The Complete Guide to OSHA Compliance

Robert D. Peterson, J.D.
Robert D. Peterson Law Corporation
Rocklin, California

Joel M. Cohen, CIH
The Cohen Group
San Mateo, California

CRC **LEWIS PUBLISHERS**

Boca Raton   New York   London   Tokyo

Library of Congress Cataloging-in-Publication Data

Cohen, Joel M.
    The complete guide to OSHA compliance / Joel Cohen and Robert Peterson.
        p.   cm.
    Includes index.
    ISBN 0-87371-681-7 (alk. paper)
    1. Industrial safety--United States--Handbooks, manuals, etc. 2. Industrial safety--Law
and legislation--United States--Handbooks, manuals, etc.   I. Peterson, Robert D. II. Title.
    T55.C578 1995
    658.4' 08--dc20   95-42176
                                                                                                  CIP

© 1996 by CRC Press, Inc.

No claim to original U.S. Government works
International Standard Book Number 0-87371-681-7
Library of Congress Card Number 95-42176
Printed in the United States of America 1 2 3 4 5 6 7 8 9 0
Printed on acid-free paper

ABOUT THE AUTHORS

Robert D. Peterson founded the Robert D. Peterson Law Corporation in 1978 and specializes in the area of OSHA defense litigation. He represents clients in defense of occupational safety and health appeals throughout the country, including both "Fed/OSHA" states and states with their own safety and health programs.

Mr. Peterson is a graduate of Portland State University and the University of Santa Clara School of Law. Prior to establishing the Robert D. Peterson Law Corporation, he served as a Deputy Attorney General for the state of California and as the first Chief Counsel to the California Occupational Safety and Health Appeals Board.

Joel M. Cohen is the founder and President of The Cohen Group, a company which has provided a complete range of environmental and occupational health services to industry and government since 1980.

Mr. Cohen received his Masters of Public Health from the University of Michigan in 1974 and is a Certified Industrial Hygienist. He is also registered in California as an Environmental Assessor and is a certified asbestos consultant. He has published numerous articles and technical journals.

Mr. Peterson and Mr. Cohen are both recognized experts in their fields, have been active in many health and safety-related seminar presentations for various associations, and have co-authored two books on Cal/OSHA compliance.

Introduction

The federal Occupational Safety and Health Act was enacted in 1970. The Act was intended to assure "so far as possible" a safe and healthy workplace for every working person in the country.

While the Act sets forth a variety of means and methods to accomplish its goal, its enforcement activities constitute its most recognized source of authority. This enforcement authority is implemented by the use of an inspection/citation scheme.

The Act imposes a two-fold responsibility upon an employer. Every employer is to furnish its employees "employment and a place of employment which are free from recognized hazards" and is also to "comply with occupational safety and health standards." The occupational safety and health standards are set forth in Title 29 of the Code of Federal Regulations ("CFR").

To enforce these responsibilities, the Act authorizes the Secretary of Labor to conduct inspections and to issue citations if it is believed that the employer has violated an occupational safety and health regulation. A penalty may also be proposed for alleged violations. In addition, a citation is to establish a reasonable time to abate (correct) the violation.

The employer may file an appeal with the Occupational Safety and Health Review Commission within 15 working days of the receipt of the citation, and a hearing will be scheduled to review the matter. The appeal may contest the violation, any abatement requirements, and the civil penalty.

The Act also allows individual states to assume responsibility for the conduct of their own safety and health programs. Approximately one-half of the states do exercise state jurisdiction over safety and health matters. Of these states, some enforce the federal rules and regulations while some have adopted and enforce their own safety and health standards. Even if the states have assumed jurisdiction of the program, generally only the Secretary of Labor may enforce safety and health on federal properties within the individual states.

To comply with OSHA rules and regulations, an employer must be familiar with what regulations apply to its place(s) of employment. The standards are divided into general areas such as construction, general industry, etc. An employer must review those areas of the OSHA rules to determine which rules and regulations apply to its operation. Additionally, if an employer does business in more than one state, it must become familiar with the occupational safety and health regulations which apply in each state.

This manual, written in lay person's language, provides a general overview of OSHA. It is intended to familiarize the reader with the means of identifying what occupational safety and health regulations might apply to his/her place of employment and to provide direction on how to comply with those rules and regulations. It additionally provides guidance on what to expect from OSHA in the event of an inspection, how to participate in the inspection, and what actions are available in the event one or more citations and penalties are issued as a result of the inspection.

This manual was written for those individuals who have the responsibility for attempting to ensure a safe and healthy place of employment. The manual is not all-inclusive.

It is our sincere hope that this manual will provide you with the "nuts and bolts" information you will need for establishing and maintaining an effective and practical safety program.

TABLE OF CONTENTS

APPENDICES

The Complete Guide to OSHA Compliance

Chapter 1

UNDERSTANDING OSHA— AN OVERVIEW

The concern for workers' well-being has extended over many years. The English Parliament enacted landmark labor legislation in 1833 called the Factory Act, which focused on the hours children were permitted to work and provided for inspections of workplaces. Additional legislation was passed in other countries in Europe.

In the U.S., legislation surrounding worker protection began to be enacted in the late 1800s by several states, including New York, Michigan, Massachusetts, and New Jersey. The legislative activity grew considerably after the turn of the century. The Bureau of Mines was created in 1910 and the federal Department of Labor was created in 1913.

State regulations moved faster than the federal programs. State and local government programs and safety standards continued to proliferate until the 1960s. Establishing a national program seemed to be an impossible task. However, the passage of three major pieces of legislation had a significant impact on establishing a national occupational health and safety program. These major pieces of legislation are:

- Metal and Nonmetallic Mine Safety Act of 1966
- Federal Coal Mine Health and Safety Act of 1969, and
- Occupational Safety and Health Act of 1970.

The Occupational Safety and Health Act has had the greatest impact on worker safety and health regulations as we know them today. It was passed at a time when the federal government believed that worker and environmental protection were of utmost importance. About the same time the

1

Occupational Safety and Health Act was passed, the Federal Hazardous Substances Act of 1966, the National Environmental Policy Act of 1969, the Coal Mine Health and Safety Act of 1969, the Clean Air Act of 1970, the Clean Water Act of 1972, The Environmental Pollution Control Act of 1972, the Safe Drinking Water Act of 1974, and the Toxic Substances Control Act of 1976 were also enacted.

Obviously, the attitude to establish a national piece of legislation to protect workers was strong. At the time the Occupational Safety and Health Act was being discussed, Congress was given the following facts:

- 14,000 deaths were due to job-related accidents
- Nearly 2-1/2 million workers were disabled
- Ten times as many person-days were lost from job-related disabilities as were from strikes
- It was estimated that there would be 300,000 new cases of occupational disease.

The principal tenet of the Occupational Safety and Health Act is to "assure so far as possible every working man and woman in the Nation safe and healthful working conditions and to preserve our human resources." The goals of the Act were to:

- Encourage employers and employees to reduce workplace hazards and to implement new or improve existing safety and health programs.
- Provide for research in occupational safety and health to develop innovative ways of dealing with occupational safety and health problems.
- Establish separate but dependent responsibilities and rights for employers and employees for the achievement of better safety and health conditions.
- Maintain a reporting and recordkeeping system to monitor job-related injuries and illnesses.
- Establish training programs to increase the number and competence of occupational safety and health personnel.
- Develop mandatory job safety and health standards and enforce them effectively.
- Provide for the development, analysis, evaluation and approval of state occupational safety and health programs.

The Occupational Safety and Health Act created several distinct government entities. Most of the power of the Occupational Safety and Health Act resides with the Occupational Safety and Health Administration (OSHA) which is located in the executive branch of the government under the Department of Labor. The specific actions that can be taken by OSHA will be discussed later.

The Occupational Safety and Health Act also established the National Institute for Occupational Safety and Health (NIOSH). NIOSH is the research arm of OSHA and is responsible for workplace investigations, training and educational programs, recommendations for new health standards, and other related activities. NIOSH is under the Department of Health and Human Services, which was previously called the Department of Health, Education and Welfare.

Other government entities created by the Occupational Safety and Health Act include the Occupational Safety and Health Review Commission, the National Advisory Committee on Occupational Safety and Health, and the National Commission on State Workers' Compensation Laws.

Not all employers are affected by the Occupational Safety and Health Act. The Act covers employers "engaged in business affecting commerce who have employees." This specifically exempts federal workers. Federal agencies are responsible for establishing their own programs that are to be consistent with those established by OSHA. Where rules do not exist, OSHA standards apply. OSHA provisions also do not apply to state and local government employees. Last, federal workers who are under the jurisdiction of another federal agency's rules for health and safety are exempt from the OSHA rules. For example, OSHA's standards and regulations do not apply to those workers who are employed in nuclear power facilities and as longshoremen. These two industries are under the jurisdiction of the Department of Energy (DOE) and the Longshoremen's and Harbor Workers' Compensation Act, respectively. Other groups like railroad workers and miners are also exempt. The Occupational Safety and Health Act also does not cover self-employed persons and farms at which only immediate members of the farm employer's family are employed.

Although federal agencies are exempt from OSHA standards, the Agency conducts workplace inspections in response to worker complaints and for federal workplaces with high hazard jobs. Federal agencies are also required to maintain injury and illness statistics, conduct self-inspections, etc.

The Occupational Safety and Health Act gave power to the states, District of Columbia, and U.S. territories to establish and manage their own occupational safety and health program as long as their rules were "at least as effective" as those enacted by the federal government. States must also cover state and local government workers in their program. States wishing to administer their own program must submit their plans to the Department of Labor for approval. The plan must demonstrate that the state has the ability to provide for:

- Standard-setting
- Enforcement
- Appeals
- Public employee protection
- Sufficient personnel for enforcement
- Training, education and technical assistance programs

There are currently 25 states with approved plans. Although all of these states have established their own enforcement arm, not all states have opted to write their own regulations. Some states have decided to enforce the federal standards as they are written. Other states have decided to establish their own safety and health standards. This is acceptable to the Department of Labor as long as the state's rules are identical to, or at least as stringent as, the federal government's regulations. As the federal government promulgates its regulations, states that establish their own regulations must do so within 6 months following the passage of a federal OSHA regulation. States that have approved plans are shown in Figure 1.1. The plans in Connecticut and New York cover public employees only. In these two states, private sector employees are covered under federal jurisdiction. Contacts for the state plans are shown in Appendix 1A.

Alaska	New York *
Arizona	North Carolina
California	Oregon
Connecticut *	Puerto Rico
Hawaii	South Carolina
Indiana	Tennessee
Iowa	Utah
Kentucky	Vermont
Maryland	Virginia
Michigan	Virgin Islands
Minnesota	Washington
Nevada	Wyoming
New Mexico	

Note * These states cover public employees only. Federal OSHA is responsible for private sector employees.

FIGURE 1.1
States with approved plans.

Chapter 2

OSHA RECORDKEEPING

This chapter covers OSHA recordkeeping requirements for occupational injuries and illnesses. This chapter is *not* all-inclusive, and you are well-advised to review the applicable federal regulations as they are extremely detailed. The applicable federal regulations are set forth in 29 CFR § 1904, et. seq. You should also review the U.S. Department of Labor, Bureau of Labor Statistics, booklet entitled *Recordkeeping Guidelines for Occupational Injuries and Illnesses*. You may obtain a copy of the booklet from one of the regional offices of the Bureau of Labor Statistics. The addresses of the regional offices are set forth in Appendix 2A. An abbreviated guide is also available for your use from the Department of Labor, Bureau of Labor Statistics and is entitled *A Brief Guide to Recordkeeping Requirements for Occupational Injuries and Illnesses*. A copy of the abbreviated guide is set forth in Appendix 2B.

With few limited exceptions, you must complete and maintain the forms discussed in this chapter. This chapter also discusses reporting requirements of a death or a serious injury or illness of a company employee. This chapter is divided into three parts:

- First, recordkeeping requirements for injuries and illnesses
- Second, how to keep OSHA records, including: The Log and Summary of Occupational Injury and Illnesses and The Supplementary Record of Occupational Injuries and Illnesses
- Third, reporting a death or serious injury.

I. RECORDKEEPING REQUIREMENTS FOR INJURIES AND ILLNESSES

If an employee suffers an occupational injury or illness, most employers must complete the documents discussed below. The coverage of the OSHA Act is extensive and covers nearly all employers in the private sector. There are certain limited exceptions to these recordkeeping requirements, which are discussed directly below.

A. No Employees

The following are examples of circumstances where OSHA recordkeeping requirements would *not* apply as there are *no employees* covered by the Fed/OSHA Act.

- Two or more partners operating a small company with no employees would not be covered by the Fed/OSHA Act. Partners are not considered employees.
- Activities of self-employed individuals are not covered by the Fed/OSHA Act. Self-employed individuals are not considered employees under the Act.
- Employers of domestic help in the employer's private residence for the usual purposes of housekeeping and/or child care are not required to keep records for the domestic help.

There are also exemptions from the recordkeeping requirements of OSHA for the following *types* of employers:

- Small employers
- Employers in low hazard industries

B. Small Employers

Although subject to the overall coverage of the Fed/OSHA Act, employers who had *no more than* 10 employees (10 or less) at any point in time during the calendar year immediately preceding a current calendar year need not comply with the recordkeeping requirements of the Act for the current year. For example, if your company employed no more than 10 employees at any point in time in 1994, you need not maintain the OSHA Log in 1995.

In determining your possible classification as a small employer, *the total number* of employees your company may have employed during the calendar year is *not* the determining factor. Rather, it is whether the company employed more than 10 employees *at any one time* during the previous calendar year.

For example, if two partners operate an automotive repair shop throughout the year with nine employees, the small employers exemption may apply to that company, for the partners are not employees. Therefore, as long as the repair shop did not have more than ten employees at any given point in time during the calendar year, it qualifies for the small employer exemption for the following calendar year.

If you have more than one business location ("establishment") under Fed/OSHA jurisdiction, the total number of employees in the entire company is included in this calculation. Therefore, if you have two separate business locations, each of which had six employees during the previous calendar year, you would need to maintain the OSHA injury and illness records during the current year for *both* establishments because the total employment of the company was greater than ten. If, on the other hand, there were never more than ten employees working at the two locations at any point in time during the calendar year, the company would not need to maintain the records in question during the following calendar year.

1. Advice

A few states do require even small employers to maintain OSHA records. If you are in a state plan state, you should check the requirements of your state regarding this requirement.

C. Employers in Low Hazard Industries

The Fed/OSHA Act creates a second exemption from its recordkeeping requirements, which applies to employers in low hazard industries. 29 CFR § 1904.16. This exemption depends upon the company's Standard Industry Classification (SIC) Code. Employers whose establishments are classified in SIC Codes 52–89, (*excluding* 52–54, 70, 75, 76, 79 and 80) need *not* comply with the recordkeeping requirements of the Fed/OSHA Act. See Appendix 2C for a list of the SIC Code exemptions.

1. Recommendation

First, you should determine the SIC Code of your company, for perhaps your company's business may fall under one of the low hazard industry exemptions. If you are uncertain of your SIC code classification, your company's income tax return may include a "principal business activity code" which should reflect a numerical designation which is generally consistent with an SIC code classification. You may also refer to the 1972 edition of the Standard Industrial Classification (SIC) Manual prepared by the Executive Office of the President, Office of Management and Budget, to determine the company's SIC code. This publication might be available in corporate offices and should be available in libraries, or it may be purchased from a government printing office. You may also contact your state officials or the U.S. Department of Labor, Bureau of Labor Statistics Regional Offices (See Appendix 2A), for assistance in determining the company's SIC code.

If you are in a state with an approved state plan, you should determine and comply with the recordkeeping requirements of your state. Some states do *not* exempt employers in low hazard industries from the recordkeeping requirements of the state. Appendix 1A includes state agency addresses and telephone numbers. Also remember to check individual state plans if some of the company's facilities are located in such states.

Large employers with multiple establishments may find that some of their establishments qualify for an exemption while others do not. For example, a manufacturer may have assembly plants and retail sales offices. The manufacturing facilities would not be exempt from OSHA recordkeeping; however, the sales offices might fall under an SIC code exemption as a low hazard type of operation.

If your company happens to be selected to participate in the "Annual Survey of Occupational Injuries and Illnesses" by the Bureau of Labor Statistics, your company would need to complete and maintain the required records for 1 year as a result of the participation in that survey, regardless of an SIC code exemption.

2. Advice

Remember that although OSHA recordkeeping requirements may be unnecessary for small employers and employers in low hazard industries, those employers must still comply with all other safety and health rules and regulations, display the OSHA poster, and orally report any work-related accidents which result in a fatality or the hospitalization of three or more employees to OSHA within 8 hours of learning of the incident.

II. HOW TO KEEP OSHA RECORDS

Only two recordkeeping forms regarding injuries and illnesses are generally used by Fed/OSHA: the Log and Summary of Occupational Injuries and Illnesses, OSHA No. 200 ("the log"), and the Supplemental Record of Occupational Injuries and Illnesses, OSHA No. 101.

A. Log and Summary of Occupational Injuries and Illnesses

The Log and Summary of Occupational Injuries and Illnesses (OSHA No. 200) is a document used for recording and classifying recordable occupational injuries and illnesses, including the extent and outcome of each case. A copy of the log is set forth in Figure 2.1.

The log shows when the occupational injury or illness occurred, to whom, what the injured or ill person's regular job was at the time of the injury and illness exposure, the department in which the person was employed at the time of injury or onset of illness, the kind of injury or illness, the extent and outcome of the injury, any lost time, and the type, extent, and outcome of the illness.

A private equivalent to the log may be used if it contains the same detail as the log itself as long as it is as "readable and comprehensible" to a person not familiar with the equivalent format.

Each recordable injury and illness is to be recorded as early as practicable, but no later than 6 working days after the company has received information that a recordable injury or illness has occurred.

You are required to maintain a log *for each establishment.* An "establishment" is defined as a single physical location where business is conducted or where services or industrial operations are performed, such as a factory, warehouse, or central administrative office. The log must reflect separately the injury and illness experience *of each establishment.*

You may perform the actual preparation and maintenance of the log at a location other than at the establishment to which it pertains. Two requirements exist if the company is to maintain and keep the log at a location other than at the establishment covered by the log. First, sufficient information must be available at the recordkeeping location to allow the log to be accurately completed within 6 workdays; and second, a copy of the log (current to within 45 calendar days) must be present at all times for each establishment in question.

That is, if you complete and retain the log for the factory at your office, send a copy of the log to the factory (the "establishment") every 45 days.

For employees working at a fixed establishment, a copy of the log is to be kept at that establishment. If you have employees who do not report to a fixed location but work elsewhere, the records should be kept at the fixed location to which the employees report each day. For example, employees engaged in activities such as agriculture and construction could fall under this category, although there may be some discretion as to the location of these records. The location of such records depends upon the nature of the operation. If the employees report to a given place each workday but work elsewhere, the records should be kept at the location to which they first report. If, on the other hand, the employees report directly to transient jobsites each day, a construction company has discretion regarding the location of the records. They may be kept at a field office or mobile base of operation, or they may be maintained at an established central location.

Some employees are subject to common supervision, yet do not report or work at a fixed establishment on a regular basis. The records for these employees may be kept at the field office or mobile office of their operations or at an established central location.

Bureau of Labor Statistics
Log and Summary of Occupational
Injuries and Illnesses

NOTE:	This form is required by Public Law 91-596 and must be kept in the establishment for 5 years. Failure to maintain and post can result in the issuance of citations and assessment of penalties. (See posting requirements on the other side of form.)			RECORDABLE CASES: You are required to record information about every occupational death; every nonfatal occupational illness; and those nonfatal occupational injuries which involve one or more of the following: loss of consciousness, restriction of work or motion, transfer to another job, or medical treatment (other than first aid). (See definitions on the other side of form.)		
Case or File Number	Date of Injury or Onset of Illness	Employee's Name	Occupation	Department	Description of Injury or Illness	
Enter a nonduplicating number which will facilitate comparisons with supplementary records.	Enter Mo./day.	Enter first name or initial, middle initial, last name.	Enter regular job title, not activity employee was performing when injured or at onset of illness. In the absence of a formal title, enter a brief description of the employee's duties.	Enter department in which the employee is regularly employed or a description of normal workplace to which employee is assigned, even though temporarily working in another department at the time of injury or illness.	Enter a brief description of the injury or illness and indicate the part or parts of body affected. Typical entries for this column might be: Amputation of 1st joint right forefinger; Strain of lower back; Contact dermatitis on both hands; Electrocution—body.	
(A)	(B)	(C)	(D)	(E)	(F)	
					PREVIOUS PAGE TOTALS →	
					TOTALS (Instructions on other side of form.) →	

OSHA No. 200   ★ U.S.GPO:1990-262-256/15419

FIGURE 2.1
Log and Summary of Occupational Injuries and Illnesses

U.S. Department of Labor

For Calendar Year 19 _____   Page ____ of____

Company Name													Form Approved O.M.B. No. 1220-0029
Establishment Name													See OMB Disclosure Statement on reverse.
Establishment Address													

Extent of and Outcome of INJURY						Type, Extent of, and Outcome of ILLNESS												
Fatalities	Nonfatal Injuries					Type of Illness								Fatalities	Nonfatal Illnesses			
Injury Related	Injuries With Lost Workdays				Injuries Without Lost Workdays	CHECK Only One Column for Each Illness (See other side of form for terminations or permanent transfers.)								Illness Related	Illnesses With Lost Workdays				Illnesses Without Lost Workdays
Enter DATE of death. Mo./day/yr.	Enter a CHECK if injury involves days away from work, or days of restricted work activity, or both.	Enter a CHECK if injury involves days away from work.	Enter number of DAYS away from work.	Enter number of DAYS of restricted work activity.	Enter a CHECK if no entry was made in columns 1 or 2 but the injury is recordable as defined above.	Occupational skin diseases or disorders	Dust diseases of the lungs	Respiratory conditions due to toxic agents	Poisoning (systemic effects of toxic materials)	Disorders due to physical agents	Disorders associated with repeated trauma	All other occupational illnesses		Enter DATE of death. Mo./day/yr.	Enter a CHECK if illness involves days away from work, or days of restricted work activity, or both.	Enter a CHECK if illness involves days away from work.	Enter number of DAYS away from work.	Enter number of DAYS of restricted work activity.	Enter a CHECK if no entry was made in columns 8 or 9.
(1)	(2)	(3)	(4)	(5)	(6)	(a)	(b)	(c)	(d)	(e)	(f)	(g) (7)		(8)	(9)	(10)	(11)	(12)	(13)

Certification of Annual Summary Totals By _____   Title _____   Date _____

FOLD

OSHA No. 200   **POST ONLY THIS PORTION OF THE LAST PAGE NO LATER THAN FEBRUARY 1.**

FIGURE 2.1
Log and Summary of Occupational Injuries and Illnesses (Continued)

The records for unsupervised employees such as traveling salespeople, consultants, or engineers who do not report or work at a single establishment, should be maintained at the location from which they are paid or at the location of their company's personnel operations. In any of these cases, such employees should be knowledgeable about the location of the log.

The log must be maintained on a calendar year basis and retained for 5 years following the end of the calendar year in question.

You are not required to maintain a copy of the log for any year during which there were no recordable cases; however, the *summary portion* of the log should be completed with zero entries and retained for the 5-year period.

1. Advice

Since the summary portion of the log is an integral portion of the log, you may want to maintain a copy of the entire log for 5 years, just for the sake of simplicity.

2. Recordable Events

Events which are recordable on the log include:

- Work-related deaths
- Lost work days
- Injuries and illnesses involving medical treatment
- Loss of consciousness
- Restriction of work or motion
- Transfer to another job

First aid treatment is not a recordable event!

The difference between first aid and medical treatment is often significant, not only for OSHA recordkeeping, but also for workers' compensation purposes. The difference between the two treatments is one of degree of treatment, not whether a physician is involved.

First aid is defined as "Any one-time treatment, and any follow-up visit for the purpose of observation, of minor scratches, cuts, burns, splinters, and so forth, which do not ordinarily require medical care. Such one-time treatment, and follow-up visit for the purpose of observation, is considered first aid even though provided by a physician or registered professional personnel."

Medical treatment is defined as "Treatment administered by a physician or by registered professional personnel under the standing orders of a physician. Medical treatment does not include first aid treatment even though provided by a physicians or registered professional personnel." See Figure 2.2 for a list generally acceptable as distinguishing first aid treatment and medical treatment.

A hospital visit (or stay) is not necessarily a controlling factor regarding the issue of the recordability of an event. The focus is also not on the length of a hospital stay, but on whether medical treatment was provided.

Each new recordable injury and illness requires a new entry. Injuries are generally the result of some new incident — such as a trip or slip — and require a new recording. Recurrences, however, do *not* require new entries, merely a revision of an earlier entry.

The distinction between a new incident and the recurrence of a further complication of a previous injury of illness can be complicated. You are referred to Chapter V of the *Recordkeeping Guidelines for Occupational Injuries and Illnesses* (Appendix 2B) to assist you in your decision.

Deciding whether the emergence of illness symptoms constitutes a new event or the recurrence of a previous illness is also often complex, and, as noted above, you should review the recordkeeping booklet for guidance.

The employee need not be presently employed to require a recordable event. As long as the underlying event occurred within the 5-year record retention period, the event is recordable in the year of the injury or illness. This may require changes to a previous year's log.

Entries for previously unrecorded injuries or illnesses which are subsequently discovered or found to be recordable after the end of the year in which the case occurred should be made upon discovery. Log totals should also be modified to reflect any such changes If an entry previously made is found at a later time to be nonrecordable, that entry may be lined out.

3. Recommendation

Strictly from an OSHA standpoint, if you question whether an injury or illness has occurred, it may be advisable to record the case within 6 workdays of learning of the condition. You may line out the entry at a later date if it is determined not to be recordable. It may be advisable to check with your workers' compensation carrier, however, to determine the ramifications of "overreporting" injuries and illnesses.

4. Completion of the Log

The log consists of three parts including a descriptive portion which identifies the employee and briefly describes an injury or illness, a section covering the extent of the *injuries,* and a similar section on the type and extent of any *illnesses.*

MEDICAL TREATMENT

Treatment of **INFECTION**
Application of **ANTISEPTICS during second or subsequent visit** to medical personnel
Treatment of **SECOND OR THIRD DEGREE BURN(S)**
Application of **SUTURES** (stitches)
Application of **BUTTERFLY ADHESIVE DRESSING(S) STRIP(S)** in lieu of sutures
Removal of **FOREIGN BODIES EMBEDDED IN EYE**
Removal of **FOREIGN BODIES FROM WOUND;** if procedure is **COMPLICATED** because of
    depth of embedment, size, or location
Use of **PRESCRIPTION MEDICATIONS** (except a single dose administered on first visit for
    minor injury or discomfort)
Use of hot or cold **SOAKING THERAPY during second or subsequent visit** to medical per-
    sonnel
Application of hot or cold **COMPRESS(ES) during second or subsequent visit** to medical
    personnel
CUTTING AWAY DEAD SKIN (surgical debridement)
Application of **HEAT THERAPY during second or subsequent visit** to medical personnel
Use of **WHIRLPOOL BATH THERAPY during second or subsequent visit** to medical per-
    sonnel
POSITIVE X-RAY DIAGNOSIS fractures, broken bones, etc.)
ADMISSION TO A HOSPITAL or equivalent medical facility **FOR TREATMENT**

FIRST AID TREATMENT

Application of **ANTISEPTICS during first visit** to medical personnel
Treatment of **FIRST DEGREE BURN(S)**
Application of **BANDAGE(S) during any visit** to medical personnel
Use of **ELASTIC BANDAGE(S) during first visit** to medical personnel
Removal of **FOREIGN BODIES NOT EMBEDDED IN EYE** if only irrigation is required
Removal of **FOREIGN BODIES FROM WOUND,** if procedure is **UNCOMPLICATED** and is,
    for example, by tweezers or other simple technique
Use of **NONPRESCRIPTION MEDICATIONS AND** administration of **single dose of PRE-**
    SCRIPTION MEDICATION on first visit for minor injury or discomfort
SOAKING THERAPY on initial visit to medical personnel or removal of bandages by **SOAK-**
    ING
Application of hot or cold **COMPRESS(ES) during first visit** to medical personnel
Application of **OINTMENTS** to abrasions to prevent drying or cracking
Application of **HEAT THERAPY during first visit** to medical personnel
Use of **WHIRLPOOL BATH THERAPY during first visit** to medical personnel
NEGATIVE X-RAY DIAGNOSIS
OBSERVATION of injury during visit to medical personnel

FIGURE 2.2
Medical and First Aid Treatment

To distinguish an injury from an illness, keep the following distinction in mind. The basic definition of an occupational *injury* includes those incidents which result from a workplace accident or an exposure involving a *single instantaneous incident* in the work environment.

For example, contact with a hot surface which produces a burn as a result of the single instantaneous moment of contact is an injury. On the other hand, sunburn or welding flash burns resulting from *prolonged* exposure are considered illnesses. This distinction is generally referred to as the "single-incident" concept. *Recordkeeping Guidelines for Occupational Injuries and Illnesses* has some excellent examples distinguishing injuries from illnesses.

The columns on the OSHA log are self-explanatory. The directions for the completion of the log are set forth on the reverse side of the form and are comprehensive and easily understood. The following comments are offered for additional assistance in completing the OSHA log.

a. General Information Columns

Column D: You must record the injured or ill employee's *regular* job title even if the employee was working outside his or her regularly assigned job at the time of the injury or illness.

Column E: You must state the department in which the injured or ill person is *regularly* employed. If, for example, an employee is regularly assigned to the maintenance department, but was injured while working in the shipping department, the correct entry would be maintenance.

Column F: While Column F on the log requests a "brief description" of the injury or illness, the entry in this column should be sufficiently detailed. For example, a proper entry regarding a finger amputation would be "amputation-first joint, ring finger, right hand." This details the degree of the injury to the finger on the hand in question.

b. Injury Portion of the Log

Although *all* work-related *deaths* and *illnesses* must be recorded, the recording of work-related *injuries* is limited to certain specific types of cases. Only work injuries involving lost work days, medical treatment, loss of consciousness, restriction of work or motion, or transfer to another job are recordable. Work injuries requiring first aid treatment are *not* recordable. "First aid treatment" is defined above. As noted, the fact that care is provided by a physician does not affect this characterization; that is, if the treatment is properly characterized as first aid treatment, it will remain in that category even if a physician renders the treatment.

Column 1:   Column 1 of the injury portion of the log requires the date of death when an occupational injury results in a fatality. Even though the death may not have occurred within 6 working days of the incident, if it occurs within 5 *years* following the end of the calendar year in which the injury occurred and the injury was work-related, the entry in the log must be changed to reflect a fatality. In such a case, any other entries on Columns 2 to 6 would be lined out and the date of death entered in Column 1.

Column 2:   If a case involves lost work days or restricted duty due to an injury, check Column 2. Lost work days include days away from work *and* days of restricted work activity. The number of lost work days should *not* include the *day of the injury* or any days which the employee would not regularly have worked (e.g., weekends, paid holidays, vacations).

Column 3 through 6: All of these columns are self-explanatory.

c. Illness Portion of the Log

Column 7:   You must make only a single entry in one of the Columns 7(a) through 7(g), depending upon which column is applicable.

Column 8:   An entry must be made in this column if a fatality does occur within 5 years following the year the illness was initially entered on the log.

Columns 9 through 13: The information required in these columns is similar to that for injuries.

For illnesses only, when a termination or a permanent transfer is involved, you must place an asterisk (*) to the right of the entry in Columns 7(a) through 7(g).

5. The Summary of Occupational Injuries and Illnesses

The portion of the log to the right of the dotted vertical line on the form is intended to record injuries and illnesses as discussed directly above and is also to be used to summarize injuries and illnesses in an establishment for the just-completed calendar year. Before preparing the summary you should review the log to ensure that each entry is accurate and correct.

Following the end of the calendar year for which the log was maintained, the summary is prepared by merely totaling the entries in Columns 1 through 13 at the bottom of the columns where indicated. Any asterisks noted on the log need not be totaled. The person certifying the accuracy of the information must complete the certification portion of the log where indicated.

If an injury or illness is continuing at the end of the year, you must *estimate* the number of future work days the employee is likely to lose in the following year as a result of the injury or illness. The estimated number of future lost work days should be added to the number of work days already lost and the combined totals entered on the log as a single entry and included in the summary. In such a situation, the log will need to be revised at a later date to reflect the number of work days that were actually lost.

For example, if an employee is injured in December and has not returned to work as of December 31, the original entry would be in the year of injury. You would calculate the total work days lost up to December 31 and then *estimate* the number of work days the employee is expected to lose the following year. Therefore, if, on December 31, the employee had lost 10 work days and you expect the employee to lose an additional 10 work days the following year, you would put the estimated total of 20 work days in either Column 4 or 5, or 11 or 12 of the log for the year of the injury or illness. When the employee does return to work and is able to perform his or her regular job, you would verify the actual number of lost work days and correct the entries on the log of the year of injury or illness as necessary. No entries would be made on the log of the year the employee returns to work.

You must **post** the summary portion of the log (post *only* that portion of the log to the right of the dotted vertical line) for each establishment for a 1-month period the following year. The summary portion of the log covering the previous calendar year shall be posted no later than February 1 of the following year and shall remain in place until March 1. The summary portion of the log is to be posted during the month of February of the following year even though there were no recordable cases during the previous year. In such a case, zeros would be entered in all the categories on the "totals" line of the summary.

The summary portion of the log must be posted in each establishment to which it pertains in a conspicuous place or in a place(s) where notices to employees are customarily posted.

If some of your employees do not work at a fixed worksite during the period February 1 through March 1, you are required to present or mail a copy of the annual summary to those employees.

If the establishment in question has closed by the time the summary is prepared or a seasonal operation is conducted at the establishment and the site is shut down during the posting period, you need not post the summary. You must, however, provide a copy of the annual summary to those permanent employees who may be employed in the seasonal operation.

As with the log itself, the use of an equivalent form (other than the summary) will be satisfactory as long as it is readable and comprehensible. You must retain the summary for five (5) years following the end of the year to which it relates.

B. The Supplementary Record of Occupational Injuries and Illnesses

For every injury or illness entered on the log, it is necessary to record additional information on the Supplementary Record of Occupational Injuries and Illnesses ("supplementary record"), the OSHA No. 101. (See: Appendix

2D.) This form is intended to provide additional information regarding the injury or illness, including a description of how the injury or illness exposure occurred, any objects or substances involved, an identification of the nature of the injury or illness, as well as the part(s) of the body affected.

If you are required to maintain the log, you are also required to complete the supplementary record in the event of a recordable event.

The supplementary record must be prepared within 6 working days after receipt of information that a recordable case has occurred.

You may use a document other than the OSHA No. 101 as long as the form or forms you use contain the same information as the OSHA form. For example, in many states a workers' compensation report of injury is required to be prepared, and such a form often contains all of the OSHA No. 101 information. In the event that you choose to use such a different form, you should ensure that the form does include all of the information that is required on the OSHA No. 101.

While completion of the OSHA No. 101 is self-explanatory, the following items are highlighted:

The "case or file number" must be the same number used to identify the case or file number in Column A of the log.

Item 8 refers to the employee's regular job title. This will be the same title as set forth in Column D of the log.

Item 9 refers to the department or the division in which the employee is regularly employed. This is the same department as indicated in Column E of the log.

1. Recommendation

Documents such as the supplementary record are often used in litigation occurring as a result of an employee's injury or illness. It is not in the company's best interest to have hurriedly completed the form or speculated as to the *cause* of the accident (paragraph 13 of the OSHA No. 101). The same advice applies to paragraphs 12 and 15 of this supplementary record.

While the supplementary record requests specificity, it may be that you do not know within 6 working days what caused the injuries to the employee or what the employee was doing at the time of his or her injury. You should *not speculate* as to the cause of the injury or illness or as to what the employee may have been doing at the time of the injury. If you do not know or if you are uncertain about these issues, you should indicate your lack of knowledge on the form. A second report prepared at a later date detailing more specific information would seemingly be acceptable to the agency. It may be, however, that the company is never able to determine the cause of the accident, a fact which should be recorded on the OSHA No. 101.

C. Reporting a Death or Serious Injury

Federal OSHA regulations require that an employer must *orally* report any work-related incident that resulted in the death of an employee or the hospitalization of three or more employees to OSHA within 8 hours. The 8-hour reporting time begins when the employer or any agent of the employer becomes aware of such an incident. This reporting requirement applies whenever an employee dies or three or more employees are hospitalized within 30 days of the incident as a result of the incident.

The rule requires an employer to make an *oral* report by telephone or in person to the OSHA Area Office nearest the incident site where a fatality or multiple hospitalizations occur. The employer can also choose to use OSHA's toll-free telephone number (800) 321-OSHA. The establishment name, the location and time of the incident, the number of fatalities or hospitalized employees, the company's contact person and his/her telephone number at work, and a brief description of the incident must be included in the report.

It is advisable that you follow up the telephone call in *writing*.

The report must include:

1. The establishment name
2. Location and time of the incident
3. A brief description of the incident
4. The number of fatalities (if any), and the extent of hospitalized employees, any injuries result from the employment accident
5. Identification of a contact person

The Area Director may require additional reports (in writing or otherwise) as he or she deems necessary. Failure to file the reports may result in the issuance of citations and the assessment of penalties. There is no small employer exemption from this reporting requirement.

1. Recommendation

Your company should ensure the existence of a procedure whereby all reportable job-related fatalities, hospitalizations, or injuries to employees are timely reported to the OSHA Area Director. It is also advisable to keep a record of when the company was made aware of the fatality, injury, or the hospitalization, and when the Area Director was contacted. If your company has a place of business within a state which operates its own OSHA program, you must become familiar with the requirements of that state plan.

Chapter 3

REGULATIONS THAT APPLY TO ALL EMPLOYERS

There are several hundred federal OSHA safety and health regulations. Some of the regulations are written for specific industries, e.g., construction, while others are for specific operations, e.g., power press, scaffolding. Still other regulations are written for protection from specific hazards, e.g., asbestos, electrical lockout. Given the fact that certain industries are subject to only a few of the OSHA standards, and others, while potentially subject to virtually all of the standards, are practically affected only by a portion of them, it is important that employers identify the regulations that apply to each of their work activities. This chapter is designed to assist employers who must comply with general workplace safety and health regulations that apply to virtually all employers.

As a general rule, *all employers are subject to the General Industry Standards.* To learn what regulations impact your business, you should:

1. Obtain a copy of the OSHA regulations. They can be found in Title 29 of the Code of Federal Regulations and are available for purchase from the Government Printing Office in Washington, D.C. Review the index for regulations that are likely to impact your business. Section 1910 applies to general industry. Read those regulations.
2. Combine compliance tasks where applicable. Your business may be subject to OSHA, EPA, state, and local government requirements that are similar. In these cases, consider dovetailing your efforts. For example, several agencies have requirements for developing and maintaining hazardous substance inventories. Combine your efforts and develop a single hazardous substance inventory that meets the OSHA Hazard Communication Standard along with the hazardous materials reporting requirements under the Environmental Protection Agency Resource Conservation and Recovery Act (RCRA).
3. Prepare plans or procedures for compliance. Make your plans as clear and straightforward as possible, responding to every point raised in a regulation. Obtain management approval if your plans go beyond what is required for a given regulation.

4. Conduct training programs to inform management about the plans being implemented. Develop an educational program for employees so they will know what is expected of them. Ensure that both groups understand how the company intends to meet the OSHA requirements.

5. Document your program. To the compliance officer, your program is only as good as your records can demonstrate during an inspection. Prepare written compliance programs. Keep written records of any changes made to the program. Maintain written records of all training programs. The records should not only include the names of those who attended, but include as well the date the training was conducted, the name of the instructor, and the class outline and/or agenda.

The following is a summary of regulations that impact nearly every employer.

I. ACCESS TO EMPLOYEE EXPOSURE AND MEDICAL RECORDS (29 CFR 1910.20 in Appendix 3A)

This regulation requires employers to provide employees and their designated representatives (e.g., collective bargaining agent, physician) with access to their exposure and medical records. Employees have a right to examine their personal records.

For the purposes of this regulation, a *medical record* consists of physician and employment questionnaires or histories, laboratory results, medical opinions, diagnoses, treatments, employee medical complaints, etc. Health insurance forms, physical specimens, and records kept for employee assistance programs (e.g., drug rehabilitation, counseling, etc.) are **not** considered medical records for the purposes of OSHA compliance.

An *exposure record* is a record of air monitoring of hazardous airborne substances, biologic monitoring required for employment (e.g., blood lead, urinary arsenic), and Material Safety Data Sheets collected for compliance with the Hazard Communication Standard.

According to this standard, you must:

a. Maintain **medical records** for 30 years beyond the duration of employment. For example, if you have a 15-year employee, you must maintain that person's records for 45 years. Do not comingle medical records with your personnel or insurance claims records.

b. Maintain all **exposure records** for 30 years. These are records directly associated with the assessment of an individual's exposure. If you collected area air samples or other forms of background environmental monitoring that were not directly related to an assessment of personal exposure, these records need only be retained for 1 year.

c. Maintain a Material Safety Data Sheet for 30 years. If you destroyed a Material Safety Data Sheet, you must keep a record of the chemicals that were used, where they were used, and when they were used.

d. Notify employees of their rights to these records. Permit employees (or their representatives) access to **their** records within a reasonable time and manner. You must provide, within 15 days of an employee's request:

- A copy of the record,
- A means of making a copy of the record at no cost to the employee, or loaning the record to the employee,

Develop a written release form for an employee's use in authorizing release of the employee's medical records to a designated representative. The release should include:

- Name and signature of the employee,
- Date of the request,
- Name of the individual or organization that is authorized to release the information,
- Name of the designated representative to receive the information,
- General description of the information to be released,
- General description of the purpose for the release, and
- Date or condition under which the authorization will expire.

A sample request letter is shown in Figure 3.1

Should you sell your business, all of the above-mentioned records are to be transferred to the new owner and the new owner is responsible to maintain the records.

If your business ceases to exist, and there is no new owner, you must notify your employees of their rights to these records 3 months prior to the business ceasing to exist.

If the business ceases to exist, and there is no new owner, or the owner intends to dispose of records (following the 30-year requirement), the employer may:

- Send the records to the Director of the National Institute for Occupational Safety and Health (NIOSH) if required by another OSHA safety standard; or
- Notify the Director of NIOSH in writing of the impending disposal of the records 3 months prior to their disposal; or
- Large employers who regularly dispose of records required to be preserved for at least 30 years may notify the Director of NIOSH with an annual notification, 3 months prior to the records being disposed.

II. EMERGENCY ACTION PLAN AND FIRE PROTECTION PLAN (29 CFR 1910.38 in Appendix 3B)

While this regulation does not make it clear whether both of these two programs are required for every employer, it is our interpretation and

I, _____, hereby authorize _____
to release to _____ the following medical information from my
personal medical records:

I give my permission for this medical information to be used for the following purpose:
_____, but I do not give permission for any other
use or re-disclosure of this information.

Expiration date:

Employee's name or legal representative:

Signature of employee or legal representative:

Date of signature:

FIGURE 3.1
Release of employee medical record information

recommendation that all employers develop and implement these programs and have them available at every place of employment.

The regulation states that small employers (i.e., employers with 10 or fewer employees for **any** time during the year) may communicate their Emergency Action Plan and their Fire Protection Plan orally to the employees. However, some documentation is required to demonstrate to OSHA that the programs are in existence.

A. Emergency Action Plan (29 CFR 1910.38[a])

Employers should develop a written Emergency Action Plan for all foreseeable emergencies, e.g., fire, chemical spill, chemical leak, tornado, hurricane, earthquake, power outage, bomb threat, etc. The plan should be in writing and contain, at a minimum, the following elements:

1. Emergency escape procedures and escape routes (e.g. evacuation routes including the locations where all employees should congregate). Consider various levels of evacuation dependent on the type of emergency, i.e., full building evacuation may not always be appropriate.

2. Procedures to be followed by employees who remain to operate critical operations that cannot be shut off, or that take time to bring to a low ebb.
3. Procedures to account for all employees following an evacuation. Generally, assigning supervisors the responsibility to perform a head count of their subordinates will suffice.
4. Procedures to be followed by those employees performing rescue and medical duties. Consider including procedures for employees who are part of an emergency response team or fire brigade if you have such groups.
5. Preferred means of reporting emergencies, e.g., call 911, call the receptionist, use the closest fire pull, etc.
6. Names or job titles of persons whom employees can contact for additional information or explanation of duties under the Emergency Action Plan.
7. Establish an alarm system in accordance with 29 CFR 1910.165. Generally, the alarm system should include the following elements:

   a. It should provide for warning for necessary emergency action as provided for in the Emergency Action Plan.
   b. It should be capable of being heard or seen above ambient noise or light levels by all employees. (Consider using flashing lights as well to accommodate the hearing impaired or in areas of high noise levels.)
   c. It should provide a distinctive and recognizable signal to evacuate or to perform actions described in the Emergency Action Plan.
   d. There should be procedures to sound the alarm
   e. The system must be installed in compliance with the OSHA requirements and local fire and building codes.
   f. The system must be able to be promptly restored following a test or alarm.
   g. The alarm system should be tested at least every 2 months.
   h. A power supply is to be maintained or replaced as often as necessary to operate properly, and a back-up alarm system (e.g., employee runners or telephones) is to be provided should the alarm system be out of operation for any time.
   i. If a manual alarm system is used (e.g., air horn, bull horn) the systems must be located in conspicuous locations and readily accessible.
   j. If the alarm system is used to alert a fire brigade, or other similar purpose, it should be distinctive and not confused with an alarm to evacuate.

All employees should be aware of the means and methods of reporting emergencies, and emergency telephone numbers should be posted near telephones or employee bulletin boards.

You must train your employees on the Emergency Action Plan:

- When the plan is first developed
- Whenever the plan is modified
- If the employee actions change

You should also train a group of employees to help implement this program.

B. Fire Protection Plan (29 CFR 1910.38[b])

Employers should develop a Fire Protection Plan. The plan should be in writing (although OSHA allows for a small employer exemption from writing this plan as well). OSHA's interest in the Fire Protection Plan seems to have intensified since a fire occurred in a chicken processing plant in North Carolina where more than 60 people died.

The requirements of a Fire Protection Plan are similar to those of the Emergency Action Plan, and therefore, you may consider incorporating the requirements of one plan with the requirements of the other plan. Elements of the Fire Protection Plan, at a minimum, include the following:

1. A list of the major workplace fire hazards and their proper handling and storage procedures.
2. A list of potential ignition sources (e.g. welding, smoking, etc.) and their control procedures.
3. Type of fire protection equipment or systems in place to control fires, e.g. fire extinguishers, sprinkler systems, Halon® systems, etc.
4. Names or job titles of employees responsible for maintenance of equipment and fire suppression equipment. Concerning maintenance, OSHA states that the employer "shall regularly and properly maintain, according to established procedures, equipment and systems installed on heat producing equipment to prevent accidental ignition of combustible materials." Maintenance procedures should be included in the written plan.
5. Names or job titles of employees responsible for control of fuel source hazards.
6. Housekeeping procedures regarding the control of the accumulation of flammable and combustible waste materials and residues.

You must inform your employees of the fire hazards, if any, to which they are exposed and train them on this plan as well. Consider dovetailing the training on the Fire Protection Plan with your training on the Emergency Action Plan.

III. MEDICAL SERVICES AND FIRST AID (29 CFR 1910.151 and 29 CFR 1926.50 in Appendix 3C)

All employers are required to have readily available medical services. The services can be provided in-house, such as through a plant infirmary or nurse's office. Alternatively, the service can be provided by a nearby clinic or hospital. OSHA does not define "near proximity" in this standard, so it is not clear how close the outside services must be to be acceptable. It has been suggested that medical services available within 4 minutes may meet the requirements of this standard.

In the absence of in-house medical services (e.g., a physician or nurse working under a physician's orders) or medical services in close proximity, employers must have on site at least one person trained in first aid (through a reputable course such as that of the American Red Cross) who could render first aid under a physician's orders.

First aid supplies approved by the consulting physician must also be available. The kit is to be maintained in a weatherproof container with individual sealed packages. The employer is to check the contents of the first aid kit regularly. For construction, the contents of the first aid kit are to be verified before being sent out on each job. Expended items are to be replaced (Construction safety orders indicate items are to be replaced at least weekly on each job).

Table 3.1 shows a recommended list of first aid supplies to be made available in the workplace. This list previously appeared in the OSHA regulations, but has since been deleted. The consulting physician should make the final determination of supplies.

Drugs, antiseptics, eye irrigation solutions, inhalants, medicines, should not be included in the first aid kit unless approved by a licensed physician.

If employees may be exposed to "injurious corrosive materials," drench showers and eye washes are to be provided within the work area.

Last, it is advisable to have the emergency telephone numbers (e.g., doctors, hospitals, or ambulance service) posted in a conspicuous location. The standard specifically requires a communication system for contacting an ambulance service or proper equipment to be provided for promptly transporting an injured person to a physician or hospital.

IV. HOUSEKEEPING (29 CFR 1910.22, 1910.176, and 1926.25 in Appendix 3D)

Housekeeping is another important requirement for all places of employment and is addressed in several OSHA regulations. For fixed workplaces (Note: 29 CFR 1910.22 applies to all permanent places of employment

TABLE 3.1
Recommended List of First Aid Supplies

Supplies for First Aid	Type of Supplies Based on Number of Employees			
	1–5	6–15	16–200	Over 200
Dressings in adequate quantities:	×	×	×	×
Adhesive dressings	×	×	×	×
Adhesive tape rolls, 1" wide	×	×	×	×
Eye dressing packet	×	×	×	×
1" gauze bandage roll or compress		×	×	×
2" gauze bandage roll or compress	×	×	×	×
4" gauze bandage roll or compress		×	×	×
Sterile gauze pads, 2" sq.	×	×	×	×
Sterile gauze pads, 4" sq.	×	×	×	×
Sterile surgical pads suitable for pressure dressings		×	×	
Triangular bandages	×	×	×	×
Safety pins	×	×	×	×
Tweezers and scissors	×	×	×	×
Cotton-tipped applicators		×	×	
Forceps			×	×
Emesis basin			×	×
Flashlight	×	×	×	×
Magnifying glass			×	×
Portable oxygen and its breathing equipment				×
Tongue depressors				×
Up-to-date first aid book	×	×	×	×

except where only domestic, mining, or agriculture work is performed), the requirements are as follows:

1. All employment locations must be kept "clean and orderly and in a sanitary condition."
2. Spills must be promptly cleaned up. Mats should be provided around wet work areas.
3. Any protruding objects, such as nails, splinters, loose boards must be removed.

Housekeeping requirements for the construction industry can be found in 29 CFR 1926.25 and require contractors to:

1. Keep all scrap lumber, debris and forms with nails clear from work areas, passageways, stairs, and in buildings and in or around structures.
2. Remove, at regular intervals, combustible scrap and debris.
3. Have waste containers at the job site. The containers must have a top if it is to be used for storage of flammable wastes. Garbage must be removed from the site at regular intervals.

V. HAZARD COMMUNICATION PROGRAM
(29 CFR 1910.1200 in Appendix 3E)

With few exceptions, every employer must comply with the Hazard Communication Standard. This is the safety standard most frequently cited by OSHA and, therefore, we strongly urge all employers, including office environments, to develop and maintain a program for compliance.

The purpose of this regulation is to ensure that employees who are or may be exposed to a hazardous substance understand the physical and health hazards associated with these substances so that they can take appropriate steps to protect themselves. This regulation also requires employers to have on hand information concerning hazardous substances and make it available to their employees.

This standard can be divided into five elements. You must comply with all of the elements in order to avoid citations. The elements are:

1. Develop a *written program* that documents the steps for compliance.
2. Prepare a *list of hazardous substances*. Keep this list current.
3. Compile *Material Safety Data Sheets* on the hazardous substances used in the workplace and make them available to all employees.
4. Ensure that all hazardous substance containers are *properly labeled*.
5. Conduct *training classes* for all affected employees.

A. What Is a Hazardous Substance?

Many employers have difficulties in understanding the difference between a hazardous substance and hazardous waste or hazardous material. Each of these terms holds a unique definition. For the purpose of this regulation, a hazardous substance is a chemical that is reported in one of the following publications:

1. OSHA—29 CFR 1910, Subpart Z, Toxic and Hazardous Substances.
2. American Conference of Governmental Industrial Hygienists (ACGIH)—Threshold Limit Values for Chemical Substances and Physical Agents in the Work Environment.
3. National Toxicology Program (NTP)—Annual Report on Carcinogens.
4. International Agency for Research on Cancer (IARC)—Monographs.

A hazardous substance may also be defined as any other substance which presents a physical or health hazard as determined by scientific evidence.

Unlike other chemical regulations, there is *no minimum quantity exemption* for this regulation. Even a small bottle of a "hazardous substance" on an employee's desk is sufficient to require an employer to develop a hazard communication standard program.

Many employers handle mixtures, e.g. cleaners, adhesives, etc., rather than individual chemicals. According to this OSHA standard, if the mixture contains 1% or more of a listed "hazardous substance," then the mixture is considered a hazardous substance. Further, if the hazardous ingredient in the mixture is a cancer-causing agent and it is present at the 0.1% or more level, the mixture would again be considered a hazardous substance.

If you are not sure whether the product is a hazardous substance, it is suggested that you assume it is hazardous unless you are notified otherwise by the manufacturer or supplier.

B. Exclusions and Exemptions

There are a few exclusions and industry exemptions from some elements of this standard. These are listed below:

1. Additional labeling is not required on:

    a. Pesticides
    b. Food, drugs, cosmetics, food additives, color additives, or medical or veterinary devices or products
    c. Alcoholic beverages
    d. Consumer products
    e. Agricultural or vegetable seed treated with pesticides

2. The following are completely exempt from this regulation:

    a. Hazardous waste regulated by the EPA
    b. Tobacco products
    c. Wood or wood products (exclusive of other materials)
    d. Articles (manufactured objects, e.g., table, chair, etc.)
    e. Food, drugs, and cosmetics for personal consumption by the employees
    f. Food, drugs, cosmetics, or alcoholic beverages which are packaged for sale in retail trade establishments.
    g. Consumer products sold at retail, unless employee exposure to the substance is greater than the exposure of the consumer to the substance
    h. Drugs administered directly to patients
    i. CERCLA hazardous substances

3. For compliance with Hazard Communication, laboratories must only ensure that:

    a. Incoming containers of chemicals are properly labeled (labels are not to be removed or defaced).
    b. Material Safety Data Sheets on incoming shipments are maintained.

     c.   Material Safety Data Sheets are available to laboratory employees.

     d.   Employees are apprised of the hazards.

4.   Warehousing, marine cargo handling, and employers who handle other forms of sealed chemical containers must:

     a.   Not remove or deface labels of incoming containers.

     b.   Maintain copies of Material Safety Data Sheets on incoming shipments.

     c.   Obtain Material Safety Data Sheets for sealed containers of hazardous chemicals received without a Material Safety Data Sheet, *if an employee requests such a sheet.*

     d.   Ensure that Material Safety Data Sheets are readily accessible to employees.

     e.   Provide training to all affected employees.

C. Required Action

You should perform the following actions to comply with this standard.

1.   Write a Hazard Communication Compliance Program. The written program should be concise, accurate, and contain the following information:

     a.   A list of the hazardous substances in the workplace.

     b   An explanation of how you will meet the requirements of labeling, collecting the Material Safety Data Sheets, and providing employee training and Information.

     c.   A plan to make employees aware of hazards encountered while performing nonroutine tasks, e.g., cleaning, maintenance.

     d.   A plan to make employees aware of chemicals in unlabeled pipes.

     e.   A plan to inform outside contractors of any hazardous substances to which their employees may be exposed during the course of their work.

It is recommended to name an individual who is to be responsible for the implementation and maintenance of this program. That person should be named in the program, and all of your employees should know how to contact this person for additional information. For multiple sites, consider naming a responsible individual for each site, but all reporting to one person who will monitor the program for consistency.

2.   Conduct an inventory of the hazardous substances on your work site. The list should include the product name, manufacturer name and address, and location in your facility where the product is being used. Due to some new hazardous materials regulations (e.g., EPA's Community Right-to-Know), some local municipalities may want a copy of

the list with quantities included. Consider local or other regulatory requirements when preparing your list so that you will not have to duplicate effort.

3. Request Material Safety Data Sheets. Based on the results from step 2 above (hazardous substance inventory), request a Material Safety Data Sheet on all listed products from each manufacturer, importer, or distributor. Keep a copy of your request letter. We encourage requesting a Material Safety Data Sheet on consumer products used in your workplace. The individual who receives your request letter will either reply with a letter stating the product does not contain any hazardous substances pursuant to this regulation **or** will send a copy of a Material Safety Data Sheet. On rare occasions, you may not receive a response. Should that occur, write a second letter 30 days following the first request. If no response is received, we suggest finding a more responsive manufacturer.

4. Ensure that all products are properly labeled. Generally, the manufacturer or supplier will have this responsibility. However, it is your responsibility to ensure completeness. Every label must contain the following three items:

    a. Identity of the hazardous substance(s)
    b. Appropriate physical and health hazard warnings
    c. Name and address of the chemical manufacturer, importer, or other responsible party

    If you purchase products in bulk and transfer the products into smaller containers, it is your responsibility to label these smaller "secondary" containers. The labels should include:

    a. Identity of the hazardous substance(s)
    b. Appropriate physical and health hazard warnings

    In lieu of a label, use signs, placards, process sheets, batch tickets, operating procedures or other such written material posted in the work area as long as the alternative labeling method conveys the required information. A Material Safety Data Sheet cannot serve as a label.

    A label is not required on a container if a product is to be in the possession of one employee for one shift and, at the end of that shift, the product will be fully consumed.

5. Conduct employee training. This subsection is the most important element of this regulation. You must provide information and training on hazardous substances to all affected employees. Training is to be provided at the time of initial assignment and whenever a new hazardous substance in introduced into the work area. Employees are to be informed of:

a. The elements of the regulation,
b. The location of any hazardous substances in their work areas, and
c. The location of the written Hazard Communication Program, including the required list of hazardous substances and the required Material Safety Data Sheets.

Employers also have the obligation to conduct training sessions with their employees where they can be taught how to read a Material Safety Data Sheet and label, how to request Material Safety Data Sheets, and steps to take for additional information. Employees must also be trained on the following topics:

a. How to detect and observe the presence or release of a hazardous substance in the work area,
b. Physical and health hazards of the hazardous substances in the work area, and,
c. How employees can protect themselves from hazards in the work area (including appropriate work practices, personal protective equipment, and emergency procedures).

Training should always be well documented. At a minimum have a sign-in sheet and an outline of topics covered. Always provide employees an opportunity to ask questions during the training. When an answer to a question cannot be immediately provided, advise the group that the answer will be provided to all of them when it has been determined.

Chapter 4

REGULATIONS THAT APPLY TO SOME EMPLOYERS

In addition to the regulations discussed in Chapter 3, OSHA has established regulations which apply to a variety of workplaces. The regulations are specific to work operations or job tasks, including such varied situations as exposure to noise, handling of asbestos, use of a punch press, erection and use of scaffolding, or work in a laboratory. These regulations comprise the largest group of OSHA regulations. Employers are likely to be subject one or more of these specific regulations.

This chapter is devoted to those operation-specific regulations most frequently cited by OSHA and those which have broad-reaching implications for employers. Understand that there are hundreds of these operation-specific regulations. A few of the more common regulations and their general requirements and content are discussed below.

I. PERSONAL PROTECTIVE EQUIPMENT
(29 CFR 1910.132 in Appendix 4A)

Personal protective equipment includes items employees may need to use while performing their job tasks such as respirators, safety glasses, face shields, hard hats, etc. If required, you are to ensure that the equipment not only is available for use, but is, in fact, used. You must also ensure that the personal protective equipment is maintained in a reliable and sanitary condition.

OSHA made recent changes to this regulation which went into effect on July 5, 1994. Two provisions, hazard assessment and training requirements, were under administrative stay at the time of this writing.

As currently written, the standard requires each employer to conduct a "hazard assessment" to determine whether hazards are present in the workplace that would require employees to use personal protective equipment (PPE).

An appendix to the regulation offers guidance to employers for conducting the assessment. The appendix indicates that the employer is to conduct a walk-through survey of the work areas and evaluate hazards that would necessitate the use of PPE such as eye, face, head, foot, or hand protection. Such hazards would include employees' exposure to falling objects, sharp objects, electrical hazards, chemical hazards, moving parts, etc. Upon completion of the hazard assessment, if it appears that there would be employee exposures to a hazardous condition, the employer is to select the appropriate PPE, based on the type of hazard and its potential for injury.

The employer must *certify in writing* that the hazard assessment was *conducted*, although it is not clear whether the assessment itself must also be documented. Following the assessment and selection of appropriate PPE, the employer must ensure that the PPE is:

- Properly fitted to the employee.
- In good working order, with all damaged or defective parts replaced.
- Designed to meet the latest editions of the pertinent American National Standards Institute (ANSI) Standards.
- Used by employees trained, and complying with the requirements of the regulation.

The final step for compliance is training. OSHA states that "each employee" must be trained in the use of the PPE and must demonstrate an "understanding" of the training. The employer also must *certify in writing* that the training was provided and was understood. Retraining of an employee is to be provided whenever:

- The employer observes inadequacies in an employee's knowledge or use of PPE.
- Changes in the workplace cause previous training to be obsolete.
- Changes in the type of PPE cause previous training to be obsolete.

Be sure to retain a copy of the documentation which details the conduct of the hazard assessment and the training and any retraining of company employees.

There are specific regulations dealing with particular types of PPE. For example, Section 1910.133 in Appendix 4A sets forth requirements for eye and face protection. Due to the nature and extent that respirators are used in the workplace, the Respiratory Protection Standard is summarized below.

II. RESPIRATORY PROTECTION (29 CFR 1910.134 in Appendix 4A)

Although the use of respiratory protection is mentioned in several OSHA regulations (e.g., asbestos, lead, arsenic), this safety standard is concerned with the general aspects of respiratory protection and the need to establish a respiratory protection plan. At the time of publication, OSHA was finalizing an amended Respiratory Protection Standard.

The scope of this standard is unique, in that it states that if employees are being exposed to hazardous dusts, fumes, mists, and the like, it is the employer's responsibility to minimize, if not completely eliminate the exposure by first using *engineering controls* to stop the release of the hazardous substance at its source. Examples of engineering controls include exhaust ventilation, enclosures, and the substitution of less toxic materials.

The standard also states that "when effective engineering controls are not feasible..." then, and only then, should respirators be used. In other words, OSHA demands that respirators be used as the last resort to control personal exposures, not the primary means of control.

According to the standard, if respirators are used, the employer must establish an effective Respiratory Protection Program. Even a paper "dust mask" used to protect against air contaminants could be considered a respirator. The Program must be in writing and include the following elements:

1. **Procedures for the selection and use of respirators.** This section involves how respirators will be selected by the employer and made available to employees. We suggest naming someone responsible for the program.

2. **Respirator selection.** Specify the type of respirators that will be used, where they will be used, and when they will be used.

3. **Employee training.** One of the most critical aspects of an effective program is employee training. Users must be trained on the proper care and use of respirators. Of special note is a fit test. A respirator is only as effective as its fit. The standard refers to a "gas-tight fit." Of particular concern are employees with facial hair which may interfere with a fit. You should consider the adoption of a company policy regarding employees with facial hair and the need for the use of respiratory protection.

4. **Cleaning and sanitizing.** Specify how respirators will be kept clean and frequency for cleaning. Some employers find it cost-effective to use disposable respirators which do not require cleaning, sanitizing or storage since they are designed for a single use.

5. **Storage.** Indicate where and how respirators will be stored. Often, a "zip-lock" bag is used to store the individual respirators. Once so stored, the respirator can then be placed in the worker's locker or in a specially designed respirator cabinet which is located out of the work area.

6. **Inspections.** Generally, there will be several levels of inspections. The user should conduct the first level inspection of his or her respirator before each use. Periodic inspections may also be established to inspect for broken or worn parts. There may also be inspections of emergency respirators which are not assigned to any one individual.

7. **Work area surveillance.** This section refers to air monitoring. Respirators are to be selected on the basis of the hazards present in the workplace. One cannot adequately select a respirator until it has been determined what exposures may be present in the workplace.
8. **Program evaluations.** As with any program, periodic evaluations should be included to measure the program effectiveness. Consider an annual evaluation.
9. **Medical surveillance.** This is likely to be one of the most discussed element of the program requirements. OSHA states that employers "should" ensure that employees assigned to use respirators are medically able to do so. OSHA continues by stating that a physician "shall" determine what health and physical conditions are pertinent. The company should consider adopting a policy regarding the assignment of employees to duties requiring the use of a respirator *and* whether the employees should be assigned a respirator unless a licensed physician has determined that the individual may wear the respirator. Such documentation should be maintained in the employee's medical records.
10. **"Approved" respirators.** Only respirators that carry the Mine Safety and Health Administration (MSHA) and National Institute for Occupational Safety and Health (NIOSH) approvals should be used.

Other issues that effect the use of respirators include the following:

Air Sources/Air Quality: If air is going to be supplied to the respirator by cylinder or air compressor, the air must be of high quality. OSHA specifies "Grade D breathing air as described in Compressed Gas Association Commodity Specification G-7.1-1966." The requirements are as follows:

Carbon monoxide	Less than 20 ppm
Carbon dioxide	Less than 1000 ppm
Condensed hydrocarbons	Less than 5 mg/m^3

Oxygen should never be used in air-line systems.

Air compressors must be carefully placed so that contaminants do not enter the system and get into the breathing air. If oil-lubricated compressors are used to supply air to the respirators, the compressor must be equipped with alarms to indicate system failure or elevated levels of carbon monoxide or temperature. If only high temperature alarms are used, a test for carbon monoxide should be taken for each use or at least weekly. The alarms should be tested periodically and the records of the tests should be maintained.

Confined Spaces/Oxygen-Deficient Atmospheres: Work which takes place in confined spaces where the atmosphere is contaminated at levels that are hazardous or in oxygen-deficient atmospheres which are immediately hazardous to life or health, require specialized procedures and the use of respiratory equipment. OSHA has established stringent regulations for work in confined spaces that can be found in 20 CFR 1910.146 in Appendix 4B. (Note: there are also requirements for agriculture, construction and shipyard employment which can be found in Parts 1928, 1926, and 1915, respectively.) The confined space requirements are not discussed in this publication.

III. OCCUPATIONAL NOISE EXPOSURE
(29 CFR 1910.95 in Appendix 4C)

When employees in a fixed workplace (i.e., excluding construction) are exposed to levels of noise above OSHA's acceptable limit, it is the employer's obligation to develop a Hearing Conservation Program. The acceptable noise exposure varies with duration of exposure as shown below:

Hours	Noise Level (dBA)
8	90
6	92
4	95
3	97
2	100
1.5	102
1	105
0.5	110
<0.25	115

Employee's exposure may not exceed an 8-hour, time-weighted average of 90 dBA. At one half that level, or 85 dBA, the employer must establish and implement an effective Hearing Conservation Program. Employers engaged in oil and gas well drilling and servicing operations are specifically exempted from this standard. The program is to be in writing and is to include the following elements:

1. **Monitoring.** The noise to which employees are exposed must be monitored if there is reason to believe that the employees' exposure may exceed OSHA limits.
2. **Employee notification.** Notify all affected employees who have been found to be exposed to noise in excess of the OSHA limit.
3. **Observation of monitoring.** Provide an opportunity for the employee or an employee representative (for employees represented by a union) to observe the testing. You are not required to have an employee representative present during testing, just afford the opportunity to a representative of the employee group to observe the testing.
4. **Periodic audiometric testing and follow-up.** This is one of the most critical elements of the program. A hearing test is required if one or more employees are exposed to noise in excess of 50% of the OSHA permissible exposure limit (or 85 dBA). A licensed or certified audiologist or other hearing specialist must conduct the audiometric examination of the employees. The test is to include a baseline audiogram to be obtained within 6 months of an employee's first exposure, and annually thereafter. Additional testing may be required if employees are found to have a degree of hearing loss.

5. **Controls.** Engineering controls are the preferred method of reducing or eliminating exposure to noise; examples of engineering controls include the construction of sound-proof enclosures around the noise-emitting source or changing the material flow so that excessive noise is not produced. Another control that is acceptable to OSHA is the use of administrative controls such as job rotation, so that an individual's exposure to noise is limited by time. OSHA believes that the least effective means of controlling noise is the use of personal protective equipment such as ear plugs or muffs. Controls you plan to use should be described in this section of your program.

6. **Hearing protectors.** Hearing protectors (i.e., ear plug or muffs) can be used if it is necessary to keep employees' average exposure (referred to as a time-weighted average) to noise within 85 dBA over an 8-hour work day. It is the employer's responsibility to provide and enforce the use of hearing protectors. Hearing protectors should also be used prior to an employee having a baseline audiogram.

7. **Hearing protector selection.** Hearing protectors vary in their ability to attenuate noise. Factors to consider in the use of hearing protectors include the level of protection they afford the user and their effectiveness in the noise environment in which they will be used. The type of hearing protectors that will be available for employee use and their location for use should be mentioned in this section of the program.

8. **Training.** A training program must be given to all affected employees who work in an environment of 85 dbA or greater level of noise for the workday. The training is to be repeated annually. Employees have access to the training materials.

9. **Recordkeeping.** You are obligated to retain records on the various aspects of this standard as follows:

    - Noise exposure measurements: two year retention period
    - Audiometric tests: retain for duration of employee's employment

    The employee has access to his/her records. All other requirements with records are consistent with "Access to Employee Medical and Exposure Records" which was briefly described in an earlier chapter.

IV. TOXIC AND HAZARDOUS SUBSTANCES (29 CFR 1910.1000 through 1910.1001 in Appendix 4D)

These sections refer to the handling of different hazardous substances, some of which are considered occupational carcinogens. If you believe that your employees may be exposed to one or more airborne contaminants, it is your responsibility to determine if their exposure is within the established limits set by OSHA. These limits of exposure are referred to as Permissible

Exposure Limits or PELs and are based on a time-weighted average concentration. There are also limits for shorter periods of time, called Short Term Exposure Limits or STELs and Ceiling Limits. A STEL refers to an exposure of 15 minutes during a workday. The Ceiling Limit is the maximum exposure, not to be exceeded for any time during the day. Affected materials are shown in Table 4.1 along with the relevant section number.

Some air contaminants have a PEL, STEL, and Ceiling Limit, while others may only have one limit.

A listing of the exposure limits for contaminants can be found in the regulations. This listing is commonly referred to as the "Z" tables, since the Tables are numbered Z 1-A, Z-2, and Z-3. About 500 of the most common industrial materials are listed in the Z tables. A change to these tables occurred in 1989, where the accepted limits were revised.

At the time of publication of this document, a federal Appeals Court ruled that the procedure OSHA used to establish the 1989 Permissible Exposure Limits (PELS) was scientifically flawed. The court order was temporarily stayed and federal OSHA was deciding if it should appeal the decision.

Since this list is extensive and it covers many industries, your company should consider the implementation of a policy including the following steps:

1. **Evaluate your operations.** Determine what substances are used in your workplace and if employees may become exposed to elevated levels of these materials.

2. **Conduct air monitoring.** Areas or operations that have been identified where workers may be exposed to elevated levels of air contaminants should be measured to determine the extent of exposure. Collecting air samples is not an easy task and should be performed by a qualified individual. Contact your workers' compensation carrier or an industrial hygiene consultant for assistance.

    The sampling survey should be designed to adequately reflect exposure. It may be necessary to sample at various times throughout the day and to monitor several workers performing their tasks. In other words, attempt to collect a "representative" exposure. This may require performing the sampling survey over several days.

3. **Compare air monitoring results.** Once you have received your air monitoring results, compare the measured levels with those PELs listed in the Z tables.

4. **Control elevated exposures.** If your measured levels exceed the PELs, you must control the exposure. There are several ways to reduce exposure such as the use of exhaust ventilation, substituting less hazardous materials for more hazardous ones, wetting down dusty operations, process changes, isolating the employee from the emitting source, etc. Again, your workers' compensation carrier or industrial hygiene consultant can assist in identifying the alternatives for you.

TABLE 4.1
Toxic and Hazardous Substances

Section	Contaminant
1910.1000	Air contaminants
1910.1001	Asbestos
1910.1002	Coal tar pitch volatiles
1910.1003	4-Nitrobiphenyl
1910.1004	alpha-Naphthylamine
1910.1006	Methyl chloromethyl ether
1910.1007	3,3'-Dichlorobenzidine (and its salts)
1910.1008	Bis-Chloromethyl ether
1910.1009	beta-Naphthylamine
1910.1010	Benzidine
1910.1011	4-Aminodiphenyl
1910.1012	Ethyleneimine
1910.1013	beta-Propiolactone
1910.1014	2-Acetylaminofluorene
1910.1015	4-Dimethylaminoazobenzene
1910.1016	N-Nitrosodimethylamine
1910.1017	Vinyl chloride
1910.1018	Inorganic arsenic
1910.1025	Lead
1910.1027	Cadmium
1910.1028	Benzene
1910.1029	Coke oven emissions
1910.1030	Bloodborne pathogens
1910.1043	Cotton dust
1910.1044	1,2-Dibromo-3-chloropropane
1910.1045	Acrylonitrile
1910.1047	Ethylene oxide
1910.1048	Formaldehyde
1910.1050	Methylenedianiline

5. **Notify employees of results**. Share your findings with employees. Explain the sampling and the findings. If corrective action is necessary, tell them what will be done to minimize exposure. If reasonable controls cannot be identified, explain the use of respirators and your respiratory protection program.

Many of the above-listed materials have detailed requirements which go well beyond the Z tables. For example, the requirements for asbestos, lead, arsenic, and formaldehyde require the employer who uses these substances to not only perform exposure monitoring as described, but may also require employee medical surveillance, personal hygiene facilities, use of protective equipment, and required employee training. If you handle any of these materials, be sure to read the regulation.

V. OCCUPATIONAL EXPOSURE TO BLOODBORNE PATHOGENS (29 CFR 1910.1030 in Appendix 4E)

This regulation, which became effective December 1991, applies to all workplaces where there is a potential for occupational exposure to blood and other potentially infectious materials. Many employers believe this regulation to be applicable only to the healthcare industry, but the standard goes well beyond hospitals, physicians' offices, dental offices, residential care facilities, and other healthcare-related employers. This regulation applies to any employer who has employees performing tasks where there could be reasonably anticipated contact with blood or other forms of infectious materials. Non-healthcare industry examples include designated emergency response personnel or teachers who are designated to render first-aid to an injured student.

Blood means human blood, human blood components, and products made from human blood.

Bloodborne Pathogens includes pathogenic microorganisms that are present in human blood. Human immunodeficiency virus (HIV) and hepatitis B are the specifically mentioned concerns.

Other Potentially Infectious Materials includes:

- Semen, vaginal secretions
- Cerebrospinal, synovial fluid
- Pleural, pericardial, peritoneal fluid
- Amniotic fluid
- Fluid visibly contaminated with blood
- All body fluids in situations where it is difficult or impossible to differentiate between fluids.
- Any unfixed tissue or organ (other than intact skin) from a human (living or dead)
- HIV-containing cell, tissue, organ cultures
- HIV- or HBV-containing culture medium, blood, organs, tissues from experimental animals infected with HIV or HBV

To comply, employers who have employees with an "occupational exposure" to bloodborne pathogens must prepare a written Exposure Control Plan that identifies tasks or jobs where exposures to blood or infectious materials may occur, without regard to protective equipment. The Exposure Control Plan must include, at a minimum, the following three sections:

1. **Exposure determination,** which includes all of the following:

   a. Job classifications in which all employees in those job classifications have occupational exposure

    b.   Job classifications in which some employees have occupational exposure

    c.   Tasks and procedures or groups of closely related tasks in which occupational exposure may occur and that are performed by employees in the job classifications listed in "b" above

    The assessment is made without regard of personal protective equipment

2.   **Schedule and method of implementation** (described below)
3.   **Procedure for evaluating exposure incidents**

Several methods of compliance or means of minimizing exposure are offered within the standard. These approaches are to be used by the employer. The approach is presented in the employer's "Schedule and Method of Implementation" portion of the Exposure Control Plan. They include:

1.   **Universal precautions.** The observance of universal precautions is a widely accepted means of infection control. According to the concept of "Universal Precautions," **all human blood and other potentially contaminated materials and devices are treated as if they are known to be infectious, whether contaminated or not.**

2.   **Engineering controls.** The goal of engineering controls is to eliminate or control the source of the potential problem, such as automating a process so that human contact with the contaminated material is not necessary. An example of an engineering control is adding exhaust ventilation to an area that emits an aerosol so that the worker will not breathe the contaminant. With regard to bloodborne pathogens, the use of biosafety cabinets is an important engineering control. Handwashing is also specifically mentioned in the standard. This may be difficult for emergency response personnel where water may not be always available. The use of antiseptic hand cleansers, followed by hand washing when feasible is an acceptable engineering control.

    The standard also discusses the handling of contaminated needles and other sharps. The standard states that these materials are not to be bent, recapped, or removed unless a procedure is used to prevent possible contamination by the handler.

3.   **Work practice controls.** This control refers to general work practices such as not eating, drinking, smoking, applying cosmetics, or handling contact lenses in work areas where an occupational exposure to blood or other potentially infectious material may be present. Prohibiting the storing of food and drink with contaminated or infectious materials is another work practice control.

4.   **Personal protective equipment.** When there is an occupational exposure to blood or other infectious materials, the employer is to provide, at no cost to the employee, appropriate personal protective equipment. The type of equipment chosen is to be based on the type of exposure, quantity, etc. of material anticipated to be encountered. **Gloves**

are to be worn when there is a potential for hand contact with the infectious materials. **Masks, eye protection** and **face shields** are to be worn if there is a possibility of splashes, sprays, etc. of infectious materials. **Gowns, aprons,** and **other body clothing** must be worn if there is the possibility of skin contact or contact with street clothing. Selection must be based on the infectious materials and duration of exposure.

5.   **Housekeeping.** The employer is to establish an appropriate written schedule for cleaning and methods of decontamination, based on the location, type of surface, type of soil present, and procedures being performed in the area.

6.   **Medical wastes (regulated wastes).** What is considered regulated biohazardous waste differs from state to state and from county to county. In general, regulated wastes include the following categories:

   a.   Liquid or semi-liquid blood or other potentially infectious material (OPIM).
   b.   Items contaminated with blood or OPIM and which would release these substances in a liquid or semi-liquid state if compressed.
   c.   Items that are caked with dried blood or OPIM and are capable of releasing these materials during handling.
   d.   Contaminated sharps.
   e.   Pathological and microbiological wastes containing blood or OPIM.

   The standard also identifies appropriate means of color-coding and labeling the wastes.

7.   **Laundry.** Laundry is to be handled as little as possible with a minimum of agitation. It also cannot be sorted or rinsed in the location of use.

8.   **Hepatitis B vaccinations.** All employees who have an occupational exposure to blood or infectious materials must be offered the hepatitis B vaccine. The vaccine is to be **made available** at **no cost** to the employee. An employee may decline the vaccination but can receive the vaccination at a later date if he/she changes his/her mind.

9.   **Communication.** An employer's ability to comply with a standard is only as good as is the ability to communicate the need for compliance to the employees. OSHA mandates that all exposed individuals receive training and education on the standard. This is accomplished in two ways, as follows:

   1.   **Signs and warnings**
   2.   **Training.** Training must be provided:

      a.   At the time of initial assignment.
      b.   Within 90 days after the effective date of the standard.
      c.   Annually thereafter.

HIV and HBV Research Laboratories and Production Facilities must follow stringent procedures to ensure employees are not contaminated. These procedures must be delineated in the Exposure Control Plan.

The last element of the standard is **recordkeeping**. Employers must establish acceptable recordkeeping practices for all occupationally exposed individuals. Items to be documented include employee training (annual training is required), incident reporting, and inspections.

Maintaining the confidentiality of these records that may show an employee to be HIV or hepatitis positive is critical. Arrangements should be made in advance for handling these records, should an incident occur.

VI. OCCUPATIONAL EXPOSURES TO HAZARDOUS CHEMICALS IN LABORATORIES (29 CFR 1910.1450 in Appendix 4F)

A. OSHA Laboratory Standard

After more than 10 years in the planning stages, OSHA released the "Lab Standard." As with the Bloodborne Pathogens regulation described above, the Laboratory Standard is broad reaching.

First, the standard applies to all laboratories which are defined as:

"a facility where the laboratory use of hazardous chemicals occurs. It is a workplace where relatively small quantities of hazardous chemicals are used on a non-production basis."

The standard applies to "laboratory use" of hazardous chemicals. OSHA defines laboratory use of chemicals as:

- Laboratory scale manipulations.
- Multiple chemical procedures or chemicals are used.
- Procedures which are not part of a production process, and do not in any way simulate a production process.
- Protective laboratory practices and equipment are available and in common use to minimize the potential for employee exposure to hazardous chemicals.

If the laboratory is an integral part of a production or manufacturing process, it is exempt from this standard. However, medical research laboratories, analytical testing laboratories, and "R&D" laboratories are included and therefore must comply with the Lab Standard.

B. Requirements of Laboratory Standard

The requirements of this standard can easily be divided into five categories. Each category is summarized below.

1. Employee Exposure Determination

The assessment phase of the standard requires employers to conduct "initial air monitoring" to characterize and determine the extent of personal exposure to a known airborne contaminant. Sampling will be performed when "there is reason to believe" an exposure exists and it is approaching the OSHA Permissible Exposure Limits. If, however, the employer believes that no exposure exists, or that the exposure is well within acceptable limits, no initial monitoring is required. You are encouraged, however, to conduct air monitoring.

Where elevated levels are found, additional "periodic monitoring" is required. OSHA specifies a frequency for re-sampling for some contaminants, such as some of the highly toxics (e.g., lead, asbestos, arsenic). When levels are within a specified acceptable limit, monitoring may be "terminated."

Employees must be notified within 15 working days in writing of the results of any monitoring. Notification can be individually, or by posting the results.

2. Chemical Hygiene Plan

As a means of protecting employees and to minimize exposure to hazardous chemicals, a written plan must be prepared. The plan must be accessible to all affected employees and include, at a minimum, the following elements:

1. Standard operating procedures relevant to safety and health considerations
2. Criteria for implementing control measures, e.g., engineering controls, personal protective devices
3. Ventilation hood performance evaluations
4. Employee information and training
5. Prior approval for new operations/processes/activities
6. Medical consultation/examinations
7. Designation of a Chemical Hygiene Officer
8. Handling of "select carcinogens" to include:

   a. establishing designated areas
   b. determining containment devices
   c. establishing methods of disposal
   d. instituting methods of decontamination

Naming the Chemical Hygiene Officer ("CHO") requires naming someone of authority who can institute change when needed. OSHA requires the

CHO to be someone who is "qualified by training or experience" to provide technical guidance for the implementation of the Chemical Hygiene Plan.

3. Employee Information and Training

Employee training is another critical element for compliance. The employees need to be apprised of the chemical hazards to which they are exposed in their work areas. The Lab Standard requires employers to provide such training upon initial assignment and prior to be assigned a new job when the hazards are different. At a minimum, the training is to include a discussion of:

1. The existence and content of the OSHA lab standard
2. The location and availability of the Chemical Hygiene Plan
3. Occupational exposure standards, such as OSHA Permissible Exposure Limits
4. Signs and symptoms associated with overexposure to chemicals
5. The location of reference materials such as Material Safety Data Sheets
6. The methods and observations that employees may use to detect the presence or release of hazardous chemicals
7. Work practices, emergency response procedures, and protective equipment to be used

Refresher training is also mandated.

4. Medical Consultation

Whenever a spill, leak, explosion, or other chemical accident occurs that may result in an exposure to a hazardous chemical, the affected laboratory worker is to be provided an opportunity for medical consultation to determine the need for a medical examination. All medical consultations and examinations are to be performed by, or under the direct supervision of, a licensed physician and provided at no cost to the employee. The medical consultation is also to be provided at a reasonable time and place for the employee, without loss of pay.

You should obtain a written opinion from the attending physician for all medical consultations provided under the Lab Standard. The opinion should include recommendations for further medical follow-up, the results of the medical examinations, and any medical conditions that may place your employee at increased risk as a result of the exposure to a hazardous chemical present in the laboratory. Only that information pertinent to the employee's performance in the job should be discussed, so that employee confidential information will not be released.

5. Special Precautions

You are also to provide additional employee protection for work with chemicals that have a high degree of acute toxicity and those chemicals of unknown toxicity, such as reproductive toxins, "select" carcinogens and acutely toxic chemicals. "Select carcinogens" are those substances that are regulated by OSHA as carcinogens, listed as known carcinogens by the National Toxicology Program, or listed as known carcinogens by the International Agency for Research on Cancer. If these types of chemicals are present in the laboratory, the employer is to establish and post a designated area where these materials must be used.

Chapter 5

ACCIDENT
PREVENTION
PLAN

What about an accident prevention plan? Does your company have such a plan? Should it have such a plan? What should be in an accident prevention plan?

It is not the intent of this manual to advise your company whether it should prepare and enforce an accident prevention plan. It would seem, however, that the existence of such a plan is a necessary tool in the accomplishment of a safe and healthy workplace.

If you are considering the adoption of an accident prevention plan, you should probably give thought to the following issues:

- Responsibility
- Training
- Communication
- Compliance
- Inspections
- Corrective measures
- Recordkeeping

I. RESPONSIBILITY

To have an effective accident prevention plan, some person (or persons) must be responsible for its implementation. Generally, such a person would be a representative of management. This person should have both the responsibility and the authority to ensure compliance with the program. The

51

identity of this person should be known to all company employees to enable the effective flow of communication of safety and health topics between management and employees.

II. TRAINING

The training of company employees about safety and health issues is perhaps the most significant element of the program. Not only is it essential that employees be informed about such matters, but many OSHA regulations require specific training, for example, the Hazard Communication standard. All employees should receive training regarding those aspects of their employment which is necessary to enable the employees to safely perform their job-required tasks. Training regarding that job should be an on-going activity. If an employee moves to a new job, training regarding that job should be accomplished.

III. COMMUNICATION

The methods by which safety and health matters are to be communicated between management and employees should be specified in the company's accident prevention plan. Safety meetings, training programs, company newsletters, postings, anonymous suggestion boxes are typical methods of communicating such topics. The accident prevention plan must provide a two-way street for communication; that is, management and employees must both have access to and be encouraged to use the communication system. Employees must be assured they will suffer no adverse consequences by speaking their mind on matters of safety and health.

IV. COMPLIANCE

All employees, from the top of the organization to the bottom, must understand that the company is serious in its intent to ensure compliance with its accident prevention plan. There are any number of ways that such an understanding may be created. Positive incentives are often a useful tool; if you do comply with the company's safety and health rules, you may expect some reward. Often, just a pat on the back and simple recognition of a job well done is enough to accomplish company goals.

It may be desirable to incorporate disciplinary provisions into the compliance portion of the accident prevention plan. If an employee does not comply with his/her training, the person may expect to be disciplined. Such a policy should be progressive; that is, the more violations by an employee, the more severe the punishment.

When considering whether to include such a policy in the accident prevention plan, consider the "message" given to an employee if management is aware that the employee has violated a company (or OSHA) rule and it looks the other way. The message is that it is okay to violate the rule. When that employee is eventually injured due to a failure to perform his/her job safely and in accordance with his/her training, what could the employee's response be? *"The company knew I was not following the rules, yet it did not care enough about me to make sure I performed my job safely. In fact, the company tacitly encouraged my unsafe activity."*

V. INSPECTIONS

The company's accident prevention plan should include provisions regarding safety and health inspections. Who should conduct them? When should they be conducted? What should be inspected? All of these questions should be addressed in this portion of your program. You may want to prepare a written checklist that can be used by the person who conducts the inspection. The checklist could include those aspects of your company's operations most likely to expose employees to unsafe or unhealthy working conditions. For example, are guards in place on machinery, or are all employees who should be wearing hearing protection, in fact, wearing such protection?

VI. CORRECTIVE MEASURES

The accident prevention plan should incorporate some method whereby any existing hazardous conditions are corrected. For example, if company maintenance personnel are to correct hazardous conditions, the program should indicate how the maintenance person is to be informed of the condition; what procedural steps are necessary to effect the correction; and how to record the corrective measures. An inspection checklist may document not only safety inspections but those corrective measures taken.

VII. RECORDKEEPING

The only sure-fire method to prove that the company's accident prevention plan has been effectively implemented is to record the activities. At a bare minimum, it is advisable to document the training of the company employees and the conduct of the safety and health inspections and any necessary corrective measures.

A. Employee Training

- Who was present?
- What was discussed?
- When was the training?
- Where was the training?

B. Inspections and Corrective Measures

- Who conducted the inspection?
- What was inspected?
- When was the inspection?
- Where was the inspection?
- What was the result of the inspection?
- What corrective measures were taken?

OSHA has no specific requirements regarding the implementation and requirements of an accident prevention plan. In 1991, California adopted a requirement that all California employers adopt a written Injury and Illness Prevention Program. As such, you may want to refer to the California plan for further guidance. The safety regulation which sets forth the requirements of such a program in California (Title 8, California Code of Regulations § 3203) and a sample Cal/OSHA Injury and Illness Prevention Program is set forth in Appendix 5A.

Chapter 6

WORKER INFORMATION AND TRAINING

I. GENERAL

Many OSHA regulations, including those discussed in the previous chapters, require the employer to provide training to the employees. Regardless of the type of business operated, OSHA requires some amount of employee training. Some of the training that is required is of a **general** nature such as Emergency Action Plan procedures, Fire Protection Plan procedures, proper selection and use of protective equipment, etc. Other regulations have requirements for **specific** topics to be covered in the training. Hazard Communication, Lab Standard, and Bloodborne Pathogens are three examples of OSHA regulations that require very specific training and topics discussed.

For the construction industry, OSHA's regulation titled "Safety Training and Education" (Title 29 CFR 1926.21 in Appendix 6A) states that construction employers must provide their workers with training on the following topics:

1. The recognition and avoidance of unsafe conditions and the regulations applicable to the work environment.
2. Proper handling practices for the use of poisons, caustics, and other harmful substances, and awareness training on personal hygiene and personal protective equipment.
3. Where harmful plants or animals are present on the job site, what are the potential hazards, how to avoid injury, and acceptable first aid procedures to be used in the event of injury.
4. Proper handling practices for flammable liquids, gases, or toxic materials.
5. If they are required to enter into confined or enclosed spaces, the nature of the hazards involved, and appropriate equipment to be used.

55

Other than the regulatory requirements to train employees, there are many good business reasons to train employees. Studies have shown that the benefits of providing employees with safety and health training include:

- Fewer work-related injuries and illnesses
- Increased productivity
- Lower insurance and workers compensation costs
- A more loyal and dependable workforce

Consider training employees:

- When the training programs are first established.
- When newly hired or when given a new assignment.
- Whenever new substances, processes, procedures, or equipment are introduced into the work environment representing a new hazard.
- Whenever a new or previously unrecognized hazard is brought to your attention.

OSHA's training requirements differ from regulation to regulation. Determine which regulations are applicable to your workplace. Carefully follow the type and format of training as called out in the regulation. OSHA's training requirements fall into one of four categories, as follows:

1. **Performance-oriented requirements**. This type of regulation requires the employer to provide training when the employees' exposure to an airborne contaminant is above an acceptable level, commonly called the Action Level. The Action Level is generally one half of the Permissible Exposure Limit. Training is required only when the employees' exposure to the airborne contaminant exceeds the Action Level. Training is not required if the airborne exposure remains below the Action Level. Examples of OSHA regulations that require training when exposure limits are exceeded include arsenic and noise.
2. **On-site requirements.** This type of regulation requires the employer to provide the employees with training, regardless of exposure. The presence of the materials on site is sufficient justification to require training. Examples of regulations that require this type of training include ionizing radiation and Hazardous Waste Operations and Emergency Response ("Hazwoper").
3. **Periodic training requirements**. Some regulations require the employer to conduct periodic refresher training. Examples of OSHA regulations that require ongoing periodic training include those for asbestos and bloodborne pathogens.
4. **One-time training requirements**. Not every OSHA training program is subject to periodic refresher requirements. Many regulations only require the employer to provide the training once, when the program is first established. Updated or refresher training would only be required

if there has been a change in the workplace, with the employer's method of compliance, or a change in the hazard. For example, Hazard Communication requires employers to train employees on the hazards to which they may be exposed in the handling of hazardous substances. Refresher training is only required if a new substance enters the environment or a change occurred with the existing substances which was brought to the attention of the employer through an updated Material Safety Data Sheet. Although the regulation states that training is required only once, it is advisable to provide employees with refresher training.

To prepare for employee training:

1. Read each regulation that affects your business to determine what are your training requirements. Familiarize yourself with the work that the employees are performing. Not every element of a regulation may be required for your operation. Determine the provisions of the regulation that impact your business. For construction, become aware of the work being performed by other trades on the job site. Their work may affect your employees, such as exposing your employees to the hazardous substances they are using.

2. Determine how the training topic should be presented. OSHA's training requirements seem to follow a similar scheme, i.e., the employer discusses the hazards; safeguards the employees' need to know to avoid exposure; company procedures for handling and monitoring the hazard; and, sources of addition information for the employees to review if desired.

   Some employers conduct the required training during company-wide meetings. The advantage of company-wide training is that all employees will be trained in the same manner, covering the material in the same way. In lieu of this approach, consider smaller group sessions. The small group training is less inhibiting for employees to ask questions and therefore can be a more beneficial experience.

   Consider offering different levels of training. Rather than training employees in large groups, train each operating unit, highlighting how they will be affected by your procedures to meet the OSHA requirement. Offer separate training for supervisors who are directly responsible for employees. In many companies, the supervisors are the trainers. If this is the case with your company, provide your "trainer" with sufficient information so that he/she can answer questions that are likely to be raised during the training.

   Supervisor training should be comprehensive so that the supervisors will have a good grasp of the topic and can more easily pass along the salient points to the subordinates. Realize, however, that not all supervisors are good instructors. Some may feel uncomfortable speaking in front of groups. If this is the case, you may want to script the presentation for the supervisor. This approach has the added benefit of assuring that all employees will hear the same information on a given topic in the same way.

Some employers find the use of outside trainers or consultants to be beneficial. Employees sometimes perceive the topic as more important if an "outside" professional is making the presentation. The use of outside training services, however, may be more costly than providing it in-house. Remember, however, that even if the training is to be completely controlled in-house, there is time and expense in preparing the program. Consider using the outside trainer to conduct the initial training and have subsequent training conducted by supervisors or in-house trainers.

Whoever performs the training, be sure that the person:

- Can give the most effective presentation
- Has the knowledge and experience on the subject
- Can achieve the respect of employees being trained
- Has credibility

3. Training activities should be scheduled to minimize disruption of work activities. Training sessions do not need to be long. A topic can be covered over several meetings.
4. Training location is also important. Pick a relatively quiet, location where distractions and interruptions can be kept to a minimum. The training area should be well lit, and equipped with all of the equipment to be used for the training, e.g., white board, transparency projector, VCR, etc.

II. PRESENTING THE TOPICS

To make a successful educational program, consider the following:

1. Present the information in a credible form. Do not overstate the topic or its severity.
2. Make the training interesting by keeping the subject moving. Consider using training aids such as:

- Pamphlets or other written handout materials
- Videotapes, films to strengthen a point or to introduce the topic
- Hands-on or simulation experience

There are many video tapes, slides, movies available on safety-related topics that can be purchased or rented. These commercially available materials should be used to supplement or strengthen the presenter's material. It is not recommended to use the audio/visual presentation as the sole source of information. The information is available from several sources, including your workers' compensation carrier, trade association, companies in your industry, and local National Safety Council office. Preview the information beforehand. Make sure it is relevant to your operations.

3.   Relate the topic to the workplace. Use examples of real life situations. Avoid discussing topics unrelated to the workplace.
4.   Give concrete examples of how the topic is relevant to the work area.
5.   At the end of the presentation, summarize the important points or have some of the workers restate them for you.

Following training, be sure to have the trainer ask if there are any questions. The trainer should answer the questions if the answer is known. If the correct answer is not known, the trainer should never guess. He/she should find out the right answer and inform the attendees of the correct response.

III. RECORDKEEPING

Keeping good records of training is as important as the training itself. There are several approaches to document the training. Listed below are some of the more commonly used approaches:

1.   **Sign in/sign out logs**. Have employees sign for themselves. Under adversarial situations, some employees may refuse to sign a log. If that is the case, assign the task to an employee, to write down names of attendees who refuse to sign. Some employers will videotape the attendees.
2.   **Test or quiz**. Some employers use a test or quiz at the conclusion of the training as a means of documenting employees' understanding of the subject matter. This is a very good approach; however, administering the test may be difficult for some employee groups. You may discover that some employees have difficulty in understanding written material or cannot read at all. You need to avoid embarrassing employees, yet everyone should be sufficiently familiar with the material to leave with a passing grade. Be prepared to sit down with some employees to go over questions incorrectly answered.
3.   **Certificates or letters of successful completion**. Consider distributing a letter or certificate at the conclusion of the class. Keep a copy of the certificate/letter as a record of attendance.

Keep good records of the class material. At a minimum, the records on the class should include:

1.   Training materials, hand-outs, scripts.
2.   Information of video, slides, etc.
3.   Agenda, topics discussed, with timetable (duration) for the presentation.
4.   Date the class was conducted and location.
5.   Names of training providers. If an outside training source was used, ask for a letter at the conclusion of the course that will document the instructor's involvement, including date, agenda, duration, and a copy of the class material.

IV. SUPERVISOR TRAINING

As stated above, supervisors generally play a key role in the overall training of employees. Not only are supervisors directly responsible for the day-to-day implementation of the program, but they are to serve as role models for the employees they supervise. A supervisor concerned with safety can have a dramatic influence on employees' safety performance. To perform their role effectively, supervisors should be afforded additional training on safety and health topics. For example, train your supervisors on hazard recognition, accident investigation and safety inspections.

V. TRAINING UNDER HAZWOPER

In March 1989, OSHA promulgated the Hazardous Waste and Emergency Response standard (29 CFR 1910.120 in Appendix 6B) that defined the level of training required for personnel involved in hazardous waste operations and emergency response actions. The standard is now commonly called the HAZWOPER regulation.

The standard covers workers involved in:

- Investigation and clean-up at hazardous waste sites
- Hazardous waste treatment, storage, or disposal (TSD) at facilities licensed under the Environmental Protection Agency's Resource Conservation and Recovery Act (RCRA)
- Any industry that responds to emergencies where hazardous substances may be released.

Not only does the standard require affected employers to develop a written safety and health plan that identifies, evaluates, and controls hazards and sets up emergency response procedures, but *specific training for workers is required*. Contractors who are involved, even incidentally, on one of the above-mentioned sites, must also train their employees **before** coming on site, where they may become exposed to the hazards.

All workers and supervisors covered under this standard must receive training on:

- Names of personnel responsible for site safety and health
- Hazard recognition and prevention
- Safe work practices to minimize risks
- Proper use of engineering controls
- Use and proper fit of personal protective equipment
- Confined space entry procedures
- Spill containment program
- Proper decontamination procedures

- Emergency Response Plan
- Medical Surveillance Requirements

The amount of instruction differs with the nature of the work operations.

Workers involved in hazardous waste clean-up who are likely to be exposed to airborne levels of hazardous substances in excess of OSHA's Permissible Exposure Limits (PELs) or who are required to wear respiratory protection must receive the following level of training:

1. 40 hours of general training
2. 3 days of on-site field training
3. 8 hours of annual refresher training
4. Special training for members of emergency response teams (time un-specified)

Workers who may occasionally work at the hazardous waste clean-up site or those involved in site characterization, e.g., groundwater monitoring, surveying, etc., who are **not** exposed to airborne levels of hazardous substances in excess of the PELs and will not be wearing respiratory protection, must receive the following level of training:

1. 24 hours of general training
2. 1 day of on-site field training
3. 8 hours of annual refresher training

Supervisors and/or managers of the above workers must also receive training equivalent in time and content to the training received by those they supervise as well as receive 8 hours of additional specialized hazardous waste management training.

Those who work on Treatment, Storage and Disposal (TSD) sites must receive the following level of training:

1. 24 hours of general training
2. 8 hours of annual refresher training
3. Special training for members of emergency response teams (time un-specified)
4. General emergency awareness training for all facility employees

There are five levels of training for emergency response personnel. These are described below:

1. **First responder training at the "awareness level".** Workers who are likely to witness or discover a release of a hazardous substance and initiate the emergency response must receive sufficient training to demonstrate competency in:

      a.   Recognition of the presence of hazardous materials in an emergency

      b.   The risks involved

      c.   Their role in securing the area and calling in the specialists

2. **First responder training at the "operations level".** Workers involved in responding to the release as part of the initial response for the purpose of protecting nearby persons and property, without actually trying to stop the release must have 8 or more hours of training plus "awareness level" competency and be able to demonstrate competency in their specific area.

3. **Hazardous materials ("Hazmat") technicians.** Workers who are responding for the purpose of stopping the release or who must enter the contaminated zone to rescue others or to survey the situation must receive 24 hours of training equivalent to the "operations level" and also be able to demonstrate competency in their specific areas.

4. **Hazardous materials ("Hazmat") specialists.** Workers who are responding to provide support and direct technicians' efforts must receive 24 hours of training equivalent to the Hazmat Technician training and show competency in their areas of specialty.

5. **On-scene incident commander.** Workers who assume control of the incident beyond the first responder awareness level must receive 24 hours of initial training plus special training according to the areas under their control.

All levels must be given annual refresher training which is to be 8 hours in duration or of sufficient content and duration for their level of compentency.

All training should be conducted at a level appropriate to the needs and abilities of the people in the course. Hands-on training and simulations should be included in the course.

A certificate is to be issued to all workers who successfully complete the course. At the time of writing this document, OSHA's certification standard was still in draft stage. Employers should therefore make a careful review of the training program to ensure its completeness. It is also advisable to review the credentials of those who are conducting the training to verify that they are qualified to conduct such a class.

Chapter 7

OSHA INSPECTIONS

This chapter provides information to your company regarding what events may result in an OSHA inspection and the scope of such an inspection. An OSHA inspection often proves to be uneventful, resulting in no citations or fines. Occasionally, however, citations and fines may be issued. Your company should understand its rights and duties during an OSHA inspection and have a sufficient understanding of the process to protect its interests. This chapter explains:

- Events that may trigger an OSHA inspection
- Unprogrammed and programmed inspections
- Comprehensive and partial inspections

I. REGULATORY AUTHORITY OF THE DEPARTMENT OF LABOR

29 CFR 1903 sets forth the regulatory enforcement authority of Fed/OSHA. 29 CFR 1903.1 authorizes the Department of Labor to conduct inspections and to issue citations and proposed penalties for alleged violations of federal health and safety rules and regulations.

29 CFR 1903.3 authorizes Compliance Safety and Health Officers of the Department of Labor ("inspectors") to enter and conduct an inspection without delay and at reasonable times of any factory, plant, establishment, construction site, or any other area, workplace, or environment where work is performed by an employee of an employer.

II. SCHEDULING AN OSHA INSPECTION—HOW AND WHY

There are any number of reasons why OSHA may conduct an inspection of your company. An employee complaint, the occurrence of an accident or a catastrophe, the presence of an imminent hazard, a notification by another agency of the existence of an allegedly unsafe condition, may all result in an OSHA inspection, and even this list is not all-inclusive.

OSHA has a priority system for scheduling inspections. The system is designed to equally distribute available OSHA resources to ensure maximum, feasible protection for all working men and women. The Area Director is responsible for creating inspection priorities. Inspections may be either programmed or unprogrammed. Unprogrammed inspections generally have a higher priority status.

III. UNPROGRAMMED INSPECTIONS

Unprogrammed inspections are generally conducted as the result of the existence of an alleged imminent danger, the occurrence of a fatality or catastrophe, or the receipt of a complaint or referral. The Area Director must prioritize unprogrammed inspections. If, for example, the Area Director has been informed of a job-related fatality at one place of employment and is also in receipt of a complaint received from an employee of a company alleging an unsafe workplace, the Area Director would need to establish the priority of the inspections.

The first priority for an unprogrammed inspection generally involves conditions posing an imminent danger.

IV. IMMINENT DANGER INSPECTIONS

29 U.S.C.A. § 662 defines imminent danger as "...any conditions or practices in any place of employment which are such that a danger exists which could reasonably be expected to cause death or serious physical harm immediately or before the imminence of such danger can be eliminated through the enforcement procedures otherwise provided by this Act."

Any alleged condition or practice which poses an imminent danger is to be inspected immediately. The source of the information regarding the alleged condition or practice is generally not important.

If, upon inspection, the inspector concludes that such a condition or practice exists, he/she is to immediately notify the employer. If the employer voluntarily and permanently eliminates the imminent danger as soon as it is pointed out, a Notice of Alleged Imminent Danger is not to be completed. Voluntary elimination of the danger shall be considered to be accomplished if an employer has removed employees from the danger area and has given satisfactory assurance that the dangerous condition will be eliminated before permitting employees back into the work area in question.

If, after being informed of the imminent danger, the employer does not take steps to reduce employee exposure to the condition, eliminate the im-

imminent danger, or give satisfactory assurance that the danger will be voluntarily eliminated, the inspector is to immediately contact the Area Director for approval to complete and post the OSHA-8 Form, "Notice of Alleged Imminent Danger." The inspector may not stop or shut down the operation or direct employees to take any action, such as leaving the area or discontinuing the practice. Once contacted by an inspector, the Area Director decides whether to order the posting of the Notice of Alleged Imminent Danger and whether to contact legal staff to obtain a temporary restraining order.

A Notice of Alleged Imminent Danger is a notice that an imminent danger is believed to exist and that OSHA may be seeking a temporary restraining order to restrain the employer from permitting employees to work in the area of the danger until it is eliminated; it does not require any particular conduct by an employer, nor does it constitute a citation. It is only with a temporary restraining order that the employer is ordered to abide by the direction of Fed/OSHA.

If it is determined that the Notice of Alleged Imminent Danger is to be posted, the original OSHA-8 Form shall be signed and posted at or near the area in which the exposed employees are working. Where there is no suitable place for posting the OSHA-8 Form, the employer shall be requested to provide a means of posting. Before the inspector leaves the workplace, he/she will advise all affected employees of the hazard and direct their attention to the OSHA-8 Form.

If an OSHA-8 Form has been posted at the worksite, the inspector shall remove the notice as soon as the imminent danger condition or practice has been eliminated or when it has been determined that a temporary restraining order will not be sought.

After an imminent danger has been found, appropriate citations and penalties may be issued. Any additional inspection activity is to take place only after resolution of the imminent danger situation. Any other violations discovered during the remainder of the inspection shall be cited and penalties proposed, whether or not they relate to the imminent danger situation.

The second priority for unprogrammed OSHA inspections involves the investigation of a fatality or catastrophe.

V. FATALITY OR CATASTROPHE INVESTIGATIONS

All job-related fatalities and catastrophes, however reported, are to be investigated by OSHA as thoroughly and expeditiously as resources and other priorities permit. For purposes of this category of inspections, a fatality is defined as an employee death resulting from an employment accident or illness — generally, from an accident or illness caused by or related to a workplace hazard.

A catastrophe is defined as the hospitalization of five or more employees resulting from an employment accident or illness—in general, from an accident caused by a workplace hazard.

Depending on the circumstances surrounding the accident, it may be necessary for the inspector to conduct a complete inspection of the workplace, including other areas or operations within the establishment which may have hazards similar to those that may have caused or contributed to the accident.

Remember to be aware of the requirement to orally report a job-related fatality or an event that resulted in the hospitalization of three or more employees to the nearest Area Director within eight (8) hours.

VI. EMERGENCY SITUATIONS

Emergencies created by fatalities or catastrophes often necessitate immediate rescue work, fire fighting, etc. When equipment which could be used in the rescue operations is available for use, OSHA is to permit its use without citing the employer, even if the equipment does not comply with all existing OSHA rules. OSHA is not to cause a delay in rescue attempts while waiting for equipment which may meet OSHA standards. The use of equipment by private employers which does not comply with OSHA requirements is limited to the actual emergency situation. Citations could be issued for the use of such equipment in a nonrescue operation such as clean-up or reconstruction work.

The third priority of unprogrammed inspections authorizes investigations of complaints and referrals.

VII. COMPLAINT AND REFERRAL INSPECTIONS

An employee complaint may result in an inspection. The complaint may be directed to an inspector or to the Area Director. The complaint must:

- Be in writing
- Be signed
- Set forth with reasonable particularity the grounds of the complaint

To initiate an inspection based upon a complaint or referral, the Area Director must ensure that the complaint satisfies the requirements discussed directly above and determine that there are reasonable grounds to believe an alleged violation exists.

If the Area Director determines that an inspection is warranted, an inspection is to be made as soon as practicable.

If the Area Director determines that an inspection is not warranted, notice of that conclusion must be given to the complainant. The complaining party may then take the complaint to the Assistant Regional Director who will make the final determination of the request. At that stage, the employer may oppose such a review.

If the complainant requests confidentiality, it will be maintained, and the identity of the individual will not be revealed to the employer. If the complaining employee does not request confidentiality, a copy of the complaint must be provided to the employer no later than the time of the inspection.

29 U.S.C.A. § 660 protects employees from discrimination for filing such a complaint.

The inspection does *not* need to be limited to only those matters referred to in the complaint.

VIII. PROGRAMMED INSPECTIONS

Unlike unprogrammed inspections, programmed inspections are inspections of workplaces which have been scheduled, based upon objective or neutral selection criteria. The workplaces to be inspected are selected according to national scheduling plans or special emphasis programs.

In scheduling programmed inspections, certain considerations are fundamental to the implementation of OSHA's targeting system. It is OSHA policy that programmed inspections are primarily in the "high-hazard" sectors of employment

A programmed inspection will generally consist of a comprehensive inspection of the entire worksite. The scope of the inspection may, nevertheless, be limited, in view of resource availability of the Area Director and other enforcement priorities. For example, low-hazard areas at the place of employment (such as office space) may be excluded from such an inspection without affecting the comprehensiveness of that inspection.

IX. COMPREHENSIVE AND PARTIAL INSPECTIONS

Inspections may be comprehensive or partial.

A comprehensive investigation consists of a substantially complete inspection of all potentially high-hazard areas of an establishment.

A partial inspection, on the other hand, consists of an inspection which may be limited to certain potentially hazardous areas, operations, conditions, or practices which may exist at the establishment.

Every inspection, whether programmed or unprogrammed, comprehensive or partial, shall include, in addition to its principal focus:

- A review of the employer's injury and illness records
- An assessment of the employer's hazard communication program
- An assessment of the employer's lockout/tagout program
- An evaluation of the employer's safety and health management program
- A brief walk-around to survey, as deemed appropriate, those areas, conditions, operations, and practices that, based on the exercise of discretion and professional judgment of the inspector, are believed to have the greatest hazard potential

In summary, for example, in the event of a fatality investigation, the inspection would be unprogrammed and would be assigned a higher inspection priority than a complaint investigation. If, in the opinion of the Area Director, a comprehensive inspection of the reporting employer's jobsite is necessary, the Area Director may direct the scope of the fatality investigation to be comprehensive rather than partial.

X. NO ADVANCE WARNING

Generally, no advance warning of an inspection is allowed. Occasionally, an advance notice may be given, for example, in a case of an apparent imminent hazard. If advance notice is given, the employer must promptly notify the authorized representative (if any) of the employees. Failure to so notify may result in a citation or penalty.

Chapter 8

OSHA CITATIONS AND PROPOSED PENALTIES

This chapter discusses citations and fines that OSHA may issue as a result of violations observed or discovered during an inspection.

Upon completion of an inspection, the inspector prepares a written report which is reviewed by the Area Director. If the documentation substantiates that an employer has violated a safety regulation or any substantive rule, a citation shall be issued to the employer.

The citation must describe the nature of the alleged violation and include a reference to the provisions of the Act, safety regulation, or order alleged to have been violated. Any citation must include a reasonable time for abatement of the alleged violation.

Generally, no citation may be issued more than 6 months after the occurrence of the alleged violation.

The employer shall also be notified of any proposed fine; which amount is determined by the Area Director, who takes into consideration such factors as the size of the employer's business, the gravity of the violation, the good faith of the employer, and the history of previous violations by the employer.

Generally, the amount of any proposed penalty is set forth on the face of the citation.

I. TYPES OF CITATIONS

OSHA citations are classified as **other-than-serious, serious, repeated,** or **willful**.

An **other-than-serious** citation is a violation that is not serious. An other-than-serious violation would generally be issued when a violation of an occupational safety and health regulation does exist, but the most likely result of the condition would probably not result in death or serious physical harm.

A proposed penalty of up to $7000 for each such violation is discretionary. A penalty for an other-than-serious violation may be adjusted downward by as much as 95%, depending on the employer's good faith (demonstrated efforts to comply with the Act), its history of previous violations (hopefully the lack thereof), the gravity of the condition, and the size of the business. When the adjusted penalty amounts to less than $50, no penalty is proposed.

A **serious** violation is defined as existing in a place of employment "...if there is a substantial probability that death or serious physical harm could result from a condition which exists, or from one or more practices, means, methods, operations, or processes which have been adopted or are in use, in such place of employment unless the employer did not, and could not with the exercise of reasonable diligence, know of the presence of the violation." (29 U.S.C.A. § 666(k).)

A mandatory penalty of up to $7000 for each serious violation may be assessed. A penalty for a serious violation may be adjusted based on the employer's good faith, history of previous violations, the gravity of the alleged violation, and the size of the employer's business.

II. ADVICE

As you can see, there is a two-fold test for proving a serious violation. The burden of proving each element of the test rests with OSHA. The inspector will make the first determination of whether each element exists during the initial inspection. OSHA must first prove that there is a substantial probability that death or serious physical harm could occur as a result of an existing condition. Second, the agency must prove that your company either had actual knowledge of the existence of the violation or, with the exercise of reasonable diligence, could have known of the presence of the violation. These are two completely different, unrelated issues. If OSHA is unable to carry its burden of proving both elements of a serious violation, the classification of the citation as serious is improper. The violation could still be upheld, but would usually be modified to allege an other-than-serious violation.

If you do not feel that the agency can prove both elements of a serious violation, after taking into consideration the amount of the civil penalty which may be imposed, you may want to consider filing an appeal from the citation, if for no other reason than to try and have the citation reduced from a serious violation to an other-than-serious violation. If the citation is modified at a hearing, the amount of the civil penalty would be significantly reduced.

A current violation will be classified as **repeated** if your company has been previously cited for a substantially similar condition and the earlier citation (the "underlying citation") has become a final order of the Review Commission. A citation becomes final one of two ways: if no timely appeal from the citation is filed with the Review Commission, or if a decision has denied the appeal of the citation.

While there is no statutory time limit as to how long the underlying citation may support a repeated citation, generally a citation will only be classified as a repeated violation if the present citation is issued within three (3) years of the final order of the underlying citation, or within 3 years of the final abatement date of the underlying citation, whichever is *later.*

If the current citation exists at a different place of employment than the underlying citation, it may or may not be properly classified as a repeated violation.

If the "gravity" of the citation is high (an injury resulting from the violation could be severe), the Area Director will determine if the employer has received any citations at any location *in the nation* over which Fed/OSHA has jurisdiction. If so, the citation may be classified as repeated.

Violations of a *lesser gravity* will generally be classified as repeated under either of two conditions; a violation at a *fixed* place of employment will generally only support a repeated violation if the alleged violation occurs at the same location. At *non-fixed* establishments (such as construction or oil and gas drilling sites) a repeated violation may exist at any site location within the jurisdiction of the same OSHA Area Office.

In summary, if your company has been previously cited within the past 3 years by OSHA for a substantially similar condition, the present citation may be classified as a repeated violation if essentially the same condition exists at the same place of employment at which the previous violation existed. For activities occurring at different locations (such as various construction projects), OSHA will look at the company's citation history throughout the same OSHA Area Office in which the present citation occurred. If a violation of a substantially similar condition occurred within the same OSHA Area Office in question within the previous 3 years, the present citation may be properly classified as repeated.

The penalties assessed for repeated violations increase significantly as the violations continue to occur. Repeated violations can bring a fine of up to $70,000 for each such violation. Repeated violations can become willful.

It may be advisable to consider appealing those citations which could be the basis for possible repeated citations. See Chapter 11.

A **willful** violation is not defined in the enabling legislation. OSHA Instruction CPL 2.45B CH-3 describes a willful violation as existing when the evidence shows either an *intentional* violation or *plain indifference* to the Act or its requirements.

Generally, it has been held that an *intentional* and *knowing* violation has occurred if an employer representative was aware of the requirements of the

Act or of the existence of an applicable standard or regulation and was also aware of a condition or practice which was in violation of those requirements.

It may be that willful conduct has occurred even though an employer representative was not aware of any legal requirements but was aware that an existing condition or practice was hazardous, and the representative made little or no effort to determine the extent of the problem or take corrective action.

Plain indifference exists when it can be established that higher management officials were aware of an OSHA requirement which was applicable to the company's business but made little or no effort to communicate the requirement to lower-level supervisors and employees.

Penalties of up to $70,000 may be proposed for each willful violation with a minimum penalty of $25,000 for each violation. A proposed penalty for a willful violation may be adjusted depending on the size of the business and its history of previous violations. Usually, no credit is given for good faith.

While not a citation per se, a Notification of Failure to Abate an Alleged Violation (OSHA-2B) is to be issued in cases where violations have not been corrected as required. Significant civil penalties can be assessed on a *daily* basis for failure to abate the violation. The Area Director has considerable discretion in calculating the amount of the daily penalty amount.

Chapter 9

GENERAL DUTY CLAUSE

Fed/OSHA requires employers to furnish employment which is free of recognized hazards. As discussed, one method that Fed/OSHA follows to ensure a safe and healthy workplace is by enforcing existing safety and health regulations. It may also enforce the "general duty" clause.

The general duty clause poses requirements which may be separate from and in addition to those included in existing safety rules and regulations. The general duty clause requires an employer to keep employees from being exposed to a recognized hazard which is likely to cause death or serious physical harm.

As the employer, you must recognize the potential for hazardous conditions. If such a condition exists, you must take those steps necessary to eliminate the hazard. If you do not eliminate an existing hazardous condition, you are subject to being cited for a violation of the general duty clause. A violation of the general duty clause consists of four elements:

- An existing hazard to which employees were exposed
- The hazard must be recognized
- The hazard was causing or was likely to cause death or serious physical harm
- Availability of a feasible existing method of abatement

These elements are discussed further below.

I. EXISTING HAZARD

A violation of the general duty clause is the result of the *existence of a hazard* in the workplace. Employee exposure is a requirement; that is, an employer may be in violation of the general duty clause *only* if its *own* employees are exposed to the hazard.

Creation of, or responsibility for, the hazard is not the key. An employer may have created the hazardous condition but, if its employees were not exposed to the condition, it may not be cited for a violation of the general duty clause.

The occurrence of an accident is also not a factor. It may be that an accident is evidence of a hazard, but the accident may also be unrelated to any existing hazard. It is the exposure of an employee to the existence of a hazard that controls.

If any of your employees are exposed to a hazardous condition, your company is subject to being cited for a violation of the general duty clause.

The hazard must be **reasonably foreseeable**. If, for example, combustible gases exist in a location but no source of ignition exists, there could be no violation of the general duty clause since it was not reasonably foreseeable that an explosion could occur.

II. RECOGNIZABLE HAZARD

The hazardous condition must be recognized as a hazard. Recognition of a hazard exists if the employer had actual knowledge of the hazard or if it is a hazard which would be recognized as such within the employer's industry.

The exercise of common sense may also establish knowledge of the existing hazard. If it looks like a duck and quacks like a duck, it is probably a duck, and you should treat it as such. So it is with a recognized hazard. Treat it as such.

III. DEATH OR SERIOUS PHYSICAL HARM

In order to constitute a general duty clause violation, the hazard must be of a magnitude likely to result in death or serious physical harm to the exposed employee(s).

If a hazardous condition exists to which one or more of your company's employees are exposed, but that condition is not likely to result in death or serious physical harm, OSHA may not issue a citation based upon the general duty clause.

Remember, however, that while an existing condition may not be subject to the general duty clause, it may, nevertheless, constitute a violation of an existing occupational safety and health standard. Therefore, when reviewing your company's operations, practices, and procedures, make sure they comply not only with your company's rules and with existing OSHA rules and regulations, but with common sense. Think about the duck.

IV. FEASIBLE, AVAILABLE ABATEMENT MEASURES EXIST

Abatement measures must be available and must be feasible before an employer may be cited for a general duty clause violation; that is, recognized hazards must be preventable.

In summary, your company may be subject to the general duty clause if a recognized hazardous condition exists (or is likely to exist) at your place of employment, which is (or should be) recognizable as a hazard to which your employees are (or are likely to be) exposed, and which may result in death or serious physical harm and an available, feasible method of controlling the condition exists.

Chapter 10

AVOIDING OSHA
INSPECTIONS AND
CONDUCT OF
SUCH INSPECTIONS

This chapter discusses methods of avoiding OSHA inspections. In the event of an inspection, this chapter also discusses what you might expect during such an inspection.

- Avoiding an OSHA inspection
- Conduct of inspection and dealing with an inspector
  - Opening conference
    - Inspection warrant
    - Inspection procedure
  - Walk-around inspection
  - Closing conference

I. AVOIDING AN OSHA INSPECTION

There is no "sure-fire" way to avoid an OSHA inspection. Without question, however, the best way to avoid an OSHA inspection is to maintain a safe workplace in compliance with existing OSHA regulations and your company's own safety and health practices and procedures.

Not only will a safe and healthful workplace tend to reduce the occurrence of injuries and illnesses, but it will reflect a positive commitment by the employer to the health and safety of its employees. Employees are less likely to file a complaint with OSHA if they believe their employer is genuinely concerned with their well-being. The absence of imminent hazards, job-related accidents, and employee complaints will reduce the employer's chances for an unprogrammed OSHA inspection.

If your company has developed and implemented an effective safety and health program and has established a good reputation with OSHA, the agency is more likely to discount unfounded complaints, and it may limit the scope of any inspection which it does conduct.

There are also steps which you may take during an inspection which may yield a positive result.

II. CONDUCT OF INSPECTION AND DEALING WITH AN INSPECTOR

The OSHA Field Operations Manual provides that at the beginning of the inspection, the inspector is to attempt to locate the owner, operator, or agent in charge of the workplace. Once located, the inspector is to present his/her credentials to the employer representative.

If the person in charge is not present, the inspector is to identify the top management official who is available. If neither the person in charge nor a top management official is present, the inspector is to request the presence of such a person.

The inspector will generally wait for a reasonable period of time (perhaps up to one hour) for the arrival of the representative of the employer.

The inspection may commence with the top management official present even if the person in charge never becomes available.

A. Opening Conference

After introductions and the presentation of credentials, the inspector is to conduct an *opening conference* which includes an explanation of the nature and purpose of the inspection, including a description of the general scope of the inspection.

As a part of the opening conference, the inspector will typically request to review certain written documents of the company prior to the commencement of the walk-around inspection (the physical inspection of the jobsite). The inspector will generally ask to review the OSHA Log 200 (OSHA No. 200) and any written programs your company should have implemented, for example, a written safety program and/or the company's written hazard communication program.

It is essential that the company's OSHA Log 200 be accurately maintained and available for review; that all necessary written programs be current and available; and that complete and properly documented safety and health training records exist. Additionally, ensure that all required posters are current and properly posted.

The inspector is to notify the employer of its right to have a representative accompany the inspector during the inspection. A representative of the employees is also given the same opportunity. The inspector is authorized to resolve any disputes as to who is the representative authorized by the employees. If there is no authorized representative of the employees, the inspector is to consult with a reasonable number of employees during the inspection concerning matters of safety and health in the workplace.

Different representatives of the employer and the employees may accompany the inspector during different phases of the inspection as long as the changes will not interfere with the conduct of the inspection.

B. Construction

On multi-employer construction worksites, the inspector is to ask for the superintendent, project manager, or other representative of the general or prime contractor. Once this contact is made, the representative of the general or prime contractor is to identify and assemble representatives of the subcontractors and any employee representatives of the subcontractor companies.

C. Inspection Warrant

An employer does have the right to request that the inspector obtain an *inspection warrant* before commencing the actual inspection of the workplace. 29 CFR 1903.4(a).

If an employer refuses the right of entry or otherwise prohibits the inspector from conducting the inspection, the inspector shall endeavor to determine the reason for such refusal or limitation and shall immediately report the refusal and the reason therefore to the Area Director. The Area Director will consult with the Regional Director, who is authorized to initiate action to obtain an inspection warrant.

The right of entry may not be negotiated with the OSHA inspector. That is, the employer may not require that the inspector agree not to issue a citation or penalty in exchange for allowing the inspector entry to the workplace without the need for an inspection warrant.

D. Advice

There is a difference of opinion regarding the advisability of requiring OSHA to obtain an inspection warrant. Remember that inspectors are human beings and may take such a request personally, which could influence the inspector's state of mind if and when he/she returns with an inspection warrant. OSHA could believe that the company had something to hide by demanding a warrant. Such a belief, proper or not, could result in a more comprehensive and time-consuming inspection than might otherwise have occurred. Since it is not unrealistic to suggest that the more time an OSHA inspector spends at your worksite, the more likely it is a violation may be observed, you may have done more harm than good by making such a request.

On the other hand, it may be that the company has instituted a policy to deny warrantless searches. Perhaps it strongly believes "probable cause" for an inspection does not exist or that there is some other existing condition which makes the inspection unreasonable. Under certain circumstances, the employer may be unwilling to permit an inspection, the result of which may be to require OSHA to seek an inspection warrant.

If it is company policy to require an inspection warrant, it is advisable to explain to the inspector why he/she is not being allowed to conduct an inspection without an inspection warrant. A reasonable explanation of why company policy requires a warrant may go a long way toward smoothing the way for any subsequent inspection in the event that OSHA does obtain an inspection warrant.

Assuming that your company policy is to permit an inspection without a warrant, or if a warrant has been obtained, the inspection will commence.

III. INSPECTION PROCEDURE RECOMMENDATIONS

It is highly advisable that you consider the appointment and training of a "key person." This person should have a basic understanding of the nature and scope of an OSHA inspection and the rights and duties of your company during an OSHA inspection.

Remember that in choosing the key person, he/she will be representing the interests of your company throughout the OSHA inspection. OSHA will consider statements made by the key person to have been made on behalf of the company; that is, he or she will be considered to be speaking for the company. The key person should:

- Verify the inspector's credentials.
- Determine the reason(s) for the inspection.
- Attempt to limit the scope of the inspection.

- Accompany the inspector throughout the inspection.
- Note apparent items of interest to the inspector.
- Note the identity of employees to whom the inspector talks.
- In the event the inspector takes photographs, the key person should take photographs of the same locations or of those items of interest to the inspector. The company's photographs may be taken either during the inspection or shortly thereafter (as long as conditions do not change).
- Taking written notes during the inspection may or may not be a good idea. It must be remembered that there is a possibility that in the event of an appeal of a citation, OSHA may attempt to obtain copies of the key person's notes. To possibly avoid this consequence, it may be advisable to prepare a written report at the request of the company attorney after the inspection is completed.

It is advisable that the key person *not speculate or offer opinions* during an OSHA inspection. The key person should respond to the inspector's questions, but only to the questions, and then as briefly as possible, and only to the extent that the answer is factual. See Appendix 10A for a proposed Company Inspection Procedure.

A. Advice

It only makes sense that company documents regarding safety and health are kept readily available at the workplace. If your key person is familiar with the documents and makes them immediately available to the inspector at the commencement of the inspection, the tenor of the walk-around inspection may be entirely different than if your company's representative appears to be unfamiliar with the basic requirements of OSHA's safety and health rules and regulations. **This is important!** First impressions are often lasting impressions. It is critical that your key person understand this basic fact and that the inspection get started on a positive footing. One other word of advice: **Treat the inspector as you would want to be treated!**

IV. WALK-AROUND INSPECTION

Generally, the scope of the inspection is left to the discretion of OSHA. It may be that in the event of an inspection warrant, the scope of the inspection is described; however, absent some type of limiting condition, there appears to be no restriction upon the authority of OSHA regarding the scope of the inspection.

When an inspector has arrived on your doorstep, your key person should attempt to learn the intent of the inspector. The key person should attempt to limit the scope of the inspection to only that operation, process, equipment, or location which may pose a potentially high-hazard exposure.

The inspection is to be conducted so as to preclude any unreasonable disruption of the operations of the company. Inspectors are to comply with all employer safety and health rules and practices at the establishment being inspected, and they are to wear and use appropriate protective clothing and equipment.

The inspector *does* have the right to talk with company employees in private. This right of confidentiality belongs to the employee. If the employee waives his/her right, you have a right to be present during discussions between the employee and the inspector. Notwithstanding this fact, if the inspector feels strongly about the privacy of the conversation, it may be advisable to allow the conversation to proceed without the presence of the key person, thereby preventing an unneeded confrontation. You may always speak with the employee after the inspection to discuss the conversation between the employee and the inspector.

The inspector has a right to take photographs, conduct sampling, and engage in those types of activities which may be necessary to determine the existence of any unsafe conditions, practices, or methods.

V. CLOSING CONFERENCE

At the conclusion of the inspection, the inspector will generally conduct a *closing conference.* During this meeting, the inspector will confer with your company's key person or other designated representatives and advise such person(s) of any apparent safety or health violations discovered during the inspection. If employee representatives were involved in the inspection, the parties may request separate closing conferences. Where it is otherwise not practicable to hold a joint closing conference, separate closing conferences shall be held.

During the closing conference, the inspector shall describe any alleged violations found during the inspection and indicate the applicable sections of the safety or health standards which may have been violated. Copies of the safety standards are to be given to both the employer and the employee representative. The representatives of both the employer and the employees are to be advised of their right to participate in any subsequent conferences, meetings, or discussions.

During the closing conference, the inspector is also to give the employer a copy of the publication, "Employer Rights and Responsibilities Following an OSHA Inspection." This document explains the responsibilities and courses of action available to the employer if a citation and fine are issued. The inspector shall then briefly discuss the information in the booklet and answer any questions. All matters discussed during the closing conference shall be documented in the inspector's case file.

During this closing conference, the employer may bring to the attention of the inspector any pertinent information regarding workplace conditions.

A closing conference does not need to be conducted immediately upon completion of the inspection. It may be held at a later date. Remember: OSHA has six (6) months to issue citations and fines for alleged violations. U.S.C.A. § 658(c).

Chapter 11

APPEAL OR NOT? AND APPEALING A CITATION OR PENALTY

Upon receipt of a Citation and Notification of Penalty from OSHA, your company is faced with a decision; perhaps it is your decision. Should you decide (or recommend) that an appeal be filed from the citation and/or the fine? This chapter is intended to give advice on whether or not to file such an appeal.

This chapter will discuss:

- Reasons to appeal
- Appealing a citation or penalty
- Informal conference

The time to decide whether or not to appeal an OSHA citation or fine is before receipt of such a document. You should establish a decision-making policy within the company regarding how such administrative agency actions are to be handled. Will the company automatically accept an adverse action without objection (as many do) or will each allegation of an administrative agency be reviewed on a case-by-case basis?

I. POSTING OF CITATION

Upon receipt of any citation, the employer must immediately post the citation or a copy at or near the place where the alleged violation occurred, unless such posting is impractical. If posting at the location of the alleged violation is no longer possible, the citation shall be posted in a prominent place, readily observable by company employees.

Where employees do not primarily work at or report to a single location, the citation may be posted at the location from which the employees operate to carry out their activities.

The citation or copy thereof must remain posted until the violation has been abated or for 3 workings days, *whichever is later.*

Filing an appeal from the citation does *not* affect this posting requirement.

II. REASONS TO APPEAL

If your company chooses to individually evaluate each proposed adverse administrative action, you should give consideration to at least the following factors:

- Existence of the violation
- Amount of civil fine
- Consequences *outside* of OSHA
- Citation improperly classified (e.g., not "serious" or not "willful")
- Possibility of a "repeat" violation
- Costs and likelihood of success
- Alienate OSHA: Yes or no?

A. Existence of the Violation

One legitimate reason for appealing an OSHA citation would be your belief that the violation did not exist. There will be occasions when a genuine factual dispute exists between you and the OSHA inspector as to the facts of an alleged violation: OSHA contends that the facts constitute a violation of a safety standard and your company disagrees.

An example of this type of situation may occur with a health standard such as 29 CFR 1910.95 whereby OSHA is alleging an employee has been exposed to a level of noise for a period of time exceeding the permissible exposure limit for such a noise level. Based on this belief, a citation (and fine) is issued to the company by OSHA. However, it is your opinion that the OSHA inspector did not perform the type of testing necessary to establish the existing noise level or did not accurately determine the length of time an employee was exposed to the alleged noise level. You believe that the citation was erroneous and that OSHA will be unable to carry *its burden* of proving a violation of the regulation.

Given such a situation, you must decide whether or not to file an appeal.

There may be occasions when OSHA has issued a citation which you believe alleges a violation of a safety regulation that did not apply to the circumstances. If you are familiar with the safety regulations, it may be your opinion that, not only did OSHA cite an improper safety order (that is, a safety regulation that was not violated), but OSHA will be unable to prove a violation of the safety regulation you believe properly applied to the existing circumstances. To prove your contention that the alleged violation did not exist, your only alternative is to file an appeal. Therefore, you are faced with the decision — appeal or not?

B. Amount of Civil Fine

Another reason for filing an appeal could be the amount of the penalties assessed as a result of the alleged violations. Penalties generally accompany a violation, and usually the more serious a condition, the higher the fine amount. It may be that the amount of the proposed penalty is too high given the circumstances or that it is excessive for your company and may pose an undue hardship on the viability of the company if upheld. The amount of the fine alone may justify the filing of an appeal.

While proposed OSHA fines are determined in accordance with a for mula, the agency may not have afforded your company proper "credits" for all possible penalty reduction factors. If the credits had been computed in accordance with your contentions, the result could be a significant reduction in the amount of the fine.

In computing the amount of the fine, OSHA considers factors such as the size of your company's business, its OSHA "history" (any previous citations), its "good faith" (does it appear that you are trying to ensure safety on the job?), and other factors such as the gravity of the violation, how widespread the condition is (is every ladder defective, or only one of 100 ladders?), and the likelihood of an accident as a result of the unsafe condition.

These factors are all considered in computing the final amount of the penalty and generally result in reductions in the proposed penalty.

Also, if you are able to persuade an administrative law judge to modify a citation to a lesser category (for example "serious" to "other-than-serious"), the amount of the proposed penalty for the violation should be significantly reduced.

C. Consequences Outside of OSHA

It may be that an OSHA citation has repercussions outside of OSHA, repercussions that could be significant. For example, the violation of a safety regulation may support a criminal charge, perhaps civil litigation, a workers' compensation claim, as well as another administrative agency's allegations of wrongdoing. **Such consequences could outweigh all other factors!** You should verify whether any such consequences are possible in the state in which you are doing business or in which the violation allegedly occurred.

For example, if an OSHA citation can support a criminal charge, this possibility alone may trigger the need to appeal the OSHA citation.

D. Violation Improperly Characterized

One factor to consider in determining whether to file an appeal from an OSHA citation may be that the violation was improperly classified. It may be that while a violation of a safety order may have existed as alleged in a citation, you believe the classification of that violation as "serious" or "willful" or "repeated" is incorrect.

For example, perhaps OSHA has issued a "serious" citation to your company. A serious citation is deemed to exist "...if there is a substantial probability that death or serious physical harm could result from a condition which exists, or from one or more practices, means, methods, operations, or processes which have been adopted or are in use, in such place of employment unless the employer did not, and could not with the exercise of reasonable diligence, know of the presence of the violation." Title 29 U.S.C.A. § 666(k).

For OSHA to establish that a citation is properly classified as serious, it has the burden of proving *both* elements of the serious test. That is, the agency has to prove with substantial evidence that there was substantial probability of death or serious physical injury because of an existing condition or practice *and* that your company either knew of the condition or practice or, with the exercise of reasonable diligence, could have known of the condition or practice.

Perhaps a condition did exist which could have resulted in a serious injury. However, it is your belief that no management representative of the company had actual knowledge of the condition or, with the exercise of reasonable diligence, could have known of the condition or practice. You believe, therefore, that OSHA will be unable to prove the "knowledge" element of a serious violation. For this reason you may want to file an appeal of the citation. If you are successful, the citation, even though it may have existed, should be reduced from "serious" to an "other-than-serious" violation (generally with a significant reduction in the amount of any proposed fine).

E. Possibility of a Repeated Violation

It may be that you are dealing with a workplace practice or condition which is difficult to immediately correct or eliminate. You are working to correct the condition, but notwithstanding your efforts to eliminate or prevent the occurrence of the given condition or practice, it continues to exist. This ongoing practice or condition could result in repeated violations in the event of future OSHA inspections. In a case such as this, you may want to consider filing an appeal from a citation alleging a violation of such a condition or practice. If successful on appeal, you have avoided the possibility of that citation being used as a basis to support a future repeated violation.

For example, you have a noisy environment which may occasionally exceed the permissible sound level. You are unable to control the noise at its source; therefore, you have implemented an effective hearing conservation program. Unfortunately, no matter how hard you try, every time you walk into the plant, there is at least one employee who is failing to use hearing protection. These occasions always involve a different employee. While you are diligently working to ensure the use of hearing protection (which you provide without cost) by all of your employees at all times, you realize that you have not quite reached that level of compliance; therefore, there may be an occasional exposure by an employee to an excessive level of noise due to the failure of the employee to use the hearing protection provided by the company.

By failing to achieve a consistent 100% compliance by the employees with the company's hearing conservation program, it is possible that every time an OSHA inspection is conducted, your company could be cited for a violation for failing to effectively enforce its hearing conservation program.

Given these conditions, you may be well-advised to appeal from any citation alleging noncompliance with the requirement of the occupational noise exposure standard to use hearing protection. On appeal, it may turn out that no employee was exposed to an excessive noise level while not wearing proper hearing protection on the occasion(s) alleged by OSHA and that, therefore, the citation was, indeed, erroneous. In such an event, the citation would be rejected (if appealed) and could not, therefore, become the basis for a future repeated citation.

F. Costs and Likelihood of Success

In the company's determination of whether to file an appeal, you must consider the cost as well as the likelihood of success. In considering cost, you should consider not only the expense of an attorney, but also the time and cost of your own staff and employees in terms of preparing for and par-ticipating in the hearing.

You should also consider the likelihood of success of an appeal. If it appears that you do not have any realistic chance of success, it may be in-advisable to expend the time and effort necessary (and the cost) to prepare for and participate in the appeal hearing. The key to any likelihood of success is often the availability of possible defenses. Possible defenses could include one or more of the following:

- No employee exposure or access to the allegedly hazardous condition
- Employee negligence
- Wrong safety order cited
- Unreliable or missing evidence
- Impossibility of compliance

G. Alienate OSHA: Yes or No?

In determining whether to file an appeal, the question of whether such an action may alienate an OSHA inspector is often raised. Like it or not, that is a legitimate concern. The filing of an appeal from a citation should *not* and generally will not upset the inspector who conducted the inspection. Most OSHA inspectors understand that an appeal is an employer's right and simply consider such an action a part of their job.

The fact that an OSHA administrative law judge may subsequently issue a decision setting aside the citation will generally not change the fact that the inspector thinks he/she acted properly in the first place. OSHA inspectors are competent professionals and understand an employer's right to contest a citation and/or fine. Filing an appeal should not alienate an inspector or put your company at risk with OSHA in the future.

III. APPEALING A CITATION OR PENALTY

If, as a result of an OSHA inspection, your company has received a citation and proposed penalty which you have analyzed pursuant to company policy and have determined to appeal, you must satisfy the procedural steps in filing an appeal.

You may appeal a citation, any abatement requirements, or a civil penalty. You may initiate your appeal by notifying the OSHA Area Director *in writing* of your intention. This written notification is referred to as the "Notice of Contest."

There is *no particular format* necessary to initiate the Notice of Contest; a simple letter will suffice. It is advisable, however, to include a copy of the Citation(s) and Notification of Penalty with each appeal you send to the Area Director. The address of the Area Director who issued the citation should be set forth on the face of the Citation and Notification of Penalty.

It is also advisable (though not required) to send the Notice of Contest to the Area Director by certified or registered mail, return receipt requested. If you are not sending the appeal by registered or certified mail, it is advisable to include a *copy* of a Declaration of Proof of Service with the written correspondence requesting the appeal. The Declaration of Proof of Service should be signed and completed by the person depositing the appeal document(s) in the mail to ensure you are able to prove the date that the appeal was mailed to the Area Director. Retain the *original* declaration for company records.

While there is no particular format you must use to initiate the appeal, you must make sure that the written appeal is postmarked *within 15 working days* of the company's *receipt* of the citation and/or proposed penalty.

If you desire to appeal *only* the amount of any proposed penalty, since the fine is generally included on the face of the citation, you must still file your written appeal with the Area Director within 15 working days of the receipt of the citation.

Under OSHA, there is *no* provision allowing late appeals; any appeal must be served on the Area Director within 15 working days of the receipt of the citation and/or fine. 29 U.S.C.A. § 659(a).

Every Notice of Contest timely filed with the Area Director must clearly identify the scope of the company's appeal. For example, does the appeal include the citation as well as any proposed civil penalty? Is the appeal intended to contest issues of abatement?

You should also consider raising possible affirmative defenses in your Notice of Contest *whether or not* you eventually pursue such a defense. An affirmative defense is a defense which you must prove (such as employee negligence or impossibility of compliance). You may wait to identify affirmative defenses until such time as your answer is to be filed in response to the complaint which will be filed on behalf of OSHA.

Your Notice of Contest will be forwarded by OSHA to the OSHA Review Commission and will be assigned a docket (case) number. Upon receipt of the docketed Notice of Contest, you must post a copy of that document in a conspicuous place at the workplace. A copy of the docketed Notice of Contest must also be given to any of the affected employees (e.g., a union representative).

After filing your appeal, the Secretary of Labor will file a written complaint alleging that the citation and civil penalty were proper. You must file a timely written response to the complaint. The appeal will be scheduled for a hearing before an administrative law judge of the OSHA Review Commission. Pay attention to all documents and comply with all orders you receive from the Occupational Safety and Health Review Commission once an appeal has been filed.

A. Advice

If your company has been charged with more than one violation as a result of an inspection and you have decided to file an appeal, you would be well-advised to file an appeal from *all* of the violations, even if your concern is limited to only one of the violations. The reason that separate appeals should be filed from all of the violations is that you may reach a point in the appeals process when you are discussing the possibility of a settlement agreement with OSHA. You will have considerably more leverage in such a negotiation if all of the violations have been appealed.

For example, if OSHA has issued five citations to your company and you are really only concerned with Citation 2, by filing an appeal from all five of the citations you are in a better negotiating posture, because OSHA may be willing to modify or possibly withdraw Citation 2 if you agree to withdraw your appeals of Citations 1, 3, 4, and 5. However, if you have only appealed Citation 2, you are not in a good negotiating posture because you have nothing to give up in exchange for OSHA's considering the possibility of modifying or withdrawing Citation 2.

IV. INFORMAL CONFERENCE

In considering the appeal process, you may want to consider requesting an informal conference.

"At the request of an affected employer, employee, or representative of employees, the Assistant Regional Director may hold an informal conference for the purpose of discussing any issues raised by an inspection, citation, notice of proposed penalty, or notice of intention to contest. ... No such conference or request for such conference shall operate as a stay of any 15-working day period for filing a notice of intention to contest a citation...." 29 CFR 1903.19.

Any request for an informal conference and the scheduling and completion of the conference do *not* operate as a stay of the appeal period; that is, the 15-day period to file a Notice of Contest *continues to run* even if an informal conference is scheduled!

Either the employer, an affected employee, or his/her representative may request an informal conference. 29 CFR 1903.19.*

The requesting party must notify all other parties of the request for the informal conference; that is, the employer must notify its employees and/or the representative(s) of the employees and vice versa.

If you request an informal conference, you may object to the presence of your employees or an employee representative, and separate informal conferences will be scheduled. Private discussions are permitted between you and the OSHA official presiding at such a conference if you so desire.

Area Directors have settlement authority, with the power to reclassify violations and modify or withdraw a penalty or citation.

---

* If you have already filed an appeal of the citation in issue, the informal conference may not be scheduled without prior approval of the Regional Solicitor.

A. Advice

Generally, you should not expect to have a citation set aside at an informal conference. If your intent is merely to accomplish a reduction in the amount of the proposed civil penalty or a reclassification of a citation (such as from "serious" to an "other-than-serious") you may be successful.

One word of advice! It is unusual for OSHA to withdraw a citation which has already been appealed. At an informal conference, your attempts to convince OSHA to consider your contentions may do more harm than good if your concerns are not resolved to your satisfaction, because you may end up providing OSHA with additional information which may then be used against you at a hearing. Always be prudent in your discussions in such a situation.

APPENDICES

Numbers at bottom of pages in appendices represent pages on which original material appeared.

APPENDICES

Appendix 1A

U.S. Department of Labor, Occupational Safety and Health Administration, Regional and Area Offices

U.S. Department of Labor, Occupational Safety and Health Administration, Regional and Area Offices

Region I
(CT,* MA, ME, NH, RI, VT*)

133 Portland Street
1st Floor
Boston, MA 02114
Telephone: (617) 565-7164

Region II
(NJ, NY,* PR,* VI*)

201 Varick Street
Room 670
New York, NY 10014
Telephone: (212) 337-2378

Region III
(DC, DE, MD,* PA, VA,* WV)

Gateway Building, Suite 2100
3535 Market Street
Philadelphia, PA 19104
Telephone: (215) 596-1201

Region IV
(AL, FL, GA, KY,* MS, NC,* SC,* TN*)

1375 Peachtree Street, N.E.
Suite 587
Atlanta, GA 30367
Telephone: (404) 347-3573

Region V
(IL, IN,* MI,* MN,* OH, WI)

230 South Dearborn Street
Room 3244
Chicago, IL 60604
Telephone: (312) 353-2220

Region VI
(AR, LA, NM,* OK, TX)

525 Griffin Street
Room 602
Dallas, TX 75202
Telephone: (214) 767-4731

Region VII
(IA,* KS, MO, NE)

911 Walnut Street
Room 406
Kansas City, MO 64106
Telephone: (816) 426-5861

Region VIII
(CO, MT, ND, SD, UT,* WY*)

Federal Building, Room 1576
1961 Stout Street
Denver, CO 80294
Telephone: (303) 844-3061

Region IX
(American Samoa, AZ,* CA,* Guam,
HI,* NV,* Trust Territories of the
Pacific)

71 Stevenson Street, Room 415
San Francisco, CA 94105
Telephone: (415) 744-6670

Region X
(AK,* ID, OR,* WA*)

111 Third Avenue, Suite 715
Seattle, WA 98101-3212
Telephone: (206) 553-5930

* These states and territories operate their own OSHA-approved job safety and health programs (Connecticut and New York plans cover public employees only). States with approved programs must have a standard that is identical to, or at least as effective as, the federal standard.

Agencies preceded by an asterisk (*) are those in which a state safety and health plan under section 18(b) of the act is in operation. This agency may be contacted directly for specific information regarding regulations in the state.

Alabama Department of Labor
  600 Administrative Building
  Montgomery, AL 36130
  Phone: (205) 261-3460

*Alaska Department of Labor
  Research and Analysis Section
  Post Office Box 1149
  Juneau, AK 99802
  Phone: (907) 465-4520

Territory of American Samoa
  Department of Manpower
    Resources
  Government of American Samoa
  Pago Pago, American Samoa 96799
  Phone: 633-5849

*Individual Commission of Arizona
  Division of Administration/
    Research and Statistics Section
  1601 W. Jefferson Street
  Post Office Box 19070
  Phoenix, AZ 85005
  Phone: (602) 255-3739

Workers' Compensation Commission,
    OSH
  Arkansas Department of Labor
  OSH Research and Statistics
  Room 502, 1022 High Street
  Little Rock, AR 72202
  Phone: (501) 371-2770

*California Department of Industrial
    Relations
  Labor Statistics and Research
  Post Office Box 603
  San Francisco, CA 94901
  Phone: (415) 557-1466

*Colorado Department of Labor and
    Employment
  Division of Labor
  1313 Sherman Street
  Room 323
  Denver, CO 80203
  Phone: (303) 866-3748

*Connecticut Department of Labor
  200 Folly Brook Boulevard
  Wethersfield, CT 06109
  Phone: (203) 566-4380

Delaware Department of Labor
  Division of Industrial Affairs
  820 N. French Street, 6th Floor
  Wilmington, DE 19801
  Phone: (302) 571-2888

Florida Department of Labor and
    Employment Security
  Division of Workers' Compensation
  2551 Executive Center Circle West
  Room 204
  Tallahassee, FL 32301-5014
  Phone: (904) 488-3044

Guam Department of Labor
  Bureau of Labor Statistics
  Post Office Box 23548
  Guam Main Facility
  Agana, Guam 96921
  Phone: 477-9241

*State of Hawaii
  Department of Labor and Industrial
    Relations
  Research and Statistics Office
  Post Office Box 3680
  Honolulu, HI 96811
  Phone: (808) 548-7638

*Indiana Department of Labor
  Research and Statistics Division
  State Office Building — Room 1013
  100 N. Senate Avenue
  Indianapolis, IN 46204
  Phone: (317) 232-2665

*Iowa Bureau of Labor
  307 East 7th Street
  Des Moines, IA 50319
  Phone: (515) 281-5151

Kansas Department of Health and
    Environment
  Division of Policy and Planning
  Occupational Safety and Health
  Topeka, KS 66620
  Phone: (913) 862-9360 Ext. 280

*Kentucky Labor Cabinet
  Occupational Safety and Health
    Program
  U.S. 127 South Building
  Frankfort, KY 40601
  Phone: (502) 564-3100

Louisiana Department of Labor
  Office of Employment
    Security — OSH
  1001 North 23rd and Fuqua
  Baton Rouge, LA 70804
  Phone: (504) 342-3126

Maine Building of Labor
  Bureau of Labor Standards
  Division of Research and Statistics
  State Office Building
  Augusta, ME 04330
  Phone: (207) 289-3331

*Maryland Department of Licensing
    and Regulation
  Division of Labor and Industry
  501 St. Paul Place
  Baltimore, MD 21202
  Phone: (301) 659-4202

Massachusetts Department of Labor
    and Industries
  Division of Industrial Safety
  100 Cambridge Street
  Boston, MS 02202
  Phone: (617) 727-3593

*Michigan Department of Labor
  7150 Harris Drive
  Secondary Complex
  Post Office Box 30015
  Lansing, MI 48909
  Phone: (517) 322-1848

*Minnesota Department of Labor and
  Industry IMSD
  444 Lafayette Road, 5th Floor
  St. Paul, MN 55101
  Phone: (612) 296-4893

Mississippi State Department of
  Health
  Office of Public Health Statistics
  Post Office Box 1700
  Jackson, MS 39215-1700
  Phone: (601) 354-7233

Missouri Department of Labor and
    Industrial Relations
  Division of Workers' Compensation
  Post Office Box 58
  Jefferson City, Missouri 65102
  Phone: (314) 751-4231

Montana Department of Labor and
    Industry
  Workers' Compensation Division
  5 South Last Chance Gulch
  Helena, MT 59601
  Phone: (406) 444-6515

Nebraska Workmens' Compensation
    Court
  State Capitol, 12th Floor
  Lincoln, NE 68509-4967
  Phone: (402) 471-3547

*Nevada Department of Industrial
   Relations
 Division of Occupational Safety and
   Health
 1370 South Curry Street
 Carson City, NV 89710
 Phone: (702) 885-5240

New Jersey Department of Labor and
   Industry
 Division of Planning and Research
 C N 056
 Trenton, NJ 08625
 Phone: (609) 292-8997

*New Mexico Health and
   Environment Department
 Environmental Improvement
   Division
 Occupational Health and Safety
 P.O. Box 968 — Crown Building
 Sante Fe, NM 87504-0968
 Phone: (505) 827-5271 Ext. 230

New York Department of Labor
 Division of Research and Statistics
 2 World Trade Center
 New York, NY 10047
 Phone: (212) 488-4661

*North Carolina Department of Labor
 Research and Statistics Division
 214 West Jones Street
 Raleigh, NC 27603
 Phone: (919) 733-4940

Ohio Department of Industrial
   Relations
 OSHA Survey Office
 Post Office Box 12355
 Columbus, OH 43212
 Phone: (614) 466-7520

Oklahoma Department of Labor
 Supplemental Data Division
 315 North Broadway Place
 Oklahoma City, OK 73105
 Phone: (405) 235-1447

*Oregon Workers' Compensation
   Department
 Research and Statistics Section
 Labor and Industries Building
 Salem, OR 97310
 Phone: (503) 378-8254

Pennsylvania Department of Labor
   and Industry
 Office of Employment Security
 7th and Forster Streets
 Labor and Industry Building
 Harrisburg, PA 17121
 Phone: (717) 787-1918

*Puerto Rico Department of Labor
   and Human Resources
 Bureau of Labor Statistics
 505 Munoz Rivera Avenue
 San Juan, PR 00918
 Phone: (809) 754-5339

Rhode Island Department of Labor
 220 Elmwood Avenue
 Providence, RI 02907
 Phone: (401) 277-2731

*South Carolina Department of Labor
 Division of Technical Support
 Post Office Box 11329
 Columbia, SC 29211
 Phone: (803) 734-9652

*Tennessee Department of Labor
 Research and Statistics
 501 Union Building, 2nd Floor
 Nashville, TN 37219
 Phone: (615) 741-1748

Texas Department of Health
 Division of Occupational Safety
 1100 West 49th Street
 Austin, TX 78756
 Phone: (512) 458-7287

*Utah Industrial Commission
  OSH Statistical Section
  160 East 300 South
  Salt Lake City, UT 84110-5800
  Phone: (801) 530-6827

*Vermont Department of Labor and
      Industry
  State Office Building
  Montpelier, VT 05602
  Phone: (802) 828-2765

*Virgin Islands Department of Labor
  Post Office Box 818
  St. Thomas, VI 00801
  Phone: (809) 776-3700

*Virginia Department of Labor and
      Industry
  Research and Statistics
  205 North 4th Street
  Post Office Box 12064
  Richmond, VA 23241
  Phone: (804) 786-2384

*State of Washington
  Department of Labor and Industries
  Division of Industrial Safety and
      Health
  Post Office Box 2589
  Olympia, WA 98504
  Phone: (206) 753-4013

West Virginia Department of Labor
  OSH Project Director
  Room 319, Bldg. 3
  Capitol Complex
  1800 Washington Street East
  Charleston, WV 25305
  Phone: (304) 348-7890

Wisconsin Department of Industry,
      Labor, and Human Resources
  Workers' Compensation Division/
      Research Section
  201 E. Washington Avenue
  Post Office Box 7901
  Madison, WI 53707
  Phone: (608) 266-7850

*Wyoming Department of Labor and
      Statistics
  Herschler Building
  Cheyenne, WY 82002
  Phone: (307) 777-6370

Offices of the
Occupational Safety and Health Administration

LEGEND

✪ Headquarters Office
◼ Regional Offices
○ Area Offices
• State Plan States
◇ District Offices

See Reverse for Regional and Area Listings

Headquarters Office
U.S. Department of Labor
Occupational Safety and
Health Administration
3rd & Constitution Ave., N.W.
Washington, D.C. 20210

OSHA 3046
1991 (Revised)

Appendix 2A

REGIONAL OFFICES OF THE BUREAU OF LABOR STATISTICS

U.S. Department of Labor
William E. Brock, Secretary

Bureau of Labor Statistics
Janet L Norwood, Commissioner
June 1986

Regional Offices of the Bureau of Labor Statistics

Region I
Kennedy Federal Building
Suite 1603
Boston, MA 02203
Phone: (617) 565-2327

Region II
Room 808
201 Varick Street
New York, NY 10014
Phone: (212) 337-2400

Region III
3535 Market Street
P.O. Box 13309
Philadelphia, PA 19101
Phone: (215) 596-1154

Region IV
1371 Peachtree Street, N.E.
Atlanta, GA 30367
Phone: (404) 347-4416

Region V
9th Floor
Federal Office Building
230 S. Dearborn Street
Chicago, IL 60604
Phone: (312) 353-1880

Region VI
Federal Building
525 Griffin Street, Room 221
Dallas, TX 75202
Phone: (214) 767-6970

Regions VII and VIII
911 Walnut Street
Kansas City, MO 64106
Phone: (816) 426-2481

Regions IX and X
71 Stevenson Street
P.O. Box 3766
San Francisco, CA 94119
Phone: (415) 744-6600

Appendix 2B

A Brief Guide to Recordkeeping Requirements for Occupational Injuries and Illnesses

U.S. Department of Labor
Bureau of Labor Statistics
June 1986

The Occupational Safety and Health Act
of 1970 and 29 CFR 1904

O.M.B. No. 1220-0029

See OMB Disclosure
Statement on page i.

Effective April 1986

Preface

The information in this pamphlet explains the requirements of the Occupational Safety and Health Act of 1970 and Title 29 of the *Code of Federal Regulations,* Part 1904 (29 CFR Part 1904) for recording and reporting occupational injuries and illnesses. The Occupational Safety and Health Act of 1970 and 29 CFR Part 1904 require employers to prepare and maintain records of occupational injuries and illnesses. The act made the Secretary of Labor responsible for the collection, compilation, and analysis of statistics of work-related injuries and illnesses. The Bureau of Labor Statistics (BLS) administers this recordkeeping and reporting system. In most States, a State agency cooperates with BLS in administering these programs.

Records of injuries and illnesses are necessary for carrying out the purposes of the act. They provide a basis for a statistical program which produces injury and illness data which are used by OSHA in measuring and directing the agency's efforts. The records are also helpful to employers and employees in identifying many of the factors which cause injuries or illnesses in the workplace. In addition, OSHA records are designed to assist safety and health compliance officers in making OSHA inspections.

This pamphlet summarizes the OSHA recordkeeping requirements of 29 CFR Part 1904, and provides basic instructions and guidelines to assist employers in fulfilling their recordkeeping and reporting obligations. Many specific standards and regulations of the Occupational Safety and Health Administration (OSHA) have additional requirements for the maintenance and retention of records of medical surveillance, exposure monitoring, inspections, accidents and other activities and incidents relevant to occupational safety and health, and for the reporting of certain information to employees and to OSHA. These additional requirements are not covered in this pamphlet. For information on these requirements, employers should refer directly to the OSHA standards or regulations or contact their OSHA Area Office.

Further information on the requirements outlined in this pamphlet is available in the free detailed report, *Recordkeeping Guidelines for Occupational Injuries and Illnesses,* which may be obtained by using the order form on page 18. Assistance can also be obtained by contacting the participating State agency or the BLS regional office for your area. The BLS regional offices are listed on the inside front cover. State agencies are listed at the end of this publication.

The following government agencies are involved in OSHA recordkeeping:

A. *The Occupational Safety and Health Administration, U.S. Department of Labor.* The Occupational Safety and Health Administration is responsible for developing, implementing, and enforcing safety and health standards and regulations. OSHA works with employers and employees to foster effective safety and health programs which reduce workplace hazards.

B. *Bureau of Labor Statistics, U.S. Department of Labor.* The Bureau of Labor Statistics is responsible for administering and maintaining the OSHA recordkeeping system, and for collecting, compiling, and analyzing work injury and illness statistics.

C. *State Agencies.* Many States cooperate with BLS in administering the OSHA recordkeeping and reporting programs. Some States have their own safety and health laws which may impose additional obligations. Employers should consult their State safety and health laws concerning these requirements.

These guidelines were prepared in the BLS Office of Occupational Safety and Health Statistics, by Stephen Newell, under the general direction of William M. Eisenberg, Associate Commissioner.

OMB DISCLOSURE STATEMENT

We estimate that the use of this supplementary instruction booklet will take an average of 6 minutes per reference, which is included in the estimate of time for completing and reviewing either a line entry on an OSHA Form No. 200 and/or an entire OSHA Form No. 101. If you have any comments regarding this estimate or any other aspect of this recordkeeping system, send them to the Bureau of Labor Statistics, Division of Management Systems (1220-0029), Washington, D.C. 20212 and to the Office of Management and Budget, Paperwork Reduction Project (1220-0029), Washington, D.C. 20503.

i

Contents

Chapter I. Employers Subject to the Recordkeeping Requirements of the Occupational Safety and Health Act of 1970

The recordkeeping requirements of the Occupational Safety and Health Act of 1970 apply to private sector employers in all States, the District of Columbia, Puerto Rico, the Virgin Islands, American Samoa, Guam, and the Trust Territories of the Pacific Islands.

A. Employers who must keep OSHA records

Employers with 11 or more employees (at any one time in the previous calendar year) in the following industries must keep OSHA records. The industries are identified by name and by the appropriate Standard Industrial Classification (SIC) code:

- Agriculture, forestry, and fishing (SIC's 01-02 and 07-09)
- Oil and gas extraction (SIC 13 and 1477)
- Construction (SIC's 15-17)
- Manufacturing (SIC's 20-39)
- Transportation and public utilities (SIC's 41-42 and 44-49)
- Wholesale trade (SIC's 50-51)
- Building materials and garden supplies (SIC 52)
- General merchandise and food stores (SIC's 53 and 54)
- Hotels and other lodging places (SIC 70)
- Repair services (SIC's 75 and 76)
- Amusement and recreation services (SIC 79), and
- Health services (SIC 80).

If employers in any of the industries listed above have more than one establishment with combined employment of 11 or more employees, records must be kept for *each* individual establishment.

B. Employers who infrequently must keep OSHA records

Employers in the industries listed below are normally exempt from OSHA recordkeeping. However, each year a small rotating sample of these employers is required to keep records and participate in a mandatory statistical survey of occupational injuries and illnesses. Their participation is necessary to produce national estimates of occupational injuries and illnesses for *all* employers (both exempt and nonexempt) in the private sector. If an employer who is regularly exempt is selected to maintain records and participate in the Annual Survey of Occupational Injuries and Illnesses, he or she will be notified in advance and supplied with the necessary forms and instructions. Employers who normally do not have to keep OSHA records include:

1. All employers with no more than 10 full- or part-time employees *at any one time* in the previous calendar year.

2. Employers in the following retail trade, finance, insurance and real estate, and services industries (identified by SIC codes):

- Automotive dealers and gasoline service stations (SIC 55)
- Apparel and accessory stores (SIC 56)
- Furniture, home furnishings, and equipment stores (SIC 57)
- Eating and drinking places (SIC 58)
- Miscellaneous retail (SIC 59)
- Banking (SIC 60)
- Credit agencies other than banks (SIC 61)
- Security, commodity brokers, and services (SIC 62)
- Insurance (SIC 63)
- Insurance agents, brokers, and services (SIC 64)
- Real estate (SIC 65)
- Combined real estate, insurance, etc. (SIC 66)
- Holding and other investment offices (SIC 67)
- Personal services (SIC 72)
- Business services (SIC 73)
- Motion pictures (SIC 78)
- Legal services (SIC 81)
- Educational services (SIC 82)
- Social services (SIC 83)
- Museums, botanical, zoological gardens (SIC 84)
- Membership organizations (SIC 86)
- Private households (SIC 88), and
- Miscellaneous services (SIC 89).

Even though recordkeeping requirements are reduced for employers in these industries, they, like nonexempt employers, must comply with OSHA standards, display the OSHA poster, and report to OSHA within 48 hours any accident which results in one or more fatalities or the hospitalization of five of more employees. Also, some State safety and health laws may require regularly exempt employers to keep injury and illness records, and some States have more stringent catastrophic reporting requirements.

1

C. Employers and individuals who never keep OSHA records

The following employers and individuals do not have to keep OSHA injury and illness records:

- *Self-employed individuals;*
- *Partners with no employees;*
- *Employers of domestics* in the employers' private residence for the purposes of housekeeping or child care, or both; and
- *Employers engaged in religious activities* concerning the conduct of religious services or rites. Employees engaged in such activities include clergy, choir members, organists and other musicians, ushers, and the like. However, records of injuries and illnesses occurring to employees while performing secular activities must be kept. Recordkeeping is also required for employees of private hospitals and certain commercial establishments owned or operated by religious organizations.

State and local government agencies are usually exempt from OSHA recordkeeping. However, in certain States, agencies of State and local governments are required to keep injury and illness records in accordance with State regulations.

D. Employers subject to other Federal safety and health regulations

Employers subject to injury and illness recordkeeping requirements of other Federal safety and health regulations are not exempt from OSHA recordkeeping. However, records used to comply with other Federal recordkeeping obligations may also be used to satisfy the OSHA recordkeeping requirements. The forms used must be equivalent to the log and summary (OSHA No. 200) and the supplementary record (OSHA No. 101).

Chapter II. OSHA Recordkeeping Forms

Only two forms are used for OSHA recordkeeping. One form, the OSHA No. 200, serves as both the Log of Occupational Injuries and Illnesses, on which the occurrence and extent of cases are recorded during the year; and as the Summary of Occupational Injuries and Illnesses, which is used to summarize the log at the end of the year to satisfy employer posting obligations. The other form, the Supplementary Record of Occupational Injuries and Illnesses, OSHA No. 101, provides additional information on each of the cases that have been recorded on the log.

A. The Log and Summary of Occupational Injuries and Illnesses, OSHA No. 200

The log is used for recording and classifying occupational injuries and illnesses, and for noting the extent of each case. The log shows when the occupational injury or illness occurred, to whom, the regular job of the injured or ill person at the time of the injury or illness exposure, the department in which the person was employed, the kind of injury or illness, how much time was lost, whether the case resulted in a fatality, etc. The log consists of three parts: A descriptive section which identifies the employee and briefly describes the injury or illness; a section covering the extent of the injuries recorded; and a section on the type and extent of illnesses.

Usually, the OSHA No. 200 form is used by employers as their record of occupational injuries and illnesses. However, a private form equivalent to the log, such as a computer printout, may be used if it contains the same detail as the OSHA No. 200 and is as readable and comprehensible as the OSHA No. 200 to a person not familiar with the equivalent form. It is important that the columns of the equivalent form have the same identifying number as the corresponding columns of the OSHA No. 200

because the instructions for completing the survey of occupational injuries and illnesses refer to log columns by number. It is advisable that employers have private equivalents of the log form reviewed by BLS to insure compliance with the regulations.

The portion of the OSHA No. 200 to the right of the dotted vertical line is used to summarize injuries and illnesses in an establishment for the calendar year. Every nonexempt employer who is required to keep OSHA records must prepare an annual summary for each establishment based on the information contained in the log for each establishment. The summary is prepared by totaling the column entries on the log (or its equivalent) and signing and dating the certification portion of the form at the bottom of the page.

B. The Supplementary Record of Occupational Injuries and Illnesses, OSHA No. 101

For every injury or illness entered on the log, it is necessary to record additional information on the supplementary record, OSHA No. 101. The supplementary record describes how the accident or illness exposure occurred, lists the objects or substances involved, and indicates the nature of the injury or illness and the part(s) of the body affected.

The OSHA No. 101 is not the only form that can be used to satisfy this requirement. To eliminate duplicate recording, workers' compensation, insurance, or other reports may be used as supplementary records if they contain all of the items on the OSHA No. 101. If they do not, the missing items must be added to the substitute or included on a separate attachment.

Completed supplementary records must be present in the establishment within 6 workdays after the employer has received information that an injury or illness has occurred.

Chapter III. Location, Retention, and Maintenance of Records

Ordinarily, injury and illness records must be kept by employers for *each* of their establishments. This chapter describes what is considered to be an establishment for recordkeeping purposes, where the records must be located, how long they must be kept, and how they should be updated.

A. Establishments

If an employer has more than one establishment, a separate set of records must be maintained for *each* one. The recordkeeping regulations define an establishment as "a single physical location where business is conducted or where services or industrial operations are performed." Examples include a factory, mill, store, hotel, restaurant, movie theater, farm, ranch, sales office, warehouse, or central administrative office.

The regulations specify that distinctly separate activities performed at the same physical location (for example, contract construction activities operated from the same physical location as a lumber yard) shall each be treated as a separate establishment for recordkeeping purposes. Production of dissimilar products; different kinds of operational procedures, different facilities; and separate management, personnel, payroll, or support staff are all indicative of separate activities and separate establishments.

B. Location of records

Injury and illness records (the log, OSHA No. 200, and the supplementary record, OSHA No. 101) must be kept for every physical location where operations are performed. Under the regulations, the location of these records depends upon whether or not the employees are associated with a fixed establishment. The distinction between fixed and nonfixed establishments generally rests on the nature and duration of the operation and not on the type of structure in which the business is located. A nonfixed establishment usually operates at a single location for a relatively short period of time. A fixed establishment remains at a given location on a long-term or permanent basis. Generally, any operation at a given site for more than 1 year is considered a fixed establishment. Also, fixed establishments are generally places where clerical, administrative, or other business records are kept.

1. *Employees associated with fixed establishments.* Re-

cords for these employees should be located as follows:

a. Records for employees working at fixed locations, such as factories, stores, restaurants, warehouses, etc., should be kept at the work location.
b. Records for employees who report to a fixed location but work elsewhere should be kept at the place where the employees report each day. These employees are generally engaged in activities such as agriculture, construction, transportation, etc.
c. Records for employees whose payroll or personnel records are maintained at a fixed location, but who do not report or work at a single establishment, should be maintained at the base from which they are paid or the base of their firm's personnel operations. This category includes generally unsupervised employees such as traveling salespeople, technicians, or engineers.

2. *Employees not associated with fixed establishments.* Some employees are subject to common supervision, but do not report or work at a fixed establishment on a regular basis. These employees are engaged in physically dispersed activities that occur in construction, installation, repair, or service operations. Records for these employees should be located as follows:

a. Records may be kept at the field office or mobile base of operations.
b. Records may also be kept at an established central location. If the records are maintained centrally: (1) The address and telephone number of the place where records are kept must be available at the worksite, and (2) there must be someone available at the central location during normal business hours to provide information from the records.

C. Location exception for the log (OSHA No. 200)

Although the supplementary record and the annual summary must be located as outlined in the previous section, it is possible to prepare and *maintain the log* at an alternate location or by means of data processing equipment, or both. Two requirements must be met: (1) Sufficient information must be available at the alternate location to complete the log within 6 workdays after receipt of information that a recordable case has occurred; and (2) a copy of the log updated to within 45 calendar days must be present at all times in the establishment. This location exception applies only to the

4

log, and not to the other OSHA records. Also, it does not affect the employer's posting obligations.

D. Retention of OSHA records

The log and summary, OSHA No. 200, and the supplementary record, OSHA No. 101, must be retained in each establishment for 5 calendar years following the end of the year to which they relate. If an establishment changes ownership, the new employer must preserve the records for the remainder of the 5-year period. However, the new employer is not responsible for updating the records of the former owner.

E. Maintenance of the log (OSHA No. 200)

In addition to keeping the log on a calendar year basis, employers are required to update this form to include newly discovered cases and to reflect changes which occur in recorded cases after the end of the calendar year. Maintenance or updating of the log is different from the retention of records discussed in the previous section. Although all OSHA injury and illness records must be retained, only the log must be updated by the employer. If, during the 5-year retention period, there is a change in the extent or outcome of an injury or illness which affects an entry on a previous year's log, then the first entry should be lined out and a corrected entry made on that log. Also, new entries should be made for previously unrecorded cases that are discovered or for cases that initially weren't recorded but were found to be recordable after the end of the year in which the case occurred. The entire entry should be lined out for recorded cases that are later found nonrecordable. Log totals should also be modified to reflect these changes.

5

Chapter IV. Deciding Whether a Case Should Be Recorded and How To Classify It

This chapter presents guidelines for determining whether a case must be recorded under the OSHA record-keeping requirements. These requirements should not be confused with recordkeeping requirements of various workers' compensation systems, internal industrial safety and health monitoring systems, the ANSI Z.16 standards for recording and measuring work injury and illness experience, and private insurance company rating systems. Reporting a case on the OSHA records should not affect recordkeeping determinations under these or other systems. Also—

Recording an injury or illness under the OSHA system does not necessarily imply that management was at fault, that the worker was at fault, that a violation of an OSHA standard has occurred, or that the injury or illness is compensable under workers' compensation or other systems.

A. Employees vs. other workers on site

Employers must maintain injury and illness records for their own employees at each of their establishments, but they are *not* responsible for maintaining records for employees of other firms or for independent contractors, even though these individuals may be working temporarily in their establishment or on one of their jobsites at the time an injury or illness exposure occurs. Therefore, before deciding whether a case is recordable an employment relationship needs to be determined.

Employee status generally exists for recordkeeping purposes when the employer supervises not only the output, product, or result to be accomplished by the person's work, but also the details, means, methods, and processes by which the work is accomplished. This means the employer who supervises the worker's day-to-day activities is responsible for recording his injuries and illnesses. Independent contractors are not considered employees; they are primarily subject to supervision by the using firm only in regard to the result to be accomplished or end product to be delivered. Independent contractors keep their own injury and illness records.

Other factors which may be considered in determining employee status are: (1) Whom the worker considers to be his or her employer; (2) who pays the worker's wages; (3) who withholds the worker's Social Security taxes;

(4) who hired the worker; and (5) who has the authority to terminate the worker's employment.

B. Method used for case analysis

The decisionmaking process consists of five steps:

1. Determine whether a case occurred; that is, whether there was a death, illness, or an injury;
2. Establish that the case was work related; that it resulted from an event or exposure in the work environment;
3. Decide whether the case is an injury or an illness; and
4. If the case is an illness, record it and check the appropriate illness category on the log; or
5. If the case is an injury, decide if it is recordable based on a finding of medical treatment, loss of consciousness, restriction of work or motion, or transfer to another job.

Chart 1 presents this methodology in graphic form.

C. Determining whether a case occurred

The first step in the decisionmaking process is the determination of whether or not an injury or illness has occurred. Employers have nothing to record unless an employee has experienced a work-related injury or illness. In most instances, recognition of these injuries and illnesses is a fairly simple matter. However, some situations have troubled employers over the years. Two of these are:

1. *Hospitalization for observation.* If an employee goes to or is sent to a hospital for a brief period of time for observation, it is not recordable, provided no medical treatment was given, or no illness was recognized. The determining factor is not that the employee went to the hospital, but whether the incident is recordable as a work-related illness or as an injury requiring medical treatment or involving loss of consciousness, restriction of work or motion, or transfer to another job.

2. *Differentiating a new case from the recurrence of a previous injury or illness.* Employers are required to make new entries on their OSHA forms for each new recordable injury or illness. However, new entries should

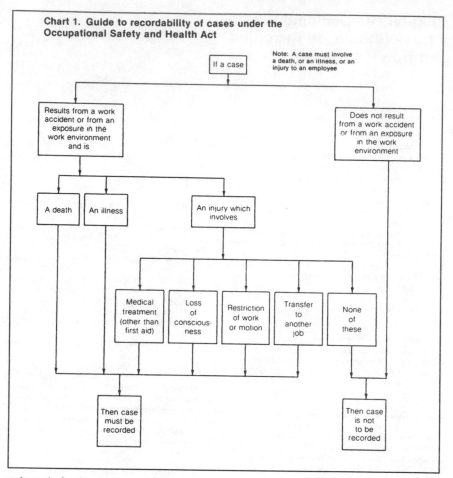

Chart 1. Guide to recordability of cases under the Occupational Safety and Health Act

Note: A case must involve a death, or an illness, or an injury to an employee

not be made for the recurrence of symptoms from previous cases, and it is sometimes difficult to decide whether or not a situation is a new case or a recurrence. The following guidelines address this problem:

a. *Injuries.* The aggravation of a previous injury almost always results from some new incident involving the employee (such as a slip, trip, fall, sharp twist, etc.). Consequently, when work related, these new incidents should be recorded as new cases.

b. *Illnesses.* Generally, each occupational illness should be recorded with a separate entry on the OSHA No. 200. However, certain illnesses, such as silicosis, may have prolonged effects which recur over time. The recurrence

of these symptoms should not be recorded as new cases on the OSHA forms. The recurrence of symptoms of previous illnesses may require adjustment of entries on the log for previously recorded illnesses to reflect possible changes in the extent or outcome of the particular case.

Some occupational illnesses, such as certain dermatitis or respiratory conditions, may recur as the result of new exposures to sensitizing agents, and should be recorded as new cases.

D.　Establishing work relationship

The Occupational Safety and Health Act of 1970

requires employers to record only those injuries and illnesses that are work related. *Work relationship is established under the OSHA recordkeeping system when the injury or illness results from an event or exposure in the work environment. The work environment is primarily composed of: (1) The employer's premises, and (2) other locations where employees are engaged in work-related activities or are present as a condition of their employment.* When an employee is off the employer's premises, work relationship must be established; when on the premises, this relationship is presumed. The employer's premises encompass the total establishment, including not only the primary work facility, but also such areas as company storage facilities. In addition to physical locations, equipment or materials used in the course of an employee's work are also considered part of the employee's work environment.

1. *Injuries and illnesses resulting from events or exposures on the employer's premises.* Injuries and illnesses that result from an event or exposure on the employer's premises are generally considered work related. The employer's premises consist of the total establishment. They include the primary work facilities and other areas which are considered part of the employer's general work area.

The presumption of work relationship for activities on the employer's premises is rebuttable. Situations where the presumption would not apply include: (1) When a worker is on the employer's premises as a member of the general public and not as an employee, and (2) when employees have symptoms that merely surface on the employer's premises, but are the result of a nonwork-related event or exposure off the premises.

The following subjects warrant special mention:

a. Company restrooms, hallways, and cafeterias are all considered to be *part* of the employer's premises and constitute part of the work environment. Therefore, injuries occurring in these places are generally considered work related.

b. For OSHA recordkeeping purposes, the definition of work premises *excludes* all employer controlled ball fields, tennis courts, golf courses, parks, swimming pools, gyms, and other similar recreational facilities which are often apart from the workplace and used by employees on a voluntary basis for their own benefit, primarily during off-work hours. Therefore, injuries to employees in these recreational facilities are not recordable unless the employee was engaged in some work-related activity, or was required by the employer to participate.

c. Company parking facilities are generally *not* considered part of the employer's premises for OSHA recordkeeping purposes. Therefore, injuries to employees on these parking lots are not presumed to be work related, and are not recordable unless the employee was engaged in some work-related activity.

2. *Injuries and illnesses resulting from events or exposures off the employer's premises.* When an employee is off the employer's premises and suffers an injury or an illness exposure, work relationship must be established; it is not presumed. Injuries and illness exposures off premises are considered work related if the employee is engaged in a work activity or if they occur in the work environment. The work environment in these instances includes locations where employees are engaged in job tasks or work-related activities, or places where employees are present due to the nature of their job or as a condition of their employment.

Employees who travel on company business shall be considered to be engaged in work-related activities all the time they spend in the interest of the company, including, but not limited to, travel to and from customer contacts, and entertaining or being entertained for the purpose of transacting, discussing, or promoting business, etc. However, an injury/illness would not be recordable if it occurred during normal living activities (eating, sleeping, recreation); or if the employee deviates from a reasonably direct route of travel (side trip for vacation or other personal reasons). He would again be in the course of employment when he returned to the normal route of travel.

When a traveling employee checks into a hotel or motel, he establishes a "home away from home." Thereafter, his activities are evaluated in the same manner as for nontraveling employees. For example, if an employee on travel status is to report each day to a fixed worksite, then injuries sustained when traveling to this worksite would be considered off the job. The rationale is that an employee's normal commute from home to office would not be considered work related. However, there are situations where employees in travel status report to, or rotate among several different worksites after they establish their "home away from home" (such as a salesperson traveling to and from different customer contacts). In these situations, the injuries sustained when traveling to and from the sales locations would be considered job related.

Traveling sales personnel may establish only one base of operations (home or company office). A sales person with his home as an office is considered at work when he is in that office and when he leaves his premises in the interest of the company.

Chart 2 provides a guide for establishing the work relationship of cases.

E. Distinguishing between injuries and illnesses

Under the OSH Act, all work-related illnesses must be recorded, while injuries are recordable *only* when they require medical treatment (other than first aid), or involve loss of consciousness, restriction of work or motion, or transfer to another job. The distinction between injuries and illnesses, therefore, has significant recordkeeping implications.

Whether a case involves an injury or illness is determined by the nature of the original event or exposure

Chart 2. Guidelines for establishing work relationship

which caused the case, not by the resulting condition of the affected employee. Injuries are caused by instantaneous events in the work environment. Cases resulting from anything other than instantaneous events are considered illnesses. This concept of illnesses includes acute illnesses which result from exposures of relatively short duration.

Some conditions may be classified as either an injury or an illness (but not both), depending upon the nature of the event that produced the condition. For example, a loss of hearing resulting from an explosion (an instantaneous event) is classified as an injury; the same condition arising from exposure to industrial noise over a period of time would be classified as an occupational illness.

F. Recording occupational illnesses

Employers are required to record the occurrence of all occupational illnesses, which are defined in the instructions of the log and summary as:

Any abnormal condition or disorder, other than one resulting from an occupational injury, caused by exposure to environmental factors associated with employment. It includes acute and chronic illnesses or diseases which may be caused by inhalation, absorption, ingestion, or direct contact.

The instructions also refer to recording illnesses which were "diagnosed or recognized." Illness exposures ultimately result in conditions of a chemical, physical, biological, or psychological nature.

Occupational illnesses must be diagnosed to be recordable. However, they do not necessarily have to be

diagnosed by a physician or other medical personnel. Diagnosis may be by a physician, registered nurse, or a person who by training or experience is capable to make such a determination. Employers, employees, and others may be able to detect some illnesses such as skin diseases or disorders without the benefit of specialized medical training. However, a case more difficult to diagnose, such as silicosis, would require evaluation by properly trained medical personnel.

In addition to recording the occurrence of occupational illnesses, employers are required to record each illness case in 1 of the 7 categories on the front of the log. The back of the log form contains a listing of types of illnesses or disorders and gives examples for each illness category. These are only examples, however, and should not be considered as a complete list of types of illnesses under each category.

Recording and classifying occupational illnesses may be difficult for employers, especially the chronic and long term latent illnesses. Many illnesses are not easily detected; and once detected, it is often difficult to determine whether an illness is work related. Also, employees may not report illnesses because the symptoms may not be readily apparent, or because they do not think their illness is serious or work related.

The following material is provided to assist in detecting occupational illnesses and in establishing their work relationship:

1. *Detection and diagnosis of occupational illnesses.* An occupational illness is defined in the instructions on

the log as any work-related abnormal condition or disorder (other than an occupational injury). Detection of these abnormal conditions or disorders, the first step in recording illnesses, is often difficult. When an occupational illness is suspected, employers may want to consider the following:

a. A medical examination of the employee's physiological systems. For example:

- Head and neck
- Eyes, ears, nose, and throat
- Endocrine
- Genitourinary
- Musculoskeletal
- Neurological
- Respiratory
- Cardiovascular, and
- Gastrointestinal;

b. Observation and evaluation of behavior related to emotional status, such as deterioration in job performance which cannot be explained;
c. Specific examination for health effects of suspected or possible disease agents by competent medical personnel;
d. Comparison of date of onset of symptoms with occupational history;
e. Evaluation of results of any past biological or medical monitoring (blood, urine, other sample analysis) and previous physical examinations;
f. Evaluation of laboratory tests: Routine (complete blood count, blood chemistry profile, urinalysis) and specific tests for suspected disease agents (e.g., blood and urine tests for specific agents, chest or other X-rays, liver function tests, pulmonary function tests); and
g. Reviewing the literature, such as Material Safety Data Sheets and other reference documents, to ascertain whether the levels to which the workers were exposed could have produced the ill effects.

2. Determining whether the illness is occupationally related.   The instructions on the back of the log define occupational illnesses as those "caused by environmental factors associated with employment." In some cases, such as contact dermatitis, the relationship between an illness and work-related exposure is easy to recognize. In other cases, where the occupational cause is not direct and apparent, it may be difficult to determine accurately whether an employee's illness is occupational in nature. In these situations, it may help employers to ask the following questions:

a. Has an illness condition clearly been established?
b. Does it appear that the illness resulted from, or was aggravated by, suspected agents or other conditions in the work environment?
c. Are these suspected agents present (or have they been present) in the work environment?
d. Was the ill employee exposed to these agents in the work environment?
e. Was the exposure to a sufficient degree and/or duration to result in the illness condition?
f. Was the illness attributable solely to a nonoccupational exposure?

G. Deciding if work-related injuries are recordable

Although the OSH Act requires that all work-related deaths and illnesses be recorded, the recording of nonfatal injuries is limited to certain specific types of cases: Those which require medical treatment or involve loss of consciousness; restriction of work or motion; or transfer to another job. Minor injuries requiring only first aid treatment are *not* recordable.

1. *Medical treatment.*   It is important to understand the distinction between medical treatment and first aid treatment since many work-related injuries are recordable only because medical treatment was given.

The regulations and the instructions on the back of the log and summary, OSHA No. 200, define medical treatment as any treatment, other than first aid treatment, administered to injured employees. Essentially, medical treatment involves the provision of medical or surgical care for injuries that are not minor through the application of procedures or systematic therapeutic measures.

The act also specifically states that work-related injuries which involve only first aid treatment should not be recorded. First aid is commonly thought to mean emergency treatment of injuries before regular medical care is available. However, first aid treatment has a different meaning for OSHA recordkeeping purposes. The regulations define first aid treatment as:

> . . . any one-time treatment, and any followup visit for the purpose of observation, of minor scratches, cuts, burns, splinters, and so forth, which do not ordinarily require medical care. Such one-time treatment, and followup visit for the purpose of observation, is considered first aid even though provided by a physician or registered professional personnel.

The distinction between medical treatment and first aid depends not only on the treatment provided, but also on the severity of the injury being treated. First aid is: (1) Limited to one-time treatment and subsequent observation; *and* (2) involves treatment of only minor injuries, *not* emergency treatment of serious injuries. Injuries are *not* minor if:

a. They must be treated only by a physician or licensed medical personnel;
b. They impair bodily function (i.e., normal use of senses, limbs, etc.);
c. They result in damage to the physical structure of a nonsuperficial nature (e.g., fractures); or
d. They involve complications requiring followup medical treatment.

Physicians or registered medical professionals, working under the standing orders of a physician, routinely treat minor injuries. Such treatment may constitute first aid. Also, some visits to a doctor do not involve treatment at all. For example, a visit to a doctor for an examination or other diagnostic procedure to determine whether the employee has an injury does not constitute medical treatment. Conversely, medical treatment can be provided to employees by lay persons; i.e., someone other than a physician or registered medical personnel.

The following classifications list certain procedures as either medical treatment or first aid treatment.

Medical Treatment:

The following are generally considered medical treatment. Work-related injuries for which this type of treatment was provided or should have been provided are almost always recordable:

- Treatment of **INFECTION**
- Application of **ANTISEPTICS during second or subsequent visit** to medical personnel
- Treatment of **SECOND OR THIRD DEGREE BURN(S)**
- Application of **SUTURES** (stitches)
- Application of **BUTTERFLY ADHESIVE DRESSING(S) or STERI STRIP(S)** in lieu of sutures
- Removal of **FOREIGN BODIES EMBEDDED IN EYE**
- Removal of **FOREIGN BODIES FROM WOUND**; if procedure is **COMPLICATED** because of depth of embedment, size, or location
- Use of **PRESCRIPTION MEDICATIONS** (except a single dose administered on first visit for minor injury or discomfort)
- Use of hot or cold **SOAKING THERAPY during second or subsequent visit** to medical personnel
- Application of hot or cold **COMPRESS(ES) during second or subsequent visit** to medical personnel
- **CUTTING AWAY DEAD SKIN** (surgical debridement)
- Application of **HEAT THERAPY during second or subsequent visit** to medical personnel
- Use of **WHIRLPOOL BATH THERAPY during second or subsequent visit** to medical personnel
- **POSITIVE X-RAY DIAGNOSIS** (fractures, broken bones, etc.)
- **ADMISSION TO A HOSPITAL** or equivalent medical facility **FOR TREATMENT.**

First Aid Treatment:

The following are generally considered first aid treatment (e.g., one-time treatment and subsequent observation of minor injuries) and should not be recorded if the work-related injury does not involve loss of consciousness, restriction of work or motion, or transfer to another job:

- Application of **ANTISEPTICS during first visit** to medical personnel
- Treatment of **FIRST DEGREE BURN(S)**
- Application of **BANDAGE(S)** during any visit to medical personnel
- Use of **ELASTIC BANDAGE(S) during first visit** to medical personnel

- Removal of **FOREIGN BODIES NOT EMBEDDED IN EYE** if only irrigation is required
- Removal of **FOREIGN BODIES FROM WOUND**; if procedure is **UNCOMPLICATED**, and is, for example, by tweezers or other simple technique
- Use of **NONPRESCRIPTION MEDICATIONS AND** administration of **single dose of PRESCRIPTION MEDICATION** on first visit for minor injury or discomfort
- **SOAKING THERAPY on initial visit** to medical personnel or removal of bandages by **SOAKING**
- Application of hot or cold **COMPRESS(ES) during first visit** to medical personnel
- Application of **OINTMENTS** to abrasions to prevent drying or cracking
- Application of **HEAT THERAPY during first visit** to medical personnel
- Use of **WHIRLPOOL BATH THERAPY during first visit** to medical personnel
- **NEGATIVE X-RAY DIAGNOSIS**
- **OBSERVATION** of injury during visit to medical personnel.

The following procedure, by itself, is not considered medical treatment:

- Administration of **TETANUS SHOT(S) or BOOSTER(S).** However, these shots are often given in conjunction with more serious injuries; consequently, injuries requiring these shots may be recordable for other reasons.

2. *Loss of consciousness.* If an employee loses consciousness as the result of a work-related injury, the case must be recorded no matter what type of treatment was provided. The rationale behind this recording requirement is that loss of consciousness is generally associated with the more serious injuries.

3. *Restriction of work or motion.* Restricted work activity occurs when the employee, because of the impact of a job-related injury, is physically or mentally unable to perform all or any part of his or her normal assignment during all or any part of the workday or shift. The emphasis is on the employee's ability to perform normal job duties. Restriction of work or motion may result in either a lost worktime injury or a nonlost-worktime injury, depending upon whether the restriction extended beyond the day of injury.

4. *Transfer to another job.* Injuries requiring transfer of the employee to another job are also considered serious enough to be recordable regardless of the type of treatment provided. Transfers are seldom the sole criterion for recordability because injury cases are almost always recordable on other grounds, primarily medical treatment or restriction of work or motion.

11

Chapter V. Categories for Evaluating the Extent of Recordable Cases

Once the employer decides that a recordable injury or illness has occurred, the case must be evaluated to determine its extent or outcome. There are three categories of recordable cases: Fatalities, lost workday cases, and cases without lost workdays. Every recordable case must be placed in only one of these categories.

A. Fatalities

All work-related fatalities must be recorded, regardless of the time between the injury and the death, or the length of the illness.

B. Lost workday cases

Lost workday cases occur when the injured or ill employee experiences either days away from work, days of restricted work activity, or both. In these situations, the injured or ill employee is affected to such an extent that: (1) Days must be taken off from the job for medical treatment or recuperation; or (2) the employee is unable to perform his or her normal job duties over a normal work shift, even though the employee may be able to continue working

1. Lost workday cases involving days away from work are cases resulting in days the employee would have worked but could not because of the job-related injury or illness. The focus of these cases is on the employee's inability, because of injury or illness, to be present in the work environment during his or her normal work shift.

2. Lost workday cases involving days of restricted work activity are those cases where, because of injury or illness, (1) the employee was assigned to another job on a temporary basis, or (2) the employee worked at a permanent job less than full time, or (3) the employee worked at his or her permanently assigned job but could not perform all the duties normally connected with it. Restricted work activity occurs when the employee, because of the job-related injury or illness, is physically or mentally unable to perform all or any part of his or her normal job duties over all or any part of his or her normal workday or shift. The emphasis is on the employee's inability to perform normal job duties over a normal work shift.

Injuries and illnesses are not considered lost workday cases unless they affect the employee beyond the day of injury or onset of illness. When counting the number of days away from work or days of restricted work activity, do not include the initial day of injury or onset of illness, or any days on which the employee would not have worked even though able to work (holidays, vacations, etc.).

C. Cases not resulting in death or lost workdays

These cases consist of the relatively less serious injuries and illnesses which satisfy the criteria for recordability but which do not result in death or require the affected employee to have days away from work or days of restricted work activity beyond the date of injury or onset of illness.

Chapter VI. Employer Obligations for Reporting Occupational Injuries and Illnesses

This chapter focuses on the requirements of Section 8(c)(2) of the Occupational Safety and Health Act of 1970 and Title 29, Part 1904, of the Code of Federal Regulations for employers to make reports of occupational injuries and illnesses. It does not include the reporting requirements of other standards or regulations of the Occupational Safety and Health Administration (OSHA) or of any other State or Federal agency.

A. The Annual Survey of Occupational Injuries and Illnesses

The survey is conducted on a sample basis, and firms required to submit reports of their injury and illness experience are contacted by BLS or a participating State agency. A firm not contacted by its State agency or BLS need not file a report of its injury and illness experience. Employers should note, however, that even if they are not selected to participate in the annual survey for a given year, they must still comply with the recordkeeping requirements listed in the preceding chapters as well as with the requirements for reporting fatalities and multiple hospitalization cases provided in the next section of this chapter.

Participants in the annual survey consist of two categories of employers: (1) Employers who maintain OSHA records on a regular basis; and (2) a small, rotating sample of employers who are regularly exempt from OSHA recordkeeping. The survey procedure is different for these two groups of employers.

1. *Participation of firms regularly maintaining OSHA records.* When employers regularly maintaining OSHA records are selected to participate in the Annual Survey of Occupational Injuries and Illnesses, they are mailed the survey questionnaire in February of the year following the reference calendar year of the survey. (A firm selected to participate in the 1985 survey would have been contacted in February of 1986.) The survey form, the Occupational Injuries and Illnesses Survey Questionnaire, OSHA No. 200-S, requests information about the establishment(s) included in the report and the injuries and illnesses experienced during the previous year. Information for the injury and illness portion of the report form usually can be copied directly from the totals on the log and summary, OSHA No. 200, which the employer should have completed and posted in the establishment oy the time the questionnaire arrives. The survey form also requests summary information about the type of business activity and number of employees and hours worked at the reporting unit during the reference year.

2. *Participation of normally exempt small employers and employers in low-hazard industries.* A few regularly exempt employers (those with fewer than 11 employees in the previous calendar year and those in designated low-hazard industries) are also required to participate in the annual survey. Their participation is necessary for the production of injury and illness statistics that are comparable in coverage to the statistics published in years prior to the exemptions. These employers are notified prior to the reference calendar year of the survey that they must maintain injury and illness records for the coming year. (A firm selected to participate in the 1985 survey would have been contacted in December 1984.) At the time of notification, they are supplied with the necessary forms and instructions. During the reference calendar year, prenotified employers make entries on the log, OSHA No. 200, but are not required to complete a Supplementary Record of Occupational Injuries and Illnesses, OSHA No. 101, or post the summary of the OSHA No. 200 the following February (regularly participating employers do both).

B. Reporting fatalities and multiple hospitalizations

All employers are required to report accidents resulting in one or more fatalities or the hospitalization of five or more employees. (Some States have more stringent catastrophic reporting requirements.)

The report is made to the nearest office of the Area Director of the Occupational Safety and Health Administration, U.S. Department of Labor, unless the State in which the accident occurred is administering an approved State plan under Section 18(b) of the OSH Act. Those 18(b) States designate a State agency to which the report must be made.

The report must contain three pieces of information: (1) Circumstances surrounding the accident(s), (2) the number of fatalities, and (3) the extent of any injuries. If necessary, the OSHA Area Director may require additional information on the accident.

The report should be made within 48 hours after the occurrence of the accident or within 48 hours after the occurrence of the fatality, regardless of the time lapse between the occurrence of the accident and the death of the employee.

Chapter VII. Access to OSHA Records and Penalties for Failure To Comply With Recordkeeping Obligations

The preceding chapters describe recordkeeping and reporting requirements. This chapter covers subjects related to insuring the integrity of the OSH recordkeeping process— access to OSHA records and penalties for recordkeeping violations.

A. Access to OSHA records

All OSHA records, which are being kept by employers for the 5-year retention period, should be available for inspection and copying by authorized Federal and State government officials. Employees, former employees, and their representatives are provided access to only the log, OSHA No. 200.

Government officials with access to the OSHA records include: Representatives of the Department of Labor, including OSHA safety and health compliance officers and BLS representatives; representatives of the Department of Health and Human Services while carrying out that department's research responsibilities; and representatives of States accorded jurisdiction for inspections or statistical compilations. "Representatives" may include Department of Labor officials inspecting a workplace or gathering information, officials of the Department of Health and Human Services, or contractors working for the agencies mentioned above, depending on the provisions of the contract under which they work.

Employee access to the log is limited to the records of the establishment in which the employee currently works or formerly worked. All current logs and those being maintained for the 5-year retention period must be made available for inspection and copying by employees, former employees, and their representatives. An employee representative can be a member of a union representing the employee, or any person designated by the employee or former employee. Access to the log is to be provided in a reasonable manner and at a reasonable time. Redress for failure to comply with the access provisions of the regulations can be obtained through a complaint to OSHA.

B. Penalties for failure to comply with recordkeeping obligations

Employers committing recordkeeping and/or reporting violations are subject to the same sanctions as employers violating other OSHA requirements such as safety and health standards and regulations.

Glossary of Terms

Annual summary. Consists of a copy of the occupational injury and illness totals for the year from the OSHA No. 200, and the following information: The calendar year covered; company name; establishment address; certification signature, title, and date.

Annual survey. Each year, BLS conducts an annual survey of occupational injuries and illnesses to produce national statistics. The OSHA injury and illness records maintained by employers in their establishments serve as the basis for this survey.

Bureau of Labor Statistics (BLS). The Bureau of Labor Statistics is the agency responsible for administering and maintaining the OSHA recordkeeping system, and for collecting, compiling, and analyzing work injury and illness statistics.

Certification. The person who supervises the preparation of the Log and Summary of Occupational Injuries and Illnesses, OSHA No. 200, certifies that it is true and complete by signing the last page of, or by appending a statement to that effect to, the annual summary.

Cooperative program. A program jointly conducted by the States and the Federal Government to collect occupational injury and illness statistics.

Employee. One who is employed in the business of his or her employer affecting commerce.

Employee representative. Anyone designated by the employee for the purpose of gaining access to the employer's log of occupational injuries and illnesses.

Employer. Any person engaged in a business affecting commerce who has employees.

Establishment. A single physical location where business is conducted or where services or industrial operations are performed; the place where the employees report for work, operate from, or from which they are paid.

Exposure. The reasonable likelihood that a worker is or was subject to some effect, influence, or safety hazard; or in contact with a hazardous chemical or physical agent at a sufficient concentration and duration to produce an illness.

Federal Register. The official source of information and notification on OSHA's proposed rulemaking, standards, regulations, and other official matters, including amendments, corrections, insertions, or deletions.

First aid. Any one-time treatment and subsequent observation of minor scratches, cuts, burns, splinters, and so forth, which do not ordinarily require medical care. Such treatment and observation are considered first aid even though provided by a physician or registered professional personnel.

First report of injury. A workers' compensation form which may qualify as a substitute for the supplementary record, OSHA No. 101.

Incidence rate. The number of injuries, illnesses, or lost workdays related to a common exposure base of 100 full-time workers. The common exposure base enables one to make accurate interindustry comparisons, trend analysis over time, or comparisons among firms regardless of size. This rate is calculated as:

$$N/EH \times 200,000$$

where:

N = number of injuries and/or illnesses or lost workdays

EH = total hours worked by all employees during calendar year

$200,000$ = base for 100 full-time equivalent workers (working 40 hours per week, 50 weeks per year).

Log and Summary (OSHA No. 200). The OSHA recordkeeping form used to list injuries and illnesses and to note the extent of each case.

Lost workday cases. Cases which involve days away from work or days of restricted work activity, or both.

Lost workdays. The number of workdays (consecutive or not), beyond the day of injury or onset of illness, the employee was away from work or limited to restricted work activity because of an occupational injury or illness.

(1) Lost workdays—away from work. The number of workdays (consecutive or not) on which the employee would have worked but could not because of occupational injury or illness.

(2) Lost workdays—restricted work activity. The number of workdays (consecutive or not) on which, because of injury or illness: (1) The employee was assigned to another job on a temporary basis; or (2) the employee worked at a permanent job less than full time; or (3) the employee worked at a permanently assigned job but could not perform all duties normally connected with it.

The number of days away from work or days of restricted work activity does not include the day of injury or onset of illness or any days on which the employee would not have worked even though able to work.

Low-hazard industries. Selected industries in retail trade; finance, insurance, and real estate; and services which are regularly exempt from OSHA recordkeeping. To be included in this exemption, an industry must fall within an SIC not targeted for general schedule inspections and must have an average lost workday case injury rate for a designated 3-year measurement period at or below 75 percent of the U.S. private sector average rate.

Medical treatment. Includes treatment of injuries administered by physicians, registered professional personnel, or lay persons (i.e., nonmedical personnel). Medical treatment does not include first aid treatment (one-time treatment and subsequent observation of minor scratches, cuts, burns, splinters, and so forth, which do not ordinarily require medical care) even though provided by a physician or registered professional personnel.

Occupational illness. Any abnormal condition or disorder, other than one resulting from an occupational injury, caused by exposure to environmental factors associated with employment. It includes acute and chronic illnesses or diseases which may be caused by inhalation, absorption, ingestion, or direct contact. The following categories should be used by employers to classify recordable occupational illnesses on the log in the columns indicated:

Column 7a. *Occupational skin diseases or disorders.*
Examples: Contact dermatitis, eczema, or rash caused by primary irritants and sensitizers or poisonous plants; oil acne; chrome ulcers; chemical burns or inflammations; etc.

Column 7b. *Dust diseases of the lungs (pneumoconioses).*
Examples: Silicosis, asbestosis, and other asbestos-related diseases, coal worker's pneumoconiosis, byssinosis, siderosis, and other pneumoconioses.

Column 7c. *Respiratory conditions due to toxic agents.*
Examples: Pneumonitis, pharyngitis, rhinitis or acute congestion due to chemicals, dusts, gases, or fumes; farmer's lung, etc.

Column 7d. *Poisoning (systemic effects of toxic materials).*
Examples: Poisoning by lead, mercury, cadmium, arsenic, or other metals; poisoning by carbon monoxide, hydrogen sulfide, or other gases; poisoning by benzol, carbon tetrachloride, or other organic solvents; poisoning by insecticide sprays such as parathion, lead arsenate; poisoning by other chemicals such as formaldehyde, plastics, and resins; etc.

Column 7e. *Disorders due to physical agents (other than toxic materials).*
Examples: Heatstroke, sunstroke, heat exhaustion, and other effects of environmental heat; freezing, frostbite, and effects of exposure to low temperatures; caisson disease; effects of ionizing radiation (isotopes, X-Rays, radium); effects of nonionizing radiation (welding flash, ultra-violet rays, microwaves, sunburn); etc.

Column 7f. *Disorders associated with repeated trauma.*
Examples: Noise-induced hearing loss; synovitis, tenosynovitis, and bursitis; Raynaud's phenomena; and other conditions due to repeated motion, vibration, or pressure.

Column 7g. *All other occupational illnesses.*
Examples: Anthrax, brucellosis, infectious hepatitis, malignant and benign tumors, food poisoning, histoplasmosis, coccidioidomycosis, etc.

Occupational injury. Any injury such as a cut, fracture, sprain, amputation, etc., which results from a work accident or from a single instantaneous exposure in the work environment.
Note: Conditions resulting from animal bites, such as insect or snake bites, and from one-time exposure to chemicals are considered to be injuries.

Occupational injuries and illnesses, extent and outcome. All recordable occupational injuries or illnesses result in either:
(1) Fatalities, regardless of the time between the injury, or the length of illness, and death;
(2) Lost workday cases, other than fatalities, that result in lost workdays; or
(3) Nonfatal cases without lost workdays.

Occupational Safety and Health Administration (OSHA). OSHA is responsible for developing, implementing, and enforcing safety and health standards and regulations. OSHA works with employers and employees to foster effective safety and health programs which reduce workplace hazards.

Posting. The annual summary of occupational injuries and illnesses must be posted at each establishment by February 1 and remain in place until March 1 to provide employees with the record of their establishment's injury and illness experience for the previous calendar year.

Premises, employer's. Consist of the employer's total establishment; they include the primary work facility and other areas in the employer's domain such as company storage facilities, cafeterias, and restrooms.

Recordable cases. All work-related deaths and illnesses, and those work-related injuries which result in: Loss of consciousness, restriction of work or motion, transfer to another job, or require medical treatment beyond first aid.

Recordkeeping system. Refers to the nationwide system for recording and reporting occupational injuries and illnesses mandated by the Occupational Safety and Health Act of 1970 and implemented by Title 29, Code of Federal Regulations, Part 1904. This system is the only source of national statistics on job-related injuries and illnesses for the private sector.

Regularly exempt employers. Employers regularly exempt from OSHA recordkeeping include: (A) All employers with no more than 10 full- or part-time employees at any one time in the previous calendar year; and (B) all employers in retail trade; finance, insurance, and real estate; and services industries; i.e., SIC's 52-89 (except building materials and garden supplies, SIC 52; general merchandise and food stores, SIC's 53 and 54; hotels and other lodging places, SIC 70; repair services, SIC's 75 and 76; amusement and recreation services, SIC 79; and health services, SIC 80). (Note: Some State safety and health laws may require these employers to keep OSHA records.)

Report form. Refers to survey form OSHA No. 200-S which is completed and returned by the surveyed reporting unit.

Restriction of work or motion. Occurs when the employee, because of the result of a job-related injury or illness, is physically or mentally unable to perform all or any part of his or her normal assignment during all or any part of the workday or shift.

Single dose (prescription medication). The measured quantity of a therapeutic agent to be taken at one time.

Small employers. Employers with no more than 10 full- and/or part-time employees among all the establishments of their firm at any one time during the previous calendar year.

Standard Industrial Classification (SIC). A classification system developed by the Office of Management and Budget, Executive Office of the President, for use in the classification of establishments by type of activity in which engaged. Each establishment is assigned an industry code for its major activity which is determined by the product manufactured or service rendered. Establishments may be classified in 2-, 3-, or 4-digit industries according to the degree of information available.

State (when mentioned alone). Refers to a State of the United States, the District of Columbia, and U.S. territories and jurisdictions.

State agency. State agency administering the OSHA recordkeeping and reporting system. Many States cooperate directly with BLS in administering the OSHA recordkeeping and reporting programs. Some States have their own safety and health laws which may impose additional obligations.

Supplementary Record (OSHA No. 101). The form (or equivalent) on which additional information is recorded for each injury and illness entered on the log.

Title 29 of the Code of Federal Regulations, Parts 1900-1999. The parts of the Code of Federal Regulations which contain OSHA regulations.

Volunteers. Workers who are not considered to be employees under the act when they serve of their own free will without compensation.

Work environment. Consists of the employer's premises and other locations where employees are engaged in work-related activities or are present as a condition of their employment. The work environment includes not only physical locations, but also the equipment or materials used by the employee during the course of his or her work.

Workers' compensation systems. State systems that provide medical benefits and/or indemnity compensation to victims of work-related injuries and illnesses.

17

ORDER FORM

Type or print

Please complete this form and mail it to the appropriate BLS regional office or participating State agency.

From:

Name _____

Firm _____

Street Address _____

City, State, Zip Code _____

Please send me the following items at no charge: *Quantity*

*A Brief Guide to Recordkeeping Requirements for Occupational Injuries
and Illnesses* (18 pp.) . . . .   _____

Recordkeeping Guidelines for Occupational Injuries and Illnesses (84 pp.) . . . .   _____

OSHA No. 200 Forms (Log and Summary of Occupational Injuries and Illnesses) . . . .   _____

OSHA No. 101 Forms (Supplementary Record of Occupational Injuries and Illnesses) . . . .   _____

ADDRESS LABEL

Name _____

Firm _____

Street Address _____

City, State, Zip Code _____

Participating State Agencies

Agencies preceded by an asterisk (*) have a State safety and health plan under section 18(b) of the act in operation and may be contacted directly for information regarding State regulations.

Alabama Department of Labor
651 Administrative Bldg.
Montgomery, AL 36130
Phone: 205 261-3460

*Alaska Department of Labor
Research and Analysis Section
P.O. Box 25501, Juneau, AK 99802
Phone: 907-465-4520

Government of American Samoa
Department of Manpower Resources
Division of Labor
Pago Pago, AS 96799
Phone: 633-5849

*Industrial Commission of Arizona
Division of Administration/Management
Research and Statistics Section
P.O. Box 19070, Phoenix, AZ 85005
Phone: 602-255-3739

Workers' Compensation Commission OSH
Arkansas Department of Labor
OSH Research and Statistics, Suite 219
1515 W. 7th St., Little Rock, AR 72201
Phone: 501-371-2770

*California Department of Industrial Relations, Labor Statistics and Research Division
P.O. Box 6880, San Francisco, CA 94101
Phone: 415-557-1466

Colorado Department of Labor and
Employment, Division of Labor
1313 Sherman St., Rm. 323
Denver, CO 80203
Phone: 303-866-3748

*Connecticut Department of Labor
200 Folly Brook Blvd.
Wethersfield, CT 06109
Phone: 203-566-4380

Delaware Department of Labor
Division of Industrial Affairs
820 N. French St., 6th Fl.
Wilmington, DE 19801
Phone: 302-571-2888

Florida Department of Labor and
Employment Security
Division of Worker's Compensation
2551 Executive Center
Circle West, Rm. 204
Tallahassee, FL 32301-5014
Phone: 904-488-3044

Guam Department of Labor
Bureau of Labor Statistics
Occupational Safety and Health Statistics
P.O. Box 23548, Guam Main Facility
Guam, M.I. 96921
Phone: 477-9241

*State of Hawaii
Department of Labor and Industrial
Relations, Research and Statistics
Office—OSHA
P.O. Box 3680, Honolulu, HI 96811
Phone: 808-548-7638

*Indiana Department of Labor
Research and Statistics Division
State Office Bldg.—Rm. 1013
100 N. Senate Ave.
Indianapolis, IN 46204
Phone: 317-232-2681

18

*Iowa Division of Labor Services
307 East 7th St., Des Moines, IA 50319
Phone: 515-281-3606

Kansas Department of Health and
Environment
Division of Policy and Planning
Research and Analysis
Topeka, KS 66620
Phone: 913-862-9360 Ext. 280

*Kentucky Labor Cabinet
Occupational Safety and Health Program
U.S. 127 South Bldg., Frankfort, KY 40601
Phone: 502-564-3100

Louisiana Department of Labor
Office of Employment Security—OSH
P.O. Box 94094
Baton Rouge, LA 70804
Phone: 504-342-3126

Maine Department of Labor
Bureau of Labor Standards
Division of Research and Statistics
State Office Bldg., Augusta, ME 04330
Phone: 207-289-4311

*Maryland Department of Licensing and
Regulation
Division of Labor and Industry
501 St. Paul Pl., Baltimore, MD 21202
Phone: 301-333-4202

Massachusetts Department of Labor and
Industries
Division of Industrial Safety
100 Cambridge St., Boston, MA 02202
Phone: 617-727-3593

*Michigan Department of Labor
7150 Harris Dr., Secondary Complex
P.O. Box 30015, Lansing, MI 48909
Phone: 517-322-1848

*Minnesota Department of Labor
and Industry IMSD
444 Lafayette Rd., 5th Fl.
St. Paul, MN 55101
Phone: 612-296-4893

Mississippi State Department of Health
Office of Public Health Statistics
P.O. Box 1700
Jackson, MS 39215-1700
Phone: 601-354-7233

Missouri Department of Labor and
Industrial Relations
Division of Workers' Compensation
P.O. Box 58, Jefferson City, MO 65102
Phone: 314-751-4231

Montana Department of Labor and
Industry
Workers' Compensation Division
5 South Last Chance Gulch
Helena, MT 59601
Phone: 406-444-6515

Nebraska Workers' Compensation Court
State Capitol, 12th Fl.
Lincoln, NE 68509-4967
Phone: 402-471-3547

*Nevada Department of Industrial Relations
Division of Occupational Safety and Health
1370 South Curry St.
Carson City, NV 89710
Phone: 702-885-5240

New Jersey Department of Labor and
Industry
Division of Planning and Research, CN 057
Trenton, NJ 08625
Phone: 609-292-8997

*New Mexico Health and Environment
Department
Environmental Improvement Division
Occupational Health and Safety
P.O. Box 968
Sante Fe, NM 87504-0968
Phone: 505-827-2875

New York Department of Labor
Division of Research and Statistics
1 Main St., Rm 907
Brooklyn, NY 11201
Phone: 718-797-7701

*North Carolina Department of Labor
Research and Statistics Division
214 West Jones St.
Raleigh, NC 27603
Phone: 919-733-4940

Ohio Department of Industrial Relations
OSH Survey Office
P.O. Box 12355, Columbus, OH 43212
Phone: 614-466-7520

Oklahoma Department of Labor
Supplemental Data Division
1315 North Broadway Pl.
Oklahoma City, OK 73105
Phone: 405-235-1447

*Oregon Workers' Compensation
Department
Research and Statistics Section
21 Labor and Industries Bldg.
Salem, OR 97310
Phone: 503-378-8254

Pennsylvania Department of Labor and
Industry
Office of Employment Security
7th and Forster Sts.
Labor and Industry Bldg.
Harrisburg, PA 17121
Phone: 717-787-1918

*Puerto Rico Department of Labor
and Human Resources
Bureau of Labor Statistics
505 Munoz Rivera Ave.
Hato Rey, PR 00918
Phone:809-754-5339

Rhode Island Department of Labor
220 Elmwood Ave., Providence, RI 02907
Phone: 401-457-1852

*South Carolina Department of Labor
Division of Technical Support
P.O. Box 11329, Columbia, SC 29211
Phone: 803-734-9652

*Tennessee Department of Labor
Research and Statistics
501 Union Bldg., 6th Fl.
Nashville, TN 37219
Phone: 615-741-1748

Texas Department of Health
Division of Occupational Safety
1100 West 49th St., Austin, TX 78756
Phone: 512-458-7287

*Utah Industrial Commission
OSH Statistical Section
160 East 300 South
Salt Lake City, UT 84145-0580
Phone: 801-530-6827

*Vermont Department of Labor
and Industry
State Office Bldg.
Montpelier, VT 05602
Phone: 802-828-2765

*Virgin Islands Department of Labor
P.O. Box 3359
St. Thomas, VI 00801
Phone: 809-776-3700

*Virginia Department of Labor and
Industry
Planning and Research
205 North 4th St.
P.O. Box 12064, Richmond, VA 23241
Phone: 804-786-2384

*State of Washington
Department of Labor and Industries
Division of Industrial Safety and Health
P.O. Box 2589
Olympia, WA 98504
Phone: 206-753-4013

West Virginia Department of Labor
OSH Project Director
Rm. 319, Bldg. 3, Capitol Complex
1800 Washington St. East
Charleston, WV 25305
Phone: 304-348-7890

Wisconsin Department of Industry, Labor
and Human Relations
Workers' Compensation Division
Research Section
201 E. Washington Ave.
P.O. Box 7901
Madison, WI 53707
Phone: 608-266-7850

*Wyoming Department of Labor and
Statistics
Herschler Bldg., 2 East
Cheyenne, WY 82002
Phone: 307-777-6370

Appendix 2C

SIC
Code Exemptions

§ 1904.16 Establishments classified in Standard Industrial Classification Codes (SIC) 52–89, (except 52–54, 70, 75, 76, 79 and 80).

An employer whose establishment is classified in SIC's 52–89, (excluding 52–54, 70, 75, 76, 79 and 80) need not comply, for such establishment, with any of the requirements of this part except the following:

(a) Obligation to report under §1904.8 concerning fatalities or multiple hospitalization accidents; and

(b) Obligation to maintain a log of occupational injuries and illnesses under §1904.21, upon being notified in writing by the Bureau of Labor Statistics that the employer has been selected to participate in a statistical survey of occupational injuries and illnesses.

[47 FR 57702, Dec. 28, 1982]

Appendix 2D

SUPPLEMENTARY RECORDS OF OCCUPATIONAL INJURIES AND ILLNESSES

Bureau of Labor Statistics
Supplementary Record of
Occupational Injuries and Illnesses

U.S. Department of Labor

This form is required by Public Law 91-596 and must be kept in the establishment for 5 years. Failure to maintain can result in the issuance of citations and assessment of penalties.	Case or File No.	Form Approved O.M.B. No. 1220-0029

Employer

1. Name

2. Mail address *(No. and street, city or town, State, and zip code)*

3. Location, if different from mail address

Injured or Ill Employee

4. Name *(First, middle, and last)* — Social Security No.

5. Home address *(No. and street, city or town, State, and zip code)*

6. Age

7. Sex: *(Check one)* Male ☐ Female ☐

8. Occupation *(Enter regular job title, not the specific activity he was performing at time of injury.)*

9. Department *(Enter name of department or division in which the injured person is regularly employed, even though he may have been temporarily working in another department at the time of injury.)*

The Accident or Exposure to Occupational Illness

If accident or exposure occurred on employer's premises, give address of plant or establishment in which it occurred. Do not indicate department or division within the plant or establishment. If accident occurred outside employer's premises at an identifiable address, give that address. If it occurred on a public highway or at any other place which cannot be identified by number and street, please provide place references locating the place of injury as accurately as possible.

10. Place of accident or exposure *(No. and street, city or town, State, and zip code)*

11. Was place of accident or exposure on employer's premises? Yes ☐ No ☐

12. What was the employee doing when injured? *(Be specific. If he was using tools or equipment or handling material, name them and tell what he was doing with them.)*

13. How did the accident occur? *(Describe fully the events which resulted in the injury or occupational illness. Tell what happened and how it happened. Name any objects or substances involved and tell how they were involved. Give full details on all factors which led to or contributed to the accident. Use separate sheet for additional space.)*

Occupational Injury or Occupational Illness

14. Describe the injury or illness in detail and indicate the part of body affected. *(E.g., amputation of right index finger at second joint; fracture of ribs; lead poisoning; dermatitis of left hand, etc.)*

15. Name the object or substance which directly injured the employee. *(For example, the machine or thing he struck against or which struck him; the vapor or poison he inhaled or swallowed; the chemical or radiation which irritated his skin; or in cases of strains, hernias, etc., the thing he was lifting, pulling, etc.)*

16. Date of injury or initial diagnosis of occupational illness

17. Did employee die? *(Check one)* Yes ☐ No ☐

Other

18. Name and address of physician

19. If hospitalized, name and address of hospital

Date of report	Prepared by	Official position

OSHA No. 101 (Feb. 1981)

29 CFR 1910.20

ACCESS TO EMPLOYEE EXPOSURE AND MEDICAL RECORDS

§ 1910.20 Access to employee exposure and medical records.

(a) *Purpose.* The purpose of this section is to provide employees and their designated representatives a right of access to relevant exposure and medical records; and to provide representatives of the Assistant Secretary a right of access to these records in order to fulfill responsibilities under the Occupational Safety and Health Act. Access by employees, their representatives, and the Assistant Secretary is necessary to yield both direct and indirect improvements in the detection, treatment, and prevention of occupational disease. Each employer is responsible for assuring compliance with this section, but the activities involved in complying with the access to medical records provisions can be carried out, on behalf of the employer, by the physician or other health care personnel in charge of employee medical records. Except as expressly provided, nothing in this section is intended to affect existing legal and ethical obligations concerning the maintenance and confidentiality of employee medical information, the duty to disclose information to a patient/employee or any other aspect of the medical-care relationship, or affect existing legal obligations concerning the protection of trade secret information.

(b) *Scope and application.* (1) This section applies to each general industry, maritime, and construction employer who makes, maintains, contracts for, or has access to employee exposure or medical records, or analyses thereof, pertaining to employees exposed to toxic substances or harmful physical agents.

(2) This section applies to all employee exposure and medical records, and analyses thereof, of such employees, whether or not the records are mandated by specific occupational safety and health standards.

(3) This section applies to all employee exposure and medical records, and analyses thereof, made or maintained in any manner, including on an in-house of contractual (e.g., fee-for-service) basis. Each employer shall assure that the preservation and access requirements of this section are complied with regardless of the manner in which the records are made or maintained.

(c) *Definitions.* (1) *Access* means the right and opportunity to examine and copy.

(2) *Analysis using exposure or medical records* means any compilation of data or any statistical study based at least in part on information collected from individual employee exposure or medical records or information collected from health insurance claims records, provided that either the analysis has been reported to the employer or no further work is currently being done by the person responsible for preparing the analysis.

(3) *Designated representative* means any individual or organization to whom an employee gives written authorization to exercise a right of access. For the purposes of access to employee exposure records and analyses using exposure or medical records, a recognized or certified collective bargaining agent shall be treated automatically as a designated representa-

tive without regard to written employee authorization.

(4) *Employee* means a current employee, a former employee, or an employee being assigned or transferred to work where there will be exposure to toxic substances or harmful physical agents. In the case of a deceased or legally incapacitated employee, the employee's legal representative may directly exercise all the employee's rights under this section.

(5) *Employee exposure record* means a record containing any of the following kinds of information:

(i) Environmental (workplace) monitoring or measuring of a toxic substance or harmful physical agent, including personal, area, grab, wipe, or other form of sampling, as well as related collection and analytical methodologies, calculations, and other background data relevant to interpretation of the results obtained;

(ii) Biological monitoring results which directly assess the absorption of a toxic substance or harmful physical agent by body systems (e.g., the level of a chemical in the blood, urine, breath, hair, fingernails, etc) but not including results which assess the biological effect of a substance or agent or which assess an employee's use of alcohol or drugs;

(iii) Material safety data sheets indicating that the material may pose a hazard to human health; or

(iv) In the absence of the above, a chemcial inventory or any other record which reveals where and when used and the identity (e.g., chemical, common, or trade name) of a toxic substance or harmful physical agent.

(6)(i) *Employee medical record* means a record concerning the health status of an employee which is made or maintained by a physician, nurse, or other health care personnel or technician, including:

(A) Medical and employment questionnaires or histories (including job description and occupational exposures),

(B) The results of medical examinations (pre-employment, pre-assignment, periodic, or episodic) and laboratory tests (including chest and other X-ray examinations taken for the purposes of establishing a base-line or de-

tecting occupational illness, and all biological monitoring not defined as an "employee exposure record"),

(C) Medical opinions, diagnoses, progress notes, and recommendations,

(D) First aid records,

(E) Descriptions of treatments and prescriptions, and

(F) Employee medical complaints.

(ii) "Employee medical record" does not include medical information in the form of:

(A) Physical specimens (e.g., blood or urine samples) which are routinely discarded as a part of normal medical practice; or

(B) Records concerning health insurance claims if maintained separately from the employer's medical program and its records, and not accessible to the employer by employee name or other direct personal identifier (e.g., social security number, payroll number, etc.); or

(C) Records created solely in preparation for litigation which are privileged from discovery under the applicable rules of procedure or evidence; or

(D) Records concerning voluntary employee assistance programs (alcohol, drug abuse, or personal counseling programs) if maintained separately from the employer's medical program and its records.

(7) *Employer* means a current employer, a former employer, or a successor employer.

(8) *Exposure* or *exposed* means that an employee is subjected to a toxic substance or harmful physical agent in the course of employment through any route of entry (inhalation, ingestion, skin contact or absorption, etc.), and includes past exposure and potential (e.g., accidental or possible) exposure, but does not include situations where the employer can demonstrate that the toxic substance or harmful physical agent is not used, handled, stored, generated, or present in the workplace in any manner different from typical nonoccupational situations.

(9) *Health Professional* means a physician, occupational health nurse, industrial hygienist, toxicologist, or epidemiologist, providing medical or other occupational health services to exposed employees.

(10) *Record* means any item, collection, or grouping of information regardless of the form or process by which it is maintained (e.g., paper document, microfiche, microfilm, X-ray film, or automated data processing).

(11) *Specific chemical identity* means the chemical name, Chemical Abstracts Service (CAS) Registry Number, or any other information that reveals the precise chemical designation of the substance.

(12)(i) *Specific written consent* means a written authorization containing the following:

(A) The name and signature of the employee authorizing the release of medical information,

(B) The date of the written authorization,

(C) The name of the individual or organization that is authorized to release the medical information,

(D) The name of the designated representative (individual or organization) that is authorized to receive the released information,

(E) A general description of the medical information that is authorized to be released,

(F) A general description of the purpose for the release of the medical information, and

(G) A date or condition upon which the written authorization will expire (if less than one year).

(ii) A written authorization does not operate to authorize the release of medical information not in existence on the date of written authorization, unless the release of future information is expressly authorized, and does not operate for more than one year from the date of written authorization.

(iii) A written authorization may be revoked in writing prospectively at any time.

(13) *Toxic substance or harmful physical agent* means any chemical substance, biological agent (bacteria, virus, fungus, etc.), or physical stress (noise, heat, cold, vibration, repetitive motion, ionizing and non-ionizing radiation, hypo—or hyperbaric pressure, etc.) which:

(i) Is listed in the least printed edition of the National Institute for Occupational Safety and Health (NIOSH)

Registry of Toxic Effects of Chemical Substances (RTECS); or

(ii) Has yielded positive evidence of an acute or chronic health hazard in testing conducted by, or known to, the employer; or

(iii) Is the subject of a material safety data sheet kept by or known to the employer indicating that the material may pose a hazard to human health.

(14) *Trade secret* means any confidential formula, pattern, process, device, or information or compilation of information that is used in an employer's business and that gives the employer an opportunity to obtain an advantage over competitors who do not know or use it.

(d) *Preservation of records.* (1) Unless a specific occupational safety and health standard provides a different period of time, each employer shall assure the preservation and retention of records as follows:

(i) *Employee medical records.* The medical record for each employee shall be preserved and maintained for at least the duration of employment plus thirty (30) years, except that the following types of records need not be retained for any specified period:

(A) Health insurance claims records maintained separately from the employer's medical program and its records,

(B) First aid records (not including medical histories) of one-time treatment and subsequent observation of minor scratches, cuts, burns, splinters, and the like which do not involve medical treatment, loss of consciousness, restriction of work or motion, or transfer to another job, if made on-site by a non-physician and if maintained separately from the employer's medical program and its records, and

(C) The medical records of employees who have worked for less than (1) year for the employer need not be retained beyond the term of employment if they are provided to the employee upon the termination of employment.

(ii) *Employee exposure records.* Each employee exposure record shall be preserved and maintained for at least thirty (30) years, except that:

(A) Background data to environmental (workplace) monitoring or measuring, such as laboratory reports and worksheets, need only be retained for one (1) year as long as the sampling results, the collection methodology (sampling plan), a description of the analytical and mathematical methods used, and a summary of other background data relevant to interpretation of the results obtained, are retained for at least thirty (30) years; and

(B) Material safety data sheets and paragraph (c)(5)(iv) records concerning the identity of a substance or agent need not be retained for any specified period as long as some record of the identity (chemical name if known) of the substance or agent, where it was used, and when it was used is retained for at least thirty (30) years;[1] and

(C) Biological monitoring results designated as exposure records by specific occupational safety and health standards shall be preserved and maintained as required by the specific standard.

(iii) *Analyses using exposure or medical records.* Each analysis using exposure or medial records shall be preserved and maintained for at least thirty (30) years.

(2) Nothing in this section is intended to mandate the form, manner, or process by which an employer preserves a record as long as the information contained in the record is preserved and retrievable, except that chest X-ray films shall be preserved in their original state.

(e) *Access to records*—(1) *General.* (i) Whenever an employee or designated representative requests access to a record, the employer shall assure that access is provided in a reasonable time, place, and manner. If the employer cannot reasonably provide access to the record within fifteen (15) working days, the employer shall within the fifteen (15) working days apprise the employee or designated representative requesting the record of the reason for the delay and the earliest date when the record can be made available.

(ii) The employer may require of the requester only such information as should be readily known to the requester and which may be necessary to

locate or identify the records being requested (e.g. dates and locations where the employee worked during the time period in question).

(iii) Whenever an employee or designated representative requests a copy of a record, the employer shall assure that either:

(A) A copy of the record is provided without cost to the employee or representative,

(B) The necessary mechanical copying facilities (e.g., photocopying) are made available without cost to the employee or representative for copying the record, or

(C) The record is loaned to the employee or representative for a reasonable time to enable a copy to be made.

(iv) In the case of an original X-ray, the employer may restrict access to on-site examination or make other suitable arrangements for the temporary loan of the X-ray.

(v) Whenever a record has been previously provided without cost to an employee or designated representative, the employer may charge reasonable, non-discriminatory administrative costs (i.e., search and copying expenses but not including overhead expenses) for a request by the employee or designated representative for additional copies of the record, except that

(A) An employer shall not charge for an initial request for a copy of new information that has been added to a record which was previously provided; and

(B) An employer shall not charge for an initial request by a recognized or certified collective bargaining agent for a copy of an employee exposure record or an analysis using exposure or medical records.

(vi) Nothing in this section is intended to preclude employees and collective bargaining agents from collectively bargaining to obtain access to information in addition to that available under this section.

(2) *Employee and designated representative access*—(i) *Employee exposure records.* (A) Except as limited by paragraph (f) of this section, each employer shall, upon request, assure the access to each employee and designated representative to employee exposure records relevant to the employee. For

---

[1] Material safety data sheets must be kept for those chemicals currently in use that are effected by the Hazard Communication Standard in accordance with 29 CFR 1910.1200(g).

the purpose of this section, an exposure record relevant to the employee consists of:

(*1*) A record which measures or monitors the amount of a toxic substance or harmful physical agent to which the employee is or has been exposed;

(*2*) In the absence of such directly relevant records, such records of other employees with past or present job duties or working conditions related to or similar to those of the employee to the extent necessary to reasonably indicate the amount and nature of the toxic substances or harmful physical agents to which the employee is or has been subjected, and

(*3*) Exposure records to the extent necessary to reasonably indicate the amount and nature of the toxic substances or harmful physical agents at workplaces or under working conditions to which the employee is being assigned or transferred.

(B) Requests by designated representatives for unconsented access to employee exposure records shall be in writing and shall specify with reasonable particularity:

(*1*) The records requested to be disclosed; and

(*2*) The occupational health need for gaining access to these records.

(ii) *Employee medical records.* (A) Each employer shall, upon request, assure the access of each employee to employee medical records of which the employee is the subject, except as provided in paragraph (e)(2)(ii)(D) of this section.

(B) Each employer shall, upon request, assure the access of each designated representative to the employee medical records of any employee who has given the designated representative specific written consent. Appendix A to this section contains a sample form which may be used to establish specific written consent for access to employee medical records.

(C) Whenever access to employee medical records is requested, a physician representing the employer may recommend that the employee or designated representative:

(*1*) Consult with the physician for the purposes of reviewing and discussing the records requested,

(*2*) Accept a summary of material facts and opinions in lieu of the records requested, or

(*3*) Accept release of the requested records only to a physician or other designated representative.

(D) Whenever an employee requests access to his or her employee medical records, and a physician representing the employer believes that direct employee access to information contained in the records regarding a specific diagnosis of a terminal illness or a psychiatric condition could be detrimental to the employee's health, the employer may inform the employee that access will only be provided to a designated representative of the employee having specific written consent, and deny the employee's request for direct access to this information only. Where a designated representative with specific written consent requests access to information so withheld, the employer shall assure the access of the designated representative to this information, even when it is known that the designated representative will give the information to the employee.

(E) A physician, nurse, or other responsible health care personnel maintaining medical records may delete from requested medical records the identity of a family member, personal friend, or fellow employee who has provided confidential information concerning an employee's health status.

(iii) *Analyses using exposure or medical records.* (A) Each employee shall, upon request, assure the access of each employee and designated representative to each analysis using exposure or medical records concerning the employee's working conditions or workplace.

(B) Whenever access is requested to an analysis which reports the contents of employee medical records by either direct identifier (name, address, social security number, payroll number, etc.) or by information which could reasonably be used under the circumstances indirectly to identify specific employees (exact age, height, weight, race, sex, date of initial employment, job title, etc.), the employer shall assure that personal identifiers are removed before access is provided. If the employer can demonstrate that removal of personal identifiers from an analysis is not feasible, access to the personally identifiable portions of the analysis need not be provided.

(3) *OSHA access.* (i) Each employer shall, upon request, and without derogation of any rights under the Constitution or the Occupational Safety and Health Act of 1970, 29 U.S.C. 651 *et seq.*, that the employer chooses to exercise, assure the prompt access of representatives of the Assistant Secretary of Labor for Occupational Safety and Health to employee exposure and medical records and to analyses using exposure or medical records. Rules of agency practice and procedure governing OSHA access to employee medical records are contained in 29 CFR 1913.10.

(ii) Whenever OSHA seeks access to personally identifiable employee medical information by presenting to the employer a written access order pursuant to 29 CFR 1913.10(d), the employer shall prominently post a copy of the written access order and its accompanying cover letter for at least fifteen (15) working days.

(f) *Trade secrets.* (1) Except as provided in paragraph (f)(2) of this section, nothing in this section precludes an employer from deleting from records requested by a health professional, employee, or designated representative any trade secret data which discloses manufacturing processes, or discloses the percentage of a chemical substance in mixture, as long as the health professional, employee, or designated representative is notified that information has been deleted. Whenever deletion of trade secret information substantially impairs evaluation of the place where or the time when exposure to a toxic substance or harmful physical agent occurred, the employer shall provide alternative information which is sufficient to permit the requesting party to identify where and when exposure occurred.

(2) The employer may withhold the specific chemical identity, including the chemical name and other specific identification of a toxic substance from a disclosable record provided that:

(i) The claim that the information withheld is a trade secret can be supported;

(ii) All other available information on the properties and effects of the toxic substance is disclosed;

(iii) The employer informs the requesting party that the specific chemical identity is being withheld as a trade secret; and

(iv) The specific chemical identity is made available to health professionals, employees and designated representatives in accordance with the specific applicable provisions of this paragraph.

(3) Where a treating physician or nurse determines that a medical emergency exists and the specific chemical identity of a toxic substance is necessary for emergency or first-aid treatment, the employer shall immediately disclose the specific chemical identity of a trade secret chemical to the treating physician or nurse, regardless of the existence of a written statement of need or a confidentiality agreement. The employer may require a written statement of need and confidentiality agreement, in accordance with the provisions of paragraphs (f)(4) and (f)(5), as soon as circumstances permit.

(4) In non-emergency situations, an employer shall, upon request, disclose a specific chemical identity, otherwise permitted to be withheld under paragraph (f)(2) of this section, to a health professional, employee, or designated representative if:

(i) The request is in writing;

(ii) The request describes with reasonable detail one or more of the following occupational health needs for the information:

(A) To assess the hazards of the chemicals to which employees will be exposed;

(B) To conduct or assess sampling of the workplace atmosphere to determine employee exposure levels;

(C) To conduct pre-assignment or periodic medical surveillance of exposed employees;

(D) To provide medical treatment to exposed employees;

(E) To select or assess appropriate personal protective equipment for exposed employees;

(F) To design or assess engineering controls or other protective measures for exposed employees; and

(G) To conduct studies to determine the health effects of exposure.

(iii) The request explains in detail why the disclosure of the specific chemical identity is essential and that, in lieu thereof, the disclosure of the following information would not enable the health professional, employee or designated representative to provide the occupational health services described in paragraph (f)(4)(ii) of this section:

(A) The properties and effects of the chemical;

(B) Measures for controlling workers' exposure to the chemical;

(C) Methods of monitoring and analyzing worker exposure to the chemical; and,

(D) Methods of diagnosing and treating harmful exposures to the chemical;

(iv) The request includes a description of the procedures to be used to maintain the confidentiality of the disclosed information; and,

(v) The health professional, employee, or designated representative and the employer or contractor of the services of the health professional or designated representative agree in a written confidentiality agreement that the health professional, employee or designated representative will not use the trade secret information for any purpose other than the health need(s) asserted and agree not to release the information under any circumstances other than to OSHA, as provided in paragraph (f)(9) of this section, except as authorized by the terms of the agreement or by the employer.

(5) The confidentiality agreement authorized by paragraph (f)(4)(iv) of this section:

(i) May restrict the use of the information to the health purposes indicated in the written statement of need;

(ii) May provide for appropriate legal remedies in the event of a breach of the agreement, including stipulation of a reasonable pre-estimate of likely damages; and,

(iii) May not include requirements for the posting of a penalty bond.

(6) Nothing in this section is meant to preclude the parties from pursuing non-contractual remedies to the extent permitted by law.

(7) If the health professional, employee or designated representative receiving the trade secret information

decides that there is a need to disclose it to OSHA, the employer who provided the information shall be informed by the health professional prior to, or at the same time as, such disclosure.

(8) If the employer denies a written request for disclosure of a specific chemical identity, the denial must:

(i) Be provided to the health professional, employee or designated representative within thirty days of the request;

(ii) Be in writing;

(iii) Include evidence to support the claim that the specific chemical identity is a trade secret;

(iv) State the specific reasons why the request is being denied; and,

(v) Explain in detail how alternative information may satisfy the specific medical or occupational health need without revealing the specific chemical identity.

(9) The health professional, employee, or designated representative whose request for information is denied under paragraph (f)(1) of this section may refer the request and the written denial of the request to OSHA for consideration.

(10) When a heath professional employee, or designated representative refers a denial to OSHA under paragraph (f)(9) of this section, OSHA shall consider the evidence to determine if:

(i) The employer has supported the claim that the specific chemical identity is a trade secret;

(ii) The health professional, employee, or designated representative has supported the claim that there is a medical or occupational health need for the information; and

(iii) The health professional, employee or designated representative has demonstrated adequate means to protect the confidentiality.

(11)(i) If OSHA determines that the specific chemical identity requested under paragraph (f)(4) of this section is not a *bona fide* trade secret, or that it is a trade secret but the requesting health professional, employee or designated representatives has a legitimate medical or occupational health need for the information, has executed a written confidentiality agreement, and has shown adequate means for complying with the terms of such agreement, the employer will be subject to citation by OSHA.

(ii) If an employer demonstrates to OSHA that the execution of a confidentiality agreement would not provide sufficient protection against the potential harm from the unauthorized disclosure of a trade secret specific chemical identity, the Assistant Secretary may issue such orders or impose such additional limitations or conditions upon the disclosure of the requested chemical information as may be appropriate to assure that the occupational health needs are met without an undue risk of harm to the employer.

(12) Notwithstanding the existence of a trade secret claim, an employer shall, upon request, disclose to the Assistant Secretary any information which this section requires the employer to make available. Where there is a trade secret claim, such claim shall be made no later than at the time the information is provided to the Assistant Secretary so that suitable determinations of trade secret status can be made and the necessary protections can be implemented.

(13) Nothing in this paragraph shall be construed as requiring the disclosure under any circumstances of process or percentage of mixture information which is trade secret.

(g) *Employee information.* (1) Upon an employee's first entering into employment, and at least annually thereafter, each employer shall inform current employees covered by this section of the following:

(i) The existence, location, and availability of any records covered by this section;

(ii) The person responsible for maintaining and providing access to records; and

(iii) Each employee's rights of access to these records.

(2) Each employer shall keep a copy of this section and its appendices, and make copies readily available, upon request, to employees. The employer shall also distribute to current employees any informational materials concerning this section which are made available to the employer by the Assistant Secretary of Labor for Occupational Safety and Health.

(h) *Transfer of records.* (1) Whenever an employer is ceasing to do business, the employer shall transfer all records subject to this section to the successor employer. The successor employer shall receive and maintain these records.

(2) Whenever an employer is ceasing to do business and there is no successor employer to receive and maintain the records subject to this standard, the employer shall notify affected current employees of their rights of access to records at least three (3) months prior to the cessation of the employer's business.

(3) Whenever an employer either is ceasing to do business and there is no successor employer to receive and maintain the records, or intends to dispose of any records required to be preserved for at least thirty (30) years, the employer shall:

(i) Transfer the records to the Director of the National Institute for Occupational Safety and Health (NIOSH) if so required by a specific occupational safety and health standard; or

(ii) Notify the Director of NIOSH in writing of the impending disposal of records at least three (3) months prior to the disposal of the records.

(4) Where an employer regularly disposes of records required to be preserved for at least thirty (30) years, the employer may, with at least (3) months notice, notify the Director of NIOSH on an annual basis of the records intended to be disposed of in the coming year.

(i) *Appendices.* The information contained in appendices A and B to this section is not intended, by itself, to create any additional obligations not otherwise imposed by this section nor detract from any existing obligation.

(Approved by the Office of Management and Budget under control number 1218–0065)

APPENDIX A TO § 1910.20—SAMPLE AUTHORIZATION LETTER FOR THE RELEASE OF EMPLOYEE MEDICAL RECORD INFORMATION TO A DESIGNATED REPRESENTATIVE (NON-MANDATORY)

I, ———— (full name of worker/patient), hereby authorize ———— (individual or organization holding the medical records) to release to ———— (individual or organization authorized to receive the medical in-

§ 1910.20

formation), the following medical information from my personal medical records:

___

(Describe generally the information desired to be released)

I give my permission for this medical information to be used for the following purpose:

___

but I do not give permission for any other use or re-disclosure of this information.

(NOTE: Several extra lines are provided below so that you can place additional restrictions on this authorization letter if you want to. You may, however, leave these lines blank. On the other hand, you may want to (1) specify a particular expiration date for this letter (if less than one year); (2) describe medical information to be created in the future that you intend to be covered by this authorization letter; or (3) describe portions of the medical information in your records which you do not intend to be released as a result of this letter.)

___

___

___

___

___

Full name of Employee or Legal Representative

___

Signature of Employee or Legal Representative

___

Date of Signature

APPENDIX B TO § 1910.20—AVAILABILITY OF NIOSH REGISTRY OF TOXIC EFFECTS OF CHEMICAL SUBSTANCES (RTECS) (NON-MANDATORY)

The final regulation, 29 CFR 1910.20, applies to all employee exposure and medical records, and analyses thereof, of employees exposed to toxic substances or harmful physical agents (paragraph (b)(2)). The term *toxic substance or harmful physical agent* is defined by paragraph (c)(13) to encompass chemical substances, biological agents, and physical stresses for which there is evidence of harmful health effects. The regulation uses the latest printed edition of the National Institute for Occupational Safety and Health (NIOSH) Registry of Toxic Effects of Chemical Substances (RTECS) as one of the chief sources of information as to whether evidence of harmful health effects exists. If a substance is listed in the latest printed RTECS, the regulation applies to exposure and medical records (and analyses of these records) relevant to employees exposed to the substance.

It is appropriate to note that the final regulation does not require that employers purchase a copy of RTECS, and many employers need not consult RTECS to ascertain whether their employee exposure or medical records are subject to the rule. Employers who do not currently have the latest printed edition of the NIOSH RTECS, however, may desire to obtain a copy. The RTECS is issued in an annual printed edition as mandated by section 20(a)(6) of the Occupational Safety and Health Act (29 U.S.C. 669(a)(6)).

The Introduction to the 1980 printed edition describes the RTECS as follows:

"The 1980 edition of the Registry of Toxic Effects of Chemical Substances, formerly known as the Toxic Substances list, is the ninth revision prepared in compliance with the requirements of Section 20(a)(6) of the Occupational Safety and Health Act of 1970 (Public Law 91-596). The original list was completed on June 28, 1971, and has been updated annually in book format. Beginning in October 1977, quarterly revisions have been provided in microfiche. This edition of the Registry contains 168,096 listings of chemical substances: 45,156 are names of different chemicals with their associated toxicity data and 122,940 are synonyms. This edition includes approximately 5,900 new chemical compounds that did not appear in the 1979 Registry. (p. xi)

"The Registry's purposes are many, and it serves a variety of users. It is a single source document for basic toxicity information and for other data, such as chemical identifiers and information necessary for the preparation of safety directives and hazard evaluations for chemical substances. The various types of toxic effects linked to literature citations provide researchers and occupational health scientists with an introduction to the toxicological literature, making their own review of the toxic hazards of a given substance easier. By presenting data on the lowest reported doses that produce effects by several routes of entry in various species, the Registry furnishes valuable information to those responsible for preparing safety data sheets for chemical substances in the workplace. Chemical and production engineers can use the Registry to identify the hazards which may be associated with chemical intermediates in the development of final products, and thus can more readily select substitutes or alternative processes which may be less hazardous. Some organizations, including health agencies and chemical companies, have included the NIOSH Registry accession numbers with the listing of chemicals in their files to reference toxicity information associated with those chemicals. By including foreign language chemical names, a start has been made toward providing rapid identification of substances produced in other countries. (p. xi)

Occupational Safety and Health Admin., Labor   **§ 1910.21**

"In this edition of the Registry, the editors intend to identify "all known toxic substances" which may exist in the environment and to provide pertinent data on the toxic effects from known doses entering an organism by any route described. (p xi)

"It must be reemphasized that the entry of a substance in the Registry does not automatically mean that it must be avoided. A listing does mean, however, that the substance has the documented potential of being harmful if misused, and care must be exercised to prevent tragic consequences. Thus, the Registry lists many substances that are common in everyday life and are in nearly every household in the United States. One can name a variety of such dangerous substances: prescription and non-prescription drugs; food additives; pesticide concentrates, sprays, and dusts; fungicides; herbicides; paints; glazes, dyes; bleaches and other household cleaning agents; alkalies; and various solvents and diluents. The list is extensive because chemicals have become an integral part of our existence."

The RTECS printed edition may be purchased from the Superintendent of Documents, U.S. Government Printing Office (GPO), Washington, DC 20402 (202–783–3238).

Some employers may desire to subscribe to the quarterly update to the RTECS which is published in a microfiche edition. An annual subscription to the quarterly microfiche may be purchased from the GPO (Order the "Microfiche Edition, Registry of Toxic Effects of Chemical Substances"). Both the printed edition and the microfiche edition of RTECS are available for review at many university and public libraries throughout the country. The latest RTECS editions may also be examined at the OSHA Technical Data Center, Room N2439—Rear, United States Department of Labor, 200 Constitution Avenue, NW., Washington, DC 20210 (202–523–9700), or at any OSHA Regional or Area Office (*See*, major city telephone directories under United States Government-Labor Department).

[53 FR 38163, Sept. 29, 1988; 53 FR 49981, Dec. 13, 1988, as amended at 54 FR 24333, June 7, 1989; 55 FR 26431, June 28, 1990]

29 CFR 1910.38
EMPLOYEE EMERGENCY PLANS AND FIRE PREVENTION PLANS

§ 1910.38 Employee emergency plans and fire prevention plans.

(a) *Emergency action plan*—(1) *Scope and application.* This paragraph (a) applies to all emergency action plans required by a particular OSHA standard. The emergency action plan shall be in writing (except as provided in the last sentence of paragraph (a)(5)(iii) of this section) and shall cover those designated actions employers and employees must take to ensure employee safety from fire and other emergencies.

(2) *Elements.* The following elements, at a minimum, shall be included in the plan:

(i) Emergency escape procedures and emergency escape route assignments;

(ii) Procedures to be followed by employees who remain to operate critical plant operations before they evacuate;

(iii) Procedures to account for all employees after emergency evacuation has been completed;

(iv) Rescue and medical duties for those employees who are to perform them;

(v) The preferred means of reporting fires and other emergencies; and

(vi) Names or regular job titles of persons or departments who can be contacted for further information or explanation of duties under the plan.

(3) *Alarm system.* (i) The employer shall establish an employee alarm system which complies with §1910.165.

(ii) If the employee alarm system is used for alerting fire brigade members, or for other purposes, a distinctive signal for each purpose shall be used.

(4) *Evacuation.* The employer shall establish in the emergency action plan the types of evacuation to be used in emergency circumstances.

(5) *Training.* (i) Before implementing the emergency action plan, the employer shall designate and train a sufficient number of persons to assist in the safe and orderly emergency evacuation of employees.

(ii) The employer shall review the plan with each employee covered by the plan at the following times:

(A) Initially when the plan is developed,

(B) Whenever the employee's responsibilities or designated actions under the plan change, and

(C) Whenever the plan is changed.

(iii) The employer shall review with each employee upon initial assignment those parts of the plan which the employee must know to protect the employee in the event of an emergency. The written plan shall be kept at the workplace and made available for employee review. For those employers with 10 or fewer employees the plan may be communicated orally to employees and the employer need not maintain a written plan.

(b) *Fire prevention plan*—(1) *Scope and application.* This paragraph (b) applies to all fire prevention plans required by a particular OSHA standard. The fire prevention plan shall be in writing, except as provided in the last sentence of paragraph (b)(4)(ii) of this section.

(2) *Elements.* The following elements, at a minimum, shall be included in the fire prevention plan:

(i) A list of the major workplace fire hazards and their proper handling and storage procedures, potential ignition sources (such as welding, smoking and others) and their control procedures, and the type of fire protection equipment or systems which can control a fire involving them;

(ii) Names or regular job titles of those personnel responsible for maintenance of equipment and systems installed to prevent or control ignitions or fires; and

(iii) Names or regular job titles of those personnel responsible for control of fuel source hazards.

(3) *Housekeeping.* The employer shall control accumulations of flammable and combustible waste materials and residues so that they do not contribute to a fire emergency. The housekeeping procedures shall be included in the written fire prevention plan.

(4) *Training.* (i) The employer shall apprise employees of the fire hazards of the materials and processes to which they are exposed.

(ii) The employer shall review with each employee upon initial assignment those parts of the fire prevention plan which the employee must know to protect the employee in the event of an emergency. The written plan shall be kept in the workplace and made available for employee review. For those employers with 10 or fewer employees, the plan may be communicated orally to employees and the employer need not maintain a written plan.

(5) *Maintenance.* The employer shall regularly and properly maintain, according to established procedures, equipment and systems installed on heat producing equipment to prevent accidental ignition of combustible materials. The maintenance procedures shall be included in the written fire prevention plan.

[45 FR 60703, Sept. 12, 1980]

Appendix 3C

29 CFR 1910.151
MEDICAL SERVICES AND FIRST AID;
29 CFR 1926.50
MEDICAL SERVICES AND FIRST AID

§ 1910.151 Medical services and first aid.

(a) The employer shall ensure the ready availability of medical personnel for advice and consultation on matters of plant health.

(b) In the absence of an infirmary, clinic, or hospital in near proximity to the workplace which is used for the treatment of all injured employees, a person or persons shall be adequately trained to render first aid. First aid supplies approved by the consulting physician shall be readily available.

(c) Where the eyes or body of any person may be exposed to injurious corrosive materials, suitable facilities for quick drenching or flushing of the eyes and body shall be provided within the work area for immediate emergency use.

§ 1926.50 Medical services and first aid.

(a) The employer shall insure the availability of medical personnel for advice and consultation on matters of occupational health.

(b) Provisions shall be made prior to commencement of the project for prompt medical attention in case of serious injury.

(c) In the absence of an infirmary, clinic, hospital, or physician, that is reasonably accessible in terms of time and distance to the worksite, which is available for the treatment of injured employees, a person who has a valid certificate in first-aid training from the U.S. Bureau of Mines, the American Red Cross, or equivalent training that can be verified by documentary evidence, shall be available at the worksite to render first aid.

(d)(1) First-aid supplies approved by the consulting physician shall be easily accessible when required.

(2) The first-aid kit shall consist of materials approved by the consulting physician in a weatherproof container with individual sealed packages for each type of item. The contents of the first-aid kit shall be checked by the employer before being sent out on each job and at least weekly on each job to ensure that the expended items are replaced.

(e) Proper equipment for prompt transportation of the injured person to a physician or hospital, or a communication system for contacting necessary ambulance service, shall be provided.

(f) The telephone numbers of the physicians, hospitals, or ambulances shall be conspicuously posted.

(g) Where the eyes or body of any person may be exposed to injurious corrosive materials, suitable facilities for quick drenching or flushing of the eyes and body shall be provided within the work area for immediate emergency use.

(The information collection requirements contained in paragraph (f) were approved by the Office of Management and Budget under control number 1218–0093.)

[44 FR 8577, Feb. 9, 1979; 44 FR 20940, Apr. 6, 1979, as amended at 49 FR 18295, Apr. 30, 1984; 58 FR 35084, June 30, 1993]

29 CFR 1910.22
GENERAL REQUIREMENTS;
29 CFR 1910.176
HANDLING MATERIALS—GENERAL;
29 CFR 1926.25
HOUSEKEEPING

§ 1910.22 General requirements.

This section applies to all permanent places of employment, except where domestic, mining, or agricultural work only is performed. Measures for the control of toxic materials are considered to be outside the scope of this section.

(a) *Housekeeping.* (1) All places of employment, passageways, storerooms, and service rooms shall be kept clean and orderly and in a sanitary condition.

(2) The floor of every workroom shall be maintained in a clean and, so far as possible, a dry condition. Where wet processes are used, drainage shall be maintained, and false floors, platforms, mats, or other dry standing places should be provided where practicable.

(3) To facilitate cleaning, every floor, working place, and passageway shall be kept free from protruding nails, splinters, holes, or loose boards.

(b) *Aisles and passageways.* (1) Where mechanical handling equipment is used, sufficient safe clearances shall be allowed for aisles, at loading docks, through doorways and wherever turns or passage must be made. Aisles and passageways shall be kept clear and in good repairs, with no obstruction across or in aisles that could create a hazard

(2) Permanent aisles and passageways shall be appropriately marked.

(c) *Covers and guardrails.* Covers and/or guardrails shall be provided to protect personnel from the hazards of open pits, tanks, vats, ditches, etc.

(d) *Floor loading protection.* (1) In every building or other structure, or part thereof, used for mercantile, business, industrial, or storage purposes, the loads approved by the building official shall be marked on plates of approved design which shall be supplied and securely affixed by the owner of the building, or his duly authorized agent, in a conspicuous place in each space to which they relate. Such plates shall not be removed or defaced but, if lost, removed, or defaced, shall be replaced by the owner or his agent.

(2) It shall be unlawful to place, or cause, or permit to be placed, on any floor or roof of a building or other structure a load greater than that for which such floor or roof is approved by the building official.

§ 1910.176 Handling materials—general.

(a) *Use of mechanical equipment.* Where mechanical handling equipment is used, sufficient safe clearances shall be allowed for aisles, at loading docks, through doorways and wherever turns or passage must be made. Aisles and passageways shall be kept clear and in good repair, with no obstruction across or in aisles that could create a hazard. Permanent aisles and passageways shall be appropriately marked.

(b) *Secure storage.* Storage of material shall not create a hazard. Bags, containers, bundles, etc., stored in tiers shall be stacked, blocked, interlocked and limited in height so that they are stable and secure against sliding or collapse.

(c) *Housekeeping.* Storage areas shall be kept free from accumulation of materials that constitute hazards from tripping, fire, explosion, or pest harborage. Vegetation control will be exercised when necessary.

(d) [Reserved]

(e) *Clearance limits.* Clearance signs to warn of clearance limits shall be provided.

(f) *Rolling railroad cars.* Derail and/or bumper blocks shall be provided on spur railroad tracks where a rolling car could contact other cars being worked, enter a building, work or traffic area.

(g) *Guarding.* Covers and/or guardrails shall be provided to protect personnel from the hazards of open pits, tanks, vats, ditches, etc.

[39 FR 23052, June 27, 1974, as amended at 43 FR 49749, Oct. 24, 1978]

§ 1926.25 Housekeeping.

(a) During the course of construction, alteration, or repairs, form and scrap lumber with protruding nails, and all other debris, shall be kept cleared from work areas, passageways, and stairs, in and around buildings or other structures.

(b) Combustible scrap and debris shall be removed at regular intervals during the course of construction. Safe means shall be provided to facilitate such removal.

(c) Containers shall be provided for the collection and separation of waste, trash, oily and used rags, and other refuse. Containers used for garbage and other oily, flammable, or hazardous wastes, such as caustics, acids, harmful dusts, etc. shall be equipped with covers. Garbage and other waste shall be disposed of at frequent and regular intervals.

29 CFR 1910.1200
Hazard
Communication

§ 1910.1200 **Hazard communication.**

(a) *Purpose.* (1) The purpose of this section is to ensure that the hazards of all chemicals produced or imported are evaluated, and ·that information concerning their hazards is transmitted to employers and employees. This transmittal of information is to be accomplished by means of comprehensive hazard communication programs, which are to include container labeling and other forms of warning, material safety data sheets and employee training.

(2) This occupational safety and health standard is intended to address comprehensively the issue of evaluating the potential hazards of chemicals, and communicating information concerning hazards and appropriate protective measures to employees, and to preempt any legal requirements of a state, or political subdivision of a state, pertaining to this subject. Evaluating the potential hazards of chemicals, and communicating information concerning hazards and appropriate protective measures to employees, may

include, for example, but is not limited to, provisions for: developing and maintaining a written hazard communication program for the workplace, including lists of hazardous chemicals present; labeling of containers of chemicals in the workplace, as well as of containers of chemicals being shipped to other workplaces; preparation and distribution of material safety data sheets to employees and downstream employers; and development and implementation of employee training programs regarding hazards of chemicals and protective measures. Under section 18 of the Act, no state or political subdivision of a state may adopt or enforce, through any court or agency, any requirement relating to the issue addressed by this Federal standard, except pursuant to a Federally-approved state plan.

(b) *Scope and application.* (1) This section requires chemical manufacturers or importers to assess the hazards of chemicals which they produce or import, and all employers to provide information to their employees about the hazardous chemicals to which they are exposed, by means of a hazard communication program, labels and other forms of warning, material safety data sheets, and information and training. In addition, this section requires distributors to transmit the required information to employers. (Employers who do not produce or import chemicals need only focus on those parts of this rule that deal with establishing a workplace program and communicating information to their workers. Appendix E of this section is a general guide for such employers to help them determine their compliance obligations under the rule.)

(2) This section applies to any chemical which is known to be present in the workplace in such a manner that employees may be exposed under normal conditions of use or in a foreseeable emergency.

(3) This section applies to laboratories only as follows:

(i) Employers shall ensure that labels on incoming containers of hazardous chemicals are not removed or defaced;

(ii) Employers shall maintain any material safety data sheets that are received with incoming shipments of haz-ardous chemicals, and ensure that they are readily accessible during each workshift to laboratory employees when they are in their work areas;

(iii) Employers shall ensure that laboratory employees are provided information and training in accordance with paragraph (h) of this section, except for the location and availability of the written hazard communication program under paragraph (h)(2)(iii) of this section; and,

(iv) Laboratory employers that ship hazardous chemicals are considered to be either a chemical manufacturer or a distributor under this rule, and thus must ensure that any containers of hazardous chemicals leaving the laboratory are labeled in accordance with paragraph (f)(1) of this section, and that a material safety data sheet is provided to distributors and other employers in accordance with paragraphs (g)(6) and (g)(7) of this section.

(4) In work operations where employees only handle chemicals in sealed containers which are not opened under normal conditions of use (such as are found in marine cargo handling, warehousing, or retail sales), this section applies to these operations only as follows:

(i) Employers shall ensure that labels on incoming containers of hazardous chemicals are not removed or defaced;

(ii) Employers shall maintain copies of any material safety data sheets that are received with incoming shipments of the sealed containers of hazardous chemicals, shall obtain a material safety data sheet as soon as possible for sealed containers of hazardous chemicals received without a material safety data sheet if an employee requests the material safety data sheet, and shall ensure that the material safety data sheets are readily accessible during each work shift to employees when they are in their work area(s); and,

(iii) Employers shall ensure that employees are provided with information and training in accordance with paragraph (h) of this section (except for the location and availability of the written hazard communication program under paragraph (h)(2)(iii) of this section), to the extent necessary to protect them in the event of a spill or leak of a hazardous chemical from a sealed container.

(5) This section does not require labeling of the following chemicals:

(i) Any pesticide as such term is defined in the Federal Insecticide, Fungicide, and Rodenticide Act (7 U.S.C. 136 *et seq.*), when subject to the labeling requirements of that Act and labeling regulations issued under that Act by the Environmental Protection Agency;

(ii) Any chemical substance or mixture as such terms are defined in the Toxic Substances Control Act (15 U.S.C. 2601 *et seq.*), when subject to the labeling requirements of that Act and labeling regulations issued under that Act by the Environmental Protection Agency.

(iii) Any food, food additive, color additive, drug, cosmetic, or medical or veterinary device or product, including materials intended for use as ingredients in such products (*e.g.* flavors and fragrances), as such terms are defined in the Federal Food, Drug, and Cosmetic Act (21 U.S.C. 301 *et seq.*) or the Virus-Serum-Toxin Act of 1913 (21 U.S.C. 151 *et seq*), and regulations issued under those Acts, when they are subject to the labeling requirements under those Acts by either the Food and Drug Administration or the Department of Agriculture;

(iv) Any distilled spirits (beverage alcohols), wine, or malt beverage intended for nonindustrial use, as such terms are defined in the Federal Alcohol Administration Act (27 U.S.C. 201 *et seq.*) and regulations issued under that Act, when subject to the labeling requirements of that Act and labeling regulations issued under that Act by the Bureau of Alcohol, Tobacco, and Firearms;

(v) Any consumer product or hazardous substance as those terms are defined in the Consumer Product Safety Act (15 U.S.C. 2051 *et seq.*) and Federal Hazardous Substances Act (15 U.S.C. 1261 *et seq.*) respectively, when subject to a consumer product safety standard or labeling requirement of those Acts, or regulations issued under those Acts by the Consumer Product Safety Commission; and,

(vi) Agricultural or vegetable seed treated with pesticides and labeled in accordance with the Federal Seed Act

(7 U.S.C. 1551 *et seq.*) and the labeling regulations issued under that Act by the Department of Agriculture.

(6) This section does not apply to: (i) Any hazardous waste as such term is defined by the Solid Waste Disposal Act, as amended by the Resource Conservation and Recovery Act of 1976, as amended (42 U.S.C. 6901 *et seq.*), when subject to regulations issued under that Act by the Environmental Protection Agency;

(ii) Any hazardous substance as such term is defined by the Comprehensive Environmental Response, Compensation, and Liability Act (CERCLA)(42 U.S.C. 9601 *et seq.*), when subject to regulations issued under that Act by the Environmental Protection Agency;

(iii) Tobacco or tobacco products;

(iv) Wood or wood products, including lumber which will not be processed, where the chemical manufacturer or importer can establish that the only hazard they pose to employees is the potential for flammability or combustibility (wood or wood products which have been treated with a hazardous chemical covered by this standard, and wood which may be subsequently sawed or cut, generating dust, are not exempted);

(v) Articles (as that term is defined in paragraph (c) of this section);

(vi) Food or alcoholic beverages which are sold, used, or prepared in a retail establishment (such as a grocery store, restaurant, or drinking place), and foods intended for personal consumption by employees while in the workplace;

(vii) Any drug, as that term is defined in the Federal Food, Drug, and Cosmetic Act (21 U.S.C. 301 *et seq.*), when it is in solid, final form for direct administration to the patient (*e.g.*, tablets or pills); drugs which are packaged by the chemical manufacturer for sale to consumers in a retail establishment (*e.g.*, over-the-counter drugs); and drugs intended for personal consumption by employees while in the workplace (*e.g.*, first aid supplies);

(viii) Cosmetics which are packaged for sale to consumers in a retail establishment, and cosmetics intended for personal consumption by employees while in the workplace;

(ix) Any consumer product or hazardous substance, as those terms are defined in the Consumer Product Safety Act (15 U.S.C. 2051 *et seq.*) and Federal Hazardous Substances Act (15 U.S.C. 1261 *et seq.*) respectively, where the employer can show that it is used in the workplace for the purpose intended by the chemical manufacturer or importer of the product, and the use results in a duration and frequency of exposure which is not greater than the range of exposures that could reasonably be experienced by consumers when used for the purpose intended;

(x) Nuisance particulates where the chemical manufacturer or importer can establish that they do not pose any physical or health hazard covered under this section;

(xi) Ionizing and nonionizing radiation; and,

(xii) Biological hazards.

(c) *Definitions.*

Article means a manufactured item other than a fluid or particle: (i) which is formed to a specific shape or design during manufacture; (ii) which has end use function(s) dependent in whole or in part upon its shape or design during end use; and (iii) which under normal conditions of use does not release more than very small quantities, *e.g.*, minute or trace amounts of a hazardous chemical (as determined under paragraph (d) of this section), and does not pose a physical hazard or health risk to employees.

Assistant Secretary means the Assistant Secretary of Labor for Occupational Safety and Health, U.S. Department of Labor, or designee.

Chemical means any element, chemical compound or mixture of elements and/or compounds.

Chemical manufacturer means an employer with a workplace where chemical(s) are produced for use or distribution.

Chemical name means the scientific designation of a chemical in accordance with the nomenclature system developed by the International Union of Pure and Applied Chemistry (IUPAC) or the Chemical Abstracts Service (CAS) rules of nomenclature, or a name which will clearly identify the chemical for the purpose of conducting a hazard evaluation.

Combustible liquid means any liquid having a flashpoint at or above 100 °F (37.8 °C), but below 200 °F (93.3 °C), except any mixture having components with flashpoints of 200 °F (93.3 °C), or higher, the total volume of which make up 99 percent or more of the total volume of the mixture.

Commercial account means an arrangement whereby a retail distributor sells hazardous chemicals to an employer, generally in large quantities over time and/or at costs that are below the regular retail price.

Common name means any designation or identification such as code name, code number, trade name, brand name or generic name used to identify a chemical other than by its chemical name.

Compressed gas means:

(i) A gas or mixture of gases having, in a container, an absolute pressure exceeding 40 psi at 70 °F (21.1 °C); or

(ii) A gas or mixture of gases having, in a container, an absolute pressure exceeding 104 psi at 130 °F (54.4 °C) regardless of the pressure at 70 °F (21.1 °C); or

(iii) A liquid having a vapor pressure exceeding 40 psi at 100 °F (37.8 °C) as determined by ASTM D–323–72.

Container means any bag, barrel, bottle, box, can, cylinder, drum, reaction vessel, storage tank, or the like that contains a hazardous chemical. For purposes of this section, pipes or piping systems, and engines, fuel tanks, or other operating systems in a vehicle, are not considered to be containers.

Designated representative means any individual or organization to whom an employee gives written authorization to exercise such employee's rights under this section. A recognized or certified collective bargaining agent shall be treated automatically as a designated representative without regard to written employee authorization.

Director means the Director, National Institute for Occupational Safety and Health, U.S. Department of Health and Human Services, or designee.

Distributor means a business, other than a chemical manufacturer or importer, which supplies hazardous chemicals to other distributors or to employers.

Employee means a worker who may be exposed to hazardous chemicals under

471

normal operating conditions or in foreseeable emergencies. Workers such as
office workers or bank tellers who encounter hazardous chemicals only in
non-routine, isolated instances are not
covered.

Employer means a person engaged in a
business where chemicals are either
used, distributed, or are produced for
use or distribution, including a contractor or subcontractor.

Explosive means a chemical that
causes a sudden, almost instantaneous
release of pressure, gas, and heat when
subjected to sudden shock, pressure, or
high temperature.

Exposure or *exposed* means that an
employee is subjected in the course of
employment to a chemical that is a
physical or health hazard, and includes
potential (*e.g.* accidental or possible)
exposure. "Subjected" in terms of
health hazards includes any route of
entry (*e.g.* inhalation, ingestion, skin
contact or absorption.)

Flammable means a chemical that
falls into one of the following categories:

(i) *Aerosol, flammable* means an aerosol that, when tested by the method described in 16 CFR 1500.45, yields a flame
projection exceeding 18 inches at full
valve opening, or a flashback (a flame
extending back to the valve) at any degree of valve opening;

(ii) *Gas, flammable* means: (A) A gas
that, at ambient temperature and pressure, forms a flammable mixture with
air at a concentration of thirteen (13)
percent by volume or less; or

(B) A gas that, at ambient temperature and pressure, forms a range of
flammable mixtures with air wider
than twelve (12) percent by volume, regardless of the lower limit;

(iii) *Liquid, flammable* means any liquid having a flashpoint below 100°F
(37.8°C), except any mixture having
components with flashpoints of 100°F
(37.8°C) or higher, the total of which
make up 99 percent or more of the total
volume of the mixture.

(iv) *Solid, flammable* means a solid,
other than a blasting agent or explosive as defined in § 1910.109(a), that is
liable to cause fire through friction,
absorption of moisture, spontaneous
chemical change, or retained heat from
manufacturing or processing, or which

can be ignited readily and when ignited
burns so vigorously and persistently as
to create a serious hazard. A chemical
shall be considered to be a flammable
solid if, when tested by the method described in 16 CFR 1500.44, it ignites and
burns with a self-sustained flame at a
rate greater than one-tenth of an inch
per second along its major axis.

Flashpoint means the minimum temperature at which a liquid gives off a
vapor in sufficient concentration to ignite when tested as follows:

(i) Tagliabue Closed Tester (See
American National Standard Method of
Test for Flash Point by Tag Closed
Tester, Z11.24–1979 (ASTM D 56–79)) for
liquids with a viscosity of less than 45
Saybolt Universal Seconds (SUS) at
100°F (37.8°C), that do not contain suspended solids and do not have a tendency to form a surface film under test;
or

(ii) Pensky-Martens Closed Tester
(see American National Standard
Method of Test for Flash Point by
Pensky-Martens Closed Tester, Z11.7–
1979 (ASTM D 93–79)) for liquids with a
viscosity equal to or greater than 45
SUS at 100°F (37.8°C), or that contain
suspended solids, or that have a tendency to form a surface film under test;
or

(iii) Setaflash Closed Tester (see
American National Standard Method of
Test for Flash Point by Setaflash
Closed Tester (ASTM D 3278–78)).

Organic peroxides, which undergo
autoaccelerating thermal decomposition, are excluded from any of the
flashpoint determination methods
specified above.

Foreseeable emergency means any potential occurrence such as, but not limited to, equipment failure, rupture of
containers, or failure of control equipment which could result in an uncontrolled release of a hazardous chemical
into the workplace.

Hazardous chemical means any chemical which is a physical hazard or a
health hazard.

Hazard warning means any words,
pictures, symbols, or combination
thereof appearing on a label or other
appropriate form of warning which convey the specific physical or health
hazard(s), including target organ effects, of the chemical(s) in the

container(s). (See the definitions for "physical hazard" and "health hazard" to determine the hazards which must be covered.)

Health hazard means a chemical for which there is statistically significant evidence based on at least one study conducted in accordance with established scientific principles that acute or chronic health effects may occur in exposed employees. The term "health hazard" includes chemicals which are carcinogens, toxic or highly toxic agents, reproductive toxins, irritants, corrosives, sensitizers, hepatotoxins, nephrotoxins, neurotoxins, agents which act on the hematopoietic system, and agents which damage the lungs, skin, eyes, or mucous membranes. Appendix A provides further definitions and explanations of the scope of health hazards covered by this section, and Appendix B describes the criteria to be used to determine whether or not a chemical is to be considered hazardous for purposes of this standard.

Identity means any chemical or common name which is indicated on the material safety data sheet (MSDS) for the chemical. The identity used shall permit cross-references to be made among the required list of hazardous chemicals, the label and the MSDS.

Immediate use means that the hazardous chemical will be under the control of and used only by the person who transfers it from a labeled container and only within the work shift in which it is transferred.

Importer means the first business with employees within the Customs Territory of the United States which receives hazardous chemicals produced in other countries for the purpose of supplying them to distributors or employers within the United States.

Label means any written, printed, or graphic material displayed on or affixed to containers of hazardous chemicals.

Material safety data sheet (MSDS) means written or printed material concerning a hazardous chemical which is prepared in accordance with paragraph (g) of this section.

Mixture means any combination of two or more chemicals if the combina-

tion is not, in whole or in part, the result of a chemical reaction.

Organic peroxide means an organic compound that contains the bivalent -O-O-structure and which may be considered to be a structural derivative of hydrogen peroxide where one or both of the hydrogen atoms has been replaced by an organic radical.

Oxidizer means a chemical other than a blasting agent or explosive as defined in § 1910.109(a), that initiates or promotes combustion in other materials, thereby causing fire either of itself or through the release of oxygen or other gases.

Physical hazard means a chemical for which there is scientifically valid evidence that it is a combustible liquid, a compressed gas, explosive, flammable, an organic peroxide, an oxidizer, pyrophoric, unstable (reactive) or water-reactive.

Produce means to manufacture, process, formulate, blend, extract, generate, emit, or repackage.

Pyrophoric means a chemical that will ignite spontaneously in air at a temperature of 130°F (54.4°C) or below.

Responsible party means someone who can provide additional information on the hazardous chemical and appropriate emergency procedures, if necessary.

Specific chemical identity means the chemical name, Chemical Abstracts Service (CAS) Registry Number, or any other information that reveals the precise chemical designation of the substance.

Trade secret means any confidential formula, pattern, process, device, information or compilation of information that is used in an employer's business, and that gives the employer an opportunity to obtain an advantage over competitors who do not know or use it. Appendix D sets out the criteria to be used in evaluating trade secrets.

Unstable (reactive) means a chemical which in the pure state, or as produced or transported, will vigorously polymerize, decompose, condense, or will become self-reactive under conditions of shocks, pressure or temperature.

Use means to package, handle, react, emit, extract, generate as a byproduct, or transfer.

Water-reactive means a chemical that reacts with water to release a gas that is either flammable or presents a health hazard.

Work area means a room or defined space in a workplace where hazardous chemicals are produced or used, and where employees are present.

Workplace means an establishment, job site, or project, at one geographical location containing one or more work areas.

(d) *Hazard determination.* (1) Chemical manufacturers and importers shall evaluate chemicals produced in their workplaces or imported by them to determine if they are hazardous. Employers are not required to evaluate chemicals unless they choose not to rely on the evaluation performed by the chemical manufacturer or importer for the chemical to satisfy this requirement.

(2) Chemical manufacturers, importers or employers evaluating chemicals shall identify and consider the available scientific evidence concerning such hazards. For health hazards, evidence which is statistically significant and which is based on at least one positive study conducted in accordance with established scientific principles is considered to be sufficient to establish a hazardous effect if the results of the study meet the definitions of health hazards in this section. Appendix A shall be consulted for the scope of health hazards covered, and Appendix B shall be consulted for the criteria to be followed with respect to the completeness of the evaluation, and the data to be reported.

(3) The chemical manufacturer, importer or employer evaluating chemicals shall treat the following sources as establishing that the chemicals listed in them are hazardous:

(i) 29 CFR part 1910, subpart Z, Toxic and Hazardous Substances, Occupational Safety and Health Administration (OSHA); or,

(ii) *Threshold Limit Values for Chemical Substances and Physical Agents in the Work Environment,* American Conference of Governmental Industrial Hygienists (ACGIH) (latest edition). The chemical manufacturer, importer, or employer is still responsible for evaluating the hazards associated with the chemicals in these source lists in ac-

cordance with the requirements of this standard.

(4) Chemical manufacturers, importers and employers evaluating chemicals shall treat the following sources as establishing that a chemical is a carcinogen or potential carcinogen for hazard communication purposes:

(i) National Toxicology Program (NTP), *Annual Report on Carcinogens* (latest edition);

(ii) International Agency for Research on Cancer (IARC) *Monographs* (latest editions); or

(iii) 29 CFR part 1910, subpart Z, Toxic and Hazardous Substances, Occupational Safety and Health Administration.

NOTE: The *Registry of Toxic Effects of Chemical Substances* published by the National Institute for Occupational Safety and Health indicates whether a chemical has been found by NTP or IARC to be a potential carcinogen.

(5) The chemical manufacturer, importer or employer shall determine the hazards of mixtures of chemicals as follows:

(i) If a mixture has been tested as a whole to determine its hazards, the results of such testing shall be used to determine whether the mixture is hazardous;

(ii) If a mixture has not been tested as a whole to determine whether the mixture is a health hazard, the mixture shall be assumed to present the same health hazards as do the components which comprise one percent (by weight or volume) or greater of the mixture, except that the mixture shall be assumed to present a carcinogenic hazard if it contains a component in concentrations of 0.1 percent or greater which is considered to be a carcinogen under paragraph (d)(4) of this section;

(iii) If a mixture has not been tested as a whole to determine whether the mixture is a physical hazard, the chemical manufacturer, importer, or employer may use whatever scientifically valid data is available to evaluate the physical hazard potential of the mixture; and,

(iv) If the chemical manufacturer, importer, or employer has evidence to indicate that a component present in the mixture in concentrations of less than one percent (or in the case of carcinogens, less than 0.1 percent) could be released in concentrations which would exceed an established OSHA permissible exposure limit or ACGIH Threshold Limit Value, or could present a health risk to employees in those concentrations, the mixture shall be assumed to present the same hazard.

(6) Chemical manufacturers, importers, or employers evaluating chemicals shall describe in writing the procedures they use to determine the hazards of the chemical they evaluate. The written procedures are to be made available, upon request, to employees, their designated representatives, the Assistant Secretary and the Director. The written description may be incorporated into the written hazard communication program required under paragraph (e) of this section.

(e) *Written hazard communication program.* (1) Employers shall develop, implement, and maintain at each workplace, a written hazard communication program which at least describes how the criteria specified in paragraphs (f), (g), and (h) of this section for labels and other forms of warning, material safety data sheets, and employee information and training will be met, and which also includes the following:

(i) A list of the hazardous chemicals known to be present using an identity that is referenced on the appropriate material safety data sheet (the list may be compiled for the workplace as a whole or for individual work areas); and,

(ii) The methods the employer will use to inform employees of the hazards of non-routine tasks (for example, the cleaning of reactor vessels), and the hazards associated with chemicals contained in unlabeled pipes in their work areas.

(2) *Multi-employer workplaces.* Employers who produce, use, or store hazardous chemicals at a workplace in such a way that the employees of other employer(s) may be exposed (for example, employees of a construction contractor working on-site) shall additionally ensure that the hazard communication programs developed and implemented under this paragraph (e) include the following:

(i) The methods the employer will use to provide the other employer(s) on-site access to material safety data sheets for each hazardous chemical the other employer(s)' employees may be exposed to while working;

(ii) The methods the employer will use to inform the other employer(s) of any precautionary measures that need to be taken to protect employees during the workplace's normal operating conditions and in foreseeable emergencies; and,

(iii) The methods the employer will use to inform the other employer(s) of the labeling system used in the workplace.

(3) The employer may rely on an existing hazard communication program to comply with these requirements, provided that it meets the criteria established in this paragraph (e).

(4) The employer shall make the written hazard communication program available, upon request, to employees, their designated representatives, the Assistant Secretary and the Director, in accordance with the requirements of 29 CFR 1910.20 (e).

(5) Where employees must travel between workplaces during a workshift, *i.e.*, their work is carried out at more than one geographical location, the written hazard communication program may be kept at the primary workplace facility.

(f) *Labels and other forms of warning.* (1) The chemical manufacturer, importer, or distributor shall ensure that each container of hazardous chemicals leaving the workplace is labeled, tagged or marked with the following information:

(i) Identity of the hazardous chemical(s);

(ii) Appropriate hazard warnings; and

(iii) Name and address of the chemical manufacturer, importer, or other responsible party.

(2)(i) For solid metal (such as a steel beam or a metal casting), solid wood, or plastic items that are not exempted as articles due to their downstream use, or shipments of whole grain, the required label may be transmitted to the customer at the time of the initial shipment, and need not be included with subsequent shipments to the same employer unless the information on the label changes;

(ii) The label may be transmitted with the initial shipment itself, or with the material safety data sheet that is to be provided prior to or at the time of the first shipment; and,

(iii) This exception to requiring labels on every container of hazardous chemicals is only for the solid material itself, and does not apply to hazardous chemicals used in conjunction with, or known to be present with, the material and to which employees handling the items in transit may be exposed (for example, cutting fluids or pesticides in grains).

(3) Chemical manufacturers, importers, or distributors shall ensure that each container of hazardous chemicals leaving the workplace is labeled, tagged, or marked in accordance with this section in a manner which does not conflict with the requirements of the Hazardous Materials Transportation Act (49 U.S.C. 1801 *et seq.*) and regulations issued under that Act by the Department of Transportation.

(4) If the hazardous chemical is regulated by OSHA in a substance-specific health standard, the chemical manufacturer, importer, distributor or employer shall ensure that the labels or other forms of warning used are in accordance with the requirements of that standard.

(5) Except as provided in paragraphs (f)(6) and (f)(7) of this section, the employer shall ensure that each container of hazardous chemicals in the workplace is labeled, tagged or marked with the following information:

(i) Identity of the hazardous chemical(s) contained therein; and,

(ii) Appropriate hazard warnings, or alternatively, words, pictures, symbols, or combination thereof, which provide at least general information regarding the hazards of the chemicals, and which, in conjunction with the other information immediately available to employees under the hazard communication program, will provide employees with the specific information regarding the physical and health hazards of the hazardous chemical.

(6) The employer may use signs, placards, process sheets, batch tickets, operating procedures, or other such written materials in lieu of affixing labels to individual stationary process containers, as long as the alternative method identifies the containers to which it is applicable and conveys the information required by paragraph (f)(5) of this section to be on a label. The written materials shall be readily accessible to the employees in their work area throughout each work shift.

(7) The employer is not required to label portable containers into which hazardous chemicals are transferred from labeled containers, and which are intended only for the immediate use of the employee who performs the transfer. For purposes of this section, drugs which are dispensed by a pharmacy to a health care provider for direct administration to a patient are exempted from labeling.

(8) The employer shall not remove or deface existing labels on incoming containers of hazardous chemicals, unless the container is immediately marked with the required information.

(9) The employer shall ensure that labels or other forms of warning are legible, in English, and prominently displayed on the container, or readily available in the work area throughout each work shift. Employers having employees who speak other languages may add the information in their language to the material presented, as long as the information is presented in English as well.

(10) The chemical manufacturer, importer, distributor or employer need not affix new labels to comply with this section if existing labels already convey the required information.

(11) Chemical manufacturers, importers, distributors, or employers who become newly aware of any significant information regarding the hazards of a chemical shall revise the labels for the chemical within three months of becoming aware of the new information. Labels on containers of hazardous chemicals shipped after that time shall contain the new information. If the chemical is not currently produced or imported, the chemical manufacturer, importers, distributor, or employer shall add the information to the label before the chemical is shipped or introduced into the workplace again.

(g) *Material safety data sheets.* (1) Chemical manufacturers and importers shall obtain or develop a material safety data sheet for each hazardous chemical they produce or import. Employers shall have a material safety data sheet in the workplace for each hazardous chemical which they use.

(2) Each material safety data sheet shall be in English (although the employer may maintain copies in other languages as well), and shall contain at least the following information:

(i) The identity used on the label, and, except as provided for in paragraph (i) of this section on trade secrets:

(A) If the hazardous chemical is a single substance, its chemical and common name(s);

(B) If the hazardous chemical is a mixture which has been tested as a whole to determine its hazards, the chemical and common name(s) of the ingredients which contribute to these known hazards, and the common name(s) of the mixture itself; or,

(C) If the hazardous chemical is a mixture which has not been tested as a whole:

(1) The chemical and common name(s) of all ingredients which have been determined to be health hazards, and which comprise 1% or greater of the composition, except that chemicals identified as carcinogens under paragraph (d) of this section shall be listed if the concentrations are 0.1% or greater; and,

(2) The chemical and common name(s) of all ingredients which have been determined to be health hazards, and which comprise less than 1% (0.1% for carcinogens) of the mixture, if there is evidence that the ingredient(s) could be released from the mixture in concentrations which would exceed an established OSHA permissible exposure limit or ACGIH Threshold Limit Value, or could present a health risk to employees; and,

(3) The chemical and common name(s) of all ingredients which have been determined to present a physical hazard when present in the mixture;

(ii) Physical and chemical characteristics of the hazardous chemical (such as vapor pressure, flash point);

(iii) The physical hazards of the hazardous chemical, including the potential for fire, explosion, and reactivity;

(iv) The health hazards of the hazardous chemical, including signs and symptoms of exposure, and any medical conditions which are generally recognized as being aggravated by exposure to the chemical;

(v) The primary route(s) of entry;

(vi) The OSHA permissible exposure limit, ACGIH Threshold Limit Value, and any other exposure limit used or recommended by the chemical manufacturer, importer, or employer preparing the material safety data sheet, where available;

(vii) Whether the hazardous chemical is listed in the National Toxicology Program (NTP) Annual Report on Carcinogens (latest edition) or has been found to be a potential carcinogen in the International Agency for Research on Cancer (IARC) Monographs (latest editions), or by OSHA;

(viii) Any generally applicable precautions for safe handling and use which are known to the chemical manufacturer, importer or employer preparing the material safety data sheet, including appropriate hygienic practices, protective measures during repair and maintenance of contaminated equipment, and procedures for clean-up of spills and leaks;

(ix) Any generally applicable control measures which are known to the chemical manufacturer, importer or employer preparing the material safety data sheet, such as appropriate engineering controls, work practices, or personal protective equipment;

(x) Emergency and first aid procedures;

(xi) The date of preparation of the material safety data sheet or the last change to it; and,

(xii) The name, address and telephone number of the chemical manufacturer, importer, employer or other responsible party preparing or distributing the material safety data sheet, who can provide additional information on the hazardous chemical and appropriate emergency procedures, if necessary.

(3) If no relevant information is found for any given category on the material safety data sheet, the chemical manufacturer, importer or employer preparing the material safety data sheet shall mark it to indicate

that no applicable information was found.

(4) Where complex mixtures have similar hazards and contents (i.e. the chemical ingredients are essentially the same, but the specific composition varies from mixture to mixture), the chemical manufacturer, importer or employer may prepare one material safety data sheet to apply to all of these similar mixtures.

(5) The chemical manufacturer, importer or employer preparing the material safety data sheet shall ensure that the information recorded, accurately reflects the scientific evidence used in making the hazard determination. If the chemical manufacturer, importer or employer preparing the material safety data sheet becomes newly aware of any significant information regarding the hazards of a chemical, or ways to protect against the hazards, this new information shall be added to the material safety data sheet within three months. If the chemical is not currently being produced or imported the chemical manufacturer or importer shall add the information to the material safety data sheet before the chemical is introduced into the workplace again.

(6)(i) Chemical manufacturers or importers shall ensure that distributors and employers are provided an appropriate material safety data sheet with their initial shipment, and with the first shipment after a material safety data sheet is updated;

(ii) The chemical manufacturer or importer shall either provide material safety data sheets with the shipped containers or send them to the distributor or employer prior to or at the time of the shipment;

(iii) If the material safety data sheet is not provided with a shipment that has been labeled as a hazardous chemical, the distributor or employer shall obtain one from the chemical manufacturer or importer as soon as possible; and,

(iv) The chemical manufacturer or importer shall also provide distributors or employers with a material safety data sheet upon request.

(7)(i) Distributors shall ensure that material safety data sheets, and updated information, are provided to other distributors and employers with their initial shipment and with the first shipment after a material safety data sheet is updated;

(ii) The distributor shall either provide material safety data sheets with the shipped containers, or send them to the other distributor or employer prior to or at the time of the shipment;

(iii) Retail distributors selling hazardous chemicals to employers having a commercial account shall provide a material safety data sheet to such employers upon request, and shall post a sign or otherwise inform them that a material safety data sheet is available;

(iv) Wholesale distributors selling hazardous chemicals to employers over-the-counter may also, as an alternative to keeping a file of material safety data sheets for all hazardous chemicals they sell, provide material safety data sheets upon the request of the employer at the time of the over-the-counter purchase, and shall post a sign or otherwise inform such employers that a material safety data sheet is available;

(v) If an employer without a commercial account purchases a hazardous chemical from a retail distributor not required to have material safety data sheets on file (i.e., the retail distributor does not have commercial accounts and does not use the materials), the retail distributor shall provide the employer, upon request, with the name, address, and telephone number of the chemical manufacturer, importer, or distributor from which a material safety data sheet can be obtained;

(vi) Wholesale distributors shall also provide material safety data sheets to employers or other distributors upon request; and,

(vii) Chemical manufacturers, importers, and distributors need not provide material safety data sheets to retail distributors that have informed them that the retail distributor does not sell the product to commercial accounts or open the sealed container to use it in their own workplaces.

(8) The employer shall maintain in the workplace copies of the required material safety data sheets for each hazardous chemical, and shall ensure that they are readily accessible during each work shift to employees when

they are in their work area(s). (Electronic access, microfiche, and other alternatives to maintaining paper copies of the material safety data sheets are permitted as long as no barriers to immediate employee access in each workplace are created by such options.)

(9) Where employees must travel between workplaces during a workshift, *i.e.*, their work is carried out at more than one geographical location, the material safety data sheets may be kept at the primary workplace facility. In this situation, the employer shall ensure that employees can immediately obtain the required information in an emergency.

(10) Material safety data sheets may be kept in any form, including operating procedures, and may be designed to cover groups of hazardous chemicals in a work area where it may be more appropriate to address the hazards of a process rather than individual hazardous chemicals. However, the employer shall ensure that in all cases the required information is provided for each hazardous chemical, and is readily accessible during each work shift to employees when they are in in their work area(s).

(11) Material safety data sheets shall also be made readily available, upon request, to designated representatives and to the Assistant Secretary, in accordance with the requirements of 29 CFR 1910.20(e). The Director shall also be given access to material safety data sheets in the same manner.

(h) *Employee information and training.* (1) Employers shall provide employees with effective information and training on hazardous chemicals in their work area at the time of their initial assignment, and whenever a new physical or health hazard the employees have not previously been trained about is introduced into their work area. Information and training may be designed to cover categories of hazards (*e.g.*, flammability, carcinogenicity) or specific chemicals. Chemical-specific information must always be available through labels and material safety data sheets.

(2) *Information.* Employees shall be informed of:

(i) The requirements of this section;

(ii) Any operations in their work area where hazardous chemicals are present; and,

(iii) The location and availability of the written hazard communication program, including the required list(s) of hazardous chemicals, and material safety data sheets required by this section.

(3) *Training.* Employee training shall include at least:

(i) Methods and observations that may be used to detect the presence or release of a hazardous chemical in the work area (such as monitoring conducted by the employer, continuous monitoring devices, visual appearance or odor of hazardous chemicals when being released, etc.);

(ii) The physical and health hazards of the chemicals in the work area;

(iii) The measures employees can take to protect themselves from these hazards, including specific procedures the employer has implemented to protect employees from exposure to hazardous chemicals, such as appropriate work practices, emergency procedures, and personal protective equipment to be used; and,

(iv) The details of the hazard communication program developed by the employer, including an explanation of the labeling system and the material safety data sheet, and how employees can obtain and use the appropriate hazard information.

(i) *Trade secrets.* (1) The chemical manufacturer, importer, or employer may withhold the specific chemical identity, including the chemical name and other specific identification of a hazardous chemical, from the material safety data sheet, provided that:

(i) The claim that the information withheld is a trade secret can be supported;

(ii) Information contained in the material safety data sheet concerning the properties and effects of the hazardous chemical is disclosed;

(iii) The material safety data sheet indicates that the specific chemical identity is being withheld as a trade secret; and,

(iv) The specific chemical identity is made available to health professionals, employees, and designated representatives in accordance with the applicable provisions of this paragraph.

(2) Where a treating physician or nurse determines that a medical emergency exists and the specific chemical identity of a hazardous chemical is necessary for emergency or first-aid treatment, the chemical manufacturer, importer, or employer shall immediately disclose the specific chemical identity of a trade secret chemical to that treating physician or nurse, regardless of the existence of a written statement of need or a confidentiality agreement. The chemical manufacturer, importer, or employer may require a written statement of need and confidentiality agreement, in accordance with the provisions of paragraphs (i) (3) and (4) of this section, as soon as circumstances permit.

(3) In non-emergency situations, a chemical manufacturer, importer, or employer shall, upon request, disclose a specific chemical identity, otherwise permitted to be withheld under paragraph (i)(1) of this section, to a health professional (i e physician, industrial hygienist, toxicologist, epidemiologist, or occupational health nurse) providing medical or other occupational health services to exposed employee(s), and to employees or designated representatives, if:

(i) The request is in writing;

(ii) The request describes with reasonable detail one or more of the following occupational health needs for the information:

(A) To assess the hazards of the chemicals to which employees will be exposed;

(B) To conduct or assess sampling of the workplace atmosphere to determine employee exposure levels;

(C) To conduct pre-assignment or periodic medical surveillance of exposed employees;

(D) To provide medical treatment to exposed employees;

(E) To select or assess appropriate personal protective equipment for exposed employees;

(F) To design or assess engineering controls or other protective measures for exposed employees; and,

(G) To conduct studies to determine the health effects of exposure.

(iii) The request explains in detail why the disclosure of the specific chemical identity is essential and that, in lieu thereof, the disclosure of the following information to the health professional, employee, or designated representative, would not satisfy the purposes described in paragraph (i)(3)(ii) of this section:

(A) The properties and effects of the chemical;

(B) Measures for controlling workers' exposure to the chemical;

(C) Methods of monitoring and analyzing worker exposure to the chemical; and,

(D) Methods of diagnosing and treating harmful exposures to the chemical;

(iv) The request includes a description of the procedures to be used to maintain the confidentiality of the disclosed information; and,

(v) The health professional, and the employer or contractor of the services of the health professional (i.e. downstream employer, labor organization, or individual employee), employee, or designated representative, agree in a written confidentiality agreement that the health professional, employee, or designated representative, will not use the trade secret information for any purpose other than the health need(s) asserted and agree not to release the information under any circumstances other than to OSHA, as provided in paragraph (i)(6) of this section, except as authorized by the terms of the agreement or by the chemical manufacturer, importer, or employer.

(4) The confidentiality agreement authorized by paragraph (i)(3)(iv) of this section:

(i) May restrict the use of the information to the health purposes indicated in the written statement of need;

(ii) May provide for appropriate legal remedies in the event of a breach of the agreement, including stipulation of a reasonable pre-estimate of likely damages; and,

(iii) May not include requirements for the posting of a penalty bond.

(5) Nothing in this standard is meant to preclude the parties from pursuing non-contractual remedies to the extent permitted by law.

(6) If the health professional, employee, or designated representative re-

ceiving the trade secret information decides that there is a need to disclose it to OSHA, the chemical manufacturer, importer, or employer who provided the information shall be informed by the health professional, employee, or designated representative prior to, or at the same time as, such disclosure.

(7) If the chemical manufacturer, importer, or employer denies a written request for disclosure of a specific chemical identity, the denial must:

(i) Be provided to the health professional, employee, or designated representative, within thirty days of the request;

(ii) Be in writing;

(iii) Include evidence to support the claim that the specific chemical identity is a trade secret;

(iv) State the specific reasons why the request is being denied; and,

(v) Explain in detail how alternative information may satisfy the specific medical or occupational health need without revealing the specific chemical identity.

(8) The health professional, employee, or designated representative whose request for information is denied under paragraph (i)(3) of this section may refer the request and the written denial of the request to OSHA for consideration.

(9) When a health professional, employee, or designated representative refers the denial to OSHA under paragraph (i)(8) of this section, OSHA shall consider the evidence to determine if:

(i) The chemical manufacturer, importer, or employer has supported the claim that the specific chemical identity is a trade secret;

(ii) The health professional, employee, or designated representative has supported the claim that there is a medical or occupational health need for the information; and,

(iii) The health professional, employee or designated representative has demonstrated adequate means to protect the confidentiality.

(10)(i) If OSHA determines that the specific chemical identity requested under paragraph (i)(3) of this section is not a *bona fide* trade secret, or that it is a trade secret, but the requesting health professional, employee, or des-

ignated representative has a legitimate medical or occupational health need for the information, has executed a written confidentiality agreement, and has shown adequate means to protect the confidentiality of the information, the chemical manufacturer, importer, or employer will be subject to citation by OSHA.

(ii) If a chemical manufacturer, importer, or employer demonstrates to OSHA that the execution of a confidentiality agreement would not provide sufficient protection against the potential harm from the unauthorized disclosure of a trade secret specific chemical identity, the Assistant Secretary may issue such orders or impose such additional limitations or conditions upon the disclosure of the requested chemical information as may be appropriate to assure that the occupational health services are provided without an undue risk of harm to the chemical manufacturer, importer, or employer.

(11) If a citation for a failure to release specific chemical identity information is contested by the chemical manufacturer, importer, or employer, the matter will be adjudicated before the Occupational Safety and Health Review Commission in accordance with the Act's enforcement scheme and the applicable Commission rules of procedure. In accordance with the Commission rules, when a chemical manufacturer, importer, or employer continues to withhold the information during the contest, the Administrative Law Judge may review the citation and supporting documentation *in camera* or issue appropriate orders to protect the confidentiality of such matters.

(12) Notwithstanding the existence of a trade secret claim, a chemical manufacturer, importer, or employer shall, upon request, disclose to the Assistant Secretary any information which this section requires the chemical manufacturer, importer, or employer to make available. Where there is a trade secret claim, such claim shall be made no later than at the time the information is provided to the Assistant Secretary so that suitable determinations of trade secret status can be made and the necessary protections can be implemented.

(13) Nothing in this paragraph shall be construed as requiring the disclosure under any circumstances of process or percentage of mixture information which is a trade secret.

(j) *Effective dates.* Chemical manufacturers, importers, distributors, and employers shall be in compliance with all provisions of this section by March 11, 1994.

NOTE: The effective date of the clarification that the exemption of wood and wood products from the Hazard Communication standard in paragraph (b)(6)(iv) only applies to wood and wood products including lumber which will not be processed, where the manufacturer or importer can establish that the only hazard they pose to employees is the potential for flammability or combustibility, and that the exemption does not apply to wood or wood products which have been treated with a hazardous chemical covered by this standard, and wood which may be subsequently sawed or cut generating dust has been stayed from March 11, 1994 to August 11, 1994.

APPENDIX A TO § 1910.1200—HEALTH HAZARD DEFINITIONS (MANDATORY)

Although safety hazards related to the physical characteristics of a chemical can be objectively defined in terms of testing requirements (e.g. flammability), health hazard definitions are less precise and more subjective. Health hazards may cause measurable changes in the body such as decreased pulmonary function. These changes are generally indicated by the occurrence of signs and symptoms in the exposed employees—such as shortness of breath, a non-measurable, subjective feeling. Employees exposed to such hazards must be apprised of both the change in body function and the signs and symptoms that may occur to signal that change.

The determination of occupational health hazards is complicated by the fact that many of the effects or signs and symptoms occur commonly in non-occupationally exposed populations, so that effects of exposure are difficult to separate from normally occurring illnesses. Occasionally, a substance causes an effect that is rarely seen in the population at large, such as angiosarcomas caused by vinyl chloride exposure, thus making it easier to ascertain that the occupational exposure was the primary causative factor. More often, however, the effects are common, such as lung cancer. The situation is further complicated by the fact that most chemicals have not been adequately tested to determine their health hazard potential, and data do not exist to substantiate these effects.

There have been many attempts to categorize effects and to define them in various ways. Generally, the terms "acute" and "chronic" are used to delineate between effects on the basis of severity or duration. "Acute" effects usually occur rapidly as a result of short-term exposures, and are of short duration. "Chronic" effects generally occur as a result of long-term exposure, and are of long duration.

The acute effects referred to most frequently are those defined by the American National Standards Institute (ANSI) standard for Precautionary Labeling of Hazardous Industrial Chemicals (Z129.1-1988)—irritation, corrosivity, sensitization and lethal dose. Although these are important health effects, they do not adequately cover the considerable range of acute effects which may occur as a result of occupational exposure, such as, for example, narcosis.

Similarly, the term chronic effect is often used to cover only carcinogenicity, teratogenicity, and mutagenicity. These effects are obviously a concern in the workplace, but again, do not adequately cover the area of chronic effects, excluding, for example, blood dyscrasias (such as anemia), chronic bronchitis and liver atrophy.

The goal of defining precisely, in measurable terms, every possible health effect that may occur in the workplace as a result of chemical exposures cannot realistically be accomplished. This does not negate the need for employees to be informed of such effects and protected from them. Appendix B, which is also mandatory, outlines the principles and procedures of hazard assessment.

For purposes of this section, any chemicals which meet any of the following definitions, as determined by the criteria set forth in Appendix B are health hazards. However, this is not intended to be an exclusive categorization scheme. If there are available scientific data that involve other animal species or test methods, they must also be evaluated to determine the applicability of the HCS.7

1. *Carcinogen:* A chemical is considered to be a carcinogen if:

(a) It has been evaluated by the International Agency for Research on Cancer (IARC), and found to be a carcinogen or potential carcinogen; or

(b) It is listed as a carcinogen or potential carcinogen in the Annual Report on Carcinogens published by the National Toxicology Program (NTP) (latest edition); or,

(c) It is regulated by OSHA as a carcinogen.

2. *Corrosive:* A chemical that causes visible destruction of, or irreversible alterations in, living tissue by chemical action at the site of contact. For example, a chemical is considered to be corrosive if, when tested on the intact skin of albino rabbits by the method described by the U.S. Department of Transportation in appendix A to 49 CFR part 173,

it destroys or changes irreversibly the structure of the tissue at the site of contact following an exposure period of four hours. This term shall not refer to action on inanimate surfaces.

3. *Highly toxic:* A chemical falling within any of the following categories:

(a) A chemical that has a median lethal dose (LD_{50}) of 50 milligrams or less per kilogram of body weight when administered orally to albino rats weighing between 200 and 300 grams each.

(b) A chemical that has a median lethal dose (LD_{50}) of 200 milligrams or less per kilogram of body weight when administered by continuous contact for 24 hours (or less if death occurs within 24 hours) with the bare skin of albino rabbits weighing between two and three kilograms each.

(c) A chemical that has a median lethal concentration (LC_{50}) in air of 200 parts per million by volume or less of gas or vapor, or 2 milligrams per liter or less of mist, fume, or dust, when administered by continuous inhalation for one hour (or less if death occurs within one hour) to albino rats weighing between 200 and 300 grams each.

4. *Irritant:* A chemical, which is not corrosive, but which causes a reversible inflammatory effect on living tissue by chemical action at the site of contact. A chemical is a skin irritant if, when tested on the intact skin of albino rabbits by the methods of 16 CFR 1500.41 for four hours exposure or by other appropriate techniques, it results in an empirical score of five or more. A chemical is an eye irritant if so determined under the procedure listed in 16 CFR 1500.42 or other appropriate techniques.

5. *Sensitizer:* A chemical that causes a substantial proportion of exposed people or animals to develop an allergic reaction in normal tissue after repeated exposure to the chemical.

6. *Toxic.* A chemical falling within any of the following categories:

(a) A chemical that has a median lethal dose (LD_{50}) of more than 50 milligrams per kilogram but not more than 500 milligrams per kilogram of body weight when administered orally to albino rats weighing between 200 and 300 grams each.

(b) A chemical that has a median lethal dose (LD_{50}) of more than 200 milligrams per kilogram but not more than 1,000 milligrams per kilogram of body weight when administered by continuous contact for 24 hours (or less if death occurs within 24 hours) with the bare skin of albino rabbits weighing between two and three kilograms each.

(c) A chemical that has a median lethal concentration (LC_{50}) in air of more than 200 parts per million but not more than 2,000 parts per million by volume of gas or vapor, or more than two milligrams per liter but not more than 20 milligrams per liter of mist, fume, or dust, when administered by

continuous inhalation for one hour (or less if death occurs within one hour) to albino rats weighing between 200 and 300 grams each.

7. *Target organ effects.*

The following is a target organ categorization of effects which may occur, including examples of signs and symptoms and chemicals which have been found to cause such effects. These examples are presented to illustrate the range and diversity of effects and hazards found in the workplace, and the broad scope employers must consider in this area, but are not intended to be all-inclusive.

a. Hepatotoxins: Chemicals which produce liver damage[3]

Signs & Symptoms: Jaundice; liver enlargement

Chemicals: Carbon tetrachloride; nitrosamines

b. Nephrotoxins: Chemicals which produce kidney damage

Signs & Symptoms: Edema; proteinuria

Chemicals: Halogenated hydrocarbons; uranium

c. Neurotoxins: Chemicals which produce their primary toxic effects on the nervous system

Signs & Symptoms: Narcosis; behavioral changes; decrease in motor functions

Chemicals: Mercury; carbon disulfide

d. Agents which act on the blood or hematopoietic system: Decrease hemoglobin function; deprive the body tissues of oxygen

Signs & Symptoms: Cyanosis; loss of consciousness

Chemicals: Carbon monoxide; cyanides

e. Agents which damage the lung: Chemicals which irritate or damage pulmonary tissue

Signs & Symptoms: Cough; tightness in chest; shortness of breath

Chemicals: Silica; asbestos

f. Reproductive toxins: Chemicals which affect the reproductive capabilities including chromosomal damage (mutations) and effects on fetuses (teratogenesis)

Signs & Symptoms: Birth defects; sterility

Chemicals: Lead; DBCP

g. Cutaneous hazards: Chemicals which affect the dermal layer of the body

Signs & Symptoms: Defatting of the skin; rashes; irritation.

Chemicals: Ketones; chlorinated compounds

h. Eye hazards: Chemicals which affect the eye or visual capacity

Signs & Symptoms: Conjunctivitis; corneal damage

Chemicals: Organic solvents; acids

APPENDIX B TO § 1910.1200—HAZARD DETERMINATION (*Mandatory*)

The quality of a hazard communication program is largely dependent upon the adequacy and accuracy of the hazard determination. The hazard determination requirement of this standard is performance-oriented. Chemical manufacturers, importers, and employers evaluating chemicals are not required to follow any specific methods for determining hazards, but they must be able to demonstrate that they have adequately ascertained the hazards of the chemicals produced or imported in accordance with the criteria set forth in this Appendix.

Hazard evaluation is a process which relies heavily on the professional judgment of the evaluator, particularly in the area of chronic hazards. The performance-orientation of the hazard determination does not diminish the duty of the chemical manufacturer, importer or employer to conduct a thorough evaluation, examining all relevant data and producing a scientifically defensible evaluation. For purposes of this standard, the following criteria shall be used in making hazard determinations that meet the requirements of this standard.

1. *Carcinogenicity:* As described in paragraph (d)(4) of this section and Appendix A of this section, a determination by the National Toxicology Program, the International Agency for Research on Cancer, or OSHA that a chemical is a carcinogen or potential carcinogen will be considered conclusive evidence for purposes of this section. In addition, however, all available scientific data on carcinogenicity must be evaluated in accordance with the provisions of this Appendix and the requirements of the rule.

2. *Human data:* Where available, epidemiological studies and case reports of adverse health effects shall be considered in the evaluation.

3. *Animal data:* Human evidence of health effects in exposed populations is generally not available for the majority of chemicals produced or used in the workplace. Therefore, the available results of toxicological testing in animal populations shall be used to predict the health effects that may be experienced by exposed workers. In particular, the definitions of certain acute hazards refer to specific animal testing results (see Appendix A).

4. *Adequacy and reporting of data.* The results of any studies which are designed and conducted according to established scientific principles, and which report statistically significant conclusions regarding the health effects of a chemical, shall be a sufficient basis for a hazard determination and reported on any material safety data sheet. *In vitro* studies alone generally do not form the basis for a definitive finding of hazard under the HCS since they have a positive or negative result rather than a statistically significant finding.

The chemical manufacturer, importer, or employer may also report the results of other scientifically valid studies which tend to refute the findings of hazard.

APPENDIX C TO § 1910.1200—INFORMATION SOURCES (ADVISORY)

The following is a list of available data sources which the chemical manufacturer, importer, distributor, or employer may wish to consult to evaluate the hazards of chemicals they produce or import:

—Any information in their own company files, such as toxicity testing results or illness experience of company employees.
—Any information obtained from the supplier of the chemical, such as material safety data sheets or product safety bulletins.
—Any pertinent information obtained from the following source list (latest editions should be used):

Condensed Chemical Dictionary

Van Nostrand Reinhold Co., 135 West 50th Street, New York, NY 10020.

The Merck Index: An Encyclopedia of Chemicals and Drugs

Merck and Company, Inc., 126 E. Lincoln Ave., Rahway, NJ 07065.

IARC Monographs on the Evaluation of the Carcinogenic Risk of Chemicals to Man

Geneva: World Health Organization, International Agency for Research on Cancer, 1972–Present. (Multivolume work). Summaries are available in supplement volumes. 49 Sheridan Street, Albany, NY 12210.

Occupational Safety and Health Admin., Labor   **§ 1910.1200, App. C**

Industrial Hygiene and Toxicology, by F.A. Patty

John Wiley & Sons, Inc., New York, NY (Multivolume work).

Clinical Toxicology of Commercial Products

Gleason, Gosselin, and Hodge.

Casarett and Doull's Toxicology; The Basic Science of Poisons

Doull, Klaassen, and Amdur, Macmillan Publishing Co., Inc., New York, NY.

Industrial Toxicology, by Alice Hamilton and Harriet L. Hardy

Publishing Sciences Group, Inc., Acton, MA.

Toxicology of the Eye, by W. Morton Grant

Charles C. Thomas, 301–327 East Lawrence Avenue, Springfield, IL.

Recognition of Health Hazards in Industry

William A. Burgess, John Wiley and Sons, 605 Third Avenue, New York, NY 10158.

Chemical Hazards of the Workplace

Nick H. Proctor and James P. Hughes, J.P. Lipincott Company, 6 Winchester Terrace, New York, NY 10022.

Handbook of Chemistry and Physics

Chemical Rubber Company, 18901 Cranwood Parkway, Cleveland, OH 44128.

Threshold Limit Values for Chemical Substances and Physical Agents in the Work Environment and Biological Exposure Indices with Intended Changes

American Conference of Governmental Industrial Hygienists (ACGIH), 6500 Glenway Avenue, Bldg. D–5, Cincinnati, OH 45211.

Information on the physical hazards of chemicals may be found in publications of the National Fire Protection Association, Boston, MA.

NOTE: The following documents may be purchased from the Superintendent of Documents, U.S. Government Printing Office, Washington, DC 20402.

Occupational Health Guidelines

NIOSH/OSHA (NIOSH Pub. No. 81–123).

NIOSH Pocket Guide to Chemical Hazards

NIOSH Pub. No. 90–117.

Registry of Toxic Effects of Chemical Substances

(Latest edition)

Miscellaneous Documents published by the National Institute for Occupational Safety and Health:
Criteria documents.
Special Hazard Reviews.
Occupational Hazard Assessments.
Current Intelligence Bulletins.

OSHA's General Industry Standards (29 CFR Part 1910)

NTP Annual Report on Carcinogens and Summary of the Annual Report on Carcinogens.

National Technical Information Service (NTIS), 5285 Port Royal Road, Springfield, VA 22161; (703) 487–4650.

Bibliographic data bases service provider	File name
Bibliographic Retrieval Services (BRS), 1200 Route 7, Latham, NY 12110.	Biosis Previews
	CA Search
	Medlars
	NTIS
	Hazardline
	American Chemical Society Journal
	Excerpta Medica
	IRCS Medical Science Journal
	Pre-Med
	Intl Pharmaceutical Abstracts
	Paper Chem
Lockheed-DIALOG Information Service, Inc., 3460 Hillview Avenue, Palo Alto, CA 94304.	Biosis Prev. Files
	CA Search Files
	CAB Abstracts
	Chemical Exposure
	Chemname
	Chemsis Files
	Chemzero
	Embase Files
	Environmental Bibliographies
	Enviroline

Bibliographic data bases service provider	File name
SDC-ORBIT, SDC Information Service, 2500 Colorado Avenue, Santa Monica, CA 90406.	Federal Research in Progress IRL Life Science Collection NTIS Occupational Safety and Health (NIOSH) Paper Chem CAS Files
National Library of Medicine .... Department of Health and Human Services, Public Health Service, National Institutes of Health, Bethesda, MD 20209.	Chemdex, 2, 3 NTIS Hazardous Substances Data Bank (NSDB) Medline Files
Pergamon International Information Corp., 1340 Old Chain Bridge Rd., McLean, VA 22101.	Toxline Files Cancerlit RTECS Chemline Laboratory Hazard Bulletin
Questel, Inc., 1625 Eye Street, NW, Suite 818, Washington, DC 20006.	CIS/ILO
Chemical Information System ICI (ICIS), Bureau of National Affairs, 1133 15th Street, NW, Suite 300, Washington, DC 20005.	Cancernet Structure and Nomenclature Search System (SANSS)
Occupational Health Services, 400 Plaza Drive, Secaucus, NJ 07094.	Acute Toxicity (RTECS) Clinical Toxicology of Commercial Products Oil and Hazardous Materials Technical Assistance Data System CCRIS CESARS MSDS Hazardline

APPENDIX D TO § 1910.1200—DEFINITION OF "TRADE SECRET" (MANDATORY)

The following is a reprint of the *Restatement of Torts* section 757, comment *b* (1939):

b. Definition of trade secret. A trade secret may consist of any formula, pattern, device or compilation of information which is used in one's business, and which gives him an opportunity to obtain an advantage over competitors who do not know or use it. It may be a formula for a chemical compound, a process of manufacturing, treating or preserving materials, a pattern for a machine or other device, or a list of customers. It differs from other secret information in a business (see s759 of the *Restatement of Torts* which is not included in this Appendix) in that it is not simply information as to single or ephemeral events in the conduct of the business, as, for example, the amount or other terms of a secret bid for a contract or the salary of certain employees, or the security investments made or contemplated, or the date fixed for the announcement of a new policy or for bringing out a new model or the like. A trade secret is a process or device for continuous use in the operations of the business. Generally it relates to the production of goods, as, for example, a machine or formula for the production of an article. It may, however, relate to the sale of goods or to other operations in the business, such as a code for determining discounts, rebates or other concessions in a price list or catalogue, or a list of specialized customers, or a method of bookkeeping or other office management.

Secrecy. The subject matter of a trade secret must be secret. Matters of public knowledge or of general knowledge in an industry cannot be appropriated by one as his secret. Matters which are completely disclosed by the goods which one markets cannot be his secret. Substantially, a trade secret is known only in the particular business in which it is used. It is not requisite that only the proprietor of the business know it. He may, without losing his protection, communicate it to employees involved in its use. He may likewise communicate it to others pledged to secrecy. Others may also know of it independently, as, for example, when they have discovered the process or formula by independent invention and are keeping it secret. Nevertheless, a substantial element of secrecy must exist, so that, except by the use of improper means, there would be difficulty in acquiring the information. An exact definition of a trade secret is not possible. Some factors to be considered in determining whether given information is one's trade secret are: (1) The extent to which the information is known outside of his business; (2) the extent to which it is known by employees and others involved in his business; (3) the extent of measures taken by him to guard the secrecy of the information; (4) the value of the information to him and his competitors; (5) the amount of effort or money expended by him in developing the information; (6) the ease or difficulty with which the information could be properly acquired or duplicated by others.

Novelty and prior art. A trade secret may be a device or process which is patentable; but it need not be that. It may be a device or process which is clearly anticipated in the prior art or one which is merely a mechanical improvement that a good mechanic can make. Novelty and invention are not requisite for a trade secret as they are for patentability. These requirements are essential to patentability because a patent protects against unlicensed use of the patented device or process even by one who discovers it properly through independent research. The patent monopoly is a reward to the inventor. But such is not the case with a trade secret. Its protection is not based on a policy of rewarding or otherwise encouraging the development of secret processes or devices. The protection is merely against breach of faith and reprehensible means of learning another's secret. For this limited protection it is not appropriate to require also the kind of novelty and invention which is a requisite of patentability. The nature of the secret is, however, an important factor in determining the kind of relief that is appropriate against one who is subject to liability under the rule stated in this Section. Thus, if the secret consists of a device or process which is a novel invention, one who acquires the secret wrongfully is ordinarily enjoined from further use of it and is required to account for the profits derived from his past use. If, on the other hand, the secret consists of mechanical improvements that a good mechanic can make without resort to the secret, the wrongdoer's liability may be limited to damages, and an injunction against future use of the improvements made with the aid of the secret may be inappropriate.

APPENDIX E TO § 1910.1200-(ADVISORY)— GUIDELINES FOR EMPLOYER COMPLIANCE

The Hazard Communication Standard (HCS) is based on a simple concept—that employees have both a need and a right to know the hazards and identities of the chemicals they are exposed to when working. They also need to know what protective measures are available to prevent adverse effects from occurring. The HCS is designed to provide employees with the information they need.

Knowledge acquired under the HCS will help employers provide safer workplaces for their employees. When employers have information about the chemicals being used, they can take steps to reduce exposures, substitute less hazardous materials, and establish proper work practices. These efforts will help prevent the occurrence of work-related illnesses and injuries caused by chemicals.

The HCS addresses the issues of evaluating and communicating hazards to workers. Evaluation of chemical hazards involves a number of technical concepts, and is a process that requires the professional judgment of experienced experts. That's why the HCS is designed so that employers who simply use chemicals, rather than produce or import them, are not required to evaluate the hazards of those chemicals. Hazard determination is the responsibility of the producers and importers of the materials. Producers and importers of chemicals are then required to provide the hazard information to employers that purchase their products.

Employers that don't produce or import chemicals need only focus on those parts of the rule that deal with establishing a workplace program and communicating information to their workers. This appendix is a general guide for such employers to help them determine what's required under the rule. It does not supplant or substitute for the regulatory provisions, but rather provides a simplified outline of the steps an average employer would follow to meet those requirements.

1. Becoming Familiar With The Rule.

OSHA has provided a simple summary of the HCS in a pamphlet entitled "Chemical Hazard Communication," OSHA Publication Number 3084. Some employers prefer to begin to become familiar with the rule's requirements by reading this pamphlet. A copy may be obtained from your local OSHA Area Office, or by contacting the OSHA Publications Office at (202) 523–9667.

The standard is long, and some parts of it are technical, but the basic concepts are simple. In fact, the requirements reflect what many employers have been doing for years. You may find that you are already largely in compliance with many of the provisions, and will simply have to modify your existing programs somewhat. If you are operating in an OSHA-approved State Plan State, you must comply with the State's requirements, which may be different than those of the Federal rule. Many of the State Plan States had hazard communication or "right-to-know" laws prior to promulgation of the Federal rule. Employers in State Plan States should contact their State OSHA offices for more information regarding applicable requirements.

The HCS requires information to be prepared and transmitted regarding all hazardous chemicals. The HCS covers both physical hazards (such as flammability), and health hazards (such as irritation, lung damage, and cancer). Most chemicals used in the workplace have some hazard potential, and thus will be covered by the rule.

One difference between this rule and many others adopted by OSHA is that this one is performance-oriented. That means that you have the flexibility to adapt the rule to the needs of your workplace, rather than having to follow specific, rigid requirements. It also means that you have to exercise more judgment to implement an appropriate and effective program.

The standard's design is simple. Chemical manufacturers and importers must evaluate the hazards of the chemicals they produce or import. Using that information, they must then prepare labels for containers, and more detailed technical bulletins called material safety data sheets (MSDS).

Chemical manufacturers, importers, and distributors of hazardous chemicals are all required to provide the appropriate labels and material safety data sheets to the employers to which they ship the chemicals. The information is to be provided automatically. Every container of hazardous chemicals you receive must be labeled, tagged, or marked with the required information. Your suppliers must also send you a properly completed material safety data sheet (MSDS) at the time of the first shipment of the chemical, and with the next shipment after the MSDS is updated with new and significant information about the hazards.

You can rely on the information received from your suppliers. You have no independent duty to analyze the chemical or evaluate the hazards of it.

Employers that "use" hazardous chemicals must have a program to ensure the information is provided to exposed employees. "Use" means to package, handle, react, or transfer. This is an intentionally broad scope, and includes any situation where a chemical is present in such a way that employees may be exposed under normal conditions of use or in a foreseeable emergency.

The requirements of the rule that deal specifically with the hazard communication program are found in this section in paragraphs (e), written hazard communication program; (f), labels and other forms of warning; (g), material safety data sheets; and (h), employee information and training. The requirements of these paragraphs should be the focus of your attention. Concentrate on becoming familiar with them, using paragraphs (b), scope and application, and (c), definitions, as references when needed to help explain the provisions.

There are two types of work operations where the coverage of the rule is limited. These are laboratories and operations where chemicals are only handled in sealed containers (e.g., a warehouse). The limited provisions for these workplaces can be found in paragraph (b) of this section, scope and application. Basically, employers having these types of work operations need only keep labels on containers as they are received;

maintain material safety data sheets that are received, and give employees access to them; and provide information and training for employees. Employers do not have to have written hazard communication programs and lists of chemicals for these types of operations.

The limited coverage of laboratories and sealed container operations addresses the obligation of an employer to the workers in the operations involved, and does not affect the employer's duties as a distributor of chemicals. For example, a distributor may have warehouse operations where employees would be protected under the limited sealed container provisions. In this situation, requirements for obtaining and maintaining MSDSs are limited to providing access to those received with containers while the substance is in the workplace, and requesting MSDSs when employees request access for those not received with the containers. However, as a distributor of hazardous chemicals, that employer will still have responsibilities for providing MSDSs to downstream customers at the time of the first shipment and when the MSDS is updated. Therefore, although they may not be required for the employees in the work operation, the distributor may, nevertheless, have to have MSDSs to satisfy other requirements of the rule.

2. Identify Responsible Staff

Hazard communication is going to be a continuing program in your facility. Compliance with the HCS is not a "one shot deal." In order to have a successful program, it will be necessary to assign responsibility for both the initial and ongoing activities that have to be undertaken to comply with the rule. In some cases, these activities may already be part of current job assignments. For example, site supervisors are frequently responsible for on-the-job training sessions. Early identification of the responsible employees, and involvement of them in the development of your plan of action, will result in a more effective program design. Evaluation of the effectiveness of your program will also be enhanced by involvement of affected employees.

For any safety and health program, success depends on commitment at every level of the organization. This is particularly true for hazard communication, where success requires a change in behavior. This will only occur if employers understand the program, and are committed to its success, and if employees are motivated by the people presenting the information to them.

3. Identify Hazardous Chemicals in the Workplace.

The standard requires a list of hazardous chemicals in the workplace as part of the written hazard communication program. The list will eventually serve as an inventory of everything for which an MSDS must be maintained. At this point, however, preparing the list will help you complete the rest of the program since it will give you some idea of the scope of the program required for compliance in your facility.

The best way to prepare a comprehensive list is to survey the workplace. Purchasing records may also help, and certainly employers should establish procedures to ensure that in the future purchasing procedures result in MSDSs being received before a material is used in the workplace.

The broadest possible perspective should be taken when doing the survey. Sometimes people think of "chemicals" as being only liquids in containers. The HCS covers chemicals in all physical forms—liquids, solids, gases, vapors, fumes, and mists—whether they are "contained" or not. The hazardous nature of the chemical and the potential for exposure are the factors which determine whether a chemical is covered. If it's not hazardous, it's not covered. If there is no potential for exposure (e.g., the chemical is inextricably bound and cannot be released), the rule does not cover the chemical.

Look around. Identify chemicals in containers, including pipes, but also think about chemicals generated in the work operations. For example, welding fumes, dusts, and exhaust fumes are all sources of chemical exposures. Read labels provided by suppliers for hazard information. Make a list of all chemicals in the workplace that are potentially hazardous. For your own information and planning, you may also want to note on the list the location(s) of the products within the workplace, and an indication of the hazards as found on the label. This will help you as you prepare the rest of your program.

Paragraph (b) of this section, scope and application, includes exemptions for various chemicals or workplace situations. After compiling the complete list of chemicals, you should review paragraph (b) of this section to determine if any of the items can be eliminated from the list because they are exempted materials. For example, food, drugs, and cosmetics brought into the workplace for employee consumption are exempt. So rubbing alcohol in the first aid kit would not be covered.

Once you have compiled as complete a list as possible of the potentially hazardous chemicals in the workplace, the next step is to determine if you have received material safety data sheets for all of them. Check your files against the inventory you have just compiled. If any are missing, contact your supplier and request one. It is a good idea to document these requests, either by copy of a letter or a note regarding telephone conversations. If you have MSDSs for chemicals that are not on your list, figure out why. Maybe you don't use the chemical

anymore. Or maybe you missed it in your survey. Some suppliers do provide MSDSs for products that are not hazardous. These do not have to be maintained by you.

You should not allow employees to use any chemicals for which you have not received an MSDS. The MSDS provides information you need to ensure proper protective measures are implemented prior to exposure.

4. Preparing and Implementing a Hazard Communication Program

All workplaces where employees are exposed to hazardous chemicals must have a written plan which describes how the standard will be implemented in that facility. Preparation of a plan is not just a paper exercise—all of the elements must be implemented in the workplace in order to be in compliance with the rule. See paragraph (e) of this section for the specific requirements regarding written hazard communication programs. The only work operations which do not have to comply with the written plan requirements are laboratories and work operations where employees only handle chemicals in sealed containers. See paragraph (b) of this section, scope and application, for the specific requirements for these two types of workplaces.

The plan does not have to be lengthy or complicated. It is intended to be a blueprint for implementation of your program—an assurance that all aspects of the requirements have been addressed.

Many trade associations and other professional groups have provided sample programs and other assistance materials to affected employers. These have been very helpful to many employers since they tend to be tailored to the particular industry involved. You may wish to investigate whether your industry trade groups have developed such materials.

Although such general guidance may be helpful, you must remember that the written program has to reflect what you are doing in your workplace. Therefore, if you use a generic program it must be adapted to address the facility it covers. For example, the written plan must list the chemicals present at the site, indicate who is to be responsible for the various aspects of the program in your facility, and indicate where written materials will be made available to employees.

If OSHA inspects your workplace for compliance with the HCS, the OSHA compliance officer will ask to see your written plan at the outset of the inspection. In general, the following items will be considered in evaluating your program.

The written program must describe how the requirements for labels and other forms of warning, material safety data sheets, and employee information and training, are going to be met in your facility. The following discussion provides the type of information compliance officers will be looking for to decide whether these elements of the hazard communication program have been properly addressed:

A. Labels and Other Forms of Warning

In-plant containers of hazardous chemicals must be labeled, tagged, or marked with the identity of the material and appropriate hazard warnings. Chemical manufacturers, importers, and distributors are required to ensure that every container of hazardous chemicals they ship is appropriately labeled with such information and with the name and address of the producer or other responsible party. Employers purchasing chemicals can rely on the labels provided by their suppliers. If the material is subsequently transferred by the employer from a labeled container to another container, the employer will have to label that container unless it is subject to the portable container exemption. See paragraph (f) of this section for specific labeling requirements.

The primary information to be obtained from an OSHA-required label is an identity for the material, and appropriate hazard warnings. The identity is any term which appears on the label, the MSDS, and the list of chemicals, and thus links these three sources of information. The identity used by the supplier may be a common or trade name ("Black Magic Formula"), or a chemical name (1,1,1,-trichloroethane). The hazard warning is a brief statement of the hazardous effects of the chemical ("flammable," "causes lung damage"). Labels frequently contain other information, such as precautionary measures ("do not use near open flame"), but this information is provided voluntarily and is not required by the rule. Labels must be legible, and prominently displayed. There are no specific requirements for size or color, or any specified text.

With these requirements in mind, the compliance officer will be looking for the following types of information to ensure that labeling will be properly implemented in your facility:

1. Designation of person(s) responsible for ensuring labeling of in-plant containers;

2. Designation of person(s) responsible for ensuring labeling of any shipped containers;

3. Description of labeling system(s) used;

4. Description of written alternatives to labeling of in-plant containers (if used); and,

5. Procedures to review and update label information when necessary.

Employers that are purchasing and using hazardous chemicals—rather than producing or distributing them—will primarily be concerned with ensuring that every purchased container is labeled. If materials are transferred into other containers, the employer must ensure that these are labeled as well, unless they fall under the portable container exemption (paragraph (f)(7) of this section).

In terms of labeling systems, you can simply choose to use the labels provided by your suppliers on the containers. These will generally be verbal text labels, and do not usually include numerical rating systems or symbols that require special training. The most important thing to remember is that this is a continuing duty—all in-plant containers of hazardous chemicals must always be labeled. Therefore, it is important to designate someone to be responsible for ensuring that the labels are maintained as required on the containers in your facility, and that newly purchased materials are checked for labels prior to use.

B. Material Safety Data Sheets

Chemical manufacturers and importers are required to obtain or develop a material safety data sheet for each hazardous chemical they produce or import. Distributors are responsible for ensuring that their customers are provided a copy of these MSDSs. Employers must have an MSDS for each hazardous chemical which they use. Employers may rely on the information received from their suppliers. The specific requirements for material safety data sheets are in paragraph (g) of this section.

There is no specified format for the MSDS under the rule, although there are specific information requirements. OSHA has developed a non-mandatory format, OSHA Form 174, which may be used by chemical manufacturers and importers to comply with the rule. The MSDS must be in English. You are entitled to receive from your supplier a data sheet which includes all of the information required under the rule. If you do not receive one automatically, you should request one. If you receive one that is obviously inadequate, with, for example, blank spaces that are not completed, you should request an appropriately completed one. If your request for a data sheet or for a corrected data sheet does not produce the information needed, you should contact your local OSHA Area Office for assistance in obtaining the MSDS.

The role of MSDSs under the rule is to provide detailed information on each hazardous chemical, including its potential hazardous effects, its physical and chemical characteristics, and recommendations for appropriate protective measures. This information should be useful to you as the employer responsible for designing protective programs, as well as to the workers. If you are not familiar with material safety data sheets and with chemical terminology, you may need to learn to use them yourself. A glossary of MSDS terms may be helpful in this regard. Generally speaking, most employers using hazardous chemicals will primarily be concerned with MSDS information regarding hazardous effects and recommended protective measures. Focus on the sections of the MSDS that are applicable to your situation.

MSDSs must be readily accessible to employees when they are in their work areas during their workshifts. This may be accomplished in many different ways. You must decide what is appropriate for your particular workplace. Some employers keep the MSDSs in a binder in a central location (*e.g.*, in the pick-up truck on a construction site). Others, particularly in workplaces with large numbers of chemicals, computerize the information and provide access through terminals. As long as employees can get the information when they need it, any approach may be used. The employees must have access to the MSDSs themselves—simply having a system where the information can be read to them over the phone is only permitted under the mobile worksite provision, paragraph (g)(9) of this section, when employees must travel between workplaces during the shift. In this situation, they have access to the MSDSs prior to leaving the primary worksite, and when they return, so the telephone system is simply an emergency arrangement.

In order to ensure that you have a current MSDS for each chemical in the plant as required, and that employee access is provided, the compliance officers will be looking for the following types of information in your written program:

1. Designation of person(s) responsible for obtaining and maintaining the MSDSs;

2. How such sheets are to be maintained in the workplace (*e.g.*, in notebooks in the work area(s) or in a computer with terminal access), and how employees can obtain access to them when they are in their work area during the work shift;

3. Procedures to follow when the MSDS is not received at the time of the first shipment;

4. For producers, procedures to update the MSDS when new and significant health information is found; and,

5. Description of alternatives to actual data sheets in the workplace, if used.

For employers using hazardous chemicals, the most important aspect of the written program in terms of MSDSs is to ensure that someone is responsible for obtaining and maintaining the MSDSs for every hazardous chemical in the workplace. The list of hazardous chemicals required to be maintained as part of the written program will serve as an inventory. As new chemicals are purchased, the list should be updated. Many companies have found it convenient to include on their purchase orders the name and address of the person designated in their company to receive MSDSs.

C. Employee Information and Training

Each employee who may be "exposed" to hazardous chemicals when working must be provided information and trained prior to

initial assignment to work with a hazardous chemical, and whenever the hazard changes. "Exposure" or "exposed" under the rule means that "an employee is subjected to a hazardous chemical in the course of employment through any route of entry (inhalation, ingestion, skin contact or absorption, etc.) and includes potential (*e.g.*, accidental or possible) exposure." See paragraph (h) of this section for specific requirements. Information and training may be done either by individual chemical, or by categories of hazards (such as flammability or carcinogenicity). If there are only a few chemicals in the workplace, then you may want to discuss each one individually. Where there are large numbers of chemicals, or the chemicals change frequently, you will probably want to train generally based on the hazard categories (*e.g.*, flammable liquids, corrosive materials, carcinogens). Employees will have access to the substance-specific information on the labels and MSDSs.

Information and training is a critical part of the hazard communication program. Information regarding hazards and protective measures are provided to workers through written labels and material safety data sheets. However, through effective information and training, workers will learn to read and understand such information, determine how it can be obtained and used in their own workplaces, and understand the risks of exposure to the chemicals in their workplaces as well as the ways to protect themselves. A properly conducted training program will ensure comprehension and understanding. It is not sufficient to either just read material to the workers, or simply hand them material to read. You want to create a climate where workers feel free to ask questions. This will help you to ensure that the information is understood. You must always remember that the underlying purpose of the HCS is to reduce the incidence of chemical source illnesses and injuries. This will be accomplished by modifying behavior through the provision of hazard information and information about protective measures. If your program works, you and your workers will better understand the chemical hazards within the workplace. The procedures you establish regarding, for example, purchasing, storage, and handling of these chemicals will improve, and thereby reduce the risks posed to employees exposed to the chemical hazards involved. Furthermore, your workers' comprehension will also be increased, and proper work practices will be followed in your workplace.

If you are going to do the training yourself, you will have to understand the material and be prepared to motivate the workers to learn. This is not always an easy task, but the benefits are worth the effort. More information regarding appropriate training can be found in OSHA Publication No. 2254 which contains voluntary training guidelines prepared by OSHA's Training Institute. A copy of this document is available from OSHA's Publications Office at (202) 219–4667.

In reviewing your written program with regard to information and training, the following items need to be considered:

1. Designation of person(s) responsible for conducting training;

2. Format of the program to be used (audiovisuals, classroom instruction, etc.);

3. Elements of the training program (should be consistent with the elements in paragraph (h) of this section); and,

4. Procedure to train new employees at the time of their initial assignment to work with a hazardous chemical, and to train employees when a new hazard is introduced into the workplace.

The written program should provide enough details about the employer's plans in this area to assess whether or not a good faith effort is being made to train employees. OSHA does not expect that every worker will be able to recite all of the information about each chemical in the workplace. In general, the most important aspects of training under the HCS are to ensure that employees are aware that they are exposed to hazardous chemicals, that they know how to read and use labels and material safety data sheets, and that, as a consequence of learning this information, they are following the appropriate protective measures established by the employer. OSHA compliance officers will be talking to employees to determine if they have received training, if they know they are exposed to hazardous chemicals, and if they know where to obtain substance-specific information on labels and MSDSs.

The rule does not require employers to maintain records of employee training, but many employers choose to do so. This may help you monitor your own program to ensure that all employees are appropriately trained. If you already have a training program, you may simply have to supplement it with whatever additional information is required under the HCS. For example, construction employers that are already in compliance with the construction training standard (29 CFR 1926.21) will have little extra training to do.

An employer can provide employees information and training through whatever means are found appropriate and protective. Although there would always have to be some training on-site (such as informing employees of the location and availability of the written program and MSDSs), employee training may be satisfied in part by general training about the requirements of the HCS and about chemical hazards on the job which is provided by, for example, trade associations, unions, colleges, and professional schools. In addition, previous training, education and experience of a worker may re-

lieve the employer of some of the burdens of informing and training that worker. Regardless of the method relied upon, however, the employer is always ultimately responsible for ensuring that employees are adequately trained. If the compliance officer finds that the training is deficient, the employer will be cited for the deficiency regardless of who actually provided the training on behalf of the employer.

D. Other Requirements

In addition to these specific items, compliance officers will also be asking the following questions in assessing the adequacy of the program:

Does a list of the hazardous chemicals exist in each work area or at a central location?

Are methods the employer will use to inform employees of the hazards of non-routine tasks outlined?

Are employees informed of the hazards associated with chemicals contained in unlabeled pipes in their work areas?

On multi-employer worksites, has the employer provided other employers with information about labeling systems and precautionary measures where the other employers have employees exposed to the initial employer's chemicals?

Is the written program made available to employees and their designated representatives?

If your program adequately addresses the means of communicating information to employees in your workplace, and provides answers to the basic questions outlined above, it will be found to be in compliance with the rule.

5. Checklist for Compliance

The following checklist will help to ensure you are in compliance with the rule:
Obtained a copy of the rule. _____
Read and understood the requirements. _____
Assigned responsibility for tasks. _____
Prepared an inventory of chemicals. _____
Ensured containers are labeled. _____
Obtained MSDS for each chemical. _____
Prepared written program. _____
Made MSDSs available to workers. _____
Conducted training of workers. _____
Established procedures to maintain current program. _____
Established procedures to evaluate effectiveness. _____

6. Further Assistance

If you have a question regarding compliance with the HCS, you should contact your local OSHA Area Office for assistance. In addition, each OSHA Regional Office has a Hazard Communication Coordinator who can answer your questions. Free consultation serv-

Occupational Safety and Health Admin., Labor   **§ 1910.1450**

ices are also available to assist employers, and information regarding these services can be obtained through the Area and Regional offices as well.

The telephone number for the OSHA office closest to you should be listed in your local telephone directory. If you are not able to obtain this information, you may contact OSHA's Office of Information and Consumer Affairs at (202) 219–8151 for further assistance in identifying the appropriate contacts.

[59 FR 6170, Feb. 9, 1994, as amended at 59 FR 17479, Apr. 13, 1994]

29 CFR 1910.132
GENERAL REQUIREMENTS;
29 CFR 1910.133
EYE AND FACE PROTECTION;
29 CFR 1910.134
RESPIRATORY PROTECTION

§ 1910.132 General requirements.

(a) *Application.* Protective equipment, including personal protective equipment for eyes, face, head, and extremities, protective clothing, respiratory devices, and protective shields and barriers, shall be provided, used, and maintained in a sanitary and reliable condition wherever it is necessary by reason of hazards of processes or environment, chemical hazards, radiological hazards, or mechanical irritants encountered in a manner capable of causing injury or impairment in the function of any part of the body through absorption, inhalation or physical contact.

(b) *Employee-owned equipment.* Where employees provide their own protective equipment, the employer shall be responsible to assure its adequacy, including proper maintenance, and sanitation of such equipment.

(c) *Design.* All personal protective equipment shall be of safe design and construction for the work to be performed.

(d) *Hazard assessment and equipment selection.* (1) The employer shall assess the workplace to determine if hazards are present, or are likely to be present, which necessitate the use of personal protective equipment (PPE). If such hazards are present, or likely to be present, the employer shall:

(i) Select, and have each affected employee use, the types of PPE that will protect the affected employee from the hazards identified in the hazard assessment;

(ii) Communicate selection decisions to each affected employee; and,

(iii) Select PPE that properly fits each affected employee.

Note: Non-mandatory Appendix B contains an example of procedures that would comply with the requirement for a hazard assessment.

(2) The employer shall verify that the required workplace hazard assessment has been performed through a written certification that identifies the workplace evaluated; the person certifying that the evaluation has been performed; the date(s) of the hazard assessment; and, which identifies the document as a certification of hazard assessment.

(e) *Defective and damaged equipment.* Defective or damaged personal protective equipment shall not be used.

(f) *Training.* (1) The employer shall provide training to each employee who is required by this section to use PPE. Each such employee shall be trained to know at least the following:

(i) When PPE is necessary;

(ii) What PPE is necessary;

(iii) How to properly don, doff, adjust, and wear PPE;

(iv) The limitations of the PPE; and,

(v) The proper care, maintenance, useful life and disposal of the PPE.

(2) Each affected employee shall demonstrate an understanding of the training specified in paragraph (f)(1) of this section, and the ability to use PPE properly, before being allowed to perform work requiring the use of PPE.

(3) When the employer has reason to believe that any affected employee who has already been trained does not have the understanding and skill required by paragraph (f)(2) of this section, the employer shall retrain each such employee. Circumstances where retraining is required include, but are not limited to, situations where:

(i) Changes in the workplace render previous training obsolete; or

(ii) Changes in the types of PPE to be used render previous training obsolete; or

(iii) Inadequacies in an affected employee's knowledge or use of assigned PPE indicate that the employee has

not retained the requisite understanding or skill.

(4) The employer shall verify that each affected employee has received and understood the required training through a written certification that contains the name of each employee trained, the date(s) of training, and that identifies the subject of the certification.

(g) Paragraphs (d) and (f) of this section apply only to §§ 1910.133, 1910.135, 1910.136, and 1910.138. Paragraphs (d) and (f) of this section do not apply to §§ 1910.134 and 1910.137.

[39 FR 23502, June 27, 1974, as amended at 59 FR 16334, Apr. 6, 1994, 59 FR 33910, July 1, 1994]

EFFECTIVE DATE NOTE: At 59 FR 16360, April 6, 1994, paragraphs (d) through (f) were added to § 1910.132, effective July 5, 1994. On July 1, 1994. At 59 FR 33910, July 1, 1994, paragraph (g) was added, effective July 5, 1994.

§1910.133　Eye and face protection.

(a) *General requirements.* (1) Each affected employee shall use appropriate eye or face protection when exposed to eye or face hazards from flying particles, molten metal, liquid chemicals, acids or caustic liquids, chemical gases or vapors, or potentially injurious light radiation.

(2) Each affected employee shall use eye protection that provides side protection when there is a hazard from flying objects. Detachable side protectors (e.g. clip-on or slide-on side shields) meeting the pertinent requirements of this section are acceptable.

(3) Each affected employee who wears prescription lenses while engaged in operations that involve eye hazards shall wear eye protection that incorporates the prescription in its design, or shall wear eye protection that can be worn over the prescription lenses without disturbing the proper position of the prescription lenses or the protective lenses.

(4) Eye and face PPE shall be distinctly marked to facilitate identification of the manufacturer.

(5) Each affected employee shall use equipment with filter lenses that have a shade number appropriate for the work being performed for protection from injurious light radiation. The following is a listing of appropriate shade numbers for various operations.

411

Filter Lenses for Protection Against Radiant Energy

Operations	Electrode Size 1/32 in.	Arc Current	Minimum* Protective Shade
Shielded metal arc welding	Less than 3	Less than 60	7
	3-5	60-160	8
	5-8	160-250	10
	More than 8	250-550	11
Gas metal arc welding and flux cored arc welding		less than 60	7
		60-160	10
		160-250	10
		250-500	10
Gas Tungsten arc welding		less than 50	8
		50-150	8
		150-500	10
Air carbon Arc cutting	(Light) .... (Heavy)	less than 500 .... 500-1000	10 11
Plasma arc welding		less than 20	6
		20 100	8
		100-400	10
		400 800	11
Plasma arc cutting	(light)** .... (medium)** .... (heavy)**	less than 300 .... 300-400 .... 400-800	8 9 10
Torch brazing			3
Torch soldering			2
Carbon arc welding			14

Filter Lenses for Protection Against Radiant Energy

Operations	Plate thickness—inches	Plate thickness—mm	Minimum* Protective Shade
Gas Welding:			
Light	Under 1/8	Under 3.2	4
Medium	1/8 to 1/2	3.2 to 12.7	5
Heavy	Over 1/2	Over 12.7	6
Oxygen cutting:			
Light	Under 1	Under 25	3
Medium	1 to 6	25 to 150	4
Heavy	Over 6	Over 150	5

* As a rule of thumb, start with a shade that is too dark to see the weld zone. Then go to a lighter shade which gives sufficient view of the weld zone without going below the minimum. In oxyfuel gas welding or cutting where the torch produces a high yellow light, it is desirable to use a filter lens that absorbs the yellow or sodium line in the visible light of the (spectrum) operation.

** These values apply where the actual arc is clearly seen. Experience has shown that lighter filters may be used when the arc is hidden by the workpiece.

(b) *Criteria for protective eye and face devices.* (1) Protective eye and face devices purchased after July 5, 1994 shall comply with ANSI Z87.1–1989, "American National Standard Practice for Occupational and Educational Eye and Face Protection," which is incorporated by reference, or shall be demonstrated by the employer to be equally effective. This incorporation by reference was approved by the Director of the Federal Register in accordance with 5 U.S.C. 552(a) and 1 CFR part 51. Copies may be obtained from the American National Standards Institute. Copies may be inspected at the Docket Office, Occupational Safety and Health Administration, U.S. Department of Labor, 200 Constitution Ave., N.W. room N2634, Washington, D.C. or at the Office of the Federal Register, 800 North Capitol Street NW., suite 700, Washington, DC.

(2) Eye and face protective devices purchased before July 5, 1994 shall comply with the ANSI "USA standard for Occupational and Educational Eye and Face Protection," Z87.1–1968 or shall be demonstrated by the employer to be equally effective. This incorporation by reference was approved by the Director of the Federal Register in accordance with 5 U.S.C. 552(a) and 1 CFR part 51. Copies may be inspected at the Docket Office, Occupational Safety and Health Administration, U.S. Department of Labor, 200 Constitution Ave., N.W. room N2634, Washington, D.C. or at the Office of the Federal Register, 800 North Capitol Street NW., suite 700, Washington, DC.

[59 FR 16360, Apr. 6, 1994; 59 FR 33911, July 1, 1994]

EFFECTIVE DATE NOTE: At 59 FR 16360, April 6, 1994, § 1910.133 was revised, effective July 5, 1994. At 59 FR 33911, July 1, 1994, in the table "Filter Lenses for Protection Against Radiant Energy", the column heading "Electric Size 1/32 in." is corrected to read "Electrode Size 1/32 in.", effective July 5, 1994. For the convenience of the user, the superseded text appears below:

§ 1910.133   Eye and face protection.

(a) *General.* (1) Protective eye and face equipment shall be required where there is a rasonable probability of injury that can be prevented by such equipment. In such cases, employees shall make conveniently available a type of protector suitable for the work to be proformed, and employees shall use such protectors. No unprotected person shall knowingly be subjected to a hazardous environmental condition. Suitable eye protectors shall be provided where machines or operations prosent the hazard of flying objects, glare, liquids, injurious radiation, or a combination of these hazards.

(2) Protectors shaall meet the following minimum requirements:

(i) They shall provide adequate protection against the particular haards for which they are designed.

(ii) They shall be reasonalby cpmfortable when worn under the designated conditions.

(iii) They shall fit snugly and shall not unduly interfere with the movements of the wearer.

(iv) They shall be durable.

(v) They shall be capable of being disinfected.

(vi) They shall be easily cleanable.

(vii) Protectors shall be kept clean and in good repair.

(3) Persons whose vision requires the use of corrective lenses in spectacles, and who are required by this standard tp wear eye protection, shall wear goggles or spectacles of one of the following types:

(i) Spectacles whose protective lenses provide optical correction.

(ii) Goggles that can be worn over corrective spectacles without disturbing the adjustment of the spectacles.

(iii) Goggles that incorporate corrective lenses mounted behind the prootective lenses.

(4) Every protector shall be distinctly marked to facilitate identification only of the manufacturer.

(5) When limitations or precautions are indicated by the manufacturer, they shall be transmitted to the user and care taken to see that such limitations and precautions are strictly observed.

(6) Design, construction, testing, and use of devices for eye and face protection shaall be in accordance with American Naational Standard for Occupational and Educaational Eye and Face Protection, Z87.1-1968.

§ 1910.134   Respiratory protection.

(a) *Permissible practice.* (1) In the control of those occupational diseases caused by breathing air contaminated with harmful dusts, fogs, fumes, mists, gases, smokes, sprays, or vapors, the primary objective shall be to prevent atmospheric contamination. This shall be accomplished as far as feasible by accepted engineering control measures (for example, enclosure or confinement of the operation, general and local ventilation, and substitution of less toxic materials). When effective engineering controls are not feasible, or while they are being instituted, appropriate respirators shall be used pursuant to the following requirements.

(2) Respirators shall be provided by the employer when such equipment is necessary to protect the health of the employee. The employer shall provide the respirators which are applicable and suitable for the purpose intended. The employer shall be responsible for the establishment and maintenance of a respiratory protective program which shall include the requirements outlined in paragraph (b) of this section.

(3) The employee shall use the provided respiratory protection in accordance with instructions and training received.

(b) *Requirements for a minimal acceptable program.* (1) Written standard operating procedures governing the selection and use of respirators shall be established.

(2) Respirators shall be selected on the basis of hazards to which the worker is exposed.

(3) The user shall be instructed and trained in the proper use of respirators and their limitations.

(4) [Reserved]

(5) Respirators shall be regularly cleaned and disinfected. Those used by more than one worker shall be thoroughly cleaned and disinfected after each use.

(6) Respirators shall be stored in a convenient, clean, and sanitary location.

(7) Respirators used routinely shall be inspected during cleaning. Worn or deteriorated parts shall be replaced. Respirators for emergency use such as self-contained devices shall be thoroughly inspected at least once a month and after each use.

(8) Appropriate surveillance of work area conditions and degree of employee exposure or stress shall be maintained.

(9) There shall be regular inspection and evaluation to determine the continued effectiveness of the program.

(10) Persons should not be assigned to tasks requiring use of respirators unless it has been determined that they are physically able to perform the work and use the equipment. The local physician shall determine what health and physical conditions are pertinent. The respirator user's medical status should be reviewed periodically (for instance, annually).

(11) Respirators shall be selected from among those jointly approved by the Mine Safety and Health Administration and the National Institute for Occupational Safety and Health under the provisions of 30 CFR part 11.

(c) *Selection of respirators.* Proper selection of respirators shall be made according to the guidance of American National Standard Practices for Respiratory Protection Z88.2–1969.

(d) *Air quality.* (1) Compressed air, compressed oxygen, liquid air, and liquid oxygen used for respiration shall be of high purity. Oxygen shall meet the requirements of the United States Pharmacopoeia for medical or breathing oxygen. Breathing air shall meet at least the requirements of the specification for Grade D breathing air as described in Compressed Gas Association Commodity Specification G–7.1–1966. Compressed oxygen shall not be used in supplied-air respirators or in open circuit self-contained breathing apparatus that have previously used compressed air. Oxygen must never be used with air line respirators.

(2) Breathing air may be supplied to respirators from cylinders or air compressors.

(i) Cylinders shall be tested and maintained as prescribed in the Shipping Container Specification Regulations of the Department of Transportation (49 CFR part 178).

(ii) The compressor for supplying air shall be equipped with necessary safety and standby devices. A breathing air-type compressor shall be used. Compressors shall be constructed and situated so as to avoid entry of contaminated air into the system and suitable in-line air purifying sorbent beds and filters installed to further assure breathing air quality. A receiver of sufficient capacity to enable the respirator wearer to escape from a contaminated atmosphere in event of compressor failure, and alarms to indicate compressor failure and overheating shall be installed in the system. If an oil-lubricated compressor is used, it shall have a high-temperature or carbon monoxide alarm, or both. If only a high-temperature alarm is used, the air from the compressor shall be frequently tested for carbon monoxide to insure that it meets the specifications in paragraph (d)(1) of this section.

(3) Air line couplings shall be incompatible with outlets for other gas systems to prevent inadvertent servicing of air line respirators with nonrespirable gases or oxygen.

(4) Breathing gas containers shall be marked in accordance with American National Standard Method of Marking Portable Compressed Gas Containers to Identify the Material Contained, Z48.1-1954; Federal Specification BB–A–1034a, June 21, 1968, Air, Compressed for Breathing Purposes; or Interim Federal Specification GG–B–00675b, April 27, 1965, Breathing Apparatus, Self-Contained.

(e) *Use of respirators.* (1) Standard procedures shall be developed for respirator use. These should include all information and guidance necessary for their proper selection, use, and care. Possible emergency and routine uses of respirators should be anticipated and planned for.

(2) The correct respirator shall be specified for each job. The respirator type is usually specified in the work procedures by a qualified individual supervising the respiratory protective program. The individual issuing them shall be adequately instructed to insure that the correct respirator is issued.

(3) Written procedures shall be prepared covering safe use of respirators in dangerous atmospheres that might be encountered in normal operations or in emergencies. Personnel shall be familiar with these procedures and the available respirators.

(i) In areas where the wearer, with failure of the respirator, could be overcome by a toxic or oxygen-deficient atmosphere, at least one additional man shall be present. Communications (visual, voice, or signal line) shall be maintained between both or all individuals present. Planning shall be such that one individual will be unaffected by any likely incident and have the proper rescue equipment to be able to assist the other(s) in case of emergency.

(ii) When self-contained breathing apparatus or hose masks with blowers are used in atmospheres immediately dangerous to life or health, standby men must be present with suitable rescue equipment.

(iii) Persons using air line respirators in atmospheres immediately hazardous to life or health shall be equipped with safety harnesses and safety lines for lifting or removing persons from hazardous atmospheres or other and equivalent provisions for the rescue of persons from hazardous atmospheres shall be used. A standby man or men with suitable self-contained breathing apparatus shall be at the nearest fresh air base for emergency rescue.

(4) Respiratory protection is no better than the respirator in use, even though it is worn conscientiously. Frequent random inspections shall be conducted by a qualified individual to assure that respirators are properly selected, used, cleaned, and maintained.

(5) For safe use of any respirator, it is essential that the user be properly instructed in its selection, use, and maintenance. Both supervisors and workers shall be so instructed by competent persons. Training shall provide the men an opportunity to handle the respirator, have it fitted properly, test its face-piece-to-face seal, wear it in normal air for a long familiarity period, and, finally, to wear it in a test atmosphere.

(i) Every respirator wearer shall receive fitting instructions including demonstrations and practice in how the respirator should be worn, how to adjust it, and how to determine if it fits properly. Respirators shall not be worn when conditions prevent a good face seal. Such conditions may be a growth of beard, sideburns, a skull cap that projects under the facepiece, or temple pieces on glasses. Also, the absence of one or both dentures can seriously affect the fit of a facepiece. The worker's diligence in observing these factors shall be evaluated by periodic check. To assure proper protection, the facepiece fit shall be checked by the wearer each time he puts on the respirator. This may be done by following the manufacturer's facepiece fitting instructions.

(ii) Providing respiratory protection for individuals wearing corrective glasses is a serious problem. A proper seal cannot be established if the temple bars of eye glasses extend through the sealing edge of the full facepiece. As a temporary measure, glasses with short temple bars or without temple bars may be taped to the wearer's head. Wearing of contact lenses in contaminated atmospheres with a respirator shall not be allowed. Systems have been developed for mounting corrective lenses inside full facepieces. When a workman must wear corrective lenses as part of the facepiece, the facepiece and lenses shall be fitted by qualified individuals to provide good vision, comfort, and a gas-tight seal.

(iii) If corrective spectacles or goggles are required, they shall be worn so as not to affect the fit of the facepiece. Proper selection of equipment will minimize or avoid this problem.

(f) *Maintenance and care of respirators.* (1) A program for maintenance and care of respirators shall be adjusted to the type of plant, working conditions, and hazards involved, and shall include the following basic services:

(i) Inspection for defects (including a leak check),

(ii) Cleaning and disinfecting,

(iii) Repair,

(iv) Storage

Equipment shall be properly maintained to retain its original effectiveness.

(2) (i) All respirators shall be inspected routinely before and after each use. A respirator that is not routinely used but is kept ready for emergency use shall be inspected after each use and at least monthly to assure that it is in satisfactory working condition.

(ii) Self-contained breathing apparatus shall be inspected monthly. Air and oxygen cylinders shall be fully charged according to the manufacturer's instructions. It shall be determined that the regulator and warning devices function properly.

(iii) Respirator inspection shall include a check of the tightness of connections and the condition of the facepiece, headbands, valves, connecting tube, and canisters. Rubber or elastomer parts shall be inspected for pliability and signs of deterioration. Stretching and manipulating rubber or elastomer parts with a massaging action will keep them pliable and flexible

and prevent them from taking a set during storage.

(iv) A record shall be kept of inspection dates and findings for respirators maintained for emergency use.

(3) Routinely used respirators shall be collected, cleaned, and disinfected as frequently as necessary to insure that proper protection is provided for the wearer. Respirators maintained for emergency use shall be cleaned and disinfected after each use.

(4) Replacement or repairs shall be done only by experienced persons with parts designed for the respirator. No attempt shall be made to replace components or to make adjustment or repairs beyond the manufacturer's recommendations. Reducing or admission valves or regulators shall be returned to the manufacturer or to a trained technician for adjustment or repair.

(5) (i) After inspection, cleaning, and necessary repair, respirators shall be stored to protect against dust, sunlight, heat, extreme cold, excessive moisture, or damaging chemicals. Respirators placed at stations and work areas for emergency use should be quickly accessible at all times and should be stored in compartments built for the purpose. The compartments should be clearly marked. Routinely used respirators, such as dust respirators, may be placed in plastic bags. Respirators should not be stored in such places as lockers or tool boxes unless they are in carrying cases or cartons.

(ii) Respirators should be packed or stored so that the facepiece and exhalation valve will rest in a normal position and function will not be impaired by the elastomer setting in an abnormal position.

(iii) Instructions for proper storage of emergency respirators, such as gas masks and self-contained breathing apparatus, are found in "use and care" instructions usually mounted inside the carrying case lid.

(g) *Identification of gas mask canisters.* (1) The primary means of identifying a gas mask canister shall be by means of properly worded labels. The secondary means of identifying a gas mask canister shall be by a color code.

(2) All who issue or use gas masks falling within the scope of this section

shall see that all gas mask canisters purchased or used by them are properly labeled and colored in accordance with these requirements before they are placed in service and that the labels and colors are properly maintained at all times thereafter until the canisters have completely served their purpose.

(3) On each canister shall appear in bold letters the following:

(i)—

Canister for ――――――――――――
(Name for atmospheric contaminant)

or

Type N Gas Mask Canister

(ii) In addition, essentially the following wording shall appear beneath the appropriate phrase on the canister label: "For respiratory protection in atmospheres containing not more than ―――――― percent by volume of ―――――――――――――."

(Name of atmospheric contaminant)

(4) Canisters having a special high-efficiency filter for protection against radionuclides and other highly toxic particulates shall be labeled with a statement of the type and degree of protection afforded by the filter. The label shall be affixed to the neck end

of, or to the gray stripe which is around and near the top of, the canister. The degree of protection shall be marked as the percent of penetration of the canister by a 0.3–micron-diameter dioctyl phthalate (DOP) smoke at a flow rate of 85 liters per minute.

(5) Each canister shall have a label warning that gas masks should be used only in atmospheres containing sufficient oxygen to support life (at least 16 percent by volume), since gas mask canisters are only designed to neutralize or remove contaminants from the air.

(6) Each gas mask canister shall be painted a distinctive color or combination of colors indicated in Table I–1. All colors used shall be such that they are clearly identifiable by the user and clearly distinguishable from one another. The color coating used shall offer a high degree of resistance to chipping, scaling, peeling, blistering, fading, and the effects of the ordinary atmospheres to which they may be exposed under normal conditions of storage and use. Appropriately colored pressure sensitive tape may be used for the stripes.

TABLE I–1

Atmospheric contaminants to be protected against	Colors assigned [1]
Acid gases	White.
Hydrocyanic acid gas	White with ½-inch green stripe completely around the canister near the bottom.
Chlorine gas	White with ½-inch yellow stripe completely around the canister near the bottom.
Organic vapors	Black.
Ammonia gas	Green.
Acid gases and ammonia gas	Green with ½-inch white stripe completely around the canister near the bottom.
Carbon monoxide	Blue.
Acid gases and organic vapors	Yellow.
Hydrocyanic acid gas and chloropicrin vapor	Yellow with ½-inch blue stripe completely around the canister near the bottom.
Acid gases, organic vapors, and ammonia gases	Brown.
Radioactive materials, excepting tritium and noble gases	Purple (Magenta).
Particulates (dusts, fumes, mists, fogs, or smokes) in combination with any of the above gases or vapors.	Canister color for contaminant, as designated above, with ½-inch gray stripe completely around the canister near the top.
All of the above atmospheric contaminants	Red with ½-inch gray stripe completely around the canister near the top.

[1] Gray shall not be assigned as the main color for a canister designed to remove acids or vapors.
NOTE: Orange shall be used as a complete body, or stripe color to represent gases not included in this table. The user will need to refer to the canister label to determine the degree of protection the canister will afford.

(Approved by the Office of Management and Budget under control number 1218–0099)

[39 FR 23502, June 27, 1974, as amended at 43 FR 49748, Oct. 24, 1978; 49 FR 5322, Feb. 10, 1984; 49 FR 18295, Apr. 30, 1984; 58 FR 35309, June 30, 1993]

29 CFR 1910.146
PERMIT REQUIRED CONFINED
SPACES

§ 1910.146 Permit-required confined spaces.

(a) *Scope and application.* This section contains requirements for practices and procedures to protect employees in general industry from the hazards of entry into permit-required confined spaces. This section does not apply to agriculture, to construction, or to shipyard employment (Parts 1928, 1926, and 1915 of this chapter, respectively).

(b) *Definitions.*

Acceptable entry conditions means the conditions that must exist in a permit space to allow entry and to ensure that employees involved with a permit-required confined space entry can safely enter into and work within the space.

Attendant means an individual stationed outside one or more permit spaces who monitors the authorized entrants and who performs all attendant's duties assigned in the employer's permit space program.

Authorized entrant means an employee who is authorized by the employer to enter a permit space.

Blanking or blinding means the absolute closure of a pipe, line, or duct by the fastening of a solid plate (such as a spectacle blind or a skillet blind) that completely covers the bore and that is capable of withstanding the maximum pressure of the pipe, line, or duct with no leakage beyond the plate.

Confined space means a space that:

(1) Is large enough and so configured that an employee can bodily enter and perform assigned work; and

(2) Has limited or restricted means for entry or exit (for example, tanks, vessels, silos, storage bins, hoppers, vaults, and pits are spaces that may have limited means of entry.); and

(3) Is not designed for continuous employee occupancy.

Double block and bleed means the closure of a line, duct, or pipe by closing and locking or tagging two in-line valves and by opening and locking or tagging a drain or vent valve in the line between the two closed valves.

Emergency means any occurrence (including any failure of hazard control or monitoring equipment) or event internal or external to the permit space that could endanger entrants.

Engulfment means the surrounding and effective capture of a person by a liquid or finely divided (flowable) solid substance that can be aspirated to cause death by filling or plugging the respiratory system or that can exert enough force on the body to cause death by strangulation, constriction, or crushing.

Entry means the action by which a person passes through an opening into a permit-required confined space. Entry includes ensuing work activities in that space and is considered to have occurred as soon as any part of the entrant's body breaks the plane of an opening into the space.

Entry permit (permit) means the written or printed document that is provided by the employer to allow and control entry into a permit space and that contains the information specified in paragraph (f) of this section.

Entry supervisor means the person (such as the employer, foreman, or crew chief) responsible for determining if acceptable entry conditions are present at a permit space where entry is planned, for authorizing entry and overseeing entry operations, and for terminating entry as required by this section.

NOTE: An entry supervisor also may serve as an attendant or as an authorized entrant, as long as that person is trained and equipped as required by this section for each role he or she fills. Also, the duties of entry supervisor may be passed from one individual to another during the course of an entry operation.

Hazardous atmosphere means an atmosphere that may expose employees to the risk of death, incapacitation, impairment of ability to self-rescue (that is, escape unaided from a permit space), injury, or acute illness from one or more of the following causes:

(1) Flammable gas, vapor, or mist in excess of 10 percent of its lower flammable limit (LFL);

(2) Airborne combustible dust at a concentration that meets or exceeds its LFL;

NOTE: This concentration may be approximated as a condition in which the dust obscures vision at a distance of 5 feet (1.52 m) or less.

(3) Atmospheric oxygen concentration below 19.5 percent or above 23.5 percent;

(4) Atmospheric concentration of any substance for which a dose or a permissible exposure limit is published in Subpart G, *Occupational Health and Environmental Control*, or in Subpart Z, *Toxic and Hazardous Substances*, of this part and which could result in employee exposure in excess of its dose or permissible exposure limit;

NOTE: An atmospheric concentration of any substance that is not capable of causing death, incapacitation, impairment of ability to self-rescue, injury, or acute illness due to its health effects is not covered by this provision.

(5) Any other atmospheric condition that is immediately dangerous to life or health.

NOTE: For air contaminants for which OSHA has not determined a dose or permissible exposure limit, other sources of information, such as Material Safety Data Sheets that comply with the Hazard Communication Standard, §1910.1200 of this part, published information, and internal documents can provide guidance in establishing acceptable atmospheric conditions.

Hot work permit means the employer's written authorization to perform operations (for example, riveting, welding, cutting, burning, and heating) capable of providing a source of ignition.

Immediately dangerous to life or health (IDLH) means any condition that poses an immediate or delayed threat to life or that would cause irreversible adverse health effects or that would interfere with an individual's ability to escape unaided from a permit space.

NOTE: Some materials—hydrogen fluoride gas and cadmium vapor, for example—may produce immediate transient effects that, even if severe, may pass without medical attention, but are followed by sudden, possibly fatal collapse 12–72 hours after exposure. The victim "feels normal" from recovery from transient effects until collapse. Such materials in hazardous quantities are considered to be "immediately" dangerous to life or health.

Inerting means the displacement of the atmosphere in a permit space by a noncombustible gas (such as nitrogen) to such an extent that the resulting atmosphere is noncombustible.

NOTE: This procedure produces an IDLH oxygen-deficient atmosphere.

Isolation means the process by which a permit space is removed from service and completely protected against the release of energy and material into the space by such means as: blanking or blinding; misaligning or removing sections of lines, pipes, or ducts; a double block and bleed system; lockout or tagout of all sources of energy; or blocking or disconnecting all mechanical linkages.

Line breaking means the intentional opening of a pipe, line, or duct that is or has been carrying flammable, corrosive, or toxic material, an inert gas, or any fluid at a volume, pressure, or temperature capable of causing injury.

Non-permit confined space means a confined space that does not contain or, with respect to atmospheric hazards, have the potential to contain any hazard capable of causing death or serious physical harm.

Oxygen deficient atmosphere means an atmosphere containing less than 19.5 percent oxygen by volume.

Oxygen enriched atmosphere means an atmosphere containing more than 23.5 percent oxygen by volume.

Permit-required confined space (permit space) means a confined space that has one or more of the following characteristics:

(1) Contains or has a potential to contain a hazardous atmosphere;

(2) Contains a material that has the potential for engulfing an entrant;

(3) Has an internal configuration such that an entrant could be trapped or asphyxiated by inwardly converging walls or by a floor which slopes downward and tapers to a smaller cross-section; or

(4) Contains any other recognized serious safety or health hazard.

Permit required confined space program (permit space program) means the employer's overall program for controlling, and, where appropriate, for protecting employees from, permit space hazards and for regulating employee entry into permit spaces.

Permit system means the employer's written procedure for preparing and issuing permits for entry and for returning the permit space to service following termination of entry.

Prohibited condition means any condition in a permit space that is not allowed by the permit during the period when entry is authorized.

Rescue service means the personnel designated to rescue employees from permit spaces.

Retrieval system means the equipment (including a retrieval line, chest or full-body harness, wristlets, if appropriate, and a lifting device or anchor) used for non-entry rescue of persons from permit spaces.

Testing means the process by which the hazards that may confront entrants of a permit space are identified and evaluated. Testing includes specifying the tests that are to be performed in the permit space.

NOTE: Testing enables employers both to devise and implement adequate control measures for the protection of authorized entrants and to determine if acceptable entry conditions are present immediately prior to, and during, entry.

(c) *General requirements.* (1) The employer shall evaluate the workplace to determine if any spaces are permit-required confined spaces.

NOTE: Proper application of the decision flow chart in Appendix A to §1910.146 would facilitate compliance with this requirement.

(2) If the workplace contains permit spaces, the employer shall inform exposed employees, by posting danger signs or by any other equally effective means, of the existence and location of and the danger posed by the permit spaces.

NOTE: A sign reading "DANGER—PERMIT-REQUIRED CONFINED SPACE, DO NOT ENTER" or using other similar language would satisfy the requirement for a sign.

(3) If the employer decides that its employees will not enter permit spaces, the employer shall take effective measures to prevent its employees from entering the permit spaces and shall comply with paragraphs (c)(1), (c)(2), (c)(6), and (c)(8) of this section.

(4) If the employer decides that its employees will enter permit spaces, the employer shall develop and implement a written permit space program that complies with this section. The written program shall be available for inspection by employees and their authorized representatives.

(5) An employer may use the alternate procedures specified in paragraph (c)(5)(ii) of this section for entering a permit space under the conditions set forth in paragraph (c)(5)(i) of this section.

(i) An employer whose employees enter a permit space need not comply with paragraphs (d) through (f) and (h) through (k) of this section, provided that:

(A) The employer can demonstrate that the only hazard posed by the permit space is an actual or potential hazardous atmosphere;

(B) The employer can demonstrate that continuous forced air ventilation alone is sufficient to maintain that permit space safe for entry;

(C) The employer develops monitoring and inspection data that supports the demonstrations required by paragraphs (c)(5)(i)(A) and (c)(5)(i)(B) of this section;

(D) If an initial entry of the permit space is necessary to obtain the data required by paragraph (c)(5)(i)(C) of this section, the entry is performed in compliance with paragraphs (d) through (k) of this section;

(E) The determinations and supporting data required by paragraphs (c)(5)(i)(A), (c)(5)(i)(B), and (c)(5)(i)(C) of this section are documented by the employer and are made available to each employee who enters the permit space under the terms of paragraph (c)(5) of this section; and

(F) Entry into the permit space under the terms of paragraph (c)(5)(i) of this section is performed in accordance with the requirements of paragraph (c)(5)(ii) of this section.

NOTE: See paragraph (c)(7) of this section for reclassification of a permit space after all hazards within the space have been eliminated.

(ii) The following requirements apply to entry into permit spaces that meet the conditions set forth in paragraph (c)(5)(i) of this section.

(A) Any conditions making it unsafe to remove an entrance cover shall be eliminated before the cover is removed.

(B) When entrance covers are removed, the opening shall be promptly guarded by a railing, temporary cover, or other temporary barrier that will prevent an accidental fall through the opening and that will protect each employee working in the space from foreign objects entering the space.

(C) Before an employee enters the space, the internal atmosphere shall be tested, with a calibrated direct-reading instrument, for the following conditions in the order given:

(1) Oxygen content,

(2) Flammable gases and vapors, and

(3) Potential toxic air contaminants.

(D) There may be no hazardous atmosphere within the space whenever any employee is inside the space.

(E) Continuous forced air ventilation shall be used, as follows:

(1) An employee may not enter the space until the forced air ventilation has eliminated any hazardous atmosphere;

(2) The forced air ventilation shall be so directed as to ventilate the immediate areas where an employee is or will be present within the space and shall continue until all employees have left the space;

(3) The air supply for the forced air ventilation shall be from a clean source and may not increase the hazards in the space.

(F) The atmosphere within the space shall be periodically tested as necessary to ensure that the continuous forced air ventilation is preventing the accumulation of a hazardous atmosphere.

(G) If a hazardous atmosphere is detected during entry:

(1) Each employee shall leave the space immediately;

(2) The space shall be evaluated to determine how the hazardous atmosphere developed; and

(3) Measures shall be implemented to protect employees from the hazardous atmosphere before any subsequent entry takes place.

(H) The employer shall verify that the space is safe for entry and that the pre-entry measures required by paragraph (c)(5)(ii) of this section have been taken, through a written certification that contains the date, the location of the space, and the signature of the person providing the certification. The certification shall be made before entry and shall be made available to each employee entering the space.

(6) When there are changes in the use or configuration of a non-permit confined space that might increase the hazards to entrants, the employer shall reevaluate that space and, if necessary, reclassify it as a permit-required confined space.

(7) A space classified by the employer as a permit-required confined space may be reclassified as a non-permit confined space under the following procedures:

(i) If the permit space poses no actual or potential atmospheric hazards and if all hazards within the space are eliminated without entry into the space, the permit space may be reclassified as a non-permit confined space for as long as the non-atmospheric hazards remain eliminated.

(ii) If it is necessary to enter the permit space to eliminate hazards, such entry shall be performed under paragraphs (d) through (k) of this section. If testing and inspection during that entry demonstrate that the hazards within the permit space have been eliminated, the permit space may be reclassified as a non-permit confined space for as long as the hazards remain eliminated.

NOTE: Control of atmospheric hazards through forced air ventilation does not constitute elimination of the hazards. Paragraph (c)(5) covers permit space entry where the employer can demonstrate that forced air ventilation alone will control all hazards in the space.

(iii) The employer shall document the basis for determining that all hazards in a permit space have been eliminated, through a certification that contains the date, the location of the space, and the signature of the person making the determination. The certification shall be made available to each employee entering the space.

(iv) If hazards arise within a permit space that has been declassified to a non-permit space under paragraph (c)(7) of this section, each employee in the space shall exit the space. The employer shall then reevaluate the space and determine whether it must be reclassified as a permit space, in accordance with other applicable provisions of this section.

(8) When an employer (host employer) arranges to have employees of another employer (contractor) perform work that involves permit space entry, the host employer shall:

(i) Inform the contractor that the workplace contains permit spaces and that permit space entry is allowed only through compliance with a permit space program meeting the requirements of this section;

(ii) Apprise the contractor of the elements, including the hazards identified and the host employer's experience with the space, that make the space in question a permit space;

(iii) Apprise the contractor of any precautions or procedures that the host employer has implemented for the protection of employees in or near permit spaces where contractor personnel will be working;

(iv) Coordinate entry operations with the contractor, when both host employer personnel and contractor personnel will be working in or near permit spaces, as required by paragraph (d)(11) of this section; and

(v) Debrief the contractor at the conclusion of the entry operations regarding the permit space program followed and regarding any hazards confronted or created in permit spaces during entry operations.

(9) In addition to complying with the permit space requirements that apply to all employers, each contractor who is retained to perform permit space entry operations shall:

(i) Obtain any available information regarding permit space hazards and entry operations from the host employer;

(ii) Coordinate entry operations with the host employer, when both host employer personnel and contractor personnel will be working in or near permit spaces, as required by paragraph (d)(11) of this section; and

(iii) Inform the host employer of the permit space program that the contractor will follow and of any hazards confronted or created in permit spaces, either through a debriefing or during the entry operation.

(d) *Permit-required confined space program* (permit space program). Under the permit space program required by paragraph (c)(4) of this section, the employer shall:

(1) Implement the measures necessary to prevent unauthorized entry;

(2) Identify and evaluate the hazards of permit spaces before employees enter them;

(3) Develop and implement the means, procedures, and practices necessary for safe permit space entry operations, including, but not limited to, the following:

(i) Specifying acceptable entry conditions;

(ii) Isolating the permit space;

(iii) Purging, inerting, flushing, or ventilating the permit space as necessary to eliminate or control atmospheric hazards;

(iv) Providing pedestrian, vehicle, or other barriers as necessary to protect entrants from external hazards; and

(v) Verifying that conditions in the permit space are acceptable for entry throughout the duration of an authorized entry.

(4) Provide the following equipment (specified in paragraphs (d)(4)(i) through (d)(4)(ix) of this section) at no cost to employees, maintain that equipment properly, and ensure that employees use that equipment properly:

(i) Testing and monitoring equipment needed to comply with paragraph (d)(5) of this section;

(ii) Ventilating equipment needed to obtain acceptable entry conditions;

(iii) Communications equipment necessary for compliance with paragraphs (h)(3) and (i)(5) of this section;

(iv) Personal protective equipment insofar as feasible engineering and work practice controls do not adequately protect employees;

(v) Lighting equipment needed to enable employees to see well enough to work safely and to exit the space quickly in an emergency;

(vi) Barriers and shields as required by paragraph (d)(3)(iv) of this section;

(vii) Equipment, such as ladders, needed for safe ingress and egress by authorized entrants;

(viii) Rescue and emergency equipment needed to comply with paragraph (d)(9) of this section, except to the extent that the equipment is provided by rescue services; and

(ix) Any other equipment necessary for safe entry into and rescue from permit spaces.

(5) Evaluate permit space conditions as follows when entry operations are conducted:

(i) Test conditions in the permit space to determine if acceptable entry conditions exist before entry is authorized to begin, except that, if isolation of the space is infeasible because the space is large or is part of a continuous system (such as a sewer), pre-entry testing shall be performed to the extent feasible before entry is authorized

and, if entry is authorized, entry conditions shall be continuously monitored in the areas where authorized entrants are working;

(ii) Test or monitor the permit space as necessary to determine if acceptable entry conditions are being maintained during the course of entry operations; and

(iii) When testing for atmospheric hazards, test first for oxygen, then for combustible gases and vapors, and then for toxic gases and vapors.

NOTE: Atmospheric testing conducted in accordance with Appendix B to § 1910.146 would be considered as satisfying the requirements of this paragraph. For permit space operations in sewers, atmospheric testing conducted in accordance with Appendix B, as supplemented by Appendix E to § 1910.146, would be considered as satisfying the requirements of this paragraph.

(6) Provide at least one attendant outside the permit space into which entry is authorized for the duration of entry operations;

NOTE: Attendants may be assigned to monitor more than one permit space provided the duties described in paragraph (i) of this section can be effectively performed for each permit space that is monitored. Likewise, attendants may be stationed at any location outside the permit space to be monitored as long as the duties described in paragraph (i) of this section can be effectively performed for each permit space that is monitored.

(7) If multiple spaces are to be monitored by a single attendant, include in the permit program the means and procedures to enable the attendant to respond to an emergency affecting one or more of the permit spaces being monitored without distraction from the attendant's responsibilities under paragraph (i) of this section;

(8) Designate the persons who are to have active roles (as, for example, authorized entrants, attendants, entry supervisors, or persons who test or monitor the atmosphere in a permit space) in entry operations, identify the duties of each such employee, and provide each such employee with the training required by paragraph (g) of this section;

(9) Develop and implement procedures for summoning rescue and emergency services, for rescuing entrants from permit spaces, for providing nec-

essary emergency services to rescued employees, and for preventing unauthorized personnel from attempting a rescue;

(10) Develop and implement a system for the preparation, issuance, use, and cancellation of entry permits as required by this section;

(11) Develop and implement procedures to coordinate entry operations when employees of more than one employer are working simultaneously as authorized entrants in a permit space, so that employees of one employer do not endanger the employees of any other employer;

(12) Develop and implement procedures (such as closing off a permit space and canceling the permit) necessary for concluding the entry after entry operations have been completed;

(13) Review entry operations when the employer has reason to believe that the measures taken under the permit space program may not protect employees and revise the program to correct deficiencies found to exist before subsequent entries are authorized; and

NOTE: Examples of circumstances requiring the review of the permit space program are: any unauthorized entry of a permit space, the detection of a permit space hazard not covered by the permit, the detection of a condition prohibited by the permit, the occurrence of an injury or near miss during entry, a change in the use or configuration of a permit space, and employee complaints about the effectiveness of the program.

(14) Review the permit space program, using the canceled permits retained under paragraph (e)(6) of this section within 1 year after each entry and revise the program as necessary, to ensure that employees participating in entry operations are protected from permit space hazards.

NOTE: Employers may perform a single annual review covering all entries performed during a 12-month period. If no entry is performed during a 12-month period, no review is necessary.

Appendix C to §1910.146 presents examples of permit space programs that are considered to comply with the requirements of paragraph (d) of this section.

(e) *Permit system.* (1) Before entry is authorized, the employer shall document the completion of measures re-

quired by paragraph (d)(3) of this section by preparing an entry permit.

NOTE: Appendix D to §1910.146 presents examples of permits whose elements are considered to comply with the requirements of this section.

(2) Before entry begins, the entry supervisor identified on the permit shall sign the entry permit to authorize entry.

(3) The completed permit shall be made available at the time of entry to all authorized entrants, by posting it at the entry portal or by any other equally effective means, so that the entrants can confirm that pre-entry preparations have been completed.

(4) The duration of the permit may not exceed the time required to complete the assigned task or job identified on the permit in accordance with paragraph (f)(2) of this section.

(5) The entry supervisor shall terminate entry and cancel the entry permit when:

(i) The entry operations covered by the entry permit have been completed; or

(ii) A condition that is not allowed under the entry permit arises in or near the permit space.

(6) The employer shall retain each canceled entry permit for at least 1 year to facilitate the review of the permit-required confined space program required by paragraph (d)(14) of this section. Any problems encountered during an entry operation shall be noted on the pertinent permit so that appropriate revisions to the permit space program can be made.

(f) *Entry permit.* The entry permit that documents compliance with this section and authorizes entry to a permit space shall identify:

(1) The permit space to be entered;

(2) The purpose of the entry;

(3) The date and the authorized duration of the entry permit;

(4) The authorized entrants within the permit space, by name or by such other means (for example, through the use of rosters or tracking systems) as will enable the attendant to determine quickly and accurately, for the duration of the permit, which authorized entrants are inside the permit space;

NOTE: This requirement may be met by inserting a reference on the entry permit as to the means used, such as a roster or tracking system, to keep track of the authorized entrants within the permit space.

(5) The personnel, by name, currently serving as attendants;

(6) The individual, by name, currently serving as entry supervisor, with a space for the signature or initials of the entry supervisor who originally authorized entry;

(7) The hazards of the permit space to be entered;

(8) The measures used to isolate the permit space and to eliminate or control permit space hazards before entry;

NOTE: Those measures can include the lockout or tagging of equipment and procedures for purging, inerting, ventilating, and flushing permit spaces.

(9) The acceptable entry conditions;

(10) The results of initial and periodic tests performed under paragraph (d)(5) of this section, accompanied by the names or initials of the testers and by an indication of when the tests were performed;

(11) The rescue and emergency services that can be summoned and the means (such as the equipment to use and the numbers to call) for summoning those services;

(12) The communication procedures used by authorized entrants and attendants to maintain contact during the entry;

(13) Equipment, such as personal protective equipment, testing equipment, communications equipment, alarm systems, and rescue equipment, to be provided for compliance with this section;

(14) Any other information whose inclusion is necessary, given the circumstances of the particular confined space, in order to ensure employee safety; and

(15) Any additional permits, such as for hot work, that have been issued to authorize work in the permit space.

(g) *Training.* (1) The employer shall provide training so that all employees whose work is regulated by this section acquire the understanding, knowledge, and skills necessary for the safe performance of the duties assigned under this section.

(2) Training shall be provided to each affected employee:

(i) Before the employee is first assigned duties under this section;

(ii) Before there is a change in assigned duties;

(iii) Whenever there is a change in permit space operations that presents a hazard about which an employee has not previously been trained;

(iv) Whenever the employer has reason to believe either that there are deviations from the permit space entry procedures required by paragraph (d)(3) of this section or that there are inadequacies in the employee's knowledge or use of these procedures.

(3) The training shall establish employee proficiency in the duties required by this section and shall introduce new or revised procedures, as necessary, for compliance with this section.

(4) The employer shall certify that the training required by paragraphs (g)(1) through (g)(3) of this section has been accomplished. The certification shall contain each employee's name, the signatures or initials of the trainers, and the dates of training. The certification shall be available for inspection by employees and their authorized representatives.

(h) *Duties of authorized entrants.* The employer shall ensure that all authorized entrants:

(1) Know the hazards that may be faced during entry, including information on the mode, signs or symptoms, and consequences of the exposure;

(2) Properly use equipment as required by paragraph (d)(4) of this section;

(3) Communicate with the attendant as necessary to enable the attendant to monitor entrant status and to enable the attendant to alert entrants of the need to evacuate the space as required by paragraph (i)(6) of this section;

(4) Alert the attendant whenever:

(i) The entrant recognizes any warning sign or symptom of exposure to a dangerous situation, or

(ii) The entrant detects a prohibited condition; and

(5) Exit from the permit space as quickly as possible whenever:

(i) An order to evacuate is given by the attendant or the entry supervisor,

(ii) The entrant recognizes any warning sign or symptom of exposure to a dangerous situation,

(iii) The entrant detects a prohibited condition, or

(iv) An evacuation alarm is activated.

(i) *Duties of attendants.* The employer shall ensure that each attendant:

(1) Knows the hazards that may be faced during entry, including information on the mode, signs or symptoms, and consequences of the exposure;

(2) Is aware of possible behavioral effects of hazard exposure in authorized entrants;

(3) Continuously maintains an accurate count of authorized entrants in the permit space and ensures that the means used to identify authorized entrants under paragraph (f)(4) of this section accurately identifies who is in the permit space;

(4) Remains outside the permit space during entry operations until relieved by another attendant;

NOTE: When the employer's permit entry program allows attendant entry for rescue, attendants may enter a permit space to attempt a rescue if they have been trained and equipped for rescue operations as required by paragraph (k)(1) of this section and if they have been relieved as required by paragraph (i)(4) of this section.

(5) Communicates with authorized entrants as necessary to monitor entrant status and to alert entrants of the need to evacuate the space under paragraph (i)(6) of this section;

(6) Monitors activities inside and outside the space to determine if it is safe for entrants to remain in the space and orders the authorized entrants to evacuate the permit space immediately under any of the following conditions:

(i) If the attendant detects a prohibited condition;

(ii) If the attendant detects the behavioral effects of hazard exposure in an authorized entrant;

(iii) If the attendant detects a situation outside the space that could endanger the authorized entrants; or

(iv) If the attendant cannot effectively and safely perform all the duties required under paragraph (i) of this section;

(7) Summon rescue and other emergency services as soon as the attendant

determines that authorized entrants may need assistance to escape from permit space hazards;

(8) Takes the following actions when unauthorized persons approach or enter a permit space while entry is underway:

(i) Warn the unauthorized persons that they must stay away from the permit space;

(ii) Advise the unauthorized persons that they must exit immediately if they have entered the permit space; and

(iii) Inform the authorized entrants and the entry supervisor if unauthorized persons have entered the permit space;

(9) Performs non-entry rescues as specified by the employer's rescue procedure; and

(10) Performs no duties that might interfere with the attendant's primary duty to monitor and protect the authorized entrants.

(j) *Duties of entry supervisors.* The employer shall ensure that each entry supervisor:

(1) Knows the hazards that may be faced during entry, including information on the mode, signs or symptoms, and consequences of the exposure;

(2) Verifies, by checking that the appropriate entries have been made on the permit, that all tests specified by the permit have been conducted and that all procedures and equipment specified by the permit are in place before endorsing the permit and allowing entry to begin;

(3) Terminates the entry and cancels the permit as required by paragraph (e)(5) of this section;

(4) Verifies that rescue services are available and that the means for summoning them are operable;

(5) Removes unauthorized individuals who enter or who attempt to enter the permit space during entry operations; and

(6) Determines, whenever responsibility for a permit space entry operation is transferred and at intervals dictated by the hazards and operations performed within the space, that entry operations remain consistent with terms of the entry permit and that acceptable entry conditions are maintained.

(k) *Rescue and emergency services.* (1) The following requirements apply to employers who have employees enter permit spaces to perform rescue services.

(i) The employer shall ensure that each member of the rescue service is provided with, and is trained to use properly, the personal protective equipment and rescue equipment necessary for making rescues from permit spaces.

(ii) Each member of the rescue service shall be trained to perform the assigned rescue duties. Each member of the rescue service shall also receive the training required of authorized entrants under paragraph (g) of this section.

(iii) Each member of the rescue service shall practice making permit space rescues at least once every 12 months, by means of simulated rescue operations in which they remove dummies, manikins, or actual persons from the actual permit spaces or from representative permit spaces. Representative permit spaces shall, with respect to opening size, configuration, and accessibility, simulate the types of permit spaces from which rescue is to be performed.

(iv) Each member of the rescue service shall be trained in basic first-aid and in cardiopulmonary resuscitation (CPR). At least one member of the rescue service holding current certification in first aid and in CPR shall be available.

(2) When an employer (host employer) arranges to have persons other than the host employer's employees perform permit space rescue, the host employer shall:

(i) Inform the rescue service of the hazards they may confront when called on to perform rescue at the host employer's facility, and

(ii) Provide the rescue service with access to all permit spaces from which rescue may be necessary so that the rescue service can develop appropriate rescue plans and practice rescue operations.

(3) To facilitate non-entry rescue, retrieval systems or methods shall be used whenever an authorized entrant enters a permit space, unless the retrieval equipment would increase the overall risk of entry or would not contribute to the rescue of the entrant. Retrieval systems shall meet the following requirements.

(i) Each authorized entrant shall use a chest or full body harness, with a retrieval line attached at the center of the entrant's back near shoulder level, or above the entrant's head. Wristlets may be used in lieu of the chest or full body harness if the employer can demonstrate that the use of a chest or full body harness is infeasible or creates a greater hazard and that the use of wristlets is the safest and most effective alternative.

(ii) The other end of the retrieval line shall be attached to a mechanical device or fixed point outside the permit space in such a manner that rescue can begin as soon as the rescuer becomes aware that rescue is necessary. A mechanical device shall be available to retrieve personnel from vertical type permit spaces more than 5 feet (1.52 m) deep.

(4) If an injured entrant is exposed to a substance for which a Material Safety Data Sheet (MSDS) or other similar written information is required to be kept at the worksite, that MSDS or written information shall be made available to the medical facility treating the exposed entrant.

[58 FR 4549, Jan. 14, 1993; 58 FR 34885, June 29, 1993, as amended at 59 FR 26114, May 19, 1994]

APPENDICES TO § 1910.146—PERMIT-
REQUIRED CONFINED SPACES

NOTE: Appendices A through E serve to provide information and non-mandatory guidelines to assist employers and employees in complying with the appropriate requirements of this section.

193

APPENDIX A TO § 1910.146—PERMIT-REQUIRED CONFINED SPACE DECISION FLOW CHART

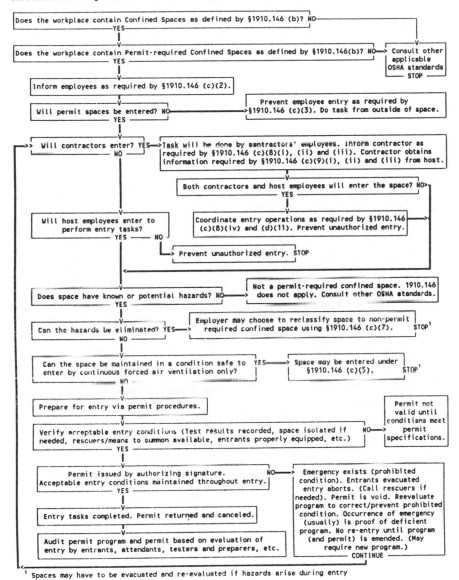

[58 FR 4549, Jan. 14, 1993; 58 FR 34846, June 29, 1993]

APPENDIX B TO § 1910.146—PROCEDURES FOR
ATMOSPHERIC TESTING

Atmospheric testing is required for two distinct purposes: evaluation of the hazards of the permit space and verification that acceptable entry conditions for entry into that space exist.

(1) *Evaluation testing.* The atmosphere of a confined space should be analyzed using equipment of sufficient sensitivity and specificity to identify and evaluate any hazardous atmospheres that may exist or arise, so that appropriate permit entry procedures can be developed and acceptable entry conditions stipulated for that space. Evaluation and interpretation of these data, and development of the entry procedure, should be done by, or reviewed by, a technically qualified professional (e.g., OSHA consultation service, or certified industrial hygienist, registered safety engineer, certified safety professional, certified marine chemist, etc.) based on evaluation of all serious hazards.

(2) *Verification testing.* The atmosphere of a permit space which may contain a hazardous atmosphere should be tested for residues of all contaminants identified by evaluation testing using permit specified equipment to determine that residual concentrations at the time of testing and entry are within the range of acceptable entry conditions. Results of testing (i.e., actual concentration, etc.) should be recorded on the permit in the space provided adjacent to the stipulated acceptable entry condition.

(3) *Duration of testing.* Measurement of values for each atmospheric parameter should be made for at least the minimum response time of the test instrument specified by the manufacturer.

(4) *Testing stratified atmospheres.* When monitoring for entries involving a descent into atmospheres that may be stratified, the atmospheric envelope should be tested a distance of approximately 4 feet (1.22 m) in the direction of travel and to each side. If a sampling probe is used, the entrant's rate of progress should be slowed to accommodate the sampling speed and detector response.

(5) *Order of testing.* A test for oxygen is performed first because most combustible gas meters are oxygen dependent and will not provide reliable readings in an oxygen deficient atmosphere. Combustible gasses are tested for next because the threat of fire or explosion is both more immediate and more life threatening, in most cases, than exposure to toxic gasses and vapors. If tests for toxic gasses and vapors are necessary, they are performed last.

APPENDIX C TO § 1910.146—EXAMPLES OF
PERMIT-REQUIRED CONFINED SPACE PROGRAMS

Example 1.

Workplace. Sewer entry.

Potential hazards. The employees could be exposed to the following:

Engulfment.

Presence of toxic gases. Equal to or more than 10 ppm hydrogen sulfide measured as an 8-hour time-weighted average. If the presence of other toxic contaminants is suspected, specific monitoring programs will be developed.

Presence of explosive/flammable gases. Equal to or greater than 10% of the lower flammable limit (LFL).

Oxygen Deficiency. A concentration of oxygen in the atmosphere equal to or less than 19.5% by volume.

A. *Entry Without Permit/Attendant*

Certification. Confined spaces may be entered without the need for a written permit or attendant provided that the space can be maintained in a safe condition for entry by mechanical ventilation alone, as provided in §1910.146(c)(5). All spaces shall be considered permit-required confined spaces until the pre-entry procedures demonstrate otherwise. Any employee required or permitted to precheck or enter an enclosed/confined space shall have successfully completed, -as a minimum, the training as required by the following sections of these procedures. *A written copy of operating and rescue procedures as required by these procedures shall be at the work site for the duration of the job.* The Confined Space Pre-Entry Check List must be completed by the LEAD WORKER before entry into a confined space. This list verifies completion of items listed below. This check list shall be kept at the job site for duration of the job. If circumstances dictate an interruption in the work, the permit space must be re-evaluated and a new check list must be completed.

Control of atmospheric and engulfment hazards.

Pumps and Lines. All pumps and lines which may reasonably cause contaminants to flow into the space shall be disconnected, blinded and locked out, or effectively isolated by other means to prevent development of dangerous air contamination or engulfment. Not all laterals to sewers or storm drains require blocking. However, where experience or knowledge of industrial use indicates there is a reasonable potential for contamination of air or engulfment into an occupied sewer, then all affected laterals shall be blocked. If blocking and/or isolation requires entry into the space the provisions for entry into a permit- required confined space must be implemented.

Surveillance. The surrounding area shall be surveyed to avoid hazards such as drifting vapors from the tanks, piping, or sewers.

Testing. The atmosphere within the space will be tested to determine whether dangerous air contamination and/or oxygen defi-

Occupational Safety and Health Admin., Labor § 1910.146

ciency exists. Detector tubes, alarm only gas monitors and explosion meters are examples of monitoring equipment that may be used to test permit space atmospheres. Testing shall be performed by the LEAD WORKER who has successfully completed the Gas Detector training for the monitor he will use. The minimum parameters to be monitored are oxygen deficiency, LFL, and hydrogen sulfide concentration. A written record of the pre-entry test results shall be made and kept at the work site for the duration of the job. The supervisor will certify in writing, based upon the results of the pre-entry testing, that all hazards have been eliminated. Affected employees shall be able to review the testing results. The most hazardous conditions shall govern when work is being performed in two adjoining, connecting spaces.

Entry Procedures. If there are no non-atmospheric hazards present and if the pre-entry tests show there is no dangerous air contamination and/or oxygen deficiency within the space and there is no reason to believe that any is likely to develop, entry into and work within may proceed. Continuous testing of the atmosphere in the immediate vicinity of the workers within the space shall be accomplished. The workers will immediately leave the permit space when any of the gas monitor alarm set points are reached as defined. Workers will not return to the area until a SUPERVISOR who has completed the gas detector training has used a direct reading gas detector to evaluate the situation and has determined that it is safe to enter.

Rescue. Arrangements for rescue services are not required where there is no attendant. See the rescue portion of section B., below, for instructions regarding rescue planning where an entry permit is required.

B. *Entry Permit Required*

Permits. Confined Space Entry Permit. All spaces shall be considered permit-required confined spaces until the pre-entry procedures demonstrate otherwise. Any employee required or permitted to pre-check or enter a permit-required confined space shall have successfully completed, as a minimum, the training as required by the following sections of these procedures. *A written copy of operating and rescue procedures as required by these procedures shall be at the work site for the duration of the job.* The Confined Space Entry Permit must be completed before approval can be given to enter a permit-required confined space. This permit verifies completion of items listed below. This permit shall be kept at the job site for the duration of the job. If circumstances cause an interruption in the work or a change in the alarm conditions for which entry was approved, a new Confined Space Entry Permit must be completed.

Control of atmospheric and engulfment hazards.

Surveillance. The surrounding area shall be surveyed to avoid hazards such as drifting vapors from tanks, piping or sewers.

Testing. The confined space atmosphere shall be tested to determine whether dangerous air contamination and/or oxygen deficiency exists. A direct reading gas monitor shall be used. Testing shall be performed by the SUPERVISOR who has successfully completed the gas detector training for the monitor he will use. The minimum parameters to be monitored are oxygen deficiency, LFL and hydrogen sulfide concentration. A written record of the pre-entry test results shall be made and kept at the work site for the duration of the job. Affected employees shall be able to review the testing results. The most hazardous conditions shall govern when work is being performed in two adjoining, connected spaces.

Space Ventilation. Mechanical ventilation systems, where applicable, shall be set at 100% outside air. Where possible, open additional manholes to increase air circulation. Use portable blowers to augment natural circulation if needed. After a suitable ventilating period, repeat the testing. Entry may not begin until testing has demonstrated that the hazardous atmosphere has been eliminated.

Entry Procedures. The following procedure shall be observed under any of the following conditions: 1.) Testing demonstrates the existence of dangerous or deficient conditions and additional ventilation cannot reduce concentrations to safe levels; 2.) The atmosphere tests as safe but unsafe conditions can reasonably be expected to develop; 3.) It is not feasible to provide for ready exit from spaces equipped with automatic fire suppression systems and it is not practical or safe to deactivate such systems; or 4.) An emergency exists and it is not feasible to wait for pre-entry procedures to take effect.

All personnel must be trained. A self contained breathing apparatus shall be worn by any person entering the space. At least one worker shall stand by the outside of the space ready to give assistance in case of emergency. The standby worker shall have a self contained breathing apparatus available for immediate use. There shall be at least one additional worker within sight or call of the standby worker. Continuous powered communications shall be maintained between the worker within the confined space and standby personnel.

If at any time there is any questionable action or non- movement by the worker inside, a verbal check will be made. If there is no response, the worker will be moved immediately. *Exception:* If the worker is disabled due to falling or impact, he/she shall not be removed from the confined space unless there is immediate danger to his/her life. Local fire department rescue personnel shall be notified immediately. The standby worker may only enter the confined space in case of an emergency (wearing the self contained breathing apparatus) and only after being relieved by another worker. Safety belt or harness with attached lifeline shall be used by all workers entering the space with the free end of the line secured outside the entry opening. The standby worker shall attempt to remove a disabled worker via his lifeline before entering the space.

When practical, these spaces shall be entered through side openings—those within 3 1/2 feet (1.07 m) of the bottom. When entry must be through a top opening, the safety belt shall be of the harness type that suspends a person upright and a hoisting device or similar apparatus shall be available for lifting workers out of the space.

In any situation where their use may endanger the worker, use of a hoisting device or safety belt and attached lifeline may be discontinued.

When dangerous air contamination is attributable to flammable and/or explosive substances, lighting and electrical equipment shall be Class 1, Division 1 rated per National Electrical Code and no ignition sources shall be introduced into the area.

Continuous gas monitoring shall be performed during all confined space operations. If alarm conditions change adversely, entry personnel shall exit the confined space and a new confined space permit issued.

Rescue. Call the fire department services for rescue. Where immediate hazards to injured personnel are present, workers at the site shall implement emergency procedures to fit the situation.

Example 2.

Workplace. Meat and poultry rendering plants.

Cookers and dryers are either batch or continuous in their operation. Multiple batch cookers are operated in parallel. When one unit of a multiple set is shut down for repairs, means are available to isolate that unit from the others which remain in operation.

Cookers and dryers are horizontal, cylindrical vessels equipped with a center, rotating shaft and agitator paddles or discs. If the inner shell is jacketed, it is usually heated with steam at pressures up to 150 psig (1034.25 kPa). The rotating shaft assembly of the continuous cooker or dryer is also steam heated.

Potential Hazards. The recognized hazards associated with cookers and dryers are the risk that employees could be:

1. Struck or caught by rotating agitator;
2. Engulfed in raw material or hot, recycled fat;
3. Burned by steam from leaks into the cooker/dryer steam jacket or the condenser duct

system if steam valves are not properly closed and locked out;
4. Burned by contact with hot metal surfaces, such as the agitator shaft assembly, or inner shell of the cooker/dryer;
5. Heat stress caused by warm atmosphere inside cooker/dryer;
6. Slipping and falling on grease in the cooker/dryer;
7. Electrically shocked by faulty equipment taken into the cooker/dryer;
8. Burned or overcome by fire or products of combustion; or
9. Overcome by fumes generated by welding or cutting done on grease covered surfaces.

Permits. The supervisor in this case is always present at the cooker/dryer or other permit entry confined space when entry is made. The supervisor must follow the pre-entry isolation procedures described in the entry permit in preparing for entry, and ensure that the protective clothing, ventilating equipment and any other equipment required by the permit are at the entry site.

Control of hazards. Mechanical. Lock out main power switch to agitator motor at main power panel. Affix tag to the lock to inform others that a permit entry confined space entry is in progress.

Engulfment. Close all valves in the raw material blow line. Secure each valve in its closed position using chain and lock. Attach a tag to the valve and chain warning that a permit entry confined space entry is in progress. The same procedure shall be used for securing the fat recycle valve.

Burns and heat stress. Close steam supply valves to jacket and secure with chains and tags. Insert solid blank at flange in cooker vent line to condenser manifold duct system. Vent cooker/dryer by opening access door at discharge end and top center door to allow natural ventilation throughout the entry. If faster cooling is needed, use an portable ventilation fan to increase ventilation. Cooling water may be circulated through the jacket to reduce both outer and inner surface temperatures of cooker/dryers faster. Check air and inner surface temperatures in cooker/dryer to assure they are within acceptable limits before entering, or use proper protective clothing.

Fire and fume hazards. Careful site preparation, such as cleaning the area within 4 inches (10.16 cm) of all welding or torch cutting operations, and proper ventilation are the preferred controls. All welding and cutting operations shall be done in accordance with the requirements of 29 CFR Part 1910, Subpart Q, OSHA's welding standard. Proper ventilation may be achieved by local exhaust ventilation, or the use of portable ventilation fans, or a combination of the two practices.

Electrical shock. Electrical equipment used in cooker/dryers shall be in serviceable condition.

Slips and falls. Remove residual grease before entering cooker/dryer.

Attendant. The supervisor shall be the attendant for employees entering cooker/dryers.

Permit. The permit shall specify how isolation shall be done and any other preparations needed before making entry. This is especially important in parallel arrangements of cooker/dryers so that the entire operation need not be shut down to allow safe entry into one unit.

Rescue. When necessary, the attendant shall call the fire department as previously arranged.

Example 3.

Workplace. Workplaces where tank cars, trucks, and trailers, dry bulk tanks and trailers, railroad tank cars, and similar portable tanks are fabricated or serviced.

A. *During fabrication.* These tanks and dry-bulk carriers are entered repeatedly throughout the fabrication process. These products are not configured identically, but the manufacturing processes by which they are made are very similar.

Sources of hazards. In addition to the mechanical hazards arising from the risks that an entrant would be injured due to contact with components of the tank or the tools being used, there is also the risk that a worker could be injured by breathing fumes from welding materials or mists or vapors from materials used to coat the tank interior. In addition, many of these vapors and mists are flammable, so the failure to properly ventilate a tank could lead to a fire or explosion.

Control of hazards.

Welding. Local exhaust ventilation shall be used to remove welding fumes once the tank or carrier is completed to the point that workers may enter and exit only through a manhole. (Follow the requirements of 29 CFR 1910, Subpart Q, OSHA's welding standard, at all times.) Welding gas tanks may never be brought into a tank or carrier that is a permit entry confined space.

Application of interior coatings/linings. Atmospheric hazards shall be controlled by forced air ventilation sufficient to keep the atmospheric concentration of flammable materials below 10% of the lower flammable limit (LFL) (or lower explosive limit (LEL), whichever term is used locally). The appropriate respirators are provided and shall be used in addition to providing forced ventilation if the forced ventilation does not maintain acceptable respiratory conditions.

Permits. Because of the repetitive nature of the entries in these operations, an "Area Entry Permit" will be issued for a 1 month period to cover those production areas where tanks are fabricated to the point that entry and exit are made using manholes.

Authorization. Only the area supervisor may authorize an employee to enter a tank within the permit area. The area supervisor must determine that conditions in the tank trailer, dry bulk trailer or truck, etc. meet permit requirements before authorizing entry.

Attendant. The area supervisor shall designate an employee to maintain communication by employer specified means with employees working in tanks to ensure their safety. The attendant may not enter any permit entry confined space to rescue an entrant or for any other reason, unless authorized by the rescue procedure and, and even then, only after calling the rescue team and being relieved by as attendant by another worker.

Communications and observation. Communications between attendant and entrant(s) shall be maintained throughout entry. Methods of communication that may be specified by the permit include voice, voice powered radio, tapping or rapping codes on tank walls, signalling tugs on a rope, and the attendant's observation that work activities such as chipping, grinding, welding, spraying, etc., which require deliberate operator control continue normally. These activities often generate so much noise that the necessary hearing protection makes communication by voice difficult.

Rescue procedures. Acceptable rescue procedures include entry by a team of employee-rescuers, use of public emergency services, and procedures for breaching the tank. The area permit specifies which procedures are available, but the area supervisor makes the final decision based on circumstances. (Certain injuries may make it necessary to breach the tank to remove a person rather than risk additional injury by removal through an existing manhole. However, the supervisor must ensure that no breaching procedure used for rescue would violate terms of the entry permit. For instance, if the tank must be breached by cutting with a torch, the tank surfaces to be cut must be free of volatile or combustible coatings within 4 inches (10.16 cm) of the cutting line and the atmosphere within the tank must be below the LFL.

Retrieval line and harnesses. The retrieval lines and harnesses generally required under this standard are usually impractical for use in tanks because the internal configuration of the tanks and their interior baffles and other structures would prevent rescuers from hauling out injured entrants. However, unless the rescue procedure calls for breaching the tank for rescue, the rescue team shall be trained in the use of retrieval lines and harnesses for removing injured employees through manholes.

B. *Repair or service of "used" tanks and bulk trailers.*

Sources of hazards. In addition to facing the potential hazards encountered in fabrication or manufacturing, tanks or trailers which have been in service may contain residues of dangerous materials, whether left over from the transportation of hazardous cargoes or generated by chemical or bacterial action on residues of non-hazardous cargoes.

Control of atmospheric hazards. A "used" tank shall be brought into areas where tank entry is authorized only after the tank has been emptied, cleansed (without employee entry) of any residues, and purged of any potential atmospheric hazards.

Welding. In addition to tank cleaning for control of atmospheric hazards, coating and surface materials shall be removed 4 inches (10.16 cm) or more from any surface area where welding or other torch work will be done and care taken that the atmosphere within the tank remains well below the LFL. (Follow the requirements of 29 CFR 1910, Subpart Q, OSHA's welding standard, at all times.)

Permits. An entry permit valid for up to 1 year shall be issued prior to authorization of entry into used tank trailers, dry bulk trailers or trucks. In addition to the pre-entry cleaning requirement, this permit shall require the employee safeguards specified for new tank fabrication or construction permit areas.

Authorization. Only the area supervisor may authorize an employee to enter a tank trailer, dry bulk trailer or truck within the permit area. The area supervisor must determine that the entry permit requirements have been met before authorizing entry.

APPENDIX D TO §1910.146—SAMPLE PERMITS

Appendix D - 1
Confined Space Entry Permit
Date & Time Issued: _____   Date and Time Expires: _____
Job site/Space I.D.: _____   Job Supervisor _____
Equipment to be worked on: _____   Work to be performed: _____

stand-by personnel _____

1. Atmospheric Checks: Time _____
   Oxygen _____ %
   Explosive _____ % L.F.L.
   Toxic _____ PPM

2. Tester's signature _____

3. Source isolation (No Entry):   N/A   Yes   No
   Pumps or lines blinded,   ( )   ( )   ( )
   disconnected, or blocked   ( )   ( )   ( )

4. Ventilation Modification: N/A   Yes   No
   Mechanical   ( )   ( )   ( )
   Natural Ventilation only   ( )   ( )   ( )

5. Atmospheric check after
   isolation and Ventilation:
   Oxygen _____   > 19.5 %
   Explosive _____ % L.F.L.   < 10 %
   Toxic _____ PPM   < 10 PPM H_2S
   Time _____
   Testers signature _____

6. Communication procedures: _____

7. Rescue procedures: _____

8. Entry, standby, and back up persons: Yes   No
   Successfully completed required
   training?   ( )   ( )
   Is it current?   ( )   ( )

9. Equipment: N/A   Yes   No
   Direct reading gas monitor -
   tested   ( )   ( )   ( )
   Safety harnesses and lifelines
   for entry and standby persons   ( )   ( )   ( )
   Hoisting equipment   ( )   ( )   ( )
   Powered communications   ( )   ( )   ( )
   SCBA's for entry and standby
   persons   ( )   ( )   ( )
   Protective Clothing   ( )   ( )   ( )
   All electric equipment listed
   Class I, Division I, Group D
   and Non-sparking tools   ( )   ( )   ( )

10. Periodic atmospheric tests:
    Oxygen _____ %   Time _____
    Oxygen _____ %   Time _____
    Explosive _____ %   Time _____
    Explosive _____ %   Time _____
    Toxic _____ %   Time _____
    Toxic _____ %   Time _____

We have reviewed the work authorized by this permit and the information contained here-in. Written instructions and safety procedures have been received and are understood. Entry cannot be approved if any squares are marked in the "No" column. This permit is not valid unless all appropriate items are completed.
Permit Prepared By: (Supervisor) _____
Approved By: (Unit Supervisor) _____
Reviewed By (Cs Operations Personnel): _____ (printed name) _____ (signature)

This permit to be kept at job site. Return job site copy to Safety Office following job completion.
Copies: White Original (Safety Office)   Yellow (Unit Supervisor)   Hard(Job site)

Appendix D - 2

ENTRY PERMIT

PERMIT VALID FOR 8 HOURS ONLY. ALL PERMIT COPIES REMAIN AT SITE UNTIL JOB COMPLETED

DATE: - -   SITE LOCATION/DESCRIPTION
PURPOSE OF ENTRY
SUPERVISOR(S) in charge of crews   Type of Crew Phone #

COMMUNICATION PROCEDURES
RESCUE PROCEDURES (PHONE NUMBERS AT BOTTOM)

* BOLD DENOTES MINIMUM REQUIREMENTS TO BE COMPLETED AND REVIEWED PRIOR TO ENTRY*

REQUIREMENTS COMPLETED	DATE TIME	REQUIREMENTS COMPLETED	DATE TIME
Lock Out/De-energize/Try-out		Full Body Harness w/"D" ring	
Line(s) Broken-Capped-Blank		Emergency Escape Retrieval Eq	
Purge-Flush and Vent		Lifelines	
Ventilation		Fire Extinguishers	
Secure Area (Post and Flag)		Lighting (Explosive Proof)	
Breathing Apparatus		Protective Clothing	
Resuscitator - Inhalator		Respirator(s) (Air Purifying)	
Standby Safety Personnel		Burning and Welding Permit	

Note: Items that do not apply enter N/A in the blank.

** RECORD CONTINUOUS MONITORING RESULTS EVERY 2 HOURS **

CONTINUOUS MONITORING**	Permissible		
TEST(S) TO BE TAKEN	Entry Level		
PERCENT OF OXYGEN	19.5% to 23.5%		
LOWER FLAMMABLE LIMIT	Under 10%		
CARBON MONOXIDE	+35 PPM		
Aromatic Hydrocarbon	+ 1 PPM * 5PPM		
Hydrogen Cyanide	(Skin) * 4PPM		
Hydrogen Sulfide	+10 PPM *15PPM		
Sulfur Dioxide	+ 2 PPM * 5PPM		
Ammonia	*35PPM		

* Short-term exposure limit:Employee can work in the area up to 15 minutes.
+ 8 hr. Time Weighted Avg.:Employee can work in area 8 hrs (longer with appropriate respiratory protection).

REMARKS:

GAS TESTER NAME & CHECK #   INSTRUMENT(S) USED MODEL &/OR TYPE   SERIAL &/OR UNIT #

SAFETY STANDBY PERSON IS REQUIRED FOR ALL CONFINED SPACE WORK
SAFETY STANDBY PERSON(S) CHECK # CONFINED SPACE ENTRANT(S) CHECK # CONFINED SPACE ENTRANT(S) CHECK #

SUPERVISOR AUTHORIZATION - ALL CONDITIONS SATISFIED

			DEPARTMENT/PHONE
AMBULANCE 2800 FIRE 2900	Safety 4901	Gas Coordinator 4529/5387	

APPENDIX E TO § 1910.146—SEWER SYSTEM
ENTRY

Sewer entry differs in three vital respects from other permit entries; first, there rarely exists any way to completely isolate the space (a section of a continuous system) to be entered; second, because isolation is not complete, the atmosphere may suddenly and unpredictably become lethally hazardous (toxic, flammable or explosive) from causes beyond the control of the entrant or employer, and third, experienced sewer workers are especially knowledgeable in entry and work in their permit spaces because of their frequent entries. Unlike other employments where permit space entry is a rare and exceptional event, sewer workers' usual work environment is a permit space.

(1) *Adherence to procedure.* The employer should designate as entrants only employees who are thoroughly trained in the employer's sewer entry procedures and who demonstrate that they follow these entry procedures exactly as prescribed when performing sewer entries.

(2) *Atmospheric monitoring.* Entrants should be trained in the use of, and be equipped with, atmospheric monitoring equipment which sounds an audible alarm, in addition to its visual readout, whenever one of the following conditions are encountered: Oxygen concentration less than 19.5 percent; flammable gas or vapor at 10 percent or more of the lower flammable limit (LFL); or hydrogen sulfide or carbon monoxide at or above 10 ppm or 35 ppm, respectively, measured as an 8-hour time-weighted average. Atmospheric monitoring equipment needs to be calibrated according to the manufacturer's instructions. The oxygen sensor/broad range sensor is best suited for initial use in situations where the actual or potential contaminants have not been identified, because broad range sensors, unlike substance-specific sensors, enable employers to obtain an overall reading of the hydrocarbons (flammables) present in the space. However, such sensors only indicate that a hazardous threshold of a class of chemicals has been exceeded. They do not measure the levels of contamination of specific substances. Therefore, substance-specific devices, which measure the actual levels of specific substances, are best suited for use where actual and potential contaminants have been identified. The measurements obtained with substance-specific devices are of vital importance to the employer when decisions are made concerning the measures necessary to protect entrants (such as ventilation or personal protective equipment) and the setting and attainment of appropriate entry conditions. However, the sewer environment may suddenly and unpredictably change, and the substance-specific devices may not detect the potentially lethal atmospheric hazards which may enter the sewer environment.

Although OSHA considers the information and guidance provided above to be appropriate and useful in most sewer entry situations, the Agency emphasizes that each employer must consider the unique circumstances, including the predictability of the atmosphere, of the sewer permit spaces in the employer's workplace in preparing for entry. Only the employer can decide, based upon his or her knowledge of, and experience with permit spaces in sewer systems, what the best type of testing instrument may be for any specific entry operation.

The selected testing instrument should be carried and used by the entrant in sewer line work to monitor the atmosphere in the entrant's environment, and in advance of the entrant's direction of movement, to warn the entrant of any deterioration in atmospheric conditions. Where several entrants are working together in the same immediate location, one instrument, used by the lead entrant, is acceptable.

(3) *Surge flow and flooding.* Sewer crews should develop and maintain liaison, to the extent possible, with the local weather bureau and fire and emergency services in their area so that sewer work may be delayed or interrupted and entrants withdrawn whenever sewer lines might be suddenly flooded by rain or fire suppression activities, or whenever flammable or other hazardous materials are released into sewers during emergencies by industrial or transportation accidents.

(4) *Special Equipment.* Entry into large bore sewers may require the use of special equipment. Such equipment might include such items as atmosphere monitoring devices with automatic audible alarms, escape self-contained breathing apparatus (ESCBA) with at least 10 minute air supply (or other NIOSH approved self-rescuer), and waterproof flashlights, and may also include boats and rafts, radios and rope stand-offs for pulling around bends and corners as needed.

[58 FR 4549, Jan. 14, 1993; 58 FR 34845, June 29, 1993, as amended at 59 FR 26114, May 19, 1994]

§ 1910.147 The control of hazardous energy (lockout/tagout).

(a) *Scope, application and purpose*—(1) *Scope.* (i) This standard covers the servicing and maintenance of machines and equipment in which the *unexpected* energization or start up of the machines or equipment, or release of stored energy could cause injury to employees. This standard establishes minimum performance requirements for the control of such hazardous energy.

(ii) This standard does not cover the following:

Appendix **4C**

29 CFR 1910.95
OCCUPATIONAL NOISE
EXPOSURE

§ 1910.95 Occupational noise exposure.

(a) Protection against the effects of noise exposure shall be provided when the sound levels exceed those shown in Table G–16 when measured on the A scale of a standard sound level meter at slow response. When noise levels are determined by octave band analysis, the equivalent A-weighted sound level may be determined as follows:

(b)(1) When employees are subjected to sound exceeding those listed in Table G–16, feasible administrative or engineering controls shall be utilized. If such controls fail to reduce sound levels within the levels of Table G–16, personal protective equipment shall be

FIGURE G–9

Equivalent sound level contours. Octave band sound pressure levels may be converted to the equivalent A-weighted sound level by plotting them on this graph and noting the A-weighted sound level corresponding to the point of highest penetration into the sound level contours. This equivalent A-weighted sound level, which may differ from the actual A-weighted sound level of the noise, is used to determine exposure limits from Table 1.G–16.

provided and used to reduce sound levels within the levels of the table.

(2) If the variations in noise level involve maxima at intervals of 1 second or less, it is to be considered continuous.

TABLE G–16—PERMISSIBLE NOISE EXPOSURES [1]

Duration per day, hours	Sound level dBA slow response
8	90
6	92
4	95
3	97
2	100
1½	102
1	105
½	110
¼ or less	115

[1] When the daily noise exposure is composed of two or more periods of noise exposure of different levels, their combined effect should be considered, rather than the individual effect of each. If the sum of the following fractions: $C_1/T_1 + C_2/T_2 \cdots C_n/T_n$ exceeds unity, then, the mixed exposure should be considered to exceed the limit value. Cn indicates the total time of exposure at a specified noise level, and Tn indicates the total time of exposure permitted at that level.

Exposure to impulsive or impact noise should not exceed 140 dB peak sound pressure level.

(c) *Hearing conservation program.* (1) The employer shall administer a continuing, effective hearing conservation program, as described in paragraphs (c) through (o) of this section, whenever employee noise exposures equal or exceed an 8-hour time-weighted average sound level (TWA) of 85 decibels measured on the A scale (slow response) or, equivalently, a dose of fifty percent. For purposes of the hearing conservation program, employee noise exposures shall be computed in accordance with appendix A and Table G–16a, and without regard to any attenuation provided by the use of personal protective equipment.

(2) For purposes of paragraphs (c) through (n) of this section, an 8-hour time-weighted average of 85 decibels or a dose of fifty percent shall also be referred to as the action level.

(d) *Monitoring.* (1) When information indicates that any employee's exposure may equal or exceed an 8-hour time-weighted average of 85 decibels, the employer shall develop and implement a monitoring program.

(i) The sampling strategy shall be designed to identify employees for inclusion in the hearing conservation program and to enable the proper selection of hearing protectors.

(ii) Where circumstances such as high worker mobility, significant variations in sound level, or a significant component of impulse noise make area monitoring generally inappropriate, the employer shall use representative personal sampling to comply with the monitoring requirements of this paragraph unless the employer can show that area sampling produces equivalent results.

(2)(i) All continuous, intermittent and impulsive sound levels from 80 decibels to 130 decibels shall be integrated into the noise measurements.

(ii) Instruments used to measure employee noise exposure shall be calibrated to ensure measurement accuracy.

(3) Monitoring shall be repeated whenever a change in production, process, equipment or controls increases noise exposures to the extent that:

(i) Additional employees may be exposed at or above the action level; or

(ii) The attenuation provided by hearing protectors being used by employees may be rendered inadequate to meet the requirements of paragraph (j) of this section.

(e) *Employee notification.* The employer shall notify each employee exposed at or above an 8-hour time-weighted average of 85 decibels of the results of the monitoring.

(f) *Observation of monitoring.* The employer shall provide affected employees or their representatives with an opportunity to observe any noise measurements conducted pursuant to this section.

(g) *Audiometric testing program.* (1) The employer shall establish and maintain an audiometric testing program as provided in this paragraph by making audiometric testing available to all employees whose exposures equal or exceed an 8-hour time-weighted average of 85 decibels.

(2) The program shall be provided at no cost to employees.

(3) Audiometric tests shall be performed by a licensed or certified audiologist, otolaryngologist, or other physician, or by a technician who is certified by the Council of Accreditation in Occupational Hearing Conservation, or who has satisfactorily demonstrated competence in administering

audiometric examinations, obtaining valid audiograms, and properly using, maintaining and checking calibration and proper functioning of the audiometers being used. A technician who operates microprocessor audiometers does not need to be certified. A technician who performs audiometric tests must be responsible to an audiologist, otolaryngologist or physician.

(4) All audiograms obtained pursuant to this section shall meet the requirements of Appendix C: *Audiometric Measuring Instruments.*

(5) *Baseline audiogram.* (i) Within 6 months of an employee's first exposure at or above the action level, the employer shall establish a valid baseline audiogram against which subsequent audiograms can be compared.

(ii) *Mobile test van exception.* Where mobile test vans are used to meet the audiometric testing obligation, the employer shall obtain a valid baseline audiogram within 1 year of an employee's first exposure at or above the action level. Where baseline audiograms are obtained more than 6 months after the employee's first exposure at or above the action level, employees shall wearing hearing protectors for any period exceeding six months after first exposure until the baseline audiogram is obtained.

(iii) Testing to establish a baseline audiogram shall be preceded by at least 14 hours without exposure to workplace noise. Hearing protectors may be used as a substitute for the requirement that baseline audiograms be preceded by 14 hours without exposure to workplace noise.

(iv) The employer shall notify employees of the need to avoid high levels of non-occupational noise exposure during the 14-hour period immediately preceding the audiometric examination.

(6) *Annual audiogram.* At least annually after obtaining the baseline audiogram, the employer shall obtain a new audiogram for each employee exposed at or above an 8-hour time-weighted average of 85 decibels.

(7) *Evaluation of audiogram.* (i) Each employee's annual audiogram shall be compared to that employee's baseline audiogram to determine if the audiogram is valid and if a standard threshold shift as defined in paragraph (g)(10) of this section has occurred. This comparison may be done by a technician.

(ii) If the annual audiogram shows that an employee has suffered a standard threshold shift, the employer may obtain a retest within 30 days and consider the results of the retest as the annual audiogram.

(iii) The audiologist, otolaryngologist, or physician shall review problem audiograms and shall determine whether there is a need for further evaluation. The employer shall provide to the person performing this evaluation the following information:

(A) A copy of the requirements for hearing conservation as set forth in paragraphs (c) through (n) of this section;

(B) The baseline audiogram and most recent audiogram of the employee to be evaluated;

(C) Measurements of background sound pressure levels in the audiometric test room as required in Appendix D: Audiometric Test Rooms.

(D) Records of audiometer calibrations required by paragraph (h)(5) of this section.

(8) *Follow-up procedures.* (i) If a comparison of the annual audiogram to the baseline audiogram indicates a standard threshold shift as defined in paragraph (g)(10) of this section has occurred, the employee shall be informed of this fact in writing, within 21 days of the determination.

(ii) Unless a physician determines that the standard threshold shift is not work related or aggravated by occupational noise exposure, the employer shall ensure that the following steps are taken when a standard threshold shift occurs:

(A) Employees not using hearing protectors shall be fitted with hearing protectors, trained in their use and care, and required to use them.

(B) Employees already using hearing protectors shall be refitted and retrained in the use of hearing protectors and provided with hearing protectors offering greater attenuation if necessary.

(C) The employee shall be referred for a clinical audiological evaluation or an otological examination, as appropriate, if additional testing is necessary or if the employer suspects that a medical pathology of the ear is caused or aggravated by the wearing of hearing protectors.

(D) The employee is informed of the need for an otological examination if a medical pathology of the ear that is unrelated to the use of hearing protectors is suspected.

(iii) If subsequent audiometric testing of an employee whose exposure to noise is less than an 8-hour TWA of 90 decibels indicates that a standard threshold shift is not persistent, the employer:

(A) Shall inform the employee of the new audiometric interpretation; and

(B) May discontinue the required use of hearing protectors for that employee.

(9) *Revised baseline.* An annual audiogram may be substituted for the baseline audiogram when, in the judgment of the audiologist, otolaryngologist or physician who is evaluating the audiogram:

(i) The standard threshold shift revealed by the audiogram is persistent; or

(ii) The hearing threshold shown in the annual audiogram indicates significant improvement over the baseline audiogram.

(10) *Standard threshold shift.* (i) As used in this section, a standard threshold shift is a change in hearing threshold relative to the baseline audiogram of an average of 10 dB or more at 2000, 3000, and 4000 Hz in either ear.

(ii) In determining whether a standard threshold shift has occurred, allowance may be made for the contribution of aging (presbycusis) to the change in hearing level by correcting the annual audiogram according to the procedure described in Appendix F: *Calculation and Application of Age Correction to Audiograms.*

(h) *Audiometric test requirements.* (1) Audiometric tests shall be pure tone, air conduction, hearing threshold examinations, with test frequencies including as a minimum 500, 1000, 2000, 3000, 4000, and 6000 Hz. Tests at each frequency shall be taken separately for each ear.

(2) Audiometric tests shall be conducted with audiometers (including microprocessor audiometers) that meet

the specifications of, and are maintained and used in accordance with, American National Standard Specification for Audiometers, S3.6–1969.

(3) Pulsed-tone and self-recording audiometers, if used, shall meet the requirements specified in Appendix C: *Audiometric Measuring Instruments.*

(4) Audiometric examinations shall be administered in a room meeting the requirements listed in Appendix D: *Audiometric Test Rooms.*

(5) *Audiometer calibration.* (i) The functional operation of the audiometer shall be checked before each day's use by testing a person with known, stable hearing thresholds, and by listening to the audiometer's output to make sure that the output is free from distorted or unwanted sounds. Deviations of 10 decibels or greater require an acoustic calibration.

(ii) Audiometer calibration shall be checked acoustically at least annually in accordance with Appendix E: *Acoustic Calibration of Audiometers.* Test frequencies below 500 Hz and above 6000 Hz may be omitted from this check. Deviations of 15 decibels or greater require an exhaustive calibration.

(iii) An exhaustive calibration shall be performed at least every two years in accordance with sections 4.1.2; 4.1.3.; 4.1.4.3; 4.2; 4.4.1; 4.4.2; 4.4.3; and 4.5 of the American National Standard Specification for Audiometers, S3.6–1969. Test frequencies below 500 Hz and above 6000 Hz may be omitted from this calibration.

(i) *Hearing protectors.* (1) Employers shall make hearing protectors available to all employees exposed to an 8-hour time-weighted average of 85 decibels or greater at no cost to the employees. Hearing protectors shall be replaced as necessary.

(2) Employers shall ensure that hearing protectors are worn:

(i) By an employee who is required by paragraph (b)(1) of this section to wear personal protective equipment; and

(ii) By any employee who is exposed to an 8-hour time-weighted average of 85 decibels or greater, and who:

(A) Has not yet had a baseline audiogram established pursuant to paragraph (g)(5)(ii); or

(B) Has experienced a standard threshold shift.

(3) Employees shall be given the opportunity to select their hearing protectors from a variety of suitable hearing protectors provided by the employer.

(4) The employer shall provide training in the use and care of all hearing protectors provided to employees.

(5) The employer shall ensure proper initial fitting and supervise the correct use of all hearing protectors.

(j) *Hearing protector attenuation.* (1) The employer shall evaluate hearing protector attenuation for the specific noise environments in which the protector will be used. The employer shall use one of the evaluation methods described in Appendix B: *Methods for Estimating the Adequacy of Hearing Protection Attenuation.*

(2) Hearing protectors must attenuate employee exposure at least to an 8-hour time-weighted average of 90 decibels as required by paragraph (b) of this section.

(3) For employees who have experienced a standard threshold shift, hearing protectors must attenuate employee exposure to an 8-hour time-weighted average of 85 decibels or below.

(4) The adequacy of hearing protector attenuation shall be re-evaluated whenever employee noise exposures increase to the extent that the hearing protectors provided may no longer provide adequate attenuation. The employer shall provide more effective hearing protectors where necessary.

(k) *Training program.* (1) The employer shall institute a training program for all employees who are exposed to noise at or above an 8-hour time-weighted average of 85 decibels, and shall ensure employee participation in such program.

(2) The training program shall be repeated annually for each employee included in the hearing conservation program. Information provided in the training program shall be updated to be consistent with changes in protective equipment and work processes.

(3) The employer shall ensure that each employee is informed of the following:

(i) The effects of noise on hearing;

(ii) The purpose of hearing protectors, the advantages, disadvantages,

and attenuation of various types, and instructions on selection, fitting, use, and care; and

(iii) The purpose of audiometric testing, and an explanation of the test procedures.

(l) *Access to information and training materials.* (1) The employer shall make available to affected employees or their representatives copies of this standard and shall also post a copy in the workplace.

(2) The employer shall provide to affected employees any informational materials pertaining to the standard that are supplied to the employer by the Assistant Secretary.

(3) The employer shall provide, upon request, all materials related to the employer's training and education program pertaining to this standard to the Assistant Secretary and the Director.

(m) *Recordkeeping*—(1) *Exposure measurements.* The employer shall maintain an accurate record of all employee exposure measurements required by paragraph (d) of this section.

(2) *Audiometric tests.* (1) The employer shall retain all employee audiometric test records obtained pursuant to paragraph (g) of this section:

(ii) This record shall include:

(A) Name and job classification of the employee;

(B) Date of the audiogram;

(C) The examiner's name;

(D) Date of the last acoustic or exhaustive calibration of the audiometer; and

(E) Employee's most recent noise exposure assessment.

(F) The employer shall maintain accurate records of the measurements of the background sound pressure levels in audiometric test rooms.

(3) *Record retention.* The employer shall retain records required in this paragraph (m) for at least the following periods.

(i) Noise exposure measurement records shall be retained for two years.

(ii) Audiometric test records shall be retained for the duration of the affected employee's employment.

(4) *Access to records.* All records required by this section shall be provided upon request to employees, former employees, representatives designated by the individual employee, and the As-

Occupational Safety and Health Admin., Labor § 1910.95

sistant Secretary. The provisions of 29 CFR 1910.20 (a)–(e) and (g)–(i) apply to access to records under this section.

(5) *Transfer of records*. If the employer ceases to do business, the employer shall transfer to the successor employer all records required to be maintained by this section, and the successor employer shall retain them for the remainder of the period prescribed in paragraph (m) (3) of this section.

(n) *Appendices*. (1) Appendices A, B, C, D, and E to this section are incorporated as part of this section and the contents of these appendices are mandatory.

(2) Appendices F and G to this section are informational and are not intended to create any additional obligations not otherwise imposed or to detract from any existing obligations.

(o) *Exemptions*. Paragraphs (c) through (n) of this section shall not apply to employers engaged in oil and gas well drilling and servicing operations.

(p) *Startup date*. Baseline audiograms required by paragraph (g) of this section shall be completed by March 1, 1984.

(Approved by the Office of Management and Budget under control number 1218–0048)

APPENDIX A TO § 1910.95—NOISE EXPOSURE COMPUTATION

This Appendix is Mandatory

I. Computation of Employee Noise Exposure

(1) Noise dose is computed using Table G–16a as follows:

(i) When the sound level, L, is constant over the entire work shift, the noise dose, D, in percent, is given by: $D=100 \ C/T$ where C is the total length of the work day, in hours, and T is the reference duration corresponding to the measured sound level, L, as given in Table G–16a or by the formula shown as a footnote to that table.

(ii) When the workshift noise exposure is composed of two or more periods of noise at different levels, the total noise dose over the work day is given by:

$$D=100 \ (C_1/T_1+C_2/T_2+\ldots+C_n/T_n),$$

where C_n indicates the total time of exposure at a specific noise level, and T_n indicates the reference duration for that level as given by Table G–16a.

(2) The eight-hour time-weighted average sound level (TWA), in decibels, may be computed from the dose, in percent, by means of the formula: $TWA=16.61 \ \log_{10} \ (D/100)+90$. For an eight-hour workshift with the noise level constant over the entire shift, the TWA is equal to the measured sound level.

(3) A table relating dose and TWA is given in Section II.

TABLE G–16a

A-weighted sound level, L (decibel)	Reference duration, T (hour)
80	32
81	27.9
82	24.3
83	21.1
84	18.4
85	16
86	13.9
87	12.1
88	10.6
89	9.2
90	8
91	7.0
92	6.1
93	5.3
94	4.6
95	4
96	3.5
97	3.0
98	2.6
99	2.3
100	2
101	1.7
102	1.5
103	1.3
104	1.1
105	1
106	0.87
107	0.76
108	0.66
109	0.57
110	0.5
111	0.44
112	0.38
113	0.33
114	0.29
115	0.25
116	0.22
117	0.19
118	0.16
119	0.14
120	0.125
121	0.11
122	0.095
123	0.082
124	0.072
125	0.063
126	0.054
127	0.047
128	0.041
129	0.036
130	0.031

In the above table the reference duration, T, is computed by

$$T = \frac{8}{2^{(L-90)/5}}$$

where L is the measured A-weighted sound level.

II. Conversion Between "Dose" and "8-Hour Time-Weighted Average" Sound Level

Compliance with paragraphs (c)–(r) of this regulation is determined by the amount of exposure to noise in the workplace. The amount of such exposure is usually measured with an audiodosimeter which gives a read-out in terms of "dose." In order to better understand the requirements of the amendment, dosimeter readings can be converted to an "8-hour time-weighted average sound level." (TWA).

In order to convert the reading of a dosimeter into TWA, see Table A–1, below. This table applies to dosimeters that are set by the manufacturer to calculate dose or percent exposure according to the relationships in Table G–16a. So, for example, a dose of 91 percent over an eight hour day results in a TWA of 89.3 dB, and, a dose of 50 percent corresponds to a TWA of 85 dB.

If the dose as read on the dosimeter is less than or greater than the values found in Table A–1, the TWA may be calculated by using the formula: $TWA = 16.61 \log_{10} (D/100) + 90$ where TWA=8-hour time-weighted average sound level and D=accumulated dose in percent exposure.

TABLE A–1—CONVERSION FROM "PERCENT NOISE EXPOSURE" OR "DOSE" TO "8-HOUR TIME-WEIGHTED AVERAGE SOUND LEVEL" (TWA)

Dose or percent noise exposure	TWA
10	73.4
15	76.3
20	78.4
25	80.0
30	81.3
35	82.4
40	83.4
45	84.2
50	85.0
55	85.7
60	86.3
65	86.9
70	87.4
75	87.9
80	88.4
81	88.5
82	88.6
83	88.7
84	88.7
85	88.8
86	88.9
87	89.0
88	89.1
89	89.2
90	89.2
91	89.3
92	89.4
93	89.5
94	89.6
95	89.6
96	89.7
97	89.8
98	89.9
99	89.9
100	90.0

TABLE A–1—CONVERSION FROM "PERCENT NOISE EXPOSURE" OR "DOSE" TO "8-HOUR TIME-WEIGHTED AVERAGE SOUND LEVEL" (TWA)—Continued

Dose or percent noise exposure	TWA
101	90.1
102	90.1
103	90.2
104	90.3
105	90.4
106	90.4
107	90.5
108	90.6
109	90.6
110	90.7
111	90.8
112	90.8
113	90.9
114	90.9
115	91.1
116	91.1
117	91.1
118	91.2
119	91.3
120	91.3
125	91.6
130	91.9
135	92.2
140	92.4
145	92.7
150	92.9
155	93.2
160	93.4
165	93.6
170	93.8
175	94.0
180	94.2
185	94.4
190	94.6
195	94.8
200	95.0
210	95.4
220	95.7
230	96.0
240	96.3
250	96.6
260	96.9
270	97.2
280	97.4
290	97.7
300	97.9
310	98.2
320	98.4
330	98.6
340	98.8
350	99.0
360	99.2
370	99.4
380	99.6
390	99.8
400	100.0
410	100.2
420	100.4
430	100.5
440	100.7
450	100.8
460	101.0
470	101.2
480	101.3
490	101.5
500	101.6
510	101.8
520	101.9

TABLE A-1—CONVERSION FROM "PERCENT
NOISE EXPOSURE" OR "DOSE" TO "8-HOUR
TIME-WEIGHTED AVERAGE SOUND LEVEL"
(TWA)—Continued

Dose or percent noise exposure	TWA
530	102.0
540	102.2
550	102.3
560	102.4
570	102.6
580	102.7
590	102.8
600	102.9
610	103.0
620	103.2
630	103.3
640	103.4
650	103.5
660	103.6
670	103.7
680	103.8
690	103.9
700	104.0
710	104.1
720	104.2
730	104.3
740	104.4
750	104.5
760	104.6
770	104.7
780	104.8
790	104.9
800	105.0
810	105.1
820	105.2
830	105.3
840	105.4
850	105.4
860	105.5
870	105.6
880	105.7
890	105.8
900	105.8
910	105.9
920	106.0
930	106.1
940	106.2
950	106.2
960	106.3
970	106.4
980	106.5
990	106.5
999	106.6

APPENDIX B TO §1910.95—METHODS FOR ESTI-
MATING THE ADEQUACY OF HEARING PROTEC-
TOR ATTENUATION

This Appendix is Mandatory

For employees who have experienced a significant threshold shift, hearing protector
attenuation must be sufficient to reduce employee exposure to a TWA of 85 dB. Employers must select one of the following methods
by which to estimate the adequacy of hearing protector attenuation.

The most convenient method is the Noise
Reduction Rating (NRR) developed by the
Environmental Protection Agency (EPA).
According to EPA regulation, the NRR must
be shown on the hearing protector package.
The NRR is then related to an individual
worker's noise environment in order to assess the adequacy of the attenuation of a
given hearing protector. This appendix describes four methods of using the NRR to determine whether a particular hearing protector provides adequate protection within a
given exposure environment. Selection
among the four procedures is dependent upon
the employer's noise measuring instruments.

Instead of using the NRR, employers may
evaluate the adequacy of hearing protector
attenuation by using one of the three methods developed by the National Institute for
Occupational Safety and Health (NIOSH),
which are described in the "List of Personal
Hearing Protectors and Attenuation Data,"
HEW Publication No. 76–120, 1975, pages 21–37.
These methods are known as NIOSH methods
#1, #2 and #3. The NRR described below is a
simplification of NIOSH method #2. The
most complex method is NIOSH method #1,
which is probably the most accurate method
since it uses the largest amount of spectral
information from the individual employee's
noise environment. As in the case of the
NRR method described below, if one of the
NIOSH methods is used, the selected method
must be applied to an individual's noise environment to assess the adequacy of the attenuation. Employers should be careful to
take a sufficient number of measurements in
order to achieve a representative sample for
each time segment.

NOTE: The employer must remember that
calculated attenuation values reflect realistic values only to the extent that the protectors are properly fitted and worn.

When using the NRR to assess hearing protector adequacy, one of the following methods must be used:

(i) When using a dosimeter that is capable
of C-weighted measurements:

(A) Obtain the employee's C-weighted dose
for the entire workshift, and convert to TWA
(see appendix A, II).

(B) Subtract the NRR from the C-weighted
TWA to obtain the estimated A-weighted
TWA under the ear protector.

(ii) When using a dosimeter that is not capable of C-weighted measurements, the following method may be used:

(A) Convert the A-weighted dose to TWA
(see appendix A).

(B) Subtract 7 dB from the NRR.

(C) Subtract the remainder from the A-
weighted TWA to obtain the estimated A-
weighted TWA under the ear protector.

(iii) When using a sound level meter set to
the A-weighting network:

(A) Obtain the employee's A-weighted
TWA.

(B) Subtract 7 dB from the NRR, and subtract the remainder from the A-weighted

TWA to obtain the estimated A-weighted TWA under the ear protector.

(iv) When using a sound level meter set on the C-weighting network:

(A) Obtain a representative sample of the C-weighted sound levels in the employee's environment.

(B) Subtract the NRR from the C-weighted average sound level to obtain the estimated A-weighted TWA under the ear protector.

(v) When using area monitoring procedures and a sound level meter set to the A-weighing network:

(A) Obtain a representative sound level for the area in question.

(B) Subtract 7 dB from the NRR and subtract the remainder from the A-weighted sound level for that area.

(vi) When using area monitoring procedures and a sound level meter set to the C-weighting network:

(A) Obtain a representative sound level for the area in question.

(B) Subtract the NRR from the C-weighted sound level for that area.

APPENDIX C TO § 1910.95—AUDIOMETRIC MEASURING INSTRUMENTS

This Appendix is Mandatory

1. In the event that pulsed-tone audiometers are used, they shall have a tone on-time of at least 200 milliseconds.

2. Self-recording audiometers shall comply with the following requirements:

(A) The chart upon which the audiogram is traced shall have lines at positions corresponding to all multiples of 10 dB hearing level within the intensity range spanned by the audiometer. The lines shall be equally spaced and shall be separated by at least 1/4 inch. Additional increments are optional. The audiogram pen tracings shall not exceed 2 dB in width.

(B) It shall be possible to set the stylus manually at the 10-dB increment lines for calibration purposes.

(C) The slewing rate for the audiometer attenuator shall not be more than 6 dB/sec except that an initial slewing rate greater than 6 dB/sec is permitted at the beginning of each new test frequency, but only until the second subject response.

(D) The audiometer shall remain at each required test frequency for 30 seconds (± 3 seconds). The audiogram shall be clearly marked at each change of frequency and the actual frequency change of the audiometer shall not deviate from the frequency boundaries marked on the audiogram by more than ± 3 seconds.

(E) It must be possible at each test frequency to place a horizontal line segment parallel to the time axis on the audiogram, such that the audiometric tracing crosses the line segment at least six times at that test frequency. At each test frequency the

threshold shall be the average of the midpoints of the tracing excursions.

APPENDIX D TO § 1910.95—AUDIOMETRIC TEST ROOMS

This Appendix is Mandatory

Rooms used for audiometric testing shall not have background sound pressure levels exceeding those in Table D-1 when measured by equipment conforming at least to the Type 2 requirements of American National Standard Specification for Sound Level Meters, S1.4–1971 (R1976), and to the Class II requirements of American National Standard Specification for Octave, Half-Octave, and Third-Octave Band Filter Sets, S1.11–1971 (R1976).

TABLE D-1—MAXIMUM ALLOWABLE OCTAVE-BAND SOUND PRESSURE LEVELS FOR AUDIOMETRIC TEST ROOMS

Octave-band center frequency (Hz)	500	1000	2000	4000	8000
Sound pressure level (dB)	40	40	47	57	62

APPENDIX E TO § 1910.95—ACOUSTIC CALIBRATION OF AUDIOMETERS

This Appendix is Mandatory

Audiometer calibration shall be checked acoustically, at least annually, according to the procedures described in this appendix. The equipment necessary to perform these measurements is a sound level meter, octave-band filter set, and a National Bureau of Standards 9A coupler. In making these measurements, the accuracy of the calibrating equipment shall be sufficient to determine that the audiometer is within the tolerances permitted by American Standard Specification for Audiometers, S3.6–1969.

(1) Sound Pressure Output Check

A. Place the earphone coupler over the microphone of the sound level meter and place the earphone on the coupler.

B. Set the audiometer's hearing threshold level (HTL) dial to 70 dB.

C. Measure the sound pressure level of the tones at each test frequency from 500 Hz through 6000 Hz for each earphone.

D. At each frequency the readout on the sound level meter should correspond to the levels in Table E-1 or Table E-2, as appropriate, for the type of earphone, in the column entitled "sound level meter reading."

(2) Linearity Check

A. With the earphone in place, set the frequency to 1000 Hz and the HTL dial on the audiometer to 70 dB.

B. Measure the sound levels in the coupler at each 10-dB decrement from 70 dB to 10 dB, noting the sound level meter reading at each setting.

Occupational Safety and Health Admin., Labor §1910.95

C. For each 10-dB decrement on the audiometer the sound level meter should indicate a corresponding 10 dB decrease.

D. This measurement may be made electrically with a voltmeter connected to the earphone terminals.

(3) Tolerances

When any of the measured sound levels deviate from the levels in Table E-1 or Table E-2 by ± 3 dB at any test frequency between 500 and 3000 Hz, 4 dB at 4000 Hz, or 5 dB at 6000 Hz, an exhaustive calibration is advised. An exhaustive calibration is required if the deviations are greater than 15 dB or greater at any test frequency.

TABLE E-1—REFERENCE THRESHOLD LEVELS FOR TELEPHONICS—TDH-39 EARPHONES

Frequency, Hz	Reference threshold level for TDH-39 earphones, dB	Sound level meter reading, dB
500	11.5	81.5
1000	7	77
2000	9	79
3000	10	80
4000	9.5	79.5
6000	15.5	85.5

TABLE E-2—REFERENCE THRESHOLD LEVELS FOR TELEPHONICS—TDH-49 EARPHONES

Frequency, Hz	Reference threshold level for TDH-49 earphones, dB	Sound level meter reading, dB
500	13.5	83.5
1000	7.5	77.5
2000	11	81.0
3000	9.5	79.5
4000	10.5	80.5
6000	13.5	83.5

APPENDIX F TO §1910.95—CALCULATIONS AND APPLICATION OF AGE CORRECTIONS TO AUDIOGRAMS

This Appendix Is Non-Mandatory

In determining whether a standard threshold shift has occurred, allowance may be made for the contribution of aging to the change in hearing level by adjusting the most recent audiogram. If the employer chooses to adjust the audiogram, the employer shall follow the procedure described below. This procedure and the age correction tables were developed by the National Institute for Occupational Safety and Health in the criteria document entitled "Criteria for

a Recommended Standard . . . Occupational Exposure to Noise," ((HSM)-11001).

For each audiometric test frequency;

(i) Determine from Tables F-1 or F-2 the age correction values for the employee by:

(A) Finding the age at which the most recent audiogram was taken and recording the corresponding values of age corrections at 1000 Hz through 6000 Hz;

(B) Finding the age at which the baseline audiogram was taken and recording the corresponding values of age corrections at 1000 Hz through 6000 Hz.

(ii) Subtract the values found in step (i)(B) from the value found in step (i)(A).

(iii) The differences calculated in step (ii) represented that portion of the change in hearing that may be due to aging.

EXAMPLE: Employee is a 32-year-old male. The audiometric history for his right ear is shown in decibels below.

Employee's age	Audiometric test frequency (Hz)				
	1000	2000	3000	4000	6000
26	10	5	5	10	5
*27	0	0	0	5	5
28	0	0	0	10	5
29	5	0	5	15	5
30	0	5	10	20	10
31	5	10	20	15	15
*32	5	10	10	25	20

The audiogram at age 27 is considered the baseline since it shows the best hearing threshold levels. Asterisks have been used to identify the baseline and most recent audiogram. A threshold shift of 20 dB exists at 4000 Hz between the audiograms taken at ages 27 and 32.

(The threshold shift is computed by subtracting the hearing threshold at age 27, which was 5, from the hearing threshold at age 32, which is 25). A retest audiogram has confirmed this shift. The contribution of aging to this change in hearing may be estimated in the following manner:

Go to Table F-1 and find the age correction values (in dB) for 4000 Hz at age 27 and age 32.

	Frequency (Hz)				
	1000	2000	3000	4000	6000
Age 32	6	5	7	10	14
Age 27	5	4	6	7	11
Difference	1	1	1	3	3

The difference represents the amount of hearing loss that may be attributed to aging in the time period between the baseline audiogram and the most recent audiogram. In this example, the difference at 4000 Hz is 3 dB. This value is subtracted from the hearing level at 4000 Hz, which in the most recent audiogram is 25, yielding 22 after adjustment. Then the hearing threshold in the baseline audiogram at 4000 Hz (5) is subtracted from the adjusted annual audiogram hearing threshold at 4000 Hz (22). Thus the age-corrected threshold shift would be 17 dB (as opposed to a threshold shift of 20 dB without age correction).

TABLE F-1—AGE CORRECTION VALUES IN DECIBELS FOR MALES

Years	Audiometric Test Frequencies (Hz)				
	1000	2000	3000	4000	6000
20 or younger	5	3	4	5	8
21	5	3	4	5	8
22	5	3	4	5	8
23	5	3	4	6	9
24	5	3	5	6	9
25	5	3	5	7	10
26	5	4	5	7	10
27	5	4	6	7	11
28	6	4	6	8	11
29	6	4	6	8	12
30	6	4	6	9	12
31	6	4	7	9	13
32	6	5	7	10	14
33	6	5	7	10	14
34	6	5	8	11	15
35	7	5	8	11	15
36	7	5	9	12	16
37	7	6	9	12	17
38	7	6	9	13	17
39	7	6	10	14	18
40	7	6	10	14	19
41	7	6	10	14	20
42	8	7	11	16	20
43	8	7	12	16	21
44	8	7	12	17	22
45	8	7	13	18	23
46	8	8	13	19	24
47	8	8	14	19	24
48	9	8	14	20	25
49	9	9	15	21	26
50	9	9	16	22	27
51	9	9	16	23	28
52	9	10	17	24	29
53	9	10	18	25	30
54	10	10	18	26	31
55	10	11	19	27	32
56	10	11	20	28	34
57	10	11	21	29	35
58	10	12	22	31	36
59	11	12	22	32	37
60 or older	11	13	23	33	38

TABLE F-2—AGE CORRECTION VALUES IN DECIBELS FOR FEMALES

Years	Audiometric Test Frequencies (Hz)				
	1000	2000	3000	4000	6000
20 or younger	7	4	3	3	6
21	7	4	4	3	6
22	7	4	4	4	6
23	7	5	4	4	7
24	7	5	4	4	7
25	8	5	4	4	7
26	8	5	5	4	8
27	8	5	5	5	8
28	8	5	5	5	8
29	8	5	5	5	9
30	8	6	5	5	9
31	8	6	6	5	9
32	9	6	6	6	10
33	9	6	6	6	10

TABLE F-2—AGE CORRECTION VALUES IN DECIBELS FOR FEMALES—Continued

Years	Audiometric Test Frequencies (Hz)				
	1000	2000	3000	4000	6000
34	9	6	6	6	10
35	9	6	7	7	11
36	9	7	7	7	11
37	9	7	7	7	12
38	10	7	7	7	12
39	10	7	8	8	12
40	10	7	8	8	13
41	10	8	8	8	13
42	10	8	9	9	13
43	11	8	9	9	14
44	11	8	9	9	14
45	11	8	10	10	15
46	11	9	10	10	15
47	11	9	10	11	16
48	12	9	11	11	16
49	12	9	11	11	16
50	12	10	11	12	17
51	12	10	12	12	17
52	12	10	12	13	18
53	13	10	13	13	18
54	13	11	13	14	19
55	13	11	14	14	19
56	13	11	14	15	20
57	13	11	15	15	20
58	14	12	15	16	21
59	14	12	16	16	21
60 or older	14	12	16	17	22

APPENDIX G TO § 1910.95—MONITORING NOISE LEVELS NON-MANDATORY INFORMATIONAL APPENDIX

This appendix provides information to help employers comply with the noise monitoring obligations that are part of the hearing conservation amendment.

WHAT IS THE PURPOSE OF NOISE MONITORING?

This revised amendment requires that employees be placed in a hearing conservation program if they are exposed to average noise levels of 85 dB or greater during an 8 hour workday. In order to determine if exposures are at or above this level, it may be necessary to measure or monitor the actual noise levels in the workplace and to estimate the noise exposure or "dose" received by employees during the workday.

WHEN IS IT NECESSARY TO IMPLEMENT A NOISE MONITORING PROGRAM?

It is not necessary for every employer to measure workplace noise. Noise monitoring or measuring must be conducted only when exposures are at or above 85 dB. Factors which suggest that noise exposures in the workplace may be at this level include employee complaints about the loudness of noise, indications that employees are losing their hearing, or noisy conditions which make normal conversation difficult. The employer should also consider any information available regarding noise emitted from specific machines. In addition, actual workplace noise measurements can suggest whether or not a monitoring program should be initiated.

HOW IS NOISE MEASURED?

Basically, there are two different instruments to measure noise exposures: the sound level meter and the dosimeter. A sound level meter is a device that measures the intensity of sound at a given moment. Since sound level meters provide a measure of sound intensity at only one point in time, it is generally necessary to take a number of measurements at different times during the day to estimate noise exposure over a workday. If noise levels fluctuate, the amount of time noise remains at each of the various measured levels must be determined.

To estimate employee noise exposures with a sound level meter it is also generally necessary to take several measurements at different locations within the workplace. After appropriate sound level meter readings are obtained, people sometimes draw "maps" of the sound levels in different areas of the workplace. By using a sound level "map" and information on employee locations throughout the day, estimates of individual exposure levels can be developed. This measurement method is generally referred to as *area* noise monitoring.

A dosimeter is like a sound level meter except that it stores sound level measurements and integrates these measurements over time, providing an average noise exposure reading for a given period of time, such as an 8-hour workday. With a dosimeter, a microphone is attached to the employee's clothing and the exposure measurement is simply read at the end of the desired time period. A reader may be used to read-out the dosimeter's measurements. Since the dosimeter is worn by the employee, it measures noise levels in those locations in which the employee travels. A sound level meter can also be positioned within the immediate vicinity of the exposed worker to obtain an individual exposure estimate. Such procedures are generally referred to as *personal* noise monitoring.

Area monitoring can be used to estimate noise exposure when the noise levels are relatively constant and employees are not mobile. In workplaces where employees move about in different areas or where the noise intensity tends to fluctuate over time, noise exposure is generally more accurately estimated by the personal monitoring approach.

In situations where personal monitoring is appropriate, proper positioning of the microphone is necessary to obtain accurate measurements. With a dosimeter, the microphone is generally located on the shoulder and remains in that position for the entire workday. With a sound level meter, the microphone is stationed near the employee's head, and the instrument is usually held by an individual who follows the employee as he or she moves about.

Manufacturer's instructions, contained in dosimeter and sound level meter operating manuals, should be followed for calibration and maintenance. To ensure accurate results, it is considered good professional practice to calibrate instruments before and after each use.

HOW OFTEN IS IT NECESSARY TO MONITOR NOISE LEVELS?

The amendment requires that when there are significant changes in machinery or production processes that may result in increased noise levels, remonitoring must be conducted to determine whether additional employees need to be included in the hearing conservation program. Many companies choose to remonitor periodically (once every year or two) to ensure that all exposed employees are included in their hearing conservation programs.

WHERE CAN EQUIPMENT AND TECHNICAL ADVICE BE OBTAINED?

Noise monitoring equipment may be either purchased or rented. Sound level meters cost about $500 to $1,000, while dosimeters range in price from about $750 to $1,500. Smaller companies may find it more economical to rent equipment rather than to purchase it. Names of equipment suppliers may be found in the telephone book (Yellow Pages) under headings such as: "Safety Equipment," "Industrial Hygiene," or "Engineers-Acoustical." In addition to providing information on obtaining noise monitoring equipment, many companies and individuals included under such listings can provide professional advice on how to conduct a valid noise monitoring program. Some audiological testing firms and industrial hygiene firms also provide noise monitoring services. Universities with audiology, industrial hygiene, or acoustical engineering departments may also provide information or may be able to help employers meet their obligations under this amendment.

Free, on-site assistance may be obtained from OSHA-supported state and private consultation organizations. These safety and health consultative entities generally give priority to the needs of small businesses. See the attached directory for a listing of organizations to contact for aid.

OSHA ONSITE CONSULTATION PROJECT DIRECTORY

State	Office and address	Contact
Alabama	Alabama Consultation Program, P.O. Box 6005, University, Alabama 35486.	(205) 348–7136, Mr. William Weems, Director.

OSHA ONSITE CONSULTATION PROJECT DIRECTORY—Continued

State	Office and address	Contact
Alaska	State of Alaska, Department of Labor, Occupational Safety & Health, 3301 Eagle St., Pouch 7–022, Anchorage, Alaska 99510.	(907) 276–5013, Mr. Stan Godsoe, Project Manager (Air Mail).
American Samoa	Service not yet available.	
Arizona	Consultation and Training, Arizona Division of Occupational Safety and Health, P.O. Box 19070, 1624 W. Adams, Phoenix, AZ 85005.	(602) 255–5795, Mr. Thomas Ramaley, Manager.
Arkansas	OSHA Consultation, Arkansas Department of Labor, 1022 High St., Little Rock, Ark. 72202.	(501) 371–2992, Mr. George Smith, Project Director.
California	CAL/OSHA Consultation Service, 2nd Floor, 525 Golden Gate Avenue, San Francisco, CA 94102.	(415) 557–2870, Mr. Emmett Jones, Chief.
Colorado	Occupational Safety & Health Section, Colorado State University, Institute of Rural Environmental Health, 110 Veterinary Science Building, Fort Collins, CO 80523.	(303) 491–6151, Dr. Roy M. Buchan, Project Director.
Connecticut	Division of Occupational Safety & Health, Connecticut Department of Labor, 200 Folly Brook Boulevard, Wethersfield, Conn. 06109.	(203) 566–4550, Mr. Leo Alix, Director.
Delaware	Delaware Department of Labor, Division of Industrial Affairs, 820 North French Street, 6th Floor, Wilmington, DE 19801.	(302) 571–3908, Mr. Bruno Salvadori, Director.
District of Columbia	Occupational Safety & Health Division, District of Columbia, Department Employment Services, Office of Labor Standards, 2900 Newton Street NE., Washington, DC 20018.	(202) 832–1230, Mr. Lorenzo M. White, Acting Associate Director.
Florida	Department of Labor & Employment Security, Bureau of Industrial Safety and Health, LaFayette Building, Room 204, 2551 Executive Center Circle West, Tallahassee, FL 32301.	(904) 488–3044, Mr. John C. Glenn, Administrator.
Georgia	Economic Development Division, Technology and Development Laboratory, Engineering Experiment Station, Georgia Institute of Technology, Atlanta, GA 30332.	(404) 094–3806, Mr. William C. Howard Assistant to Director, Mr. James Burson, Project Manager.
Guam	Department of Labor, Government of Guam, 23548 Guam Main Facility, Agana, Guam 96921.	(671) 772–6291, Joe R. San Agustin, Director.
Hawaii	Education and Information Branch, Division of Occupational Safety and Health, Suite 910, 677 Ala Moana, Honolulu, HI 96813.	(808) 548–2511, Mr. Don Alper, Manager (Air Mail).
Idaho	OSHA Onsite Consultation Program, Boise State University, Community and Environmental Health, 1910 University Drive, Boise, ID 83725.	(208) 385–3929, Dr. Eldon Edmundson, Director.
Illinois	Division of Industrial Services, Dept. of Commerce and Community Affairs, 310 S. Michigan Avenue, 10 Floor, Chicago, IL 60601.	(800) 972–4140/4216 (Toll-free in State), (312) 793–3270, Mr. Stan Czwinski, Assistant Director.
Iowa	Bureau of Labor, 307 E. Seventh Street, Des Moines, IA 50319.	(515) 281–3606, Mr. Allen J. Meier, Commissioner.
Indiana	Bureau of Safety, Education and Training, Indiana Division of Labor, 1013 State Office Building, Indianapolis, IN 46204.	(317) 633–5845, Mr. Harold Mills, Director.
Kansas	Kansas Dept. of Human Resources, 401 Topeka Ave., Topeka, KS 66603.	(913) 296–4086, Mr. Jerry Abbott, Secretary.
Kentucky	Education and Training, Occupational Safety and Health, Kentucky Department of Labor, 127 Building, 127 South, Frankfort, KY 40601.	(502) 564–6895, Mr. Larry Potter, Director.
Louisiana	No services available as yet (Pending FY 83).	
Maine	Division of Industrial Safety, Maine Dept. of Labor, Labor Station 45, State Office Building, Augusta, ME 04333.	(207) 289–3331, Mr. Lester Wood, Director.
Maryland	Consultation Services, Division of Labor & Industry, 501 St. Paul Place, Baltimore, Maryland 21202.	(301) 659–4210, Ms. Ileana O'Brien, Project Manager, 7(c)(1) Agreement.
Massachusetts	Division of Industrial Safety, Massachusetts Department of Labor and Industries, 100 Cambridge Street, Boston, MA 02202.	(617) 727–3567, Mr. Edward Noseworthy, Project Director.
Michigan (Health)	Special Programs Section, Division of Occupational Health, Michigan Dept. of Public Health, 3500 N. Logan, Lansing. MI 48909.	(517) 373–1410, Mr. Irving Davis, Chief.
Michigan (Safety)	Safety Education & Training Division Bureau of Safety and Regulation, Michigan Department of Labor, 7150 Harris Drive, Box 30015, Lansing, Michigan 48909.	(517) 322–1809, Mr. Alan Harvie, Chief.

Occupational Safety and Health Admin., Labor §1910.95

OSHA ONSITE CONSULTATION PROJECT DIRECTORY—Continued

State	Office and address	Contact
Minnesota	Training and Education Unit, Department of Labor and Industry, 5th Floor, 444 Lafayette Road, St. Paul, MN 55101.	(612) 296–2973, Mr. Timothy Tierney, Project Manager.
Mississippi	Division of Occupational Safety and Health, Mississippi State Board of Health, P.O. Box 1700, Jackson, MS 39205.	(601) 982–6315, Mr. Henry L. Laird, Director.
Missouri	Missouri Department of Labor and Industrial Relations, 722 Jefferson Street, Jefferson City, MO 65101.	1–(800) 392–0208, (314) 751–3403, Ms. Paula Smith, Mr. Jim Brake.
Montana	Montana Bureau of Safety & Health, Division of Workers Compensation, 815 Front Street, Helena, MT 59601.	(406) 449–3402, Mr. Ed Gatzemeier, Chief.
Nebraska	Nebraska Department of Labor, State House Station, State Capitol, P.O. Box 94600, Lincoln, NB 68509.	475–8451 Ext. 258, Mr. Joseph Carroll, Commissioner.
Nevada	Department of Occupational Safety and Health, Nevada Industrial Commission, 515 E. Muffer Street, Carson City, NV 89714.	(702) 885–5240, Mr. Allen Traenkner, Director.
New Hampshire	For information contact	Office of Consultation Programs, Room N3472 200 Constitution Avenue, NW. Washington, DC 20210, Phone: (202) 523–8985.
New Jersey	New Jersey Department of Labor and Industry Division of Work Place Standards, CN–054, Trenton, NJ 08625.	(609) 292–2313, FTS–8–477–2313, Mr. William Clark, Assistant Commissioner.
New Mexico	OSHA Consultation, Health and Environment Department, Environmental Improvement Division, Occupational Health & Safety Section, 4215 Montgomery Boulevard, NE., Albuquerque, NM 87109.	(505) 842–3387, Mr. Albert M. Stevens, Project Manager.
New York	Division of Safety and Health, New York State Department of Labor, 2 World Trade Center, Room 6995, New York, NY 10047.	(212) 488–7746/7, Mr. Joseph Alleva, Project Manager, DOSH.
North Carolina	Consultation Services, North Carolina Department of Labor, 4 West Edenton Street, Raleigh, NC 27601.	(919) 733–4885, Mr. David Pierce, Director.
North Dakota	Division of Environmental Research, Department of Health, Missouri Office Building, 1200 Missouri Avenue, Bismarck, ND 58505.	(701) 224–2348, Mr. Jay Crawford, Director.
Ohio	Department of Industrial Relations, Division of Onsite Consultation, P.O. Box 825, 2323 5th Avenue, Columbus, OH 43216.	(800) 282–1425 (Toll-free in State), (614) 466–7485, Mr. Andrew Doehrel, Project Manager.
Oklahoma	OSHA Division, Oklahoma Department of Labor, State Capitol, Suite 118, Oklahoma City, OK 73105.	(405) 521–2461, Mr. Charles W. McGlon, Director.
Oregon	Consultative Section, Department of Workers' Compensation, Accident Prevention Division, Room 102, Building 1, 2110 Front Street NE., Salem, OR 97310.	(503) 378–2890, Mr. Jack Buckland, Supervisor.
Pennsylvania	For information contact	Office of Consultation Programs, Room N3472, 200 Constitution Avenue NW., Washington, DC 20210, Phone: (202) 523–8985.
Puerto Rico	Occupational Safety & Health, Puerto Rico Department of Labor and Human Resources, 505 Munoz Rivera Ave., 21st Floor, Hato Rey, Puerto Rico 00919.	(809) 754–2134, Mr. John Cinque, Assistant Secretary, (Air Mail).
Rhode Island	Division of Occupational Health, Rhode Island Department of Health, The Cannon Building, 206 Health Department Building, Providence, RI 02903.	(401) 277–2438, Mr. James E. Hickey, Chief.
South Carolina	Consultation and Monitoring, South Carolina Department of Labor, P.O. Box 11329, Columbia, SC 29211.	(803) 758–8921, Mr. Robert Peck, Director, 7(c)(1), Project.
South Dakota	South Dakota Consultation Program, South Dakota State University, S.T.A.T.E.-Engineering Extension, 201 Pugsley Center-SDSO, Brookings, SD 57007.	(605) 688–4101, Mr. James Ceglian, Director.
Tennessee	OSHA Consultative Services, Tennessee Department of Labor, 2nd Floor, 501 Union Building, Nashville, TN 37219.	(615) 741–2793, Mr. L. H. Craig Director.
Texas	Division of Occupational Safety and State Safety Engineer, Texas Department of Health and Resources, 1100 West 49th Street, Austin, TX 78756.	(512) 458–7287, Mr. Walter G. Martin, P.E. Director.
Trust Territories	Service not yet available.	
Utah	Utah Job Safety and Health Consultation Service, Suite 4004, Crane Building, 307 West 200 South, Salt Lake City, UT 84101.	(801) 533–7927/8/9, Mr. H. M. Bergeson, Project Director.
Vermont	Division of Occupational Safety and Health, Vermont Department of Labor and Industry, 118 State Street, Montpelier, VT 05602.	(802) 828–2765, Mr. Robert Mcleod, Project Director.

OSHA ONSITE CONSULTATION PROJECT DIRECTORY—Continued

State	Office and address	Contact
Virginia	Department of Labor and Industry, P.O. Box 12064, 205 N. 4th Street, Richmond, Va. 23241.	(804) 786–5875, Mr. Robert Beard, Commissioner.
Virgin Islands	Division of Occupational Safety and Health, Virgin Islands Department of Labor, Lagoon Street, Room 207, Frederiksted, Virgin Islands 00840.	(809) 772–1315, Mr. Louis Llanos, Deputy Director-DOSH.
Washington	Department of Labor and Industry, P.O. Box 207, Olympia, WA 98504.	(206) 753–6500, Mr. James Sullivan, Assistant Director.
West Virginia	West Virginia Department of Labor, Room 451B, State Capitol, 1900 Washington Street, Charleston, WV 25305.	FTS 8–885–7890, Mr. Lawrence Barker, Commissioner.
Wisconsin (Health)	Section of Occupational Health, Department of Health and Social Services, P.O. Box 309, Madison, WI 53701.	(608) 266–0417, Ms. Patricia Natzke, Acting Chief.
Wisconsin (Safety)	Division of Safety and Buildings, Department of Industry, Labor and Human Relations, 1570 E. Moreland Blvd., Waukesha, WI 53186.	(414) 544–8686, Mr. Richard Michalski, Supervisor.
Wyoming	Wyoming Occupational Health and Safety Department, 200 East 8th Avenue, Cheyenne, Wyo. 82002.	(307) 777–7786, Mr. Donald Owsley, Health and Safety Administrator.

APPENDIX H TO § 1910.95—AVAILABILITY OF REFERENCED DOCUMENTS

Paragraphs (c) through (o) of 29 CFR 1910.95 and the accompanying appendices contain provisions which incorporate publications by reference. Generally, the publications provide criteria for instruments to be used in monitoring and audiometric testing. These criteria are intended to be mandatory when so indicated in the applicable paragraphs of § 1910.95 and appendices.

It should be noted that OSHA does not require that employers purchase a copy of the referenced publications. Employers, however, may desire to obtain a copy of the referenced publications for their own information.

The designation of the paragraph of the standard in which the referenced publications appear, the titles of the publications, and the availability of the publications are as follows:

Paragraph designation	Referenced publication	Available from—
Appendix B	"List of Personal Hearing Protectors and Attenuation Data," HEW Pub. No. 76–120, 1975. NTIS–PB267461.	National Technical Information Service, Port Royal Road, Springfield, VA 22161.
Appendix D	"Specification for Sound Level Meters," S1.4–1971 (R1976).	American National Standards Institute, Inc., 1430 Broadway, New York, NY 10018.
§ 1910.95(k)(2), appendix E	"Specifications for Audiometers," S3.6–1969.	American National Standards Institute, Inc., 1430 Broadway, New York, NY 10018.
Appendix D	"Specification for Octave, Half-Octave and Third-Octave Band Filter Sets," S1.11–1971 (R1976).	Back Numbers Department, Dept. STD, American Institute of Physics, 333 E. 45th St., New York, NY 10017; American National Standards Institute, Inc., 1430 Broadway, New York, NY 10018.

The referenced publications (or a microfiche of the publications) are available for review at many universities and public libraries throughout the country. These publications may also be examined at the OSHA Technical Data Center, Room N2439, United States Department of Labor, 200 Constitution Avenue, NW., Washington, DC 20210, (202) 523–9700 or at any OSHA Regional Office (see telephone directories under United States Government—Labor Department).

APPENDIX I TO § 1910.95—DEFINITIONS

These definitions apply to the following terms as used in paragraphs (c) through (n) of 29 CFR 1910.95.

Action level—An 8-hour time-weighted average of 85 decibels measured on the A-scale, slow response, or equivalently, a dose of fifty percent.

Audiogram—A chart, graph, or table resulting from an audiometric test showing an individual's hearing threshold levels as a function of frequency.

Audiologist—A professional, specializing in the study and rehabilitation of hearing, who is certified by the American Speech-Language-Hearing Association or licensed by a state board of examiners.

Baseline audiogram—The audiogram against which future audiograms are compared.

Occupational Safety and Health Admin., Labor   **§ 1910.96**

Criterion sound level—A sound level of 90 decibels.

Decibel (dB)—Unit of measurement of sound level.

Hertz (Hz)—Unit of measurement of frequency, numerically equal to cycles per second.

Medical pathology—A disorder or disease. For purposes of this regulation, a condition or disease affecting the ear, which should be treated by a physician specialist.

Noise dose—The ratio, expressed as a percentage, of (1) the time integral, over a stated time or event, of the 0.6 power of the measured SLOW exponential time-averaged, squared A-weighted sound pressure and (2) the product of the criterion duration (8 hours) and the 0.6 power of the squared sound pressure corresponding to the criterion sound level (90 dB).

Noise dosimeter—An instrument that integrates a function of sound pressure over a period of time in such a manner that it directly indicates a noise dose.

Otolaryngologist—A physician specializing in diagnosis and treatment of disorders of the ear, nose and throat.

Representative exposure—Measurements of an employee's noise dose or 8-hour time-weighted average sound level that the employers deem to be representative of the exposures of other employees in the workplace.

Sound level—Ten times the common logarithm of the ratio of the square of the measured A-weighted sound pressure to the square of the standard reference pressure of 20 micropascals. Unit: decibels (dB). For use with this regulation, SLOW time response, in accordance with ANSI S1.4–1971 (R1976), is required.

Sound level meter—An instrument for the measurement of sound level.

Time-weighted average sound level—That sound level, which if constant over an 8-hour exposure, would result in the same noise dose as is measured.

[39 FR 23502, June 27, 1974, as amended at 46 FR 4161, Jan. 16, 1981; 46 FR 62845, Dec. 29, 1981; 48 FR 9776, Mar. 8, 1983; 48 FR 29687, June 28, 1983; 54 FR 24333, June 7, 1989]

29 CFR 1910.1000– 1910.1001

AIR CONTAMINANTS

§ 1910.1000   Air contaminants.

An employee's exposure to any substance listed in Tables Z–1, Z–2, or Z–3 of this section shall be limited in accordance with the requirements of the following paragraphs of this section.

(a) *Table Z–1.* (1) *Substances with limits preceded by "C"—Ceiling Values.* An employee's exposure to any substance in Table Z–1, the exposure limit of which is preceded by a "C", shall at no time exceed the exposure limit given for that substance. If instantaneous monitoring is not feasible, then the ceiling shall be assessed as a 15-minute time weighted average exposure which shall not be exceeded at any time during the working day.

(2) *Other substances—8-hour Time Weighted Averages.* An employee's exposure to any substance in Table Z–1, the exposure limit of which is not preceded by a "C", shall not exceed the 8-hour Time Weighted Average given for that substance in any 8-hour work shift of a 40-hour work week.

(b) *Table Z–2.* An employee's exposure to any substance listed in Table Z–2 shall not exceed the exposure limits specified as follows:

(1) *8-hour time weighted averages.* An employee's exposure to any substance listed in Table Z–2, in any 8-hour work shift of a 40-hour work week, shall not exceed the 8-hour time weighted average limit given for that substance in Table Z–2.

(2) *Acceptable ceiling concentrations.* An employee's exposure to a substance listed in Table Z–2 shall not exceed at any time during an 8-hour shift the ac-

ceptable ceiling concentration limit given for the substance in the table, except for a time period, and up to a concentration not exceeding the maximum duration and concentration allowed in the column under "acceptable maximum peak above the acceptable ceiling concentration for an 8-hour shift."

(3) *Example*. During an 8-hour work shift, an employee may be exposed to a concentration of Substance A (with a 10 ppm TWA, 25 ppm ceiling and 50 ppm peak) above 25 ppm (but never above 50 ppm) only for a maximum period of 10 minutes. Such exposure must be compensated by exposures to concentrations less than 10 ppm so that the cumulative exposure for the entire 8-hour work shift does not exceed a weighted average of 10 ppm.

(c) *Table Z–3*. An employee's exposure to any substance listed in Table Z–3, in any 8-hour work shift of a 40-hour work week, shall not exceed the 8-hour time weighted average limit given for that substance in the table.

(d) *Computation formulae*. The computation formula which shall apply to employee exposure to more than one substance for which 8-hour time weighted averages are listed in subpart Z of 29 CFR part 1910 in order to determine whether an employee is exposed over the regulatory limit is as follows:

(1)(i) The cumulative exposure for an 8-hour work shift shall be computed as follows:

$$E=(C_a T_a+C_b T_b+. . .C_n T_n)\div 8$$

Where:

E is the equivalent exposure for the working shift.
C is the concentration during any period of time T where the concentration remains constant.
T is the duration in hours of the exposure at the concentration C.

The value of E shall not exceed the 8-hour time weighted average specified in subpart Z of 29 CFR part 1910 for the substance involved.

(ii) To illustrate the formula prescribed in paragraph (d)(1)(i) of this section, assume that Substance A has an 8-hour time weighted average limit of 100 ppm noted in Table Z–1. Assume that an employee is subject to the following exposure:

Two hours exposure at 150 ppm
Two hours exposure at 75 ppm

Four hours exposure at 50 ppm

Substituting this information in the formula, we have

$(2\times150+2\times75+4\times50)\div8=81.25$ ppm

Since 81.25 ppm is less than 100 ppm, the 8-hour time weighted average limit, the exposure is acceptable.

(2)(i) In case of a mixture of air contaminants an employer shall compute the equivalent exposure as follows:

$$E_m=(C_1\div L_1+C_2\div L_2)+. . .(C_n\div L_n)$$

Where:

E_m is the equivalent exposure for the mixture.
C is the concentration of a particular contaminant.
L is the exposure limit for that substance specified in subpart Z of 29 CFR part 1910.

The value of E_m shall not exceed unity (1).

(ii) To illustrate the formula prescribed in paragraph (d)(2)(i) of this section, consider the following exposures:

Substance	Actual concentration of 8-hour exposure (ppm)	8-hour TWA PEL (ppm)
B	500	1,000
C	45	200
D	40	200

Substituting in the formula, we have:
$E_m=500\div1,000+45\div200+40\div200$
$E_m=0.500+0.225+0.200$
$E_m=0.925$

Since E_m is less than unity (1), the exposure combination is within acceptable limits.

(e) To achieve compliance with paragraphs (a) through (d) of this section, administrative or engineering controls must first be determined and implemented whenever feasible. When such controls are not feasible to achieve full compliance, protective equipment or any other protective measures shall be used to keep the exposure of employees to air contaminants within the limits prescribed in this section. Any equipment and/or technical measures used for this purpose must be approved for each particular use by a competent industrial hygienist or other technically qualified person. Whenever respirators are used, their use shall comply with 1910.134.

(f) *Effective dates*. The exposure limits specified have been in effect with the method of compliance specified in paragraph (e) of this section since May 29, 1971.

TABLE Z-1.—LIMITS FOR AIR CONTAMINANTS

Substance	CAS No. (c)	ppm (a) [1]	mg/m³ (b) [1]	Skin designation
Acetaldehyde	75-07-0	200	360	
Acetic acid	64-19-7	10	25	
Acetic anhydride	108-24-7	5	20	
Acetone	67-64-1	1000	2400	
Acetonitrile	75-05-8	40	70	
2-Acetylaminofluorine; see 1910.1014	53-96-3			
Acetylene dichloride; see 1,2-Dichloroethylene.				
Acetylene tetrabromide	79-27-6	1	14	
Acrolein	107-02-8	0.1	0.25	
Acrylamide	79-06-1		0.3	X
Acrylonitrile; see 1910.1045	107-13-1			
Aldrin	309-00-2		0.25	X
Allyl alcohol	107-18-6	2	5	X
Allyl chloride	107-05-1	1	3	
Allyl glycidyl ether (AGE)	106-92-3	(C)10	(C)45	
Allyl propyl disulfide	2179-59-1	2	12	
alpha-Alumina	1344-28-1			
Total dust			15	
Respirable fraction			5	
Aluminum, metal (as Al)	7429-90-5			
Total dust			15	
Respirable fraction			5	
4-Aminodiphenyl; see 1910.1011	92-67-1			
2-Aminoethanol, see Ethanolamine.				
2-Aminopyridine	504-29-0	0.5	2	
Ammonia	7664-41-7	50	35	
Ammonium sulfamate	7773-06-0			
Total dust			15	
Respirable fraction			5	
n-Amyl acetate	628-63-7	100	525	
sec-Amyl acetate	626-38-0	125	650	
Aniline and homologs	62-53-3	5	19	X
Anisidine (o-, p-isomers)	29191-52-4		0.5	X
Antimony and compounds (as Sb)	7440-36-0		0.5	
ANTU (alpha Naphthylthiourea)	86-88-4		0.3	
Arsenic, inorganic compounds (as As); see 1910.1018.	7440-38-2			
Arsenic, organic compounds (as As)	7440-38-2		0.5	
Arsine	7784-42-1	0.05	0.2	
Asbestos; see 1910.1001	(4)			
Azinphos-methyl	86-50-0		0.2	X
Barium, soluble compounds (as Ba)	7440-39-3		0.5	
Barium sulfate	7727-43-7			
Total dust			15	
Respirable fraction			5	
Benomyl	17804-35-2			
Total dust			15	
Respirable fraction			5	
Benzene; see 1910.1028	71-43-2			
See Table Z-2 for the limits applicable in the operations or sectors excluded in 1910.1028 [d]				
Benzidine; see 1910.1010	92-87-5			
p-Benzoquinone; see Quinone.				
Benzo(a)pyrene; see Coal tar pitch volatiles..				
Benzoyl peroxide	94-36-0		5	
Benzyl chloride	100-44-7	1	5	
Beryllium and beryllium compounds (as Be).	7440-41-7		(2)	
Biphenyl; see Diphenyl.				
Bismuth telluride, Undoped	1304-82-1			
Total dust			15	
Respirable fraction			5	
Boron oxide	1303-86-2			
Total dust			15	

8

Occupational Safety and Health Admin., Labor   **§ 1910.1000**

TABLE Z–1.—LIMITS FOR AIR CONTAMINANTS—Continued

Substance	CAS No. (c)	ppm (a) [1]	mg/m³ (b) [1]	Skin designation
Boron trifluoride	7637–07–2	(C)1	(C)3	
Bromine	7726–95–6	0.1	0.7	
Bromoform	75–25–2	0.5	5	X
Butadiene (1,3-Butadiene)	106–99–0	1000	2200	
Butanethiol; see Butyl mercaptan.				
2-Butanone (Methyl ethyl ketone)	78–93–3	200	590	
2-Butoxyethanol	111–76–2	50	240	X
n-Butyl-acetate	123–86–4	150	710	
sec-Butyl acetate	105–46–4	200	950	
tert-Butyl acetate	540–88–5	200	950	
n-Butyl alcohol	71–36–3	100	300	
sec-Butyl alcohol	78–92–2	150	450	
tert-Butyl alcohol	75–65–0	100	300	
Butylamine	109–73–9	(C)5	(C)15	X
tert-Butyl chromate (as CrO₃)	1189–85–1		(C)0.1	X
n-Butyl glycidyl ether (BGE)	2426–08–6	50	270	
Butyl mercaptan	109–79–5	10	35	
p-tert-Butyltoluene	98–51–1	10	60	
Cadmium (as Cd); see 1910.1027	7440–43–9			
Calcium carbonate	1317–65–3			
Total dust			15	
Respirable fraction			5	
Calcium hydroxide	1305–62–0			
Total dust			15	
Respirable fraction			5	
Calcium oxide	1305–78–8		5	
Calcium silicate	1344–95–2			
Total dust			15	
Respirable fraction			5	
Calcium sulfate	7778–18–9			
Total dust			15	
Respirable fraction			5	
Camphor, synthetic	76–22–2		2	
Carbaryl (Sevin)	63–25–2		5	
Carbon black	1333–86–4		3.5	
Carbon dioxide	124–38–9	5000	9000	
Carbon disulfide	75–15–0		(²)	
Carbon monoxide	630–08–0	50	55	
Carbon tetrachloride	56–23–5		(²)	
Cellulose	9004–34–6			
Total dust			15	
Respirable fraction			5	
Chlordane	57–74–9		0.5	X
Chlorinated camphene	8001–35–2		0.5	X
Chlorinated diphenyl oxide	55720–99–5		0.5	
Chlorine	7782–50–5	(C)1	(C)3	
Chlorine dioxide	10049–04–4	0.1	0.3	
Chlorine trifluoride	7790–91–2	(C)0.1	(C)0.4	
Chloroacetaldehyde	107–20–0	(C)1	(C)3	
a-Chloroacetophenone (Phenacyl chloride).	532–27–4	0.05	0.3	
Chlorobenzene	108–90–7	75	350	
o-Chlorobenzylidene malononitrile	2698–41–1	0.05	0.4	
Chlorobromomethane	74–97–5	200	1050	
2-Chloro-1,3-butadiene; see beta-Chloroprene.				
Chlorodiphenyl (42% Chlorine) (PCB) .	53469–21–9		1	X
Chlorodiphenyl (54% Chlorine) (PCB) .	11097–69–1		0.5	X
1-Chloro-2,3-epoxypropane; see Epichlorohydrin.				
2-Chloroethanol; see Ethylene chlorohydrin.				
Chloroethylene; see Vinyl chloride.				
Chloroform (Trichloromethane)	67–66–3	(C)50	(C)240	
bis(Chloromethyl) ether; see 1910.1008.	542–88–1			
Chloromethyl methyl ether; see 1910.1006.	107–30–2			
1-Chloro-1-nitropropane	600–25–9	20	100	
Chloropicrin	76–06–2	0.1	0.7	
beta-Chloroprene	126–99–8	25	90	X
2-Chloro-6-(trichloromethyl) pyridine	1929–82–4			

9

TABLE Z-1.—LIMITS FOR AIR CONTAMINANTS—Continued

Substance	CAS No. (c)	ppm (a) [1]	mg/m³ (b) [1]	Skin designation
Total dust			15	
Respirable fraction			5	
Chromic acid and chromates (as CrO₃)	([4])		([2])	
Chromium (II) compounds.				
(as Cr)	7440–47–3		0.5	
Chromium (III) compounds.				
(as Cr)	7440–47–3		0.5	
Chromium metal and insol. salts (as Cr).	7440–47–3		1	
Chrysene; see Coal tar pitch volatiles.				
Clopidol	2971–90–6			
Total dust			15	
Respirable fraction			5	
Coal dust (less than 5% SiO₂), respirable fraction.			([3])	
Coal dust (greater than or equal to 5% SiO₂), respirable fraction.			([3])	
Coal tar pitch volatiles (benzene soluble fraction), anthracene, BaP, phenanthrene, acridine, chrysene, pyrene.	65966–93–2		0.2	
Cobalt metal, dust, and fume (as Co)	7440–48–4		0.1	
Coke oven emissions; see 1910.1029.				
Copper	7440–50–8			
Fume (as Cu)			0.1	
Dusts and mists (as Cu)			1	
Cotton dust ᵉ; see 1910.1043			1	
Crag herbicide (Sesone)	136–78–7			
Total dust			15	
Respirable fraction			5	
Cresol, all isomers	1319–77–3	5	22	X
Crotonaldehyde	123–73–9; 4170–30–3	2	6	
Cumene	98–82–8	50	245	X
Cyanides (as CN)	([4])		5	
Cyclohexane	110–82–7	300	1050	
Cyclohexanol	108–93–0	50	200	
Cyclohexanone	108–94–1	50	200	
Cyclohexene	110–83–8	300	1015	
Cyclopentadiene	542–92–7	75	200	
2,4-D (Dichlorophenoxyacetic acid)	94–75–7		10	
Decaborane	17702–41–9	0.05	0.3	X
Demeton (Systox)	8065–48–3		0.1	X
Diacetone alcohol (4-Hydroxy-4-methyl-2-pentanone).	123–42–2	50	240	
1,2-Diaminoethane; see Ethylenediamine.				
Diazomethane	334–88–3	0.2	0.4	
Diborane	19287–45–7	0.1	0.1	
1,2-Dibromo-3-chloropropane (CBCP); see 1910.1044.	96–12–8			
1,2-Dibromoethane; see Ethylene dibromide.				
Dibutyl phosphate	107–66–4	1	5	
Dibutyl phthalate	84–74–2		5	
o-Dichlorobenzene	95–50–1	(C)50	(C)300	
p-Dichlorobenzene	106–46–7	75	450	
3,3′-Dichlorobenzidine; see 1910.1007	91–94–1			
Dichlorodifluoromethane	75–71–8	1000	4950	
1,3-Dichloro-5,5-dimethyl hydantoin	118–52–5		0.2	
Dichlorodiphenyltrichloroethane (DDT)	50–29–3		1	X
1,1-Dichloroethane	75–34–3	100	400	
1,2-Dichloroethane; see Ethylene dichloride.				
1,2-Dichloroethylene	540–59–0	200	790	
Dichloroethyl ether	111–44–4	(C)15	(C)90	X
Dichloromethane; see Methylene chloride.				
Dichloromonofluoromethane	75–43–4	1000	4200	
1,1-Dichloro-1-nitroethane	594–72–9	(C)10	(C)60	
1,2-Dichloropropane; see Propylene dichloride.				
Dichlorotetrafluoroethane	76–14–2	1000	7000	

Occupational Safety and Health Admin., Labor §1910.1000

TABLE Z-1.—LIMITS FOR AIR CONTAMINANTS—Continued

Substance	CAS No. (c)	ppm (a)[1]	mg/m³ (b)[1]	Skin designation
Dichlorvos (DDVP)	62–73–7		1	X
Dicyclopentadienyl iron	102–54–5			
Total dust			15	
Respirable fraction			5	
Dieldrin	60–57–1		0.25	X
Diethylamine	109–89–7	25	75	
2-Diethylaminoethanol	100–37–8	10	50	X
Diethyl ether; see Ethyl ether.				
Difluorodibromomethane	75–61–6	100	860	
Diglycidyl ether (DGE)	2238–07–5	(C)0.5	(C)2.8	
Dihydroxybenzene; see Hydroquinone.				
Diisobutyl ketone	108–83–8	50	290	
Diisopropylamine	108–18–9	5	20	X
4-Dimethylaminoazobenzene; see 1910.1015.	60–11–7			
Dimethoxymethane; see Methylal.				
Dimethyl acetamide	127–19–5	10	35	X
Dimethylamine	124–40–3	10	18	
Dimethylaminobenzene; see Xylidine.				
Dimethylaniline (N,N-Dimethylaniline)	121–69–7	5	25	X
Dimethylbenzene; see Xylene.				
Dimethyl-1,2-dibromo-2,2-dichloroethyl phosphate.	300–76–5		3	
Dimethylformamide	68–12–2	10	30	X
2,6-Dimethyl-4-heptanone; see Diisobutyl ketone.				
1,1-Dimethylhydrazine	57–14–7	0.5	1	X
Dimethylphthalate	131–11–3		5	
Dimethyl sulfate	77–78–1	1	5	X
Dinitrobenzene (all isomers)			1	X
(ortho)	528–29–0			
(meta)	99–65–0			
(para)	100–25–4			
Dinitro-o-cresol	534–52–1		0.2	X
Dinitrotoluene	25321–14–6		1.5	X
Dioxane (Diethylene dioxide)	123–91–1	100	360	X
Diphenyl (Biphenyl)	92–52–4	0.2	1	
Diphenylmethane diisocyanate; see Methylene bisphenyl isocyanate.				
Dipropylene glycol methyl ether	34590–94–8	100	600	X
Di-sec octyl phthalate (Di-(2-ethylhexyl) phthalate).	117–81–7		5	
Emery	12415–34–8			
Total dust			15	
Respirable fraction			5	
Endosulfan	115–29–7		0.1	X
Endrin	72–20–8		0.1	X
Epichlorohydrin	106–89–8	5	19	X
EPN	2104–64–5		0.5	X
1,2-Epoxypropane; see Propylene oxide.				
2,3-Epoxy-1-propanol; see Glycidol.				
Ethanethiol; see Ethyl mercaptan.				
Ethanolamine	141–43–5	3	6	
2-Ethoxyethanol (Cellosolve)	110–80–5	200	740	X
2-Ethoxyethyl acetate (Cellosolve acetate).	111–15–9	100	540	X
Ethyl acetate	141–78–6	400	1400	
Ethyl acrylate	140–88–5	25	100	X
Ethyl alcohol (Ethanol)	64–17–5	1000	1900	
Ethylamine	75–04–7	10	18	
Ethyl amyl ketone (5-Methyl-3-heptanone).	541–85–5	25	130	
Ethyl benzene	100–41–4	100	435	
Ethyl bromide	74–96–4	200	890	
Ethyl butyl ketone (3-Heptanone)	106–35–4	50	230	
Ethyl chloride	75–00–3	1000	2600	
Ethyl ether	60–29–7	400	1200	
Ethyl formate	109–94–4	100	300	
Ethyl mercaptan	75–08–1	(C)10	(C)25	
Ethyl silicate	78–10–4	100	850	
Ethylene chlorohydrin	107–07–3	5	16	X

§ 1910.1000

TABLE Z-1.—LIMITS FOR AIR CONTAMINANTS—Continued

Substance	CAS No. (c)	ppm (a) [1]	mg/m³ (b) [1]	Skin designation
Ethylenediamine	107-15-3	10	25	
Ethylene dibromide	106-93-4		(2)	
Ethylene dichloride (1,2-Dichloroethane).	107-06-2		(2)	
Ethylene glycol dinitrate	628-96-6	(C)0.2	(C)1	X
Ethylene glycol methyl acetate; see Methyl cellosolve acetate.				
Ethyleneimine; see 1910.1012	151-56-4			
Ethylene oxide; see 1910.1047	75-21-8			
Ethylidene chloride; see 1,1-Dichloroethane.				
N-Ethylmorpholine	100-74-3	20	94	X
Ferbam	14484-64-1			
Total dust			15	
Ferrovanadium dust	12604-58-9		1	
Fluorides (as F)	(4)		2.5	
Fluorine	7782-41-4	0.1	0.2	
Fluorotrichloromethane (Trichlorofluoromethane).	75-69-4	1000	5600	
Formaldehyde; see 1910.1048	50-00-0			
Formic acid	64-18-6	5	9	
Furfural	98-01-1	5	20	X
Furfuryl alcohol	98-00-0	50	200	
Grain dust (oat, wheat, barley)			10	
Glycerin (mist)	56-81-5			
Total dust			15	
Respirable fraction			5	
Glycidol	556-52-5	50	150	
Glycol monoethyl ether; see 2-Ethoxyethanol.				
Graphite, natural, respirable dust	7782-42-5		(3)	
Graphite, synthetic				
Total dust			15	
Respirable fraction			5	
Guthion; see Azinphos methyl.				
Gypsum	13397-24-5			
Total dust			15	
Respirable fraction			5	
Hafnium	7440-58-6		0.5	
Heptachlor	76-44-8		0.5	X
Heptane (n-Heptane)	142-82-5	500	2000	
Hexachloroethane	67-72-1	1	10	X
Hexachloronaphthalene	1335-87-1		0.2	X
n-Hexane	110-54-3	500	1800	
2-Hexanone (Methyl n-butyl ketone)	591-78-6	100	410	
Hexone (Methyl isobutyl ketone)	108-10-1	100	410	
sec-Hexyl acetate	108-84-9	50	300	
Hydrazine	302-01-2	1	1.3	X
Hydrogen bromide	10035-10-6	3	10	
Hydrogen chloride	7647-01-0	(C)5	(C)7	
Hydrogen cyanide	74-90-8	10	11	X
Hydrogen fluoride (as F)	7664-39-3		(2)	
Hydrogen peroxide	7722-84-1	1	1.4	
Hydrogen selenide (as Se)	7783-07-5	0.05	0.2	
Hydrogen sulfide	7783-06-4		(2)	
Hydroquinone	123-31-9		2	
Iodine	7553-56-2	(C)0.1	(C)1	
Iron oxide fume	1309-37-1		10	
Isoamyl acetate	123-92-2	100	525	
Isoamyl alcohol (primary and secondary).	123-51-3	100	360	
Isobutyl acetate	110-19-0	150	700	
Isobutyl alcohol	78-83-1	100	300	
Isophorone	78-59-1	25	140	
Isopropyl acetate	108-21-4	250	950	
Isopropyl alcohol	67-63-0	400	980	
Isopropylamine	75-31-0	5	12	
Isopropyl ether	108-20-3	500	2100	
Isopropyl glycidyl ether (IGE)	4016-14-2	50	240	
Kaolin	1332-58-7			
Total dust			15	
Respirable fraction			5	

Occupational Safety and Health Admin., Labor §1910.1000

TABLE Z–1.—LIMITS FOR AIR CONTAMINANTS—Continued

Substance	CAS No. (c)	ppm (a) [1]	mg/m³ (b) [1]	Skin designation
Ketene	463–51–4	0.5	0.9	
Lead, inorganic (as Pb); see 1910.1025.	7439–92–1			
Limestone	1317–65–3			
Total dust			15	
Respirable fraction			5	
Lindane	58–89–9		0.5	X
Lithium hydride	7580–67–8		0.025	
L.P.G. (Liquefied petroleum gas)	68476–85–7	1000	1800	
Magnesite	546–93–0			
Total dust			15	
Respirable fraction			5	
Magnesium oxide fume	1309–48–4			
Total particulate			15	
Malathion	121–75–5			
Total dust			15	X
Maleic anhydride	108–31–6	0.25	1	
Manganese compounds (as Mn)	7439–96–5		(C)5	
Manganese fume (as Mn)	7439–96–5		(C)5	
Marble	1317–65–3			
Total dust			15	
Respirable fraction			5	
Mercury (aryl and inorganic) (as Hg)	7439–97–6		(2)	
Mercury (organo) alkyl compounds (as Hg).	7439–97–6		(2)	
Mercury (vapor) (as Hg)	7439–97–6		(2)	
Mesityl oxide	141–79–7	25	100	
Methanethiol; see Methyl mercaptan.				
Methoxychlor	72–43–5			
Total dust			15	
2-Methoxyethanol (Methyl cellosolve)	109–86–4	25	80	X
2-Methoxyethyl acetate (Methyl cellosolve acetate).	110–49–6	25	120	X
Methyl acetate	79–20–9	200	610	
Methyl acetylene (Propyne)	74–99–7	1000	1650	
Methyl acetylene-propadiene mixture (MAPP).		1000	1800	
Methyl acrylate	96–33–3	10	35	X
Methylal (Dimethoxy-methane)	109–87–5	1000	3100	
Methyl alcohol	67–56–1	200	260	
Methylamine	74–89–5	10	12	
Methyl amyl alcohol; see Methyl isobutyl carbinol.				
Methyl n-amyl ketone	110–43–0	100	465	
Methyl bromide	74–83–9	(C)20	(C)80	X
Methyl butyl ketone; see 2-Hexanone.				
Methyl cellosolve; see 2-Methoxyethanol.				
Methyl cellosolve acetate; see 2-Methoxyethyl acetate.				
Methyl chloride	74–87–3		(2)	
Methyl chloroform (1,1,1-Trichloroethane).	71–55–6	350	1900	
Methylcyclohexane	108–87–2	500	2000	
Methylcyclohexanol	25639–42–3	100	470	
o-Methylcyclohexanone	583–60–8	100	460	X
Methylene chloride	75–09–2		(2)	
Methyl ethyl ketone (MEK); see 2-Butanone.				
Methyl formate	107–31–3	100	250	
Methyl hydrazine (Monomethyl hydrazine).	60–34–4	(C)0.2	(C)0.35	X
Methyl iodide	74–88–4	5	28	X
Methyl isoamyl ketone	110–12–3	100	475	
Methyl isobutyl carbinol	108–11–2	25	100	X
Methyl isobutyl ketone; see Hexone.				
Methyl isocyanate	624–83–9	0.02	0.05	X
Methyl mercaptan	74–93–1	(C)10	(C)20	
Methyl methacrylate	80–62–6	100	410	
Methyl propyl ketone; see 2-Pentanone.				
alpha-Methyl styrene	98–83–9	(C)100	(C)480	

13

TABLE Z-1.—LIMITS FOR AIR CONTAMINANTS—Continued

Substance	CAS No. (c)	ppm (a)[1]	mg/m³ (b)[1]	Skin designation
Methylene bisphenyl isocyanate (MDI)	101-68-8	(C)0.02	(C)0.2	
Mica; see Silicates.				
Molybdenum (as Mo)	7439-98-7			
Soluble compounds			5	
Insoluble compounds.				
Total dust			15	
Monomethyl aniline	100-61-8	2	9	X
Monomethyl hydrazine; see Methyl hydrazine.				
Morpholine	110-91-8	20	70	X
Naphtha (Coal tar)	8030-30-6	100	400	
Naphthalene	91-20-3	10	50	
alpha-Naphthylamine; see 1910.1004 .	134-32-7			
beta-Naphthylamine; see 1910.1009 ...	91-59-8			
Nickel carbonyl (as Ni)	13463-39-3	0.001	0.007	
Nickel, metal and insoluble compounds (as Ni).	7440-02-0		1	
Nickel, soluble compounds (as Ni)	7440-02-0		1	
Nicotine	54-11-5		0.5	X
Nitric acid	7697-37-2	2	5	
Nitric oxide	10102-43-9	25	30	
p-Nitroaniline	100-01-6	1	6	X
Nitrobenzene	98-95-3	1	5	X
p-Nitrochlorobenzene	100-00-5		1	X
4-Nitrodiphenyl; see 1910.1003	92-93-3			
Nitroethane	79-24-3	100	310	
Nitrogen dioxide	10102-44-0	(C)5	(C)9	
Nitrogen trifluoride	7783-54-2	10	29	
Nitroglycerin	55-63-0	(C)0.2	(C)2	X
Nitromethane	75-52-5	100	250	
1-Nitropropane	108-03-2	25	90	
2-Nitropropane	79-46-9	25	90	
N-Nitrosodimethylamine; see 1910.1016.				
Nitrotoluene (all isomers)		5	30	X
o-isomer	88-72-2			
m-isomer	99-08-1			
p-isomer	99-99-0			
Nitrotrichloromethane; see Chloropicrin.				
Octachloronaphthalene	2234-13-1		0.1	X
Octane	111-65-9	500	2350	
Oil mist, mineral	8012-95-1		5	
Osmium tetroxide (as Os)	20816-12-0		0.002	
Oxalic acid	144-62-7		1	
Oxygen difluoride	7783-41-7	0.05	0.1	
Ozone	10028-15-6	0.1	0.2	
Paraquat, respirable dust	4685-14-7; 1910-42-5; 2074-50-2		0.5	X
Parathion	56-38-2		0.1	X
Particulates not otherwise regulated (PNOR)[f].				
Total dust			15	
Respirable fraction			5	
PCB; see Chlorodiphenyl (42% and 54% chlorine).				
Pentaborane	19624-22-7	0.005	0.01	
Pentachloronaphthalene	1321-64-8		0.5	X
Pentachlorophenol	87-86-5		0.5	X
Pentaerythritol	115-77-5			
Total dust			15	
Respirable fraction			5	
Pentane	109-66-0	1000	2950	
2-Pentanone (Methyl propyl ketone)	107-87-9	200	700	
Perchloroethylene (Tetrachloroethylene).	127-18-4		(²)	
Perchloromethyl mercaptan	594-42-3	0.1	0.8	
Perchloryl fluoride	7616-94-6	3	13.5	
Perlite	93763-70-3			
Total dust			15	
Respirable fraction			5	

Occupational Safety and Health Admin., Labor § 1910.1000

TABLE Z–1.—LIMITS FOR AIR CONTAMINANTS—Continued

Substance	CAS No. (c)	ppm (a) [1]	mg/m³ (b) [1]	Skin designation
Petroleum distillates (Naphtha) (Rubber Solvent).		500	2000	
Phenol	108–95–2	5	19	X
p-Phenylene diamine	106–50–3		0.1	X
Phenyl ether, vapor	101–84–8	1	7	
Phenyl ether-biphenyl mixture, vapor		1	7	
Phenylethylene; see Styrene.				
Phenyl glycidyl ether (PGE)	122–60–1	10	60	
Phenylhydrazine	100–63–0	5	22	X
Phosdrin (Mevinphos)	7786–34–7		0.1	X
Phosgene (Carbonyl chloride)	75–44–5	0.1	0.4	
Phosphine	7803–51–2	0.3	0.4	
Phosphoric acid	7664–38–2		1	
Phosphorus (yellow)	7723–14–0		0.1	
Phosphorus pentachloride	10026–13–8		1	
Phosphorus pentasulfide	1314–80–3		1	
Phosphorus trichloride	7719–12–2	0.5	3	
Phthalic anhydride	85–44–9	2	12	
Picloram	1918–02–1			
Total dust			15	
Respirable fraction			5	
Picric acid	88–89–1		0.1	X
Pindone (2-Pivalyl-1,3-indandione)	83–26–1		0.1	
Plaster of Paris	26499–65–0			
Total dust			15	
Respirable fraction			5	
Platinum (as Pt)	7440–06–4			
Metal				
Soluble salts			0.002	
Portland cement	65997–15–1			
Total dust			15	
Respirable fraction			5	
Propane	74–98–6	1000	1800	
beta-Propriolactone; see 1910.1013	57–57–8			
n-Propyl acetate	109–60–4	200	840	
n-Propyl alcohol	71–23–8	200	500	
n-Propyl nitrate	627–13–4	25	110	
Propylene dichloride	78–87–5	75	350	
Propylene imine	75–55–8	2	5	X
Propylene oxide	75–56–9	100	240	
Propyne; see Methyl acetylene.				
Pyrethrum	8003–34–7		5	
Pyridine	110–86–1	5	15	
Quinone	106–51–4	0.1	0.4	
RDX; see Cyclonite.				
Rhodium (as Rh), metal fume and insoluble compounds.	7440–16–6		0.1	
Rhodium (as Rh), soluble compounds	7440–16–6		0.001	
Ronnel	299–84–3		15	
Rotenone	83–79–4		5	
Rouge				
Total dust			15	
Respirable fraction			5	
Selenium compounds (as Se)	7782–49–2		0.2	
Selenium hexafluoride (as Se)	7783–79–1	0.05	0.4	
Silica, amorphous, precipitated and gel	112926–00–8		(3)	
Silica, amorphous, diatomaceous earth, containing less than 1% crystalline silica.	61790–53–2		(3)	
Silica, crystalline cristobalite, respirable dust.	14464–46–1		(3)	
Silica, crystalline quartz, respirable dust.	14808–60–7		(3)	
Silica, crystalline tripoli (as quartz), respirable dust.	1317–95–9		(3)	
Silica, crystalline tridymite, respirable dust.	15468–32–3		(3)	
Silica, fused, respirable dust	60676–86–0		(3)	
Silicates (less than 1% crystalline silica).				
Mica (respirable dust)	12001–26–2		(3)	
Soapstone, total dust			(3)	

15

§ 1910.1000   **29 CFR Ch. XVII (7-1-94 Edition)**

TABLE Z–1.—LIMITS FOR AIR CONTAMINANTS—Continued

Substance	CAS No. (c)	ppm (a)[1]	mg/m³ (b)[1]	Skin designation
Soapstone, respirable dust	....		(3)	
Talc (containing asbestos); use asbestos limit; see 29 CFR 1910.1001.	....		(3)	
Talc (containing no asbestos), respirable dust.	14807–96–6		(3)	
Tremolite, asbestiform; see 1910.1001.				
Silicon	7440–21–3			
Total dust		....	15	
Respirable fraction		....	5	
Silicon carbide	409–21–2			
Total dust		....	15	
Respirable fraction		....	5	
Silver, metal and soluble compounds (as Ag).	7440–22–4	....	0.01	
Soapstone; see Silicates.				
Sodium fluoroacetate	62–74–8		0.05	X
Sodium hydroxide	1310–73–2	....	2	
Starch	9005–25–8			
Total dust		....	15	
Respirable fraction		....	5	
Stibine	7803–52–3	0.1	0.5	
Stoddard solvent	8052–41–3	500	2900	
Strychnine	57–24–9		0.15	
Styrene	100–42–5		(2)	
Sucrose	57–50–1			
Total dust		....	15	
Respirable fraction		....	5	
Sulfur dioxide	7446–09–5	5	13	
Sulfur hexafluoride	2551–62–4	1000	6000	
Sulfuric acid	7664–93–9	....	1	
Sulfur monochloride	10025–67–9	1	6	
Sulfur pentafluoride	5714–22–7	0.025	0.25	
Sulfuryl fluoride	2699–79–8	5	20	
Systox; see Demeton.				
2,4,5–T (2,4,5-trichlorophenoxyacetic acid).	93–76–5	....	10	
Talc; see Silicates.				
Tantalum, metal and oxide dust	7440–25–7		5	
TEDP (Sulfotep)	3689–24–5	....	0.2	X
Tellurium and compounds (as Te)	13494–80–9	....	0.1	
Tellurium hexafluoride (as Te)	7783–80–4	0.02	0.2	
Temephos	3383–96–8			
Total dust		....	15	
Respirable fraction		....	5	
TEPP (Tetraethyl pyrophosphate)	107–49–3	....	0.05	X
Terphenyls	26140–60–3	(C)1	(C)9	
1,1,1,2-Tetrachloro-2,2-difluoroethane .	76–11–9	500	4170	
1,1,2,2-Tetrachloro-1,2-difluoroethane .	76–12–0	500	4170	
1,1,2,2-Tetrachloroethane	79–34–5	5	35	X
Tetrachloroethylene; see Perchloroethylene.				
Tetrachloromethane; see Carbon tetrachloride.				
Tetrachloronaphthalene	1335–88–2		2	X
Tetraethyl lead (as Pb)	78–00–2	....	0.075	X
Tetrahydrofuran	109–99–9	200	590	
Tetramethyl lead (as Pb)	75–74–1		0.075	X
Tetramethyl succinonitrile	3333–52–6	0.5	3	X
Tetranitromethane	509–14–8	1	8	
Tetryl (2,4,6-Trinitrophenylmethylnitramine).	479–45–8		1.5	X
Thallium, soluble compounds (as Tl) ...	7440–28–0	....	0.1	X
4,4′-Thiobis (6-tert, Butyl-m-cresol)	96–69–5			
Total dust		....	15	
Respirable fraction		....	5	
Thiram	137–26–8		5	
Tin, inorganic compounds (except oxides) (as Sn).	7440–31–5		2	
Tin, organic compounds (as Sn)	7440–31–5	....	0.1	
Titanium dioxide	13463–67–7			

Occupational Safety and Health Admin., Labor §1910.1000

TABLE Z–1.—LIMITS FOR AIR CONTAMINANTS—Continued

Substance	CAS No. (c)	ppm (a) [1]	mg/m³ (b) [1]	Skin designation
Total dust			15	
Toluene	108–88–3		[2]	
Toluene-2,4-diisocyanate (TDI)	584–84–9	(C)0.02	(C)0.14	
o-Toluidine	95–53–4	5	22	X
Toxaphene; see Chlorinated camphene.				
Tremolite; see Silicates.				
Tributyl phosphate	126–73–8		5	
1,1,1-Trichloroethane; see Methyl chloroform.				
1,1,2-Trichloroethane	79–00–5	10	45	X
Trichloroethylene	79–01–6		[2]	
Trichloromethane; see Chloroform.				
Trichloronaphthalene	1321–65–9		5	X
1,2,3-Trichloropropane	96–18–4	50	300	
1,1,2-Trichloro-1,2,2-trifluoroethane	76–13–1	1000	7600	
Triethylamine	121–44–8	25	100	
Trifluorobromomethane	75–63–8	1000	6100	
2,4,6-Trinitrophenyl; see Picric acid.				
2,4,6-Trinitrophenylmethylnitramine; see Tetryl.				
2,4,6-Trinitrotoluene (TNT)	118–96–7		1.5	X
Triorthocresyl phosphate	78–30–8		0.1	
Triphenyl phosphate	115–86–6		3	
Turpentine	8006–64–2	100	560	
Uranium (as U)	7440–61–1			
Soluble compounds			0.05	
Insoluble compounds			0.05	
Vanadium	1314–62–1			
Respirable dust (as V₂O₅)			(C)0.5	
Fume (as V₂O₅)			(C)0.1	
Vegetable oil mist				
Total dust			15	
Respirable fraction			5	
Vinyl benzene; see Styrene.				
Vinyl chloride; see 1910.1017	75–01–4			
Vinyl cyanide; see Acrylonitrile.				
Vinyl toluene	25013–15–4	100	480	
Warfarin	81–81–2		0.1	
Xylenes (o-, m-, p-isomers)	1330–20–7	100	435	
Xylidine	1300–73–8	5	25	X
Yttrium	7440–65–5		1	
Zinc chloride fume	7646–85–7		1	
Zinc oxide fume	1314–13–2		5	
Zinc oxide	1314–13–2			
Total dust			15	
Respirable fraction			5	
Zinc stearate	557–05–1			
Total dust			15	
Respirable fraction			5	
Zirconium compounds (as Zr)	7440–67–7		5	

[1] The PELs are 8-hour TWAs unless otherwise noted; a (C) designation denotes a ceiling limit. They are to be determined from breathing-zone air samples.

(a) Parts of vapor or gas per million parts of contaminated air by volume at 25 °C and 760 torr.

(b) Milligrams of substance per cubic meter of air. When entry is in this column only, the value is exact; when listed with a ppm entry, it is approximate.

(c) The CAS number is for information only. Enforcement is based on the substance name. For an entry covering more than one metal compound, measured as the metal, the CAS number for the metal is given—not CAS numbers for the individual compounds.

(d) The final benzene standard in 1910.1028 applies to all occupational exposures to benzene except in some circumstances the distribution and sale of fuels, sealed containers and pipelines, coke production, oil and gas drilling and production, natural gas processing, and the percentage exclusion for liquid mixtures; for the excepted subsegments, the benzene limits in Table Z–2 apply. See 1910.1028 for specific circumstances.

(e) This 8-hour TWA applies to respirable dust as measured by a vertical elutriator cotton dust sampler or equivalent instrument. The time-weighted average applies to the cottom waste processing operations of waste recycling (sorting, blending, cleaning and willowing) and garnetting. See also 1910.1043 for cotton dust limits applicable to other sectors.

(f) All inert or nuisance dusts, whether mineral, inorganic, or organic, not listed specifically by substance name are covered by the Particulates Not Otherwise Regulated (PNOR) limit which is the same as the inert or nuisance dust limit of Table Z–3.

[2] See Table Z–2.

[3] See Table Z–3.

[4] Varies with compound.

§ 1910.1000

TABLE Z-2

Substance	8-hour time weighted average	Acceptable ceiling concentration	Acceptable maximum peak above the acceptable ceiling concentration for an 8-hr shift	
			Concentration	Maximum duration
Benzene[a] (Z37.40–1969)	10 ppm	25 ppm	50 ppm	10 minutes.
Beryllium and beryllium compounds (Z37.29–1970)	2 µg/m³	5 µg/m³	25 µg/m³	30 minutes.
Cadmium fume[b] (Z37.5–1970)	0.1 mg/m³	0.3 mg/m³		
Cadmium dust[b] (Z37.5–1970)	0.2 mg/m³	0.6 mg/m³.		
Carbon disulfide (Z37.3–1968)	20 ppm	30 ppm	100 ppm	30 minutes.
Carbon tetrachloride (Z37.17–1967)	10 ppm	25 ppm	200 ppm	5 min. in any 4 hrs.
Chromic acid and chromates (Z37.7–1971)		1 mg/10m³.		
Ethylene dibromide (Z37.31–1970)	20 ppm	30 ppm	50 ppm	5 minutes.
Ethylene dichloride (Z37.21–1969)	50 ppm	100 ppm	200 ppm	3 min. in any 3 hrs.
Fluoride as dust (Z37.28–1969)	2.5 mg/m³			
Formaldehyde; see 1910.1048				
Hydrogen fluoride (Z37.28–1969)	3 ppm			
Hydrogen sulfide (Z37.2–1966)		20 ppm	50 ppm	10 mins. once, only if no other meas. exp. occurs.
Mercury (Z37.8–1971)		1 mg/10m³		
Methyl chloride (Z37.18–1969)	100 ppm	200 ppm	300 ppm	5 mins. in any 3 hrs.
Methylene chloride (Z37.23–1969)	500 ppm	1,000 ppm	2,000 ppm	5 mins. in any 2 hrs.
Organo (alkyl) mercury (Z37.30–1969)	0.01 mg/m³	0.04 mg/m³		
Styrene (Z37.15–1969)	100 ppm	200 ppm	600 ppm	5 mins. in any 3 hrs.
Tetrachloroethylene (Z37.22–1967)	100 ppm	200 ppm	300 ppm	5 mins. in any 3 hrs
Toluene (Z37.12–1967)	200 ppm	300 ppm	500 ppm	10 minutes.
Trichloroethylene (Z37.19–1967)	100 ppm	200 ppm	300 ppm	5 mins. in any 2 hrs.

[a] This standard applies to the industry segments exempt from the 1 ppm 8-hour TWA and 5 ppm STEL of the benzene standard at 1910.1028.
[b] This standard applies to any operations or sectors for which the Cadmium standard, 1910.1027, is stayed or otherwise not in effect.

TABLE Z-3 MINERAL DUSTS

Substance	mppcf [a]	mg/m³
Silica:		
Crystalline		
Quartz (Respirable)	$\dfrac{250 \text{ [b]}}{\%SiO_2+5}$	$\dfrac{10 \text{ mg/m}^3 \text{ [c]}}{\% SiO_2 + 2}$
Quartz (Total Dust)		$\dfrac{30 \text{ mg/m}^3}{\% SiO_2 + 2}$
Cristobalite: Use ½ the value calculated from the count or mass formulae for quartz		
Tridymite: Use ½ the value calculated from the formulae for quartz		
Amorphous, including natural diatomaceous earth	20	$\dfrac{80 \text{ mg/m}^3}{\%SiO_2}$
Silicates (less than 1% crystalline silica):		
Mica	20	
Soapstone	20	
Talc (not containing asbestos)	20 [c]	
Talc (containing asbestos) Use asbestos limit.		

Occupational Safety and Health Admin., Labor §1910.1001

TABLE Z–3 MINERAL DUSTS—Continued

Substance	mppcf [a]	mg/m³
Tremolite, asbestiform (see 29 CFR 1910.1001). Portland cement	50	
Graphite (Natural)	15	
Coal Dust:		
Respirable fraction less than 5% SiO_2	....	2.4 mg/m³ [e]
		$\%SiO_2+2$
Respirable fraction greater than 5% SiO_2	....	10 mg/m³ [e]
		$\%SiO_2+2$
Inert or Nuisance Dust: [d]		
Respirable fraction	15	5 mg/m³
Total dust	50	15 mg/m³

Note—Conversion factors - mppcf X 35.3 = million particles per cubic meter = particles per c.c.

[a] Millions of particles per cubic foot of air, based on impinger samples counted by light-field techniques.

[b] The percentage of crystalline silica in the formula is the amount determined from airborne samples, except in those instances in which other methods have been shown to be applicable.

[c] Containing less than 1% quartz; if 1% quartz or more, use quartz limit.

[d] All inert or nuisance dusts, whether mineral, inorganic, or organic, not listed specifically by substance name are covered by this limit, which is the same as the Particulates Not Otherwise Regulated (PNOR) limit in Table Z–1.

[e] Both concentration and percent quartz for the application of this limit are to be determined from the fraction passing a size-selector with the following characteristics:

Aerodynamic diameter (unit density sphere)	Percent passing selector
2	90
2.5	75
3.5	50
5.0	25
10	0

The measurements under this note refer to the use of an AEC (now NRC) instrument. The respirable fraction of coal dust is determined with an MRE; the figure corresponding to that of 2.4 mg/m³ in the table for coal dust is 4.5 mg/m³K.

[58 FR 35340, June 30. 1993; 58 FR 40191, July 27, 1993]

§1910.1001 Asbestos.

(a) *Scope and application.* (1) This section applies to all occupational exposures to asbestos in all industries covered by the Occupational Safety and Health Act, except as provided in paragraph (a)(2) of this section.

(2) This section does not apply to construction work as defined in 29 CFR 1910.12(b). [Exposure to asbestos in construction work is covered by 29 CFR 1926.58.]

(b) *Definitions.* Action level means an airborne concentration of asbestos, of 0.1 fiber per cubic centimeter (f/cc) of air calculated as an eight (8)—hour time-weighted average.

Asbestos includes chrysotile, amosite, crocidolite, tremolite asbestos, anthophyllite asbestos, actinolite asbestos, and any of these minerals that have been chemically treated and/or altered.

Assistant Secretary means the Assistant Secretary of Labor for Occupational Safety and Health, U.S. Department of Labor, or designee.

Authorized person means any person authorized by the employer and required by work duties to be present in regulated areas.

Director means the Director of the National Institute for Occupational Safety and Health, U.S. Department of

Health and Human Services, or designee.

Employee exposure means that exposure to airborne asbestos that would occur if the employee were not using respiratory protective equipment.

Fiber means a particulate form of asbestos, 5 micrometers or longer, with a length-to-diameter ratio of at least 3 to 1.

High-efficiency particulate air (HEPA) filter means a filter capable of trapping and retaining at least 99.97 percent of 0.3 micrometer diameter mono-disperse particles.

Regulated area means an area established by the employer to demarcate areas where airborne concentrations of asbestos exceed, or can reasonably be expected to exceed, the permissible exposure limit.

(c) *Permissible exposure limits (PELS)*— (1) *Time-weighted average limit (TWA)*. The employer shall ensure that no employee is exposed to an airborne concentration of asbestos in excess of 0.2 fiber per cubic centimeter of air as an eight (8)-hour time-weighted average (TWA) as determined by the method prescribed in Appendix A of this section, or by an equivalent method.

(2) *Excursion limit*. The employer shall ensure that no employee is exposed to an airborne concentration of asbestos in excess of 1.0 fiber per cubic centimeter of air (1 f/cc) as averaged over a sampling period of thirty (30) minutes.

(d) *Exposure monitoring*—(1) *General.* (i) Determinations of employee exposure shall be made from breathing zone air samples that are representative of the 8-hour TWA and 30-minute short-term exposures of each employee.

(ii) Representative 8-hour TWA employee exposures shall be determined on the basis of one or more samples representing full-shift exposures for each shift for each employee in each job classification in each work area. Representative 30-minute short-term employee exposures shall be determined on the basis of one or more samples representing 30 minute exposures associated with operations that are most likely to produce exposures above the excursion limit for each shift for each job classification in each work area.

(2) *Initial monitoring.* (i) Each employer who has a workplace or work operation covered by this standard, except as provided for in paragraphs (d)(2)(ii) and (d)(2)(iii) of this section, shall perform initial monitoring of employees who are, or may reasonably be expected to be exposed to airborne concentrations at or above the action level and/or excursion limit.

(ii) Where the employer has monitored after December 20, 1985, for the TWA and after March 14, 1988, for the excursion limit, and the monitoring satisfies all other requirements of this section, the employer may rely on such earlier monitoring results to satisfy the requirements of paragraph (d)(2)(i) of this section.

(iii) Where the employer has relied upon objective data that demonstrates that asbestos is not capable of being released in airborne concentrations at or above the action level and/or excursion limit under the expected conditions of processing, use, or handling, then no initial monitoring is required.

(3) *Monitoring frequency (periodic monitoring) and patterns.* After the initial determinations required by paragraph (d)(2)(i) of this section, samples shall be of such frequency and pattern as to represent with reasonable accuracy the levels of exposure of the employees. In no case shall sampling be at intervals greater than six months for employees whose exposures may reasonably be foreseen to exceed the action level and/or excursion limit.

(4) *Changes in monitoring frequency.* If either the initial or the periodic monitoring required by paragraphs (d)(2) and (d)(3) of this section statistically indicates that employee exposures are below the action level and/or excursion limit, the employer may discontinue the monitoring for those employees whose exposures are represented by such monitoring.

(5) *Additional monitoring.* Notwithstanding the provisions of paragraphs (d)(2)(ii) and (d)(4) of this section, the employer shall institute the exposure monitoring required under paragraphs (d)(2)(i) and (d)(3) of this section whenever there has been a change in the production, process, control equipment, personnel or work practices that may result in new or additional expo-

sures above the action level and/or excursion limit or when the employer has any reason to suspect that a change may result in new or additional exposures above the action level and/or excursion limit.

(6) *Method of monitoring.* (i) All samples taken to satisfy the monitoring requirements of paragraph (d) shall be personal samples collected following the procedures specified in Appendix A.

(ii) All samples taken to satisfy the monitoring requirements of paragraph (d) shall be evaluated using the OSHA Reference Method (ORM) specified in Appendix A of this section, or an equivalent counting method.

(iii) If an equivalent method to the ORM is used, the employer shall ensure that the method meets the following criteria:

(A) Replicate exposure data used to establish equivalency are collected in side-by-side field and laboratory comparisons; and

(B) The comparison indicates that 90% of the samples collected in the range 0.5 to 2.0 times the permissible limit have an accuracy range of plus or minus 25 percent of the ORM results with a 95% confidence level as demonstrated by a statistically valid protocol; and

(C) The equivalent method is documented and the results of the comparison testing are maintained.

(iv) To satisfy the monitoring requirements of paragraph (d) of this section, employers must use the results of monitoring analysis performed by laboratories which have instituted quality assurance programs that include the elements as prescribed in Appendix A.

(7) *Employee notification of monitoring results.* (i) The employer shall, within 15 working days after the receipt of the results of any monitoring performed under the standard, notify the affected employees of these results in writing either either individually or by posting of results in an appropriate location that is accessible to affected employees.

(ii) The written notification required by paragraph (d)(7)(i) of this section shall contain the corrective action being taken by the employer to reduce employee exposure to or below the TWA and/or excursion limit, wherever

monitoring results indicated that the TWA and/or excursion limit had been exceeded.

(e) *Regulated Areas*—(1) *Establishment.* The employer shall establish regulated areas wherever airborne concentrations of asbestos are in excess of the .TWA and/or excursion limit prescribed in paragraph (c) of this section.

(2) *Demarcation.* Regulated areas shall be demarcated from the rest of the workplace in any manner that minimizes the number of persons who will be exposed to asbestos.

(3) *Access.* Access to regulated areas shall be limited to authorized persons or to persons authorized by the Act or regulations issued pursuant thereto.

(4) *Provision of respirators.* Each person entering a regulated area shall be supplied with and required to use a respirator, selected in accordance with paragraph (g)(2) of this section.

(5) *Prohibited activities.* The employer shall ensure that employees do not eat, drink, smoke, chew tobacco or gum, or apply cosmetics in the regulated areas.

(f) *Methods of compliance*—(1) *Engineering controls and work practices.* (i) The employer shall institute engineering controls and work practices to reduce and maintain employee exposure to or below the TWA and/or excursion limit, prescribed in paragraph (c) of this section, except to the extent that such controls are not feasible.

(ii) Wherever the feasible engineering controls and work practices that can be instituted are not sufficient to reduce employee exposure to or below the TWA and/or excursion limit prescribed in paragraph (c) of this section, the employer shall use them to reduce employee exposure to the lowest levels achievable by these controls and shall supplement them by the use of respiratory protection that complies with the requirements of paragraph (g) of this section.

(iii) For the following operations, wherever feasible engineering controls and work practices that can be instituted are not sufficient to reduce the employee exposure to or below the TWA and/or excursion limit, prescribed in paragraph (c) of this section, the employer shall use them to reduce employee exposure to or below 0.5 fiber per cubic centimeter of air (as an eight-hour time-weighted average) or 2.5 fibers/cc for 30 minutes (short-term exposure) and shall supplement them by the use of any combination of respiratory protection that complies with the requirements of paragraph (g) of this section, work practices and feasible engineering controls that will reduce employee exposure to or below the TWA and to or below the excursion limit prescribed in paragraph (c) of this section: Coupling cutoff in primary asbestos cement pipe manufacturing; sanding in primary and secondary asbestos cement sheet manufacturing; grinding in primary and secondary friction product manufacturing; carding and spinning in dry textile processes; and grinding and sanding in primary plastics manufacturing.

(iv) *Local exhaust ventilation.* Local exhaust ventilation and dust collection systems shall be designed, constructed, installed, and maintained in accordance with good practices such as those found in the American National Standard Fundamentals Governing the Design and Operation of Local Exhaust Systems, ANSI Z9.2–1979

(v) *Particular tools.* All hand-operated and power-operated tools which would produce or release fibers of asbestos so as to expose employees to levels in excess of the TWA and/or excursion limit prescribed in paragraph (c) of this section, such as, but not limited to saws, scorers, abrasive wheels, and drills, shall be provided with local exhaust ventilation systems which comply with paragraph (f)(1)(iv) of this section.

(vi) *Wet methods.* Insofar as practicable, asbestos shall be handled, mixed, applied, removed, cut, scored, or otherwise worked in a wet state sufficient to prevent the emission of airborne fibers so as to expose employees to levels in excess of the TWA and/or excursion limit, prescribed in paragraph (c) of this section, unless the usefulness of the product would be diminished thereby.

(vii) [Reserved]

(viii) *Particular products and operations.* No asbestos cement, mortar, coating, grout, plaster, or similar material containing asbestos shall be removed from bags, cartons, or other containers in which they are shipped, without being either wetted, or en-

closed, or ventilated so as to prevent effectively the release of airborne fibers of asbestos so as to expose employees to levels in excess of the TWA and/or excursion limit prescribed in paragraph (c) of this section.

(ix) *Compressed air.* Compressed air shall not be used to remove asbestos or materials containing asbestos, unless the compressed air is used in conjunction with a ventilation system designed to capture the dust cloud created by the compressed air.

(2) *Compliance program.* (i) Where the TWA and/or excursion limit is exceeded, the employer shall establish and implement a written program to reduce employee exposure to or below the TWA and to or below the excursion limit by means of engineering and work practice controls as required by paragraph (f)(1) of this section, and by the use of respiratory protection where required or permitted under this section.

(ii) Such programs shall be reviewed and updated as necessary to reflect significant changes in the status of the employer's compliance program.

(iii) Written programs shall be submitted upon request for examination and copying to the Assistant Secretary, the Director, affected employees and designated employee representatives.

(iv) The employer shall not use employee rotation as a means of compliance with the TWA and/or excursion limit.

(g) *Respiratory protection—*(1) *General.* The employer shall provide respirators, and ensure that they are used, where required by this section. Respirators shall be used in the following circumstances:

(i) During the interval necessary to install or implement feasible engineering and work practice controls;

(ii) In work operations, such as maintenance and repair activities, or other activities for which engineering and work practice controls are not feasible;

(iii) In work situations where feasible engineering and work practice controls are not yet sufficient to reduce exposure to or below the TWA and/or excursion limit; and

(iv) In emergencies.

Occupational Safety and Health Admin., Labor   **§1910.1001**

(2) *Respirator selection.* (i) Where respirators are required under this section, the employer shall select and provide, at no cost to the employee, the appropriate respirator as specified in Table 1. The employer shall select respirators from among those jointly approved as being acceptable for protection by the Mine Safety and Health Administration (MSHA) and by the National Institute for Occupational Safety and Health (NIOSH) under the provisions of 30 CFR Part 11.

(ii) The employer shall provide a powered, air-purifying respirator in lieu of any negative pressure respirator specified in Table 1 whenever:

(A) An employee chooses to use this type of respirator; and

(B) This respirator will provide adequate protection to the employee.

TABLE 1—RESPIRATORY PROTECTION FOR ASBESTOS FIBERS

Airborne concentration of asbestos	Required respirator
Not in excess of 2 f/cc (10 X PEL).	1. Half-mask air-purifying respirator, other than a disposable respirator, equipped with high-efficiency filters.
Not in excess of 10 f/cc (50 X PEL).	1. Full facepiece air-purifying respirator equipped with high-efficiency filters.
Not in excess of 20 f/cc (100 X PEL).	1. Any powered air-purifying respirator equipped with high-efficiency filters. 2. Any supplied-air respirator operated in continuous flow mode.
Not in excess of 200 f/cc (1000 X PEL).	1. Full facepiece supplied-air respirator operated in pressure demand mode.
Greater than 200 f/cc (> 1,000 X PEL) or unknown concentration.	1. Full facepiece supplied air respirator operated in pressure demand mode equipped with an auxiliary positive pressure self-contained breathing apparatus.

NOTE: a. Respirators assigned for higher environmental concentrations may be used at lower concentrations.
b. A high-efficiency filter means a filter that is at least 99.97 percent efficient against mono-dispersed particles of 0.3 micrometers or larger.

(3) *Respirator program.* (i) Where respiratory protection is required, the employer shall institute a respirator program in accordance with 29 CFR 1910.134(b), (d), (e), and (f).

(ii) The employer shall permit each employee who uses a filter respirator to change the filter elements whenever an increase in breathing resistance is detected and shall maintain an adequate supply of filter elements for this purpose.

(iii) Employees who wear respirators shall, be permitted to leave the regulated area to wash their faces and res-

pirator facepieces whenever necessary to prevent skin irritation associated with respirator use.

(iv) No employee shall be assigned to tasks requiring the use of respirators if, based upon his or her most recent examination, an examining physician determines that the employee will be unable to function normally wearing a respirator, or that the safety or health of the employee or other employees will be impaired by the use of a respirator. Such employee shall be assigned to another job or given the opportunity to transfer to a different position whose duties he or she is able to perform with the same employer, in the same geographical area and with the same seniority, status, and rate of pay the employee had just prior to such transfer, if such a different position is available.

(4) *Respirator fit testing.* (i) The employer shall ensure that the respirator issued to the employee exhibits the least possible facepiece leakage and that the respirator is fitted properly.

(ii) For each employee wearing negative pressure respirators, employers shall perform either quantitative or qualitative face fit tests at the time of initial fitting and at least every six months thereafter. The qualitative fit tests may be used only for testing the fit of half-mask respirators where they are permitted to be worn, and shall be conducted in accordance with Appendix C. The tests shall be used to select facepieces that provide the required protection as prescribed in Table I.

(h) *Protective work clothing and equipment*—(1) *Provision and use.* If an employee is exposed to asbestos above the TWA and/or excursion limit, or where the possibility of eye irritation exists, the employer shall provide at no cost to the employee and ensure that the employee uses appropriate work clothing and equipment such as, but not limited to:

(i) **Coveralls** or similar full-body work clothing;

(ii) **Gloves** head coverings, and foot coverings; and

(iii) **Face** shields, vented goggles, or other appropriate protective equipment which complies with §1910.133 of this Part.

(2) *Removal and storage.* (i) The employer shall ensure that employees remove work clothing contaminated with asbestos only in change rooms provided in accordance with paragraph (i)(1) of this section.

(ii) The employer shall ensure that no employee takes contaminated work clothing out of the change room, except those employees authorized to do so for the purpose of laundering, maintenance, or disposal.

(iii) Contaminated work clothing shall be placed and stored in closed containers which prevent dispersion of the asbestos outside the container.

(iv) Containers of contaminated protective devices or work clothing which are to be taken out of change rooms or the workplace for cleaning, maintenance or disposal, shall bear labels in accordance with paragraph (j)(2) of this section.

(3) *Cleaning and replacement.* (i) The employer shall clean, launder, repair, or replace protective clothing and equipment required by this paragraph to maintain their effectiveness. The employer shall provide clean protective clothing and equipment at least weekly to each affected employee.

(ii) The employer shall prohibit the removal of asbestos from protective clothing and equipment by blowing or shaking.

(iii) Laundering of contaminated clothing shall be done so as to prevent the release of airborne fibers of asbestos in excess of the permissible exposure limits prescribed in paragraph (c) of this section.

(iv) Any employer who gives contaminated clothing to another person for laundering shall inform such person of the requirement in paragraph (h)(3)(iii) of this section to effectively prevent the release of asbestos in excess of the permissible exposure limits.

(v) The employer shall inform any person who launders or cleans protective clothing or equipment contaminated with asbestos of the potentially harmful effects of exposure to asbestos.

(vi) Contaminated clothing shall be transported in sealed impermeable bags, or other closed, impermeable containers, and labeled in accordance with paragraph (j) of this seciton.

(i) *Hygiene facilities and practices*—(1) *Change rooms.* (i) The employer shall provide clean change rooms for employees who work in areas where their airborne exposure to asbestos is above the TWA and/or excursion limit.

(ii) The employer shall ensure that change rooms are in accordance with § 1910.141(e) of this part, and are equipped with two separate lockers or storage facilities, so separated as to prevent contamination of the employee's street clothes from his protective work clothing and equipment.

(2) *Showers.* (i) The employer shall ensure that employees who work in areas where their airborne exposure is above the TWA and/or excursion limit shower at the end of the work shift.

(ii) The employer shall provide shower facilities which comply with § 1910.141(d)(3) of this part.

(iii) The employer shall ensure that employees who are required to shower pursuant to paragraph (i)(2)(i) of this section do not leave the workplace wearing any clothing or equipment worn during the work shift.

(3) *Lunchrooms.* (i) The employer shall provide lunchroom facilities for employees who work in areas where their airborne exposure is above the TWA and/or excursion limit.

(ii) The employer shall ensure that lunchroom facilities have a positive pressure, filtered air supply, and are readily accessible to employees.

(iii) The employer shall ensure that employees who work in areas where their airborne exposure is above the TWA and/or excursion limit wash their hands and faces prior to eating, drinking or smoking.

(iv) The employer shall ensure that employees do not enter lunchroom facilities with protective work clothing or equipment unless surface asbestos fibers have been removed from the clothing or equipment by vacuuming or other method that removes dust without causing the asbestos to become airborne.

(4) *Smoking in work areas.* The employer shall ensure that employees do not smoke in work areas where they are occupationally exposed to asbestos because of activities in that work area.

(j) *Communication of hazards to employees*—(1) *Warning signs.* (i) Posting.

Warning signs shall be provided and displayed at each regulated area. In addition, warning signs shall be posted at all approaches to regulated areas so that an employee may read the signs and take necessary protective steps before entering the area.

(ii) Sign specifications. The warning signs required by paragraph (j)(1)(i) of this section shall bear the following information:

DANGER
ASBESTOS
CANCER AND LUNG DISEASE HAZARD
AUTHORIZED PERSONNEL ONLY
RESPIRATORS AND PROTECTIVE CLOTHING
ARE REQUIRED IN THIS AREA

(iii) [Reserved]

(iv) The employer shall ensure that employees working in and contiguous to regulated areas comprehend the warning signs required to be posted by paragraph (j)(1)(i) of this section. Means to ensure employee comprehension may include the use of foreign languages, pictographs and graphics.

(2) *Warning labels.* (i) Labeling. Warning labels shall be affixed to all raw materials, mixtures, scrap, waste, debris, and other products containing asbestos fibers, or to their containers.

(ii) Label specifications. The labels shall comply with the requirements of 29 CFR 1910.1200(f) of OSHA's Hazard Communication standard, and shall include the following information:

DANGER
CONTAINS ASBESTOS FIBERS
AVOID CREATING DUST
CANCER AND LUNG DISEASE HAZARD

(3) *Material safety data sheets.* Employers who are manufacturers or importers of asbestos or asbestos products shall comply with the requirements regarding development of material safety data sheets as specified in 29 CFR 1910.1200(g) of OSHA's Hazard Communication standard, except as provided by paragraph (j)(4) of this section.

(4) The provisions for labels required by paragraph (j)(2) or for material safety data sheets required by paragraph (j)(3) do not apply where:

(i) Asbestos fibers have been modified by a bonding agent, coating, binder, or other material provided that the manufacturer can demonstrate that during any reasonably foreseeable use, handling, storage, disposal, processing, or transportation, no airborne concentrations of fibers of asbestos in excess of the action level and/or excursion limit will be released or

(ii) Asbestos is present in a product in concentrations less than 0.1%.

(5) *Employee information and training.* (i) The employer shall institute a training program for all employees who are exposed to airborne concentrations of asbestos at or above the action level and/or excursion limit and ensure their participation in the program.

(ii) Training shall be provided prior to or at the time of initial assignment and at least annually thereafter.

(iii) The training program shall be conducted in a manner which the employee is able to understand. The employer shall ensure that each employee is informed of the following:

(A) The health effects associated with asbestos exposure;

(B) The relationship between smoking and exposure to asbestos in producing lung cancer:

(C) The quantity, location, manner of use, release, and storage of asbestos, and the specfic nature of operations which could result in exposure to asbestos;

(D) The engineering controls and work practices associated with the employee's job assignment;

(E) The specific procedures implemented to protect employees from exposure to asbestos, such as appropriate work practices, emergency and cleanup procedures, and personal protective equipment to be used;

(F) The purpose, proper use, and limitations of respirators and protective clothing;

(G) The purpose and a description of the medical surveillance program required by paragraph (l) of this section;

(H) The content of this standard, including appendices.

(I) The names, addresses and phone numbers of public health organizations which provide information, materials, and/or conduct programs concerning smoking cessation. The employer may distribute the list of such organizations contained in Appendix I, to comply with this requirement.

(J) The requirements for posting signs and affixing labels and the meaning of the required legends for such signs and labels.

(iv) Access to information and training materials.

(A) The employer shall make a copy of this standard and its appendices readily available without cost to all affected employees.

(B) The employer shall provide, upon request, all materials relating to the employee information and training program to the Assistant Secretary and the training program to the Assistant Secretary and the Director.

(C) The employer shall inform all employees concerning the availability of self-help smoking cessation program material. Upon employee request, the employer shall distribute such material, consisting of NIH Publication No. 89–1647, or equivalent self-help material, which is approved or published by a public health organization listed in appendix I.

(k) *Housekeeping.* (1) All surfaces shall be maintained as free as practicable of accumulations of dusts and waste containing asbestos.

(2) All spills and sudden releases of material containing asbestos shall be cleaned up as soon as possible.

(3) Surfaces contaminated with asbestos may not be cleaned by the use of compressed air.

(4) Vacuuming. HEPA-filtered vacuuming equipment shall be used for vacuuming. The equipment shall be used and emptied in a manner which minimizes the reentry of asbestos into the workplace.

(5) Shoveling, dry sweeping and dry clean-up of asbestos may be used only where vacuuming and/or wet cleaning are not feasible.

(6) Waste disposal. Waste, scrap, debris, bags, containers, equipment, and clothing contaminated with asbestos consigned for disposal, shall be collected and disposed of in sealed impermeable bags, or other closed, impermeable containers.

(l) *Medical surveillance*—(1) *General.* (i) The employer shall institute a medical surveillance program for all employees who are or will be exposed to airborne concentrations of asbestos at or above the action level and/or excursion limit.

(ii) *Examination by a physician.* (A) The employer shall ensure that all medical examinations and procedures are performed by or under the supervision of a licensed physician, and shall be provided without cost to the employee and at a reasonable time and place.

(B) Persons other than licensed physicians, who administer the pulmonary function testing required by this section, shall complete a training course in spirometry sponsored by an appropriate academic or professional institution.

(2) *Preplacement examinations.* (i) Before an employee is assigned to an occupation exposed to airborne concentrations of asbestos fibers, a preplacement medical examination shall be provided or made available by the employer.

(ii) Such examination shall include, as a minimum, a medical and work history; a complete physical examination of all systems with emphasis on the respiratory system, the cardiovascular system and digestive tract; completion of the respiratory disease standardized questionnaire in Appendix D, Part 1, a chest roentgenogram (posterior-anterior 14x17 inches); pulmonary function tests to include forced vital capacity (FVC) and forced expiratory volume at 1 second ($FEV_{1.0}$); and any additional tests deemed appropriate by the examining physician. Interpretation and classification of chest roentgenograms shall be conducted in accordance with Appendix E.

(3) *Periodic examinations.* (i) Periodic medical examinations shall be made available annually.

(ii) The scope of the medical examination shall be in conformance with the protocol established in paragraph (l)(2)(ii) of this section, except that the frequency of chest roentgenograms shall be conducted in accordance with Table 2, and the abbreviated standardized questionnaire contained in Appendix D, Part 2, shall be administered to the employee.

Occupational Safety and Health Admin., Labor   **§ 1910.1001**

TABLE 2—FREQUENCY OF CHEST ROENTGENOGRAMS

Years since first exposure	Age of employee		
	15 to 35	35+ to 45	45+
0 to 10	Every 5 years	Every 5 years	Every 5 years.
10+	Every 5 years	Every 2 years	Every 1 year.

(4) *Termination of employment examinations.* (i) The employer shall provide, or make available, a termination of employment medical examination for any employee who has been exposed to airborne concentrations of fibers of asbestos at or above the action level and/or excursion limit.

(ii) The medical examination shall be in accordance with the requirements of the periodic examinations stipulated in paragraph (1)(3) of this section, and shall be given within 30 calendar days before or after the date of termination of employment.

(5) *Recent examinations.* No medical examination is required of any employee, if adequate records show that the employee has been examined in accordance with any of the preceding paragraphs [(1)(2)–(1)(4)] within the past 1 year period.

(6) *Information provided to the physician.* The employer shall provide the following information to the examining physician:

(i) A copy of this standard and Appendices D and E.

(ii) A description of the affected employee's duties as they relate to the employee's exposure.

(iii) The employee's representative exposure level or anticipated exposure level.

(iv) A description of any personal protective and respiratory equipment used or to be used.

(v) Information from previous medical examinations of the affected employee that is not otherwise available to the examining physician.

(7) *Physician's written opinion.* (i) The employer shall obtain a written signed opinion from the examining physician. This written opinion shall contain the results of the medical examination and shall include:

(A) The physician's opinion as to whether the employee has any detected medical conditions that would place the employee at an increased risk of

material health impairment from exposure to asbestos;

(B) Any recommended limitations on the employee or upon the use of personal protective equipment such as clothing or respirators; and

(C) A statement that the employee has been informed by the physician of the results of the medical examination and of any medical conditions resulting from asbestos exposure that require further explanation or treatment.

(D) A statement that the employee has been informed by the physician of the increased risk of lung cancer attributable to the combined effect of smoking and asbestos exposure.

(ii) The employer shall instruct the physician not to reveal in the written opinion given to the employer specific findings or diagnoses unrelated to occupational exposure to asbestos.

(iii) The employer shall provide a copy of the physician's written opinion to the affected employee within 30 days from its receipt.

(m) *Recordkeeping—(1) Exposure measurements.* (i) The employer shall keep an accurate record of all measurements taken to monitor employee exposure to asbestos as prescribed in paragraph (d) of this section.

(ii) This record shall include at least the following information:

(A) The date of measurement;

(B) The operation involving exposure to asbestos which is being monitored;

(C) Sampling and analytical methods used and evidence of their accuracy;

(D) Number, duration, and results of samples taken;

(E) Type of respiratory protective devices worn, if any; and

(F) Name, social security number and exposure of the employees whose exposure are represented.

(iii) The employer shall maintain this record for at least thirty (30) years, in accordance with 29 CFR 1910.20.

(2) *Objective data for exempted operations.* (i) Where the processing, use, or handling of products made from or containing asbestos is exempted from other requirements of this section under paragraph (d)(2)(iii) of this section, the employer shall establish and maintain an accurate record of objective data reasonably relied upon in support of the exemption.

(ii) The record shall include at least the following:

(A) The product qualifying for exemption;

(B) The source of the objective data;

(C) The testing protocol, results of testing, and/or analysis of the material for the release of asbestos;

(D) A description of the operation exempted and how the data support the exemption; and

(E) Other data relevant to the operations, materials, processing, or employee exposures covered by the exemption.

(iii) The employer shall maintain this record for the duration of the employer's reliance upon such objective data.

NOTE: The employer may utilize the services of competent organizations such as industry trade associations and employee associations to maintain the records required by this section.

(3) *Medical surveillance.* (1) The employer shall establish and maintain an accurate record for each employee subject to medical surveillance by paragraph (l)(1)(i) of this section, in accordance with 29 CFR 1910.20.

(ii) The record shall include at least the following information:

(A) The name and social security number of the employee;

(B) Physician's written opinions;

(C) Any employee medical complaints related to exposure to asbestos; and

(D) A copy of the information provided to the physician as required by paragraph (l)(6) of this section.

(iii) The employer shall ensure that this record is maintained for the duration of employment plus thirty (30) years, in accordance with 29 CFR 1910.20.

(4) *Training.* The employer shall maintain all employee training records

for one (1) year beyond the last date of employment of that employee.

(5) *Availability.* (i) The employer, upon written request, shall make all records required to be maintained by this section available to the Assistant Secretary and the Director for examination and copying.

(ii) The employer, upon request shall make any exposure records required by paragraph (m)(1) of this section available for examination and copying to affected employees, former employees, designated representatives and the Assistant Secretary, in accordance with 29 CFR 1910.20 (a)–(e) and (g)–(i).

(iii) The employer, upon request, shall make employee medical records required by paragraph (m)(2) of this section available for examination and copying to the subject employee, to anyone having the specific written consent of the subject employee, and the Assistant Secretary, in accordance with 29 CFR 1910.20.

(6) *Transfer of records.* (i) The employer shall comply with the requirements concerning transfer of records set forth in 29 CFR 1910.20(h).

(ii) Whenever the employer ceases to do business and there is no successor employer to receive and retain the records for the prescribed period, the employer shall notify the Director at least 90 days prior to disposal of records and, upon request, transmit them to the Director.

(n) *Observation of monitoring*—(1) *Employee observation.* The employer shall provide affected employees or their designated representatives an opportunity to observe any monitoring of employee exposure to asbestos conducted in accordance with paragraph (d) of this section.

(2) *Observation procedures.* When observation of the monitoring of employee exposure to asbestos requires entry into an area where the use of protective clothing or equipment is required, the observer shall be provided with and be required to use such clothing and equipment and shall comply with all other applicable safety and health procedures.

(o) *Dates*—(1) *Effective date.* This standard shall become effective July 21, 1986. The requirements in the amended paragraphs in this section which pertain only to or are triggered by the excursion limit shall become effective October 14, 1988,

(2) *Start-up dates.* All obligations of this standard commence on the effective date except as follows:

(i) *Exposure monitoring.* Initial monitoring required by paragraph (d)(2) of this section shall be completed as soon as possible but no later than October 20, 1986.

(ii) *Regulated areas.* Regulated areas required to be established by paragraph (e) of this section as a result of initial monitoring shall be set up as soon as possible after the results of that monitoring are known and not later than November 17, 1986.

(iii) *Respiratory protection.* Respiratory protection required by paragraph (g) of this section shall be provided as soon as possible but no later than the following schedule:

(A) Employees whose 8-hour TWA exposure exceeds 2 fibers/cc—July 21, 1986.

(B) Employees whose 8-hour TWA exposure exceeds the PEL but is less than 2 fibers/cc—November 17, 1986.

(C) Powered air-purifying respirators provided under paragraph (g)(2)(ii)—January 16, 1987.

(iv) *Hygiene and lunchroom facilities.* Construction plans for changerooms, showers, lavatories, and lunchroom facilities shall be completed no later than January 16, 1987; and these facilities shall be constructed and in use no later than July 20, 1987. However, if as part of the compliance plan it is predicted by an independent engineering firm that engineering controls and work practices will reduce exposures below the permissible exposure limit by July 20, 1988, for affected employees, then such facilities need not be completed until 1 year after the engineering controls are completed, if such controls have not in fact succeeded in reducing exposure to below the permissible exposure limit.

(v) *Employee information and training.* Employee information and training required by paragraph (j)(5) of this section shall be provided as soon as possible but no later than October 20, 1986.

(vi) *Medical surveillance.* Medical examinations required by paragraph (l) of this section shall be provided as soon

as possible but no later than November 17, 1986.

(vii) *Compliance program.* Written compliance programs required by paragraph (f)(2) of this section as a result of initial monitoring shall be completed and available for inspection and copying as soon as possible but no later than July 20, 1987.

(viii) *Methods of compliance.* The engineering and work practice controls as required by paragraph (f)(1) shall be implemented as soon as possible but no later than July 20, 1988.

(3) *Start-up dates for excursion limit.* Compliance with the excursion limit requirements in this section shall be as follows:

(i) Paragraphs (c), (d), (e), (g), (h), (j), (k), (l), (m) of this section, shall be complied with by December 13, 1988.

(ii) Paragraph (f) of this section, shall be complied with by March 13, 1989.

(iii) Paragraph (i) of this section, shall be complied with by September 14, 1989.

(4) *Compliance date.* The requirements of paragraphs (i)(4), (j)(l)(iv), (j)(5)(iii)(I), (j)(5)(iii)(J), (j)(5)(iv)(C), and (l)(7)(i)(D) shall be complied with by May 7, 1990.

(p) *Appedices.* (1) Appendices A, C, D, and E to this section are incorporated as part of this section and the contents of these Appendices are mandatory.

(2) Appendices B, F, G, H, and I to this section are informational and are not intended to create any additional obligation not otherwise imposed or to detract from any existing obligation.

APPENDIX A TO § 1910.1001—OSHA REFERENCE METHOD—MANDATORY

This mandatory appendix specifies the procedure for analyzing air samples for asbestos and specifies quality control procedures that must be implemented by laboratories performing the analysis. The sampling and analytical methods described below represent the elements of the available monitoring methods (such as the NIOSH 7400 method) which OSHA considers to be essential to achieve adequate employee exposure monitoring while allowing employers to use methods that are already established within their organizations. All employers who are required to conduct air monitoring under paragraph (d) of the standard are required to utilize analytical laboratories that use this procedure, or an equivalent method, for collecting and analyzing samples.

Sampling and Analytical Procedure

1. The sampling medium for air samples shall be mixed cellulose ester filter membranes. These shall be designated by the manufacturer as suitable for asbestos counting. See below for rejection of blanks.

2. The preferred collection device shall be the 25-mm diameter cassette with an open-faced 50-mm electrically conductive extension cowl. The 37-mm cassette may be used if necessary but only if written justification for the need to use the 37-mm filter cassette accompanies the sample results in the employee's exposure monitoring record.

3. An air flow rate between 0.5 liter/min and 2.5 liters/min shall be selected for the 25-mm cassette. If the 37-mm cassette is used, an air flow rate between 1 liter/min and 2.5 liters/min shall be selected.

4. Where possible, a sufficient air volume for each air sample shall be collected to yield between 100 and 1,300 fibers per square millimeter on the membrane filter. If a filter darkens in appearance or if loose dust is seen on the filter, a second sample shall be started.

5. Ship the samples in a rigid container with sufficient packing material to prevent dislodging the collected fibers. Packing material that has a high electrostatic charge on its surface (e.g., expanded polystyrene) cannot be used because such material can cause loss of fibers to the sides of the cassette.

6. Calibrate each personal sampling pump before and after use with a representative filter cassette installed between the pump and the calibration devices.

7. Personal samples shall be taken in the "breathing zone" of the employee (i.e., attached to or near the collar or lapel near the worker's face).

8. Fiber counts shall be made by positive phase contrast using a microscope with an 8 to 10 X eyepiece and a 40 to 45 X objective for a total magnification of approximately 400 X and a numerical aperture of 0.65 to 0.75. The microscope shall also be fitted with a green or blue filter.

9. The microscope shall be fitted with a Walton-Beckett eyepiece graticule calibrated for a field diameter of 100 micrometers (+/−2 micrometers).

10. The phase-shift detection limit of the microscope shall be about 3 degrees measured using the HSE phase shift test slide as outlined below.

a. Place the test slide on the microscope stage and center it under the phase objective.

b. Bring the blocks of grooved lines into focus.

NOTE: The slide consists of seven sets of grooved lines (ca. 20 grooves to each block) in descending order of visibility from sets 1

to 7, seven being the least visible. The requirements for asbestos counting are that the microscope optics must resolve the grooved lines in set 3 completely, although they may appear somewhat faint, and that the grooved lines in sets 6 and 7 must be invisible. Sets 4 and 5 must be at least partially visible but may vary slightly in visibility between microscopes. A microscope that fails to meet these requirements has either too low or too high a resolution to be used for asbestos counting.

c. If the image deteriorates, clean and adjust the microscope optics. If the problem persists, consult the microscope manufacturer.

11. Each set of samples taken will include 10 percent blanks or a minimum of 2 blanks. The blank results shall be averaged and subtracted from the analytical results before reporting. Any samples represented by a blank having a fiber count in excess of 7 fibers/100 fields shall be rejected.

12. The samples shall be mounted by the acetone/triacetin method or a method with an equivalent index of refraction and similar clarity.

13. Observe the following counting rules.

a. Count only fibers equal to or longer than 5 micrometers. Measure the length of curved fibers along the curve.

b. In the absence of other information, count all particles as asbestos that have a length-to-width ratio (aspect ratio) of 3:1 or greater.

c. Fibers lying entirely within the boundary of the Walton-Beckett graticule field shall receive a count of 1. Fibers crossing the boundary once, having one end within the circle, shall receive the count of one half (½). Do not count any fiber that crosses the graticule boundary more than once. Reject and do not count any other fibers even though they may be visible outside the graticule area.

d. Count bundles of fibers as one fiber unless individual fibers can be identified by observing both ends of an individual fiber.

e. Count enough graticule fields to yield 100 fibers. Count a minimum of 20 fields; stop counting at 100 fields regardless of fiber count.

14. Blind recounts shall be conducted at the rate of 10 percent.

Quality Control Procedures

1. Intralaboratory program. Each laboratory and/or each company with more than one microscopist counting slides shall establish a statistically designed quality assurance program involving blind recounts and comparisons between microscopists to monitor the variability of counting by each microscopist and between microscopists. In a company with more than one laboratory, the program shall include all laboratories and

shall also evaluate the laboratory-to-laboratory variability.

2. Interlaboratory program. Each laboratory analyzing asbestos samples for compliance determination shall implement an interlaboratory quality assurance program that as a minimum includes participation of at least two other independent laboratories. Each laboratory shall participate in round robin testing at least once every 6 months with at least all the other laboratories in its interlaboratory quality assurance group. Each laboratory shall submit slides typical of its own work load for use in this program. The round robin shall be designed and results analyzed using appropriate statistical methodology.

3. All individuals performing asbestos analysis must have taken the NIOSH course for sampling and evaluating airborne asbestos dust or an equalivalent course.

4. When the use of different microscopes contributes to differences between counters and laboratories, the effect of the different microscope shall be evaluated and the microscope shall be replaced, as necessary.

5. Current results of these quality assurance programs shall be posted in each laboratory to keep the microscopists informed.

APPENDIX B TO §1910.1001—DETAILED PROCEDURE FOR ASBESTOS SAMPLING AND ANALYSIS—NON-MANDATORY

This appendix contains a detailed procedure for sampling and analysis and includes those critical elements specified in Appendix A. Employers are not required to use this procedure, but they are required to use Appendix A. The purpose of Appendix B is to provide a detailed step-by-step sampling and analysis procedure that conforms to the elements specified in Appendix A. Since this procedure may also standardize the analysis and reduce variability, OSHA encourages employers to use this appendix.

Asbestos Sampling and Analysis Method

Technique: Microscopy, Phase Contrast
Analyte: Fibers (manual count)
Sample Preparation: Acetone/triacetin method
Calibration: Phase-shift detection limit about 3 degrees
Range: 100 to 1300 fibers/mm² filter area
Estimated limit of detection: 7 fibers/mm² filter area
Sampler: Filter (0.8–1.2 um mixed cellulose ester membrane, 25-mm diameter)
Flow rate: 0.5 L/min to 2.5 L/min (25-mm cassette) 1.0 L/min to 2.5 L/min (37-mm cassette)
Sample volume: Adjust to obtain 100 to 1300 fibers/mm²
Shipment: Routine
Sample stability: Indefinite
Blanks: 10% of samples (minimum 2)

Standard analytical error: 0.25.

Applicability: The working range is 0.02 f/cc (1920–L air sample) to 1.25 f/cc (400–L air sample). The method gives an index of airborne asbestos fibers but may be used for other materials such as fibrous glass by inserting suitable parameters into the counting rules. The method does not differentiate between asbestos and other fibers. Asbestos fibers less than ca. 0.25 um diameter will not be detected by this method.

Interferences: Any other airborne fiber may interfere since all particles meeting the counting criteria are counted. Chainlike particles may appear fibrous. High levels of nonfibrous dust particles may obscure fibers in the field of view and raise the detection limit.

Reagents: 1. Acetone. 2. Triacetin (glycerol triacetate), reagent grade

Special precautions: Acetone is an extremely flammable liquid and precautions must be taken not to ignite it. Heating of acetone must be done in a ventilated laboratory fume hood using a flameless, spark-free heat source.

Equipment: 1. Collection device: 25-mm cassette with 50-mm electrically conductive extension cowl with cellulose ester filter, 0.8 to 1.2 mm pore size and backup pad.

NOTE: Analyze representative filters for fiber background before use and discard the filter lot if more than 5 fibers/100 fields are found.

2. Personal sampling pump, greater than or equal to 0.5 L/min. with flexible connecting tubing.

3. Microscope, phase contrast, with green or blue filter, 8 to 10X eyepiece, and 40 to 45X phase objective (total magnification ca 400X; numerical aperture = 0.65 to 0.75.

4. Slides, glass, single-frosted, pre-cleaned, 25 x 75 mm.

5. Cover slips, 25 x 25 mm, no. 1½ unless otherwise specified by microscope manufacturer.

6. Knife, No. 1 surgical steel, curved blade.

7. Tweezers.

8. Flask, Guth-type, insulated neck, 250 to 500 mL (with single-holed rubber stopper and elbow-jointed glass tubing, 16 to 22 cm long).

9. Hotplate, spark-free, stirring type; heating mantle; or infrared lamp and magnetic stirrer.

10. Syringe, hypodermic, with 22-gauge needle.

11. Graticule, Walton-Beckett type with 100 um diameter circular field at the specimen plane (area = 0.00785 mm²). (Type G–22).

NOTE: the graticule is custom-made for each microscope.

12. HSE/NPL phase contrast test slide, Mark II.

13. Telescope, ocular phase-ring centering.

14. Stage micrometer (0.01 mm divisions).

Sampling

1. Calibrate each personal sampling pump with a representative sampler in line.

2. Fasten the sampler to the worker's lapel as close as possible to the worker's mouth. Remove the top cover from the end of the cowl extension (open face) and orient face down. Wrap the joint between the extender and the monitor's body with shrink tape to prevent air leaks.

3. Submit at least two blanks (or 10% of the total samples, whichever is greater) for each set of samples. Remove the caps from the field blank cassettes and store the caps and cassettes in a clean area (bag or box) during the sampling period. Replace the caps in the cassettes when sampling is completed.

4. Sample at 0.5 L/min or greater. Do not exceed 1 mg total dust loading on the filter. Adjust sampling flow rate, Q (L/min), and time to produce a fiber density, E (fibers/mm^2), of 100 to 1300 fibers/m^2 [3.85x10^4 to 5x10^5 fibers per 25-mm filter with effective collection area (A$_c$=385 mm^2)] for optimum counting precision (see step 21 below). Calculate the minimum sampling time, t$_{minimum}$ (min) at the action level (one-half of the current standard), L (f/cc) of the fibrous aerosol being sampled:

$$t_{minimum} = \frac{(Ac)(E)}{(Q)(L)10^3}$$

5. Remove the field monitor at the end of sampling, replace the plastic top cover and small end caps, and store the monitor.

6. Ship the samples in a rigid container with sufficient packing material to prevent jostling or damage.

NOTE: Do not use polystyrene foam in the shipping container because of electrostatic forces which may cause fiber loss from the sample filter.

Sample Preparation

NOTE: The object is to produce samples with a smooth (non-grainy) background in a medium with a refractive index equal to or less than 1.46. The method below collapses the filter for easier focusing and produces permanent mounts which are useful for quality control and interlaboratory comparison. Other mounting techniques meeting the above criteria may also be used, e.g., the nonpermanent field mounting technique used in P & CAM 239.

7. Ensure that the glass slides and cover slips are free of dust and fibers.

8. Place 40 to 60 ml of acetone into a Guth-type flask. Stopper the flask with a single-hole rubber stopper through which a glass tube extends 5 to 8 cm into the flask. The portion of the glass tube that exits the top of the stopper (8 to 10 cm) is bent downward in an elbow that makes an angle of 20 to 30 degrees with the horizontal.

9. Place the flask in a stirring hotplate or wrap in a heating mantle. Heat the acetone gradually to its boiling temperature (ca. 58 °C).

CAUTION.—The acetone vapor must be generated in a ventilated fume hood away from all open flames and spark sources. Alternate heating methods can be used, providing no open flame or sparks are present.

10. Mount either the whole sample filter or a wedge cut from the sample filter on a clean glass slide.

a. Cut wedges of ca. 25 percent of the filter area with a curved-blade steel surgical knife using a rocking motion to prevent tearing.

b. Place the filter or wedge, dust side up, on the slide. Static electricity will usually keep the filter on the slide until it is cleared.

c. Hold the glass slide supporting the filter approximately 1 to 2 cm from the glass tube port where the acetone vapor is escaping from the heated flask. The acetone vapor stream should cause a condensation spot on the glass slide ca. 2 to 3 cm in diameter. Move the glass slide gently in the vapor stream. The filter should clear in 2 to 5 sec. If the filter curls, distorts, or is otherwise rendered unusable, the vapor stream is probably not strong enough. Periodically wipe the outlet port with tissue to prevent liquid acetone dripping onto the filter.

d. Using the hypodermic syringe with a 22-gauge needle, place 1 to 2 drops of triacetin on the filter. Gently lower a clean 25-mm square cover slip down onto the filter at a slight angle to reduce the possibility of forming bubbles. If too many bubbles form or the amount of triacetin is insufficient, the cover slip may become detached within a few hours.

e. Glue the edges of the cover slip to the glass slide using a lacquer or nail polish.

NOTE: If clearing is slow, the slide preparation may be heated on a hotplate (surface temperature 50 °C) for 15 min to hasten clearing. Counting may proceed immediately after clearing and mounting are completed.

Calibration and Quality Control

11. Calibration of the Walton-Beckett graticule. The diameter, d$_c$(mm), of the circular counting area and the disc diameter must be specified when ordering the graticule.

a. Insert any available graticule into the eyepiece and focus so that the graticule lines are sharp and clear.

b. Set the appropriate interpupillary distance and, if applicable, reset the binocular head adjustment so that the magnification remains constant.

c. Install the 40 to 45X phase objective.

d. Place a stage micrometer on the microscope object stage and focus the microscope on the graduated lines.

Occupational Safety and Health Admin., Labor   **§ 1910.1001, App. B**

e. Measure the magnified grid length, L_o(mm), using the stage micrometer.

f. Remove the graticule from the microscope and measure its actual grid length, L_a(mm). This can best be accomplished by using a stage fitted with verniers.

g. Calculate the circle diameter, d_c(mm), for the Walton-Beckett graticule:

$$d_c = \frac{L_a \times D}{L_o}$$

EXAMPLE.—If L_o = 108 um, L_a = 2.93 mm and D = 100 um, then d_c = 2.71 mm.

h. Check the field diameter, D(acceptable range 100 mm ± 2 mm) with a stage micrometer upon receipt of the graticule from the manufacturer. Determine field area (mm²).

12. Microscope adjustments. Follow the manufacturer's instructions and also the following:

a. Adjust the light source for even illumination across the field of view at the condenser iris.

NOTE: Kohler illumination is preferred, where available.

b. Focus on the particulate material to be examined.

c. Make sure that the field iris is in focus, centered on the sample, and open only enough to fully illuminate the field of view.

d. Use the telescope ocular supplied by the manufacturer to ensure that the phase rings (annular diaphragm and phase-shifting elements) are concentric.

13. Check the phase-shift detection limit of the microscope periodically.

a. Remove the HSE/NPL phase-contrast test slide from its shipping container and center it under the phase objective.

b. Bring the blocks of grooved lines into focus.

NOTE: The slide consists of seven sets of grooves (ca. 20 grooves to each block) in descending order of visibility from sets 1 to 7. The requirements for counting are that the microscope optics must resolve the grooved lines in set 3 completely, although they may appear somewhat faint, and that the grooved lines in sets 6 to 7 be invisible. Sets 4 and 5 must be at least partially visible but may vary slightly in visibility between microscopes. A microscope which fails to meet these requirements has either too low or too high a resolution to be used for asbestos counting.

c. If the image quality deteriorates, clean the microscope optics and, if the problem persists, consult the microscope manufacturer.

14. Quality control of fiber counts.

a. Prepare and count field blanks along with the field samples. Report the counts on each blank. Calculate the mean of the field blank counts and subtract this value from each sample count before reporting the results.

NOTE 1: The identity of the blank filters should be unknown to the counter until all counts have been completed.

NOTE 2: If a field blank yields fiber counts greater than 7 fibers/100 fields, report possible contamination of the samples.

b. Perform blind recounts by the same counter on 10 percent of filters counted (slides relabeled by a person other than the counter).

15. Use the following test to determine whether a pair of counts on the same filter should be rejected because of possible bias. This statistic estimates the counting repeatability at the 95% confidence level. Discard the sample if the difference between the two counts exceeds $2.77(F)s_r$, where F=average of the two fiber counts and s_r=relative standard deviation, which should be derived by each laboratory based on historical in-house data.

NOTE: If a pair of counts is rejected as a result of this test, recount the remaining samples in the set and test the new counts against the first counts. Discard all rejected paired counts.

16. Enroll each new counter in a training course that compares performance of counters on a variety of samples using this procedure.

NOTE: To ensure good reproducibility, all laboratories engaged in asbestos counting are required to participate in the Proficiency Analytical Testing (PAT) Program and should routinely participate with other asbestos fiber counting laboratories in the exchange of field samples to compare performance of counters.

Measurement

17. Place the slide on the mechanical stage of the calibrated microscope with the center of the filter under the objective lens. Focus the microscope on the plane of the filter.

18. Regularly check phase-ring alignment and Kohler illumination.

19. The following are the counting rules:

a. Count only fibers longer than 5 um. Measure the length of curved fibers along the curve.

b. Count only fibers with a length-to-width ratio equal to or greater than 3:1.

c. For fibers that cross the boundary of the graticule field, do the following:

1. Count any fiber longer tha 5 um that lies entirely within the graticule area.

2. Count as ½ fiber any fiber with only one end lying within the graticule area.

3. Do not count any fiber that crosses the graticule boundary more than once.

4. Reject and do not count all other fibers.

d. Count bundles of fibers as one fiber unless individual fibers can be identified by observing both ends of a fiber.

e. Count enough graticule fields to yield 100 fibers. Count a minimum of 20 fields. Stop at 100 fields regardless of fiber count.

20. Start counting from one end of the filter and progress along a radial line to the other end, shift either up or down on the filter, and continue in the reverse direction. Select fields randomly by looking away from the eyepiece briefly while advancing the mechanical stage. When an agglomerate covers ca. ⅛ or more of the field of view, reject the field and select another. Do not report rejected fields in the number of total fields counted.

NOTE: When counting a field, continuously scan a range of focal planes by moving the fine focus knob to detect very fine fibers which have become embedded in the filter. The small-diameter fibers will be very faint but are an important contribution to the total count.

Calculations

21. Calculate and report fiber density on the filter, E (fibers/mm^2); by dividing the total fiber count, F; minus the mean field blank count, B, by the number of fields, n; and the field area, A_f (0.00785 mm^2 for a properly calibrated Walton-Beckett graticule):

$$E = \frac{(F/n_f - (B/n_b))}{A_f} \quad \text{fibers/} \atop mm^2$$

where:
n_f=number of fields in submission sample
n_b=number of fields in blank sample

22. Calculate the concentration, C (f/cc), of fibers in the air volume sampled, V (L), using the effective collection area of the filter, A_c (385 mm^2 for a 25-mm filter):

$$C = \frac{(E)(Ac)}{V(10^3)} \text{*COM001*}$$

NOTE: Periodically check and adjust the value of A_c, if necessary.

APPENDIX C TO § 1910.1001—QUALITATIVE AND QUANTITATIVE FIT TESTING PROCEDURES— MANDATORY

QUALITATIVE FIT TEST PROTOCOLS

I. Isoamyl Acetate Protocol.

A. Odor Threshold Screening

1. Three 1-liter glass jars with metal lids (e.g. Mason or Bell jars) are required.

2. Odor-free water (e.g. distilled or spring water) at approximately 25°C shall be used for the solutions.

3. The isoamyl acetate (IAA) (also known as isopentyl acetate) stock solution is prepared by adding 1 cc of pure IAA to 800 cc of odor free water in a 1-liter jar and shaking for 30 seconds. This solution shall be prepared new at least weekly.

4. The screening test shall be conducted in a room separate from the room used for actual fit testing. The two rooms shall be well ventilated but shall not be connected to the same recirculating ventilation system.

5. The odor test solution is prepared in a second jar by placing 0.4 cc of the stock solution into 500 cc of odor free water using a clean dropper or pipette. Shake for 30 seconds and allow to stand for two to three minutes so that the IAA concentration above the liquid may reach equilibrium. This solution may be used for only one day.

6. A test blank is prepared in a third jar by adding 500 cc of odor free water.

7. The odor test and test blank jars shall be labelled 1 and 2 for jar identification. If the labels are put on the lids they can be periodically peeled, dried off and switched to maintain the integrity of the test.

8. The following instructions shall be typed on a card and placed on the table in front of the two test jars (i.e. 1 and 2): "The purpose of this test is to determine if you can smell banana oil at a low concentration. The two bottles in front of you contain water. One of these bottles also contains a small amount of banana oil. Be sure the covers are on tight, then shake each bottle for two seconds. Unscrew the lid of each bottle, one at a time, and sniff at the mouth of the bottle. Indicate to the test conductor which bottle contains banana oil."

9. The mixtures used in the IAA odor detection test shall be prepared in an area separate from where the test is performed, in order to prevent olfactory fatigue in the subject.

10. If the test subject is unable to correctly identify the jar containing the odor test solution, the IAA qualitative fit test may not be used.

11. If the test subject correctly identifies the jar containing the odor test solution, the test subject may proceed to respirator selection and fit testing.

B. Respirator Selection

1. The test subject shall be allowed to pick the most comfortable respirator from a selection including respirators of various sizes from different manufacturers. The selection shall include at least five sizes of elastomeric half facepieces, from at least two manufacturers.

2. The selection process shall be conducted in a room separate from the fit-test chamber to prevent odor fatigue. Prior to the selection process, the test subject shall be shown how to put on a respirator, how it should be positioned on the face, how to set strap tension and how to determine a "comfortable" respirator. A mirror shall be available to as-

Occupational Safety and Health Admin., Labor   **§ 1910.1001, App. C**

sist the subject in evaluating the fit and positioning of the respirator. This instruction may not constitute the subject's formal training on respirator use, as it is only a review.

3. The test subject should understand that the employee is being asked to select the respirator which provides the most comfortable fit. Each respirator represents a different size and shape and, if fit properly and used properly will provide adequate protection.

4. The test subject holds each facepiece up to the face and eliminates those which obviously do not give a comfortable fit. Normally, selection will begin with a half-mask and if a good fit cannot be found, the subject will be asked to test the full facepiece respirators. (A small percentage of users will not be able to wear any half-mask.)

5. The more comfortable facepieces are noted; the most comfortable mask is donned and *worn at least five minutes* to assess comfort. All donning and adjustments of the facepiece shall be performed by the test subject without assistance from the test conductor or other person. Assistance in assessing comfort can be given by discussing the points in #6 below. If the test subject is not familiar with using a particular respirator, the test subject shall be directed to don the mask several times and to adjust the straps each time to become adept at setting proper tension on the straps.

6. Assessment of comfort shall include reviewing the following points with the test subject and allowing the test subject adequate time to determine the comfort of the respirator:
- Positioning of mask on nose.
- Room for eye protection.
- Room to talk.
- Positioning mask on face and cheeks.

7. The following criteria shall be used to help determine the adequacy of the respirator fit:
- Chin properly placed.
- Strap tension.
- Fit across nose bridge.
- Distance from nose to chin.
- Tendency to slip.
- Self-observation in mirror.

8. The test subject shall conduct the conventional negative and positive-pressure fit checks (e.g. see ANSI Z88.2–1980). Before conducting the negative- or positive-pressure test the subject shall be told to "seat" the mask by rapidly moving the head from side-to-side and up and down, while taking a few deep breaths.

9. The test subject is now ready for fit testing.

10. After passing the fit test, the test subject shall be questioned again regarding the comfort of the respirator. If it has become uncomfortable, another model of respirator shall be tried.

11. The employee shall be given the opportunity to select a different facepiece and be retested if the chosen facepiece becomes increasingly uncomfortable at any time.

C. Fit Test

1. The fit test chamber shall be similar to a clear 55 gal drum liner suspended inverted over a 2 foot diameter frame, so that the top of the chamber is about 6 inches above the test subject's head. The inside top center of the chamber shall have a small hook attached.

2. Each respirator used for the fitting and fit testing shall be equipped with organic vapor cartridges or offer protection against organic vapors. The cartridges or masks shall be changed at least weekly.

3. After selecting, donning, and properly adjusting a respirator, the test subject shall wear it to the fit testing room. This room shall be separate from the room used for odor threshold screening and respirator selection, and shall be well ventilated, as by an exhaust fan or lab hood, to prevent general room contamination.

4. A copy of the following test exercises and rainbow passage shall be taped to the inside of the test chamber:

Test Exercises

i. Breathe normally.

ii. Breathe deeply. Be certain breaths are *deep* and *regular*.

iii. Turn head all the way from one side to the other. Inhale on each side. Be certain movement is complete. Do not bump the respirator against the shoulders.

iv. Nod head up-and-down. Inhale when head is in the full up position (looking toward ceiling). Be certain motions are complete and made about every second. Do not bump the respirator on the chest.

v. Talking. Talk aloud and slowly for several minutes. The following paragraph is called the Rainbow Passage. Reading it will result in a wide range of facial movements, and thus be useful to satisfy this requirement. Alternative passages which serve the same purpose may also be used.

vi. Jogging in place.

vii. Breathe normally.

Rainbow Passage

When the sunlight strikes raindrops in the air, they act like a prism and form a rainbow. The rainbow is a division of white light into many beautiful colors. These take the shape of a long round arch, with its path high above, and its two ends apparently beyond the horizon. There is, according to legend, a boiling pot of gold at one end. People look but no one ever finds it. When a man looks for something beyond reach, his friends say he is looking for the pot of gold at the end of the rainbow.

5. Each test subject shall wear the respirator for at least 10 minutes before starting the fit test.

6. Upon entering the test chamber, the test subject shall be given a 6 inch by 5 inch piece of paper towel or other porous absorbent single ply material, folded in half and wetted with three-quarters of one cc of pure IAA. The test subject shall hang the wet towel on the hook at the top of the chamber.

7. Allow two minutes for the IAA test concentration to be reached before starting the fit-test exercises. This would be an appropriate time to talk with the test subject, to explain the fit test, the importance of cooperation, the purpose for the head exercises, or to demonstrate some of the exercises.

8. Each exercise described in #4 above shall be performed for at least one minute.

9. If at any time during the test, the subject detects the banana-like odor of IAA, the test has failed. The subject shall quickly exit from the test chamber and leave the test area to avoid olfactory fatigue.

10. If the test is failed, the subject shall return to the selection room and remove the respirator, repeat the odor sensitivity test, select and put on another respirator, return to the test chamber, and again begin the procedure described in the c(4) through c(8) above. The process continues until a respirator that fits well has been found. Should the odor sensitivity test be failed, the subject shall wait about 5 minutes before retesting. Odor sensitivity will usually have returned by this time.

11. If a person cannot pass the fit test described above wearing a half-mask respirator from the available selection, full facepiece models must be used.

12. When a respirator is found that passes the test, the subject breaks the faceseal and takes a breath before exiting the chamber. This is to assure that the reason the test subject is not smelling the IAA is the good fit of the respirator facepiece seal and not olfactory fatigue.

13. When the test subject leaves the chamber, the subject shall remove the saturated towel and return it to the person conducting the test. To keep the area from becoming contaminated, the used towels shall be kept in a self-sealing bag so there is no significant IAA concentration buildup in the test chamber during subsequent tests.

14. At least two facepieces shall be selected for the IAA test protocol. The test subject shall be given the opportunity to wear them for one week to choose the one which is more comfortable to wear.

15. Persons who have successfully passed this fit test with a half-mask respirator may be assigned the use of the test respirator in atmospheres with up to 10 times the PEL of airborne asbestos.

16. The test shall not be conducted if there is any hair growth between the skin the facepiece sealing surface.

17. If hair growth or apparel interfere with a satisfactory fit, then they shall be altered or removed so as to eliminate interference and allow a satisfactory fit. If a satisfactory fit is still not attained, the test subject must use a positive-pressure respirator such as powered air-purifying respirators, supplied air respirator, or self-contained breathing apparatus.

18. If a test subject exhibits difficulty in breathing during the tests, she or he shall be referred to a physician trained in respirator diseases or pulmonary medicine to determine whether the test subject can wear a respirator while performing her or his duties.

19. Qualitative fit testing shall be repeated at least every six months.

20. In addition, because the sealing of the respirator may be affected, qualitative fit testing shall be repeated immediately when the test subject has a:

(1) Weight change of 20 pounds or more,

(2) Significant facial scarring in the area of the facepiece seal,

(3) Significant dental changes; i.e., multiple extractions without prothesis, or acquiring dentures,

(4) Reconstructive or cosmetic surgery, or

(5) Any other condition that may interfere with facepiece sealing.

D. Recordkeeping

A summary of all test results shall be maintained in each office for 3 years. The summary shall include:

(1) Name of test subject.

(2) Date of testing.

(3) Name of the test conductor.

(4) Respirators selected (indicate manufacturer, model, size and approval number).

(5) Testing agent.

II. Saccharin Solution Aerosol Protocol

A. Respirator Selection

Respirators shall be selected as described in section IB (respirator selection) above, except that each respirator shall be equipped with a particulate filter.

B. Taste Threshold Screening

1. An enclosure about head and shoulders shall be used for threshold screening (to determine if the individual can taste saccharin) and for fit testing. The enclosure shall be approximately 12 inches in diameter by 14 inches tall with at least the front clear to allow free movement of the head when a respirator is worn.

2. The test enclosure shall have a three-quarter inch hole in front of the test subject's nose and mouth area to accommodate the nebulizer nozzle.

3. The entire screening and testing procedure shall be explained to the test subject prior to conducting the screening test.

4. During the threshold screening test, the test subject shall don the test enclosure and breathe with open mouth with tongue extended.

5. Using a DeVilbiss Model 40 Inhalation Medication Nebulizer or equivalent, the test conductor shall spray the threshold check solution into the enclosure. This nebulizer shall be clearly marked to distinguish it from the fit test solution nebulizer.

6. The threshold check solution consists of 0.83 grams of sodium saccharin, USP in water. It can be prepared by putting 1 cc of the test solution (see C 7 below) in 100 cc of water.

7. To produce the aerosol, the nebulizer bulb is firmly squeezed so that it collapses completely, then is released and allowed to fully expand.

8. Ten squeezes of the nebulizer bulb are repeated rapidly and then the test subject is asked whether the saccharin can be tasted.

9. If the first response is negative, ten more squeezes of the nebulizer bulb are repeated rapidly and the test subject is again asked whether the saccharin can be tasted.

10. If the second response is negative ten more squeezes are repeated rapidly and the test subject is again asked whether the saccharin can be tasted.

11. The test conductor will take note of the number of squeezes required to elicit a taste response.

12. If the saccharin is not tasted after 30 squeezes (Step 10), the saccharin fit test cannot be performed on the test subject.

13. If a taste response is elicited, the test subject shall be asked to take note of the taste for reference in the fit test.

14. Correct use of the nebulizer means that approximately 1 cc of liquid is used at a time in the nebulizer body.

15. The nebulizer shall be thoroughly rinsed in water, shaken dry, and refilled at least every four hours.

C. Fit Test

1. The test subject shall don and adjust the respirator without the assistance from any person.

2. The fit test uses the same enclosure described in IIB above.

3. Each test subject shall wear the respirator for at least 10 minutes before starting the fit test.

4. The test subject shall don the enclosure while wearing the respirator selected in section 1B above. This respirator shall be properly adjusted and equipped with a particulate filter.

5. The test subject may not eat, drink (except plain water), or chew gum for 15 minutes before the test.

6. A second DeVilbiss Model 40 Inhalation Medication Nebulizer is used to spray the fit test solution into the enclosure. This nebulizer shall be clearly marked to distinguish it from the screening test solution nebulizer.

7. The fit test solution is prepared by adding 83 grams of sodium saccharin to 100 cc of warm water.

8. As before, the test subject shall breathe with mouth open and tongue extended.

9. The nebulizer is inserted into the hole in the front of the enclosure and the fit test solution is sprayed into the enclosure using the same technique as for the taste threshold screening and the same number of squeezes required to elicit a taste response in the screening. (See B8 through B10 above).

10. After generation of the aerosol read the following instructions to the test subject. The test subject shall perform the exercises for one minute each.

i. Breathe normally.

ii. Breathe deeply. Be certain breaths are *deep* and *regular*.

iii. Turn head all the way from one side *to the other*. Be certain movement is complete. Inhale on each side. Do not bump the respirator against the shoulders.

iv. Nod head up-and-down. Be certain motions are complete. Inhale when head is in the full up position (when looking toward the ceiling). Do not bump the respirator on the chest.

v. Talking. Talk aloud and slowly for several minutes. The following paragraph is called the Rainbow Passage. Reading it will result in a wide range of facial movements, and thus be useful to satisfy this requirement. Alternative passages which serve the same purpose may also be used.

vi. Jogging in place.

vii. Breathe normally.

Rainbow Passage

When the sunlight strikes raindrops in the air, they act like a prism and form a rainbow. The rainbow is a division of white light into many beautiful colors. These take the shape of a long round arch, with its path high above, and its two ends apparently beyond the horizon. There is, according to legend, a boiling pot of gold at one end. People look, but no one ever finds it. When a man looks for something beyond his reach, his friends say he is looking for the pot of gold at the end of the rainbow.

11. At the beginning of each exercise, the aerosol concentration shall be replenished using one-half the number of squeezes as initially described in C9.

12. The test subject shall indicate to the test conductor if at any time during the fit test the taste of saccharin is detected.

13. If the saccharin is detected the fit is deemed unsatisfactory and a different respirator shall be tried.

14. At least two facepieces shall be selected by the saccharin solution aerosol test protocol. The test subject shall be given the opportunity to wear them for one week to choose the one which is more comfortable to wear.

15. Successful completion of the test protocol shall allow the use of the half mask tested respirator in contaminated atmospheres up to 10 times the PEL of asbestos. In other words this protocol may be used to assign protection factors no higher than ten.

16. The test shall not be conducted if there is any hair growth between the skin and the facepiece sealing surface.

17. If hair growth or apparel interfere with a satisfactory fit, then they shall be altered or removed so as to eliminate interference and allow a satisfactory fit. If a satisfactory fit is still not attained, the test subject must use a positive-pressure respirator such as powered air-purifying respirators, supplied air respirator, or self-contained breathing apparatus.

18. If a test subject exhibits difficulty in breathing during the tests, she or he shall be referred to a physician trained in respirator diseases or pulmonary medicine to determine whether the test subject can wear a respirator while performing her or his duties.

19. Qualitative fit testing shall be repeated at least every six months.

20. In addition, because the sealing of the respirator may be affected, qualitative fit testing shall be repeated immediately when the test subject has a:

(1) Weight change of 20 pounds or more.

(2) Significant facial scarring in the area of the facepiece seal,

(3) Significant dental changes; i.e.; multiple extractions without prothesis, or acquiring dentures,

(4) Reconstructive or cosmetic surgery, or

(5) Any other condition that may interfere with facepiece sealing.

D. Recordkeeping

A summary of all test results shall be maintained in each office for 3 years. The summary shall include:

(1) Name of test subject.

(2) Date of testing.

(3) Name of test conductor.

(4) Respirators selected (indicate manufacturer, model, size and approval number).

(5) Testing agent.

III. Irritant Fume Protocol

A. Respirator selection

Respirators shall be selected as described in section IB above, except that each respirator shall be equipped with a high-efficiency cartridge.

B. Fit test

1. The test subject shall be allowed to smell a weak concentration of the irritant smoke to familiarize the subject with the characteristic odor.

2. The test subject shall properly don the respirator selected as above, and wear it for at least 10 minutes before starting the fit test.

3. The test conductor shall review this protocol with the test subject before testing.

4. The test subject shall perform the conventional positive pressure and negative pressure fit checks (see ANSI Z88.2 1980). Failure of either check shall be cause to collect an alternate respirator.

5. Break both ends of a ventilation smoke tube containing stannic oxychloride, such as the MSA part #5645, or equivalent. Attach a short length of tubing to one end of the smoke tube. Attach the other end of the smoke tube to a low pressure air pump set to deliver 200 milliliters per minute.

6. Advise the test subject that the smoke can be irritating to the eyes and instruct the subject to keep the eyes closed while the test is performed.

7. The test conductor shall direct the stream of irritant smoke from the tube towards the faceseal area of the test subject. The person conducting the test shall begin with the tube at least 12 inches from the facepiece and gradually move to within one inch, moving around the whole perimeter of the mask.

8. The test subject shall be instructed to do the following exercises while the respirator is being challenged by the smoke. Each exercise shall be performed for one minute.

i. Breathe normally.

ii. Breathe deeply. Be certain breaths are *deep* and *regular*.

iii. Turn head all the way from one side to the other. Be certain movement is complete. Inhale on each side. Do not bump the respirator against the shoulders.

iv. Nod head up-and-down. Be certain motions are complete and made every second. Inhale when head is in the full up position (looking toward ceiling). Do not bump the respirator against the chest.

v. Talking. Talk aloud and slowly for several minutes. The following paragraph is called the Rainbow Passage. Repeating it after the test conductor (keeping eyes closed) will result in a wide range of facial movements, and thus be useful to satisfy this requirement. Alternative passages which serve the same purpose may also be used.

Rainbow Passage

When the sunlight strikes raindrops in the air, they act like a prism and form a rainbow. The rainbow is a division of white light into many beautiful colors. These take the shape of a long round arch, with its path high above, and its two ends apparently beyond the horizon. There is, according to legend, a boiling pot of gold at one end. People look, but no one ever finds it. When a man looks for something beyond his reach, his friends say he is looking for the pot of gold at the end of the rainbow.

vi. Jogging in Place.

vii. Breathe normally.

9. The test subject shall indicate to the test conductor if the irritant smoke is detected. If smoke is detected, the test conductor shall stop the test. In this case, the tested respirator is rejected and another respirator shall be selected.

10. Each test subject passing the smoke test (i.e. without detecting the smoke) shall be given a sensitivity check of smoke from the same tube to determine if the test subject reacts to the smoke. Failure to evoke a response shall void the fit test.

11. Steps B4, B9, B10 of this fit test protocol shall be performed in a location with exhaust ventilation sufficient to prevent general contamination of the testing area by the test agents.

12. At least two facepieces shall be selected by the irritant fume test protocol. The test subject shall be given the opportunity to wear them for one week to choose the one which is more comfortable to wear.

13. Respirators successfully tested by the protocol may be used in contaminated atmospheres up to ten times the PEL of asbestos.

14. The test shall not be conducted if there is any hair growth between the skin and the facepiece sealing surface.

15. If hair growth or apparel interfere with a satisfactory fit, then they shall be altered or removed so as to eliminate interference and allow a satisfactory fit. If a satisfactory fit is still not attained, the test subject must use a positive-pressure respirator such as powered air-purifying respirators, supplied air respirator, or self-contained breathing apparatus.

16. If a test subject exhibits difficulty in breathing during the tests, she or he shall be referred to a physician trained in respirator diseases or pulmonary medicine to determine whether the test subject can wear a respirator while performing her or his duties.

17. Qualitative fit testing shall be repeated at least every six months.

18. In addition, because the sealing of the respirator may be affected, qualitative fit testing shall be repeated immediately when the test subject has a:

(1) Weight change of 20 pounds or more,

(2) Significant facial scarring in the area of the facepiece seal,

(3) Significant dental changes; i.e.; multiple extractions without prothesis, or acquiring dentures,

(4) Reconstructive or cosmestic surgery, or

(5) Any other condition that may interfere with facepiece sealing.

C. Recordkeeping

A summary of all test results shall be maintained in each office for 3 years. The summary shall include:

(1) Name of test subject.

(2) Date of testing.

(3) Name of test conductor.

(4) Respirators selected (indicate manufacturer, model, size and approval number).

(5) Testing agent

Quantitative Fit Test Procedures

1. General.

a. The method applies to the negative-pressure nonpowered air-purifying respirators only.

b. The employer shall assign one individual who shall assume the full responsibility for implementing the respirator quantitative fit test program.

2. *Definition.*

a. *Quantitative Fit Test* means the measurement of the effectiveness of a respirator seal in excluding the ambient atmosphere. The test is performed by dividing the measured concentration of challenge agent in a test chamber by the measured concentration of the challenge agent inside the respirator facepiece when the normal air purifying element has been replaced by an essentially perfect purifying element.

b. *Challenge Agent* means the air contaminant introduced into a test chamber so that its concentration inside and outside the respirator may be compared.

c. *Test Subject* means the person wearing the respirator for quantitative fit testing.

d. *Normal Standing Position* means standing erect and straight with arms down along the sides and looking straight ahead.

e. *Fit Factor* means the ratio of challenge agent concentration outside with respect to the inside of a respirator inlet covering (facepiece or enclosure).

3. *Apparatus.*

a. *Instrumentation.* Corn oil, sodium chloride or other appropriate aerosol generation, dilution, and measurement systems shall be used for quantitative fit test.

b. *Test chamber.* The test chamber shall be large enough to permit all test subjects to freely perform all required exercises without distributing the challenge agent concentration or the measurement apparatus. The test chamber shall be equipped and constructed so that the challenge agent is effectively isolated from the ambient air yet uniform in concentration throughout the chamber.

c. When testing air-purifying respirators, the normal filter or cartridge element shall be replaced with a high-efficiency particulate filter supplied by the same manufacturer.

d. The sampling instrument shall be selected so that a strip chart record may be made of the test showing the rise and fall of challenge agent concentration with each inspiration and expiration at fit factors of at least 2,000.

e. The combination of substitute air-purifying elements (if any), challenge agent, and challenge agent concentration in the test chamber shall be such that the test subject is not exposed in excess of PEL to the challenge agent at any time during the testing process.

f. The sampling port on the test specimen respirator shall be placed and constructed so that there is no detectable leak around the port, a free air flow is allowed into the sampling line at all times and so there is no interference with the fit or performance of the respirator.

g. The test chamber and test set-up shall permit the person administering the test to observe one test subject inside the chamber during the test.

h. The equipment generating the challenge atmosphere shall maintain the concentration of challenge agent constant within a 10 percent variation for the duration of the test.

i. The time lag (interval between an event and its being recorded on the strip chart) of the instrumentation may not exceed 2 seconds.

j. The tubing for the test chamber atmosphere and for the respirator sampling port shall be the same diameter, length and material. It shall be kept as short as possible. The smallest diameter tubing recommended by the manufacturer shall be used.

k. The exhaust flow from the test chamber shall pass through a high-efficiency filter before release to the room.

l. When sodium chloride aerosol is used, the relative humidity inside the test chamber shall not exceed 50 percent.

4. *Procedural Requirements.*

a. The fitting of half-mask respirators should be started with those having multiple sizes and a variety of interchangeable cartridges and canisters such as the MSA Comfo II-M, North M. Survivair M, A-O M, or Scott-M. Use either of the tests outlined below to assure that the facepiece is properly adjusted.

(1) *Positive pressure test.* With the exhaust port(s) blocked, the negative pressure of slight inhalation should remain constant for several seconds.

(2) *Negative pressure test.* With the intake port(s) blocked, the negative pressure slight inhalation should remain constant for several seconds.

b. After a facepiece is adjusted, the test subject shall wear the facepiece for at least 5 minutes before conducting a qualitive test by using either of the methods described

below and using the exercise regime described in 5.a., b., c., d, and e.

(1) *Isoamyl acetate test.* When using organic vapor cartridges, the test subject who can smell the odor should be unable to detect the odor of isoamyl acetate squirted into the air near the most vulnerable portions of the facepiece seal. In a location which is separated from the test area, the test subject shall be instructed to close her/his eyes during the test period. A combination cartridge or canister with organic vapor and high-efficiency filters shall be used when available for the particular mask being tested. The test subject shall be given an opportunity to smell the odor of isoamyl acetate before the test is conducted.

(2) *Irritant fume test.* When using high-efficiency filters, the test subject should be unable to detect the odor of irritant fume (stannic chloride or titanium tetrachloride ventilation smoke tubes) squirted into the air near the most vulnerable portions of the facepiece seal. The test subject shall be instructed to close her/his eyes during the test period.

c. The test subject may enter the quantitative testing chamber only if she or he has obtained a satisfactory fit as stated in 4.b. of this Appendix.

d. Before the subject enters the test chamber, a reasonably stable challenge agent concentration shall be measured in the test chamber.

e. Immediately after the subject enters the test chamber, the challenge agent concentration inside the respirator shall be measured to ensure that the peak penetration does not exceed 5 percent for a half-mask and 1 percent for a full facepiece.

f. A stable challenge agent concentration shall be obtained prior to the actual start of testing.

(1) Respirator restraining straps may not be overtightened for testing. The straps shall be adjusted by the wearer to give a reasonably comfortable fit typical of normal use.

5. *Exercise Regime.* Prior to entering the test chamber, the test subject shall be given complete instructions as to her/his part in the test procedures. The test subject shall perform the following exercises, in the order given, for each independent test.

a. *Normal Breathing (NB).* In the normal standing position, without talking, the subject shall breathe normally for at least one minute.

b. *Deep Breathing (DB).* In the normal standing position the subject shall do deep breathing for at least one minute pausing so as not to hyperventilate.

c. *Turning head side to side (SS).* Standing in place the subject shall slowly turn his/her head from side between the extreme positions to each side. The head shall be held at each extreme position for at least 5 seconds. Perform for at least three complete cycles.

d. *Moving head up and down (UD)*. Standing in place, the subject shall slowly move his/her head up and down between the extreme position straight up and the extreme position straight down. The head shall be held at each extreme position for at least 5 seconds. Perform for at least three complete cycles.

e. *Reading (R)*. The test subject (keeping eyes closed) shall repeat after the test conductor the 'rainbow passage' at the end of this section. The subject shall talk slowly and aloud so as to be heard clearly by the test conductor or monitor.

f. *Grimace (G)*. The test subject shall grimace, smile, frown, and generally contort the face using the facial muscles. Continue for at least 15 seconds.

g. *Bend over and touch toes (B)*. The test subject shall bend at the waist and touch toes and return to upright position. Repeat for at least 30 seconds.

h. *Jogging in place (J)*. The test subject shall perform jog in place for at least 30 seconds.

i. *Normal Breathing (NB)*. Same as exercise a.

Rainbow Passage

When the sunlight strikes raindrops in the air, they act like a prism and form a rainbow. The rainbow is a division of white light into many beautiful colors. These take the shape of a long round arch, with its path high above, and its two ends apparently beyond the horizon. There is, according to legend, a boiling pot of gold at one end. People look, but no one ever finds it. When a man looks for something beyond reach, his friends say he is looking for the pot of gold at the end of the rainbow.

6. The test shall be terminated whenever any single peak penetration exceeds 5 percent for half-masks and 1 percent for full facepieces. The test subject may be refitted and retested. If two of the three required tests are terminated, the fit shall be deemed inadequate.

7. *Calculation of Fit Factors*.

a. The fit factor determined by the quantitative fit test equals the average concentration inside the respirator.

b. The average test chamber concentration is the arithmetic average of the test chamber concentration at the beginning of and the end of the test.

c. The average peak concentration of the challenge agent inside the respirator shall be the arithmetic average peak concentrations for each of the nine exercises of the test which are computed as the arithmetic average of the peak concentrations found for each breath during the exercise.

d. The average peak concentration for an exercise may be determined graphically if there is not a great variation in the peak concentrations during a single exercise.

8. *Interpretation of Test Results*. The fit factor measured by the quantitative fit testing shall be the lowest of the three protection factors resulting from three independent tests.

9. *Other Requirements*.

a. The test subject shall not be permitted to wear a half-mask or full facepiece mask if the minimum fit factor of 100 or 1,000, respectively, cannot be obtained. If hair growth or apparel interfere with a satisfactory fit, then they shall be altered or removed so as to eliminate interference and allow a satisfactory fit. If a satisfactory fit is still not attained, the test subject must use a positive-pressure respirator such as powered air-purifying respirators, supplied air respirator, or self-contained breathing apparatus.

b. The test shall not be conducted if there is any hair growth between the skin and the facepiece sealing surface.

c. If a test subject exhibits difficulty in breathing during the tests, she or he shall be referred to a physician trained in respirator diseases or pulmonary medicine to determine whether the test subject can wear a respirator while performing her or his duties.

d. The test subject shall be given the opportunity to wear the assigned respirator for one week. If the respirator does not provide a satisfactory fit during actual use, the test subject may request another QNFT which shall be performed immediately.

e. A respirator fit factor card shall be issued to the test subject with the following information:

(1) Name.

(2) Date of fit test.

(3) Protection factors obtained through each manufacturer, model and approval number of respirator tested.

(4) Name and signature of the person that conducted the test.

f. Filters used for qualitative or quantitative fit testing shall be replaced weekly, whenever increased breathing resistance is encountered, or when the test agent has altered the integrity of the filter media. Organic vapor cartridges/canisters shall be replaced daily or sooner if there is any indication of breakthrough by the test agent.

10. In addition, because the sealing of the respirator may be affected, quantitative fit testing shall be repeated immediately when the test subject has a:

(1) Weight change of 20 pounds or more,

(2) Significant facial scarring in the area of the facepiece seal,

(3) Significant dental changes; i.e., multiple extractions without prothesis, or acquiring dentures.

(4) Reconstructive or cosmetic surgery, or

(5) Any other condition that may interfere with facepiece sealing.

11. *Recordkeeping*.

A summary of all test results shall be maintained for 3 years. The summary shall include:

(1) Name of test subject.

(2) Date of testing.

(3) Name of the test conductor.

(4) Fit factors obtained from every respirator tested (indicate manufacturer, model, size and approval number).

APPENDIX D TO § 1910.1001—MEDICAL QUESTIONNAIRES; MANDATORY

This mandatory appendix contains the medical questionnaires that must be administered to all employees who are exposed to asbestos above the action level, and who will therefore be included in their employer's medical surveillance program. Part 1 of the appendix contains the Initial Medical Questionnaire, which must be obtained for all new hires who will be covered by the medical surveillance requirements. Part 2 includes the abbreviated Periodical Medical Questionnaire, which must be administered to all employees who are provided periodic medical examinations under the medical surveillance provisions of the standard.

Occupational Safety and Health Admin., Labor §1910.1001, App. D

Part 1
INITIAL MEDICAL QUESTIONNAIRE

1. NAME _____

2. SOCIAL SECURITY # ___ ___ ___ ___ ___ ___ ___ ___ ___
                          1   2   3   4   5   6   7   8   9

3. CLOCK NUMBER ___ ___ ___ ___ ___ ___
                        10 11 12 13 14 15

4. PRESENT OCCUPATION _____

5. PLANT _____

6. ADDRESS _____

7. _____
                          (Zip Code)

8. TELEPHONE NUMBER _____

9. INTERVIEWER _____

10. DATE _____ ___ ___ ___ ___ ___ ___
                                16 17 18 19 20 21

11. Date of Birth _____ ___ ___ ___ ___ ___ ___
                 Month   Day   Year 22 23 24 25 26 27

12. Place of Birth _____

13. Sex
                          1. Male ___
                          2. Female ___

14. What is your marital status?   1. Single ___   4. Separated/
                                  2. Married ___   Divorced ___
                                  3. Widowed ___

15. Race   1. White ___ 4. Hispanic ___
                            2. Black ___ 5. Indian ___
                            3. Asian ___ 6. Other ___

16. What is the highest grade completed in school? _____
    (For example 12 years is completion of high school)

OCCUPATIONAL HISTORY

17A. Have you ever worked full time (30 hours   1. Yes ___   2. No ___
    per week or more) for 6 months or more?

     IF YES TO 17A:

B. Have you ever worked for a year or more in   1. Yes ___   2. No ___
    any dusty job?   3. Does Not Apply ___

Specify job/industry _____   Total Years Worked ____

Was dust exposure: 1. Mild ___   2. Moderate ___   3. Severe ___

C. Have you even been exposed to gas or   1. Yes ___ 2. No ___
chemical fumes in your work?
Specify job/industry _____   Total Years Worked ___

Was exposure: 1. Mild ___   2. Moderate ___   3. Severe ___

D. What has been your usual occupation or job--the one you have
worked at the longest?

1. Job occupation _____

2. Number of years employed in this occupation _____

3. Position/job title _____

4. Business, field or
industry _____

(Record on lines the years in which you have worked in any of these
industries, e.q. 1960-1969)

Have you ever worked:

		YES	NO
E.	In a mine?................................	[_]	[_]
F.	In a quarry?.............................	[_]	[_]
G.	In a foundry?,..........................	[_]	[_]
H.	In a pottery?........................	[_]	[_]
I.	In a cotton, flax or hemp mill?...........	[_]	[_]
J.	With asbestos?............................	[_]	[_]

18. PAST MEDICAL HISTORY

	YES	NO
A. Do you consider yourself to be in good health?	[_]	[_]

If "NO" state reason _____

B. Have you any defect of vision?............... [_]   [_]

If "YES" state nature of defect _____

C. Have you any hearing defect?.................. [_]   [_]

If "YES" state nature of defect _____

Occupational Safety and Health Admin., Labor §1910.1001, App. D

D. Are you suffering from or have you ever suffered from:

a. Epilepsy (or fits, seizures, convulsions)?   [_]   [_]

b. Rheumatic fever?   [_]   [_]

c. Kidney disease?   [_]   [_]

d. Bladder disease?   [_]   [_]

e. Diabetes?   [_]   [_]

f. Jaundice?   [_]   [_]

19. CHEST COLDS AND CHEST ILLNESSES

19A. If you get a cold, does it <u>usually</u> go to your   1. Yes __   2. No __
chest? (Usually means more than 1/2 the time)   3. Don't get colds __

20A. During the past 3 years, have you had any chest   1. Yes __   2. No __
illnesses that have kept you off work, indoors at
home, or in bed?

IF YES TO 20A:
B. Did you produce phlegm with any of these chest   1. Yes __   2. No __
illnesses?   3. Does Not Apply __

C. In the last 3 years, how many such illnesses   Number of illnesses __
with (increased) phlegm did you have which   No such illnesses __
lasted a week or more?

21. Did you have any lung trouble before the age of   1. Yes __   2. No __
16?

22. Have you ever had any of the following?

1A. Attacks of bronchitis?   1. Yes __   2. No __

IF YES TO 1A:
B. Was it confirmed by a doctor?   1. Yes __   2. No __
     3. Does Not Apply __

C. At what age was your first attack?   Age in Years __
     Does Not Apply __

2A. Pneumonia (include bronchopneumonia)?   1. Yes __   2. No __

IF YES TO 2A:
B. Was it confirmed by a doctor?   1. Yes __   2. No __
     3. Does Not Apply __

C. At what age did you first have it?   Age in Years __
     Does Not Apply __

45

3A. Hay Fever?   1. Yes __   2. No __

    IF YES TO 3A:
  B. Was it confirmed by a doctor?   1. Yes __   2. No __
                                                     3. Does Not Apply __

  C. At what age did it start?   Age in Years   __
                                                     Does Not Apply __

23A. Have you ever had chronic bronchitis?   1. Yes __   2. No __

    IF YES TO 23A:
  B. Do you still have it?   1. Yes __   2. No __
                                                     3. Does Not Apply __

  C. Was it confirmed by a doctor?   1. Yes __   2. No __
                                                   3. Does Not Apply __

D. At what age did it start?   Age in Years   __
                                                     Does Not Apply __

24A. Have you ever had emphysema?   1. Yes __   2. No __

    IF YES TO 24A:
  B. Do you still have it?   1. Yes __   2. No __
                                                     3. Does Not Apply __

  C. Was it confirmed by a doctor?   1. Yes __   2. No __
                                                   3. Does Not Apply __

  D. At what age did it start?   Age in Years   __
                                                     Does Not Apply __

25A. Have you ever had asthma?   1. Yes __   2. No __

    IF YES TO 25A:
  B. Do you still have it?   1. Yes __   2. No __
                                                     3. Does Not Apply __

  C. Was it confirmed by a doctor?   1. Yes __   2. No __
                                                   3. Does Not Apply __

  D. At what age did it start?   Age in Years   __
                                                     Does Not Apply __

  E. If you no longer have it, at what age did it   Age stopped   __
    stop?   Does Not Apply __

26. Have you ever had:

  A. Any other chest illness?   1. Yes __   2. No __

    If yes, please specify _____

Occupational Safety and Health Admin., Labor   **§ 1910.1001, App. D**

B. Any chest operations?   1. Yes __   2. No __

    If yes, please specify _____

C. Any chest injuries?   1. Yes __   2. No __

    If yes, please specify _____

27A. Has a doctor ever told you that you had heart   1. Yes __   2. No __
     trouble?

     IF YES TO 27A:
  B. Have you ever had treatment for heart trouble   1. Yes __   2. No __
     in the past 10 years?   3. Does Not Apply __

28A. Has a doctor ever told you that you had high   1. Yes __   2. No __
     blood pressure?

     IF YES TO 28A:
  B. Have you had any treatment for high blood   1. Yes __   2. No __
     pressure (hypertension) in the past 10 years?   3. Does Not Apply __

29. When did you last have your chest X-rayed?   (Year) __ __ __ __
                                                      25 26 27 28

30. Where did you last have your chest X-rayed (if known)? _____

    What was the outcome? _____

FAMILY HISTORY

31. Were either of your natural parents ever told by a doctor that they had a
    chronic lung condition such as:

	FATHER			MOTHER		
	1. Yes	2. No	3. Don't Know	1. Yes	2. No	3. Don't Know
A. Chronic Bronchitis?	__	__	__	__	__	__
B. Emphysema?	__	__	__	__	__	__
C. Asthma?	__	__	__	__	__	__
D. Lung cancer?	__	__	__	__	__	__
E. Other chest conditions	__	__	__	__	__	__
F. Is parent currently alive?	__	__	__	__	__	__

G. Please Specify   ___ Age if Living   ___ Age if Living
                    ___ Age at Death   ___ Age at Death
                    ___ Don't Know   ___ Don't Know

H. Please specify cause of death

_____   _____

COUGH

32A. Do you usually have a cough? (Count   1. Yes __   2. No __
a cough with first smoke or on first
going out of doors. Exclude clearing
of throat.) [If no, skip to question
32C.]

B. Do you usually cough as much as 4 to   1. Yes __   2. No __
6 times a day 4 or more days out of
the week?

C. Do you usually cough at all on getting   1. Yes __   2. No __
up or first thing in the morning?

D. Do you usually cough at all during the   1. Yes __   2. No __
rest of the day or at night?

IF YES TO ANY OF ABOVE (32A, B, C, or D), ANSWER THE FOLLOWING. IF NO
TO ALL, CHECK DOES NOT APPLY AND SKIP TO NEXT PAGE

E. Do you usually cough like this on most   1. Yes __   2. No __
days for 3 consecutive months or more   3. Does not apply __
during the year?

F. For how many years have you had the cough?   Number of years __
                                                 Does not apply __

33A. Do you usually bring up phlegm from your   1. Yes __   2. No __
chest?
(Count phlegm with the first smoke or
on first going out of doors. Exclude
phlegm from the nose. Count swallowed
phlegm.) (If no, skip to 33C)

B. Do you usually bring up phlegm like this   1. Yes __   2. No __
as much as twice a day 4 or more days
out of the week?

C. Do you usually bring up phlegm at all on   1. Yes __   2. No __
getting up or first thing in the morning?

D. Do you usually bring up phlegm at all   1. Yes __   2. No __
during the rest of the day or at night?

IF YES TO ANY OF THE ABOVE (33A, B, C, or D), ANSWER THE FOLLOWING:
IF NO TO ALL, CHECK DOES NOT APPLY AND SKIP TO 34A.

E. Do you bring up phlegm like this on most   1. Yes __   2. No __
days for 3 consecutive months or more   3. Does not apply __
during the year?

Occupational Safety and Health Admin., Labor   § 1910.1001, App. D

F. For how many years have you had trouble   Number of years __
   with phlegm?   Does not apply __

EPISODES OF COUGH AND PHLEGM

34A. Have you had periods or episodes of (in-   1. Yes __   2. No __
     creased*) cough and phlegm lasting for 3
     weeks or more each year?
     *(For persons who usually have cough and/or
      phlegm)

     If YES TO 34A
 B. For how long have you had at least 1 such   Number of years __
    episode per year?   Does not apply __

WHEEZING

35A. Does your chest ever sound wheezy or
     whistling
              1.   When you have a cold?   1. Yes __   2. No __
              2.   Occasionally apart from colds?   1. Yes __   2. No __
              3.   Most days or nights?   1. Yes __   2. No __

              IF YES TO 1, 2, or 3 in 35A
 B. For how many years has this been present?   Number of years __
                                                     Does not apply __

36A. Have you ever had an attack of wheezing   1. Yes __   2. No __
     that has made you feel short of breath?

              IF YES TO 36A
 B. How old were you when you had your first   Age in years   __
    such attack?   Does not apply __

 C. Have you had 2 or more such episodes?   1. Yes __   2. No __
                                                     3. Does not apply __

 D. Have you ever required medicine or   1. Yes __   2. No __
    treatment for the(se) attack(s.)?   3. Does not apply __

BREATHLESSNESS

37. If disabled from walking by any condition
     other than heart or lung disease, please
     describe and proceed to question 39A.
     Nature of condition(s)_____

38A. Are you troubled by shortness of breath when   1. Yes __   2. No __
     hurrying on the level or walking up a
     slight hill?

IF YES TO 38A

B. Do you have to walk slower than people of your age on the level because of breathlessness?

1. Yes __   2. No __
3. Does not apply __

C. Do you ever have to stop for breath when walking at your own pace on the level?

1. Yes __   2. No __
3. Does not apply __

D. Do you ever have to stop for breath after walking about 100 yards (or after a few minutes) on the level?

1. Yes __   2. No __
3. Does not apply __

E. Are you too breathless to leave the house or breathless on dressing or climbing one flight of stairs?

1. Yes __   2. No __
3. Does not apply __

TOBACCO SMOKING

39A. Have you ever smoked cigarettes? (No means less than 20 packs of cigarettes or 12 oz. of tobacco in a lifetime or less than 1 cigarette a day for 1 year.)

1. Yes __   2. No __

IF YES TO 39A

B. Do you now smoke cigarettes (as of one month ago)

1. Yes __   2. No __
3. Does not apply __

C. How old were you when you first started regular cigarette smoking?

Age in years   __
Does not apply   __

D. If you have stopped smoking cigarettes completely, how old were you when you stopped?

Age stopped   __
Check if still smoking __
Does not apply   __

E. How many cigarettes do you smoke per day now?

Cigarettes per day   __
Does not apply   __

F. On the average of the entire time you smoked, how many cigarettes did you smoke per day?

Cigarettes per day   __
Does not apply   __

G. Do or did you inhale the cigarette smoke?

1. Does not apply   __
2. Not at all   __
3. Slightly   __
4. Moderately   __
5. Deeply   __

40A. Have you ever smoked a pipe regularly? (Yes means more than 12 oz. of tobacco in a lifetime.)

1. Yes __   2. No __

Occupational Safety and Health Admin., Labor § 1910.1001, App. D

IF YES TO 40A:
FOR PERSONS WHO HAVE EVER SMOKED A PIPE

B. 1. How old were you when you started to
smoke a pipe regularly?   Age __

2. If you have stopped smoking a pipe   Age stopped   __
completely, how old were you when you   Check if still
stopped?   smoking pipe
                                            Does not apply   __

C. On the average over the entire time you   __ oz. per week (a standard
smoked a pipe, how much pipe tobacco did   pouch of tobacco contains
you smoke per week?   1 1/2 oz.)
                                            __ Does not apply

D. How much pipe tobacco are you smoking now? oz. per week   __
                                            Not currently
                                            smoking a pipe   __

E. Do you or did you inhale the pipe smoke?   1. Never smoked   __
                                            2. Not at all   __
                                            3. Slightly   __
                                            4. Moderately   __
                                            5. Deeply   __

41A. Have you ever smoked cigars regularly?   1. Yes __   2. No __
(Yes means more than 1 cigar a week for a
year)

IF YES TO 41A
FOR PERSONS WHO HAVE EVER SMOKED CIGARS

B. 1. How old were you when you started   Age __
smoking cigars regularly?

2. If you have stopped smoking cigars   Age stopped   __
completely, how old were you when   Check if still
you stopped.   smoking cigars
                                            Does not apply   __

C. On the average over the entire time you   Cigars per week   __
smoked cigars, how many cigars did you   Does not apply   __
smoke per week?

D. How many cigars are you smoking per week   Cigars per week   __
now?   Check if not
                                            smoking cigars
                                            currently   __

E. Do or did you inhale the cigar smoke?   1. Never smoked   __
                                            2. Not at all   __
                                            3. Slightly   __
                                            4. Moderately   __
                                            5. Deeply   __

Signature _____   Date _____

51

Part 2
PERIODIC MEDICAL QUESTIONNAIRE

1.   NAME _____

2.   SOCIAL SECURITY # ___ ___ ___ ___ ___ ___ ___ ___ ___ ___
                            1   2   3   4   5   6 7 8   9

3.   CLOCK NUMBER   ___ ___ ___ ___ ___ ___
                                     10 11 12 13 14 15

4.   PRESENT OCCUPATION _____

5.   PLANT _____

6.   ADDRESS _____

7.   _____
                                      (Zip Code)

8.   TELEPHONE NUMBER _____

9.   INTERVIEWER _____

10. DATE _____ ___ ___ ___ ___ ___ ___
                                           16 17 18 19 20 21

11. What is your marital status?   1. Single ___   4. Separated/
                                       2. Married ___   Divorced ___
                                       3. Widowed ___

12. OCCUPATIONAL HISTORY

12A. In the past year, did you work   1. Yes ___   2. No ___
     full time (30 hours per week
     or more) for 6 months or more?

     IF YES TO 12A:

12B. In the past year, did you work   1. Yes ___   2. No ___
     in a dusty job?   3. Does Not Apply ___

12C. Was dust exposure: 1. Mild ___   2. Moderate ___   3. Severe ___

12D. In the past year, were you   1. Yes ___   2. No ___
     exposed to gas or chemical
     fumes in your work?

12E. Was exposure: 1. Mild ___   2. Moderate ___   3. Severe ___

12F. In the past year,
     what was your: 1. Job/occupation? _____
                             2. Position/job title? _____

52

Occupational Safety and Health Admin., Labor §1910.1001, App. D

13. RECENT MEDICAL HISTORY

13A. Do you consider yourself to
be in good health?   Yes ___   No ___

If NO, state reason _____

13B. In the past year, have you
developed: Yes   No
                              Epilepsy?   ___   ___
                              Rheumatic fever? ___   ___
                              Kidney disease? ___   ___
                              Bladder disease? ___   ___
                              Diabetes?   ___   ___
                              Jaundice?   ___   ___
                              Cancer?   ___   ___

14. CHEST COLDS AND CHEST ILLNESSES

14A. If you get a cold, does it usually go to your chest?
(Usually means more than 1/2 the time)
                                        1. Yes ___   2. No ___
                                        3. Don't get colds ___

15A. During the past year, have you had
any chest illnesses that have kept you   1. Yes ___   2. No ___
off work, indoors at home, or in bed?   3. Does Not Apply ___

IF YES TO 15A:

15B. Did you produce phlegm with any   1. Yes ___   2. No ___
of these chest illnesses?   3. Does Not Apply ___

15C. In the past year, how many such   Number of illnesses ___
illnesses with (increased) phlegm   No such illnesses ___
did you have which lasted a week
or more?

16. RESPIRATORY SYSTEM

In the past year have you had:

	Yes or No	Further Comment on Positive Answers
Asthma	_____	
Bronchitis	_____	
Hay Fever	_____	
Other Allergies	_____	

	Yes or No	Further Comment on Positive Answers
Pneumonia	_____	
Tuberculosis	_____	
Chest Surgery	_____	
Other Lung Problems	_____	
Heart Disease	_____	

Do you have:

	Yes or No	Further Comment on Positive Answers
Frequent colds	_____	
Chronic cough	_____	
Shortness of breath when walking or climbing one flight or stairs	_____	

Do you:

Wheeze	_____
Cough up phlegm	_____
Smoke cigarettes	_____

Smoke cigarettes _____ Packs per day ___ How many years ___

Date _____   Signature _____

APPENDIX E TO § 1910.1001—INTERPRETATION AND CLASSIFICATION OF CHEST ROENTGENO-GRAMS—MANDATORY

(a) Chest roentgenograms shall be interpreted and classified in accordance with a professionally accepted Classification system and recorded on an interpretation form following the format of the CDC/NIOSH (M) 2.8 form. As a minimum, the content within the bold lines of this form (items 1 though 4) shall be included. This form is not to be submitted to NIOSH.

(b) Roentgenograms shall be interpreted and classified only by a B-reader, a board eligible/certified radiologist, or an experienced physician with known expertise in pneumoconioses.

(c) All interpreters, whenever interpreting chest roentgenograms made under this section, shall have immediately available for reference a complete set of the ILO-U/C International Classification of Radiographs for Pneumoconioses, 1980.

APPENDIX F TO § 1910.1001—WORK PRACTICES AND ENGINEERING CONTROLS FOR AUTO-MOTIVE BRAKE REPAIR OPERATIONS—NON-MANDATORY

This appendix is intended as guidance for employers in the automotive brake and clutch repair industry who wish to reduce their employees' asbestos exposures during repair operations to levels below the new standard's action level (0.1 f/cc). OSHA believes that employers in this industry sector are likely to be able to reduce their employees' exposures to asbestos by employing the engineering and work practice controls described in Sections A and B of this appendix. Those employers who choose to use these controls and who achieve exposures below the action level will thus be able to avoid any burden that might be imposed by complying with such requirements as medical surveillance, recordkeeping, training, respiratory protection, and regulated areas, which are triggered when employee exposures exceed the action level or PEL.

Asbestos exposure in the automotive brake and clutch repair industry occurs primarily during the replacement of clutch plates and brake pads, shoes, and linings. Asbestos fibers may become airborne when an automotive mechanic removes the asbestos-containing residue that has been deposited as brakes and clutches wear. Employee exposures to asbestos occur during the cleaning of the brake drum or clutch housing.

Based on evidence in the rulemaking record (Exs. 84-74, 84-263, 90-148), OSHA believes that employers engaged in brake repair operations who implement any of the work practices and engineering controls described in Sections A and B of this appendix may be able to reduce their employees' exposures to levels below the action level (0.1 fiber/cc). These control methods and the relevant record evidence on these and other methods are described in the following sections.

A. Enclosed Cylinder/HEPA Vacuum System Method

The enclosed cylinder-vacuum system used in one of the facilities visited by representatives of the National Institute for Occupational Safety and Health (NIOSH) during a health hazard evaluation of brake repair facilities (Ex. 84-263) consists of three components:

(1) A wheel-shaped cylinder designed to cover and enclose the wheel assembly;

(2) A compressed-air hose and nozzle that fits into a port in the cylinder; and

(3) A HEPA-filtered vacuum used to evacuate airborne dust generated within the cylinder by the compressed air.

To operate the system, the brake assembly is enclosed in a cylinder that has viewing ports to provide visibility and cotton sleeves through which the mechanic can handle the brake assembly parts. The cylinder effectively isolates asbestos dust in the drum from the mechanic's breathing zone. One company manufactures the brake assembly isolation cylinder in two sizes to fit brake drums in the 7-to-12-inch size range common to automobiles and light trucks and the 12-to-19-inch size range common to large commercial vehicles. The cylinder is equipped with built-in compressed-air guns and a connection for a vacuum cleaner equipped with a High Efficiency Particulate Air (HEPA) filter. This type of filter is capable of removing all particles greater than 0.3 microns from the air. When the vacuum cleaner's filter is full, it must be replaced according to the manufacturer's instruction, and appropriate HEPA-filtered dual cartridge respirators should be worn during the process. The filter of the vacuum cleaner is assumed to be contaminated with asbestos fibers and should be handled carefully, wetted with a fine mist of water, placed immediately in a labelled plastic bag, and disposed of properly. When the cylinder is in place around the brake assembly and the HEPA vacuum is connected, compressed air is blown into the cylinder to loosen the residue from the brake assembly parts. The vacuum then evacuates the loosened material from within the cylinder, capturing the airborne material on the HEPA filter.

The HEPA vacuum system can be disconnected from the brake assembly isolation cylinder when the cylinder is not being used. The HEPA vacuum can then be used for clutch facing work, grinding, or other routine cleaning.

B. Compressed Air/Solvent System Method

A compressed-air hose fitted at the end with a bottle of solvent can be used to loosen the asbestos-containing residue and to capture the resulting airborne particles in the solvent mist. The mechanic should begin spraying the asbestos-contaminated parts with the solvent at a sufficient distance to ensure that the asbestos particles are not dislodged by the velocity of the solvent spray. After the asbestos particles are thoroughly wetted, the spray may be brought closer to the parts and the parts may be sprayed as necessary to remove grease and other material. The automotive parts sprayed with the mist are then wiped with a rag, which must then be disposed of appropriately. Rags should be placed in a labelled plastic bag or other container while they are still wet. This ensures that the asbestos fibers will not become airborne after the brake and clutch parts have been cleaned. (If clean-up rags are laundered rather than disposed of, they must be washed using methods appropriate for the laundering of asbestos-contaminated materials.)

OSHA believes that a variant of this compressed-air/solvent mist process offers advantages over the compressed-air/solvent mist technique discussed above, both in terms of costs and employee protection. The variant involves the use of spray cans filled with any of several solvent cleaners commercially available from auto supply stores. Spray cans of solvent are inexpensive, readily available, and easy to use. These cans will also save time, because no solvent delivery system has to be asembled, i.e., no compressed-air hose/mister ensemble. OSHA believes that a spray can will deliver solvent to the parts to be cleaned with considerably less force than the alternative compressed-air delivery system described above, and will thus generate fewer airborne asbestos fibers than the compressed-air method. The Agency therefore believes that the exposure levels of automotive repair mechanics using the spray can/solvent mist process will be even lower than the exposures reported by NIOSH (Ex. 84-263) for the compressed-air/solvent mist system (0.08 f/cc).

C. Information on the Effectiveness of Various Control Measures

The amount of airborne asbestos generated during brake and clutch repair operations depends on the work practices and engineering controls used during the repair or removal activity. Data in the rulemaking record document the 8-hour time-weighted average (TWA_8) asbestos exposure levels associated with various methods of brake and clutch repair and removal.

NIOSH submitted a report to the record entitled "Health Hazard Evaluation for Automotive Brake Repair" (Ex. 84-263). In addition, Exhibits 84-74 and 90-148 provided exposure data for comparing the airborne concentrations of asbestos generated by the use of various work practices during brake repair operations. These reports present exposure data for brake repair operations involving a variety of controls and work practices, including:

• Use of compressed air to blow out the brake drums;

• Use of a brush, without a wetting agent, to remove the asbestos-containing residue;

• Use of a brush dipped in water or a solvent to remove the asbestos-containing residue;

• Use of an enclosed vacuum cleaning system to capture the asbestos-containing residue; and

• Use of a solvent mixture applied with compressed air to remove the residue.

Prohibited Methods

The use of compressed air to blow the asbestos-containing residue off the surface of the brake drum removes the residue effectively but simultaneously produces an airborne cloud of asbestos fibers. According to NIOSH (Ex. 84-263), the peak exposures of mechanics using this technique were as high as 15 fibers/cc, and 8-hour TWA exposures ranged from 0.03 to 0.19 f/cc.

Dr. William J. Nicholson of the Mount Sinai School of Medicine (Ex. 84-74) cited data from Knight and Hickish (1970) that indicated that the concentration of asbestos ranged from 0.84 to 5.35 f/cc over a 60-minute sampling period when compressed air was being used to blow out the asbestos-containing residue from the brake drum. In the same study, a peak concentration of 87 f/cc was measured for a few seconds during brake cleaning performed with compressed air. Rohl et al. (1976) (Ex. 90-148) measured area concentrations (of unspecified duration) within 3-5 feet of operations involving the cleaning of brakes with compressed air and obtained readings ranging from 6.6 to 29.8 f/cc. Because of the high exposure levels that result from cleaning brake and clutch parts using compressed air, OSHA has prohibited this practice in the revised standard.

Ineffective Methods

When dry brushing was used to remove the asbestos-containing residue from the brake drums and wheel assemblies, peak exposures measured by NIOSH ranged from 0.61 to 0.81 f/cc, while 8-hour TWA levels were at the new standard's permissible exposure limit (PEL) of 0.2 f/cc (Ex. 84-263). Rohl and his colleagues (Ex. 90-148) collected area samples 1-3 feet from a brake cleaning operation being performed with a dry brush, and measured concentrations ranging from 1.3 to 3.6 f/cc; however, sampling times and TWA concentrations were not presented in the Rohl et al. study.

When a brush wetted with water, gasoline, or Stoddart solvent was used to clean the asbestos-containing residue from the affected parts, exposure levels (8-hour TWAs) measured by NIOSH also exceeded the new 0.2 f/cc PEL, and peak exposures ranged as high as 2.62 f/cc (Ex. 84–263).

Preferred Methods

Use of an engineering control system involving a cylinder that completely encloses the brake shoe assembly and a High Efficiency Particulate Air (HEPA) filter-equipped vacuum produced 8-hour TWA employee exposures of 0.01 f/cc and peak exposures ranging from nondetectable to 0.07 f/cc (Ex. 84–263). (Because this system achieved exposure levels below the standard's action level, it is described in detail above.) Data collected by the Mount Sinai Medical Center (Ex. 90–148) for Nilfisk of America, Inc., the manufacturer of the brake assembly enclosure system, showed that for two of three operations sampled, the exposure of mechanics to airborne asbestos fibers was nondetectable. For the third operator sampled by Mt. Sinai researchers, the exposure was 0.5 f/cc, which the authors attributed to asbestos that had contaminated the operator's clothing in the course of previous brake repair operations performed without the enclosed cylinder/vacuum system.

Some automotive repair facilities use a compressed-air hose to apply a solvent mist to remove the asbestos-containing residue from the brake drums before repair. The NIOSH data (Ex. 84–263) indicated that mechanics employing this method experienced exposures (8-hour TWAs) of 0.8 f/cc, with peaks of 0.25 to 0.68 f/cc. This technique, and a variant of it that OSHA believes is both less costly and more effective in reducing employee exposures, is described in greater detail above in Sections A and B.

D. Summary

In conclusion, OSHA believes that it is likely that employers in the brake and clutch repair industry will be able to avail themselves of the action level trigger built into the revised standard if they conscientiously employ one of the three control methods described above: the enclosed cylinder/HEPA vacuum system, the compressed air/solvent method, or the spray can/solvent mist system.

APPENDIX G TO §1910.1001—SUBSTANCE TECHNICAL INFORMATION FOR ASBESTOS—NON-MANDATORY

I. Substance Identification

A. Substance: "Asbestos" is the name of a class of magnesium-silicate minerals that occur in fibrous form. Minerals that are included in this group are chrysotile, crocidolite, amosite, tremolite asbestos, anthophyllite asbestos, and actinolite asbestos.

B. Asbestos is used in the manufacture of heat-resistant clothing, automotive brake and clutch linings, and a variety of building materials including floor tiles, roofing felts, ceiling tiles, asbestos-cement pipe and sheet, and fire-resistant drywall. Asbestos is also present in pipe and boiler insulation materials, and in sprayed-on materials located on beams, in crawlspaces, and between walls.

C. The potential for a product containing asbestos to release breatheable fibers depends on its degree of friability. Friable means that the material can be crumbled with hand pressure and is therefore likely to emit fibers. The fibrous or fluffy sprayed-on materials used for fireproofing, insulation, or sound proofing are considered to be friable, and they readily release airborne fibers if disturbed. Materials such as vinyl-asbestos floor tile or roofing felts are considered nonfriable and generally do not emit airborne fibers unless subjected to sanding or sawing operations. Asbestos-cement pipe or sheet can emit airborne fibers if the materials are cut or sawed, or if they are broken during demolition operations.

D. Permissible exposure: Exposure to airborne asbestos fibers may not exceed 0.2 fibers per cubic centimeter of air (0.2 f/cc) averaged over the 8-hour workday.

II. Health Hazard Data

A. Asbestos can cause disabling respiratory disease and various types of cancers if the fibers are inhaled. Inhaling or ingesting fibers from contaminated clothing or skin can also result in these diseases. The symptoms of these diseases generally do not appear for 20 or more years after initial exposure.

B. Exposure to asbestos has been shown to cause lung cancer, mesothelioma, and cancer of the stomach and colon. Mesothelioma is a rare cancer of the thin membrane lining of the chest and abdomen. Symptoms of mesothelioma include shortness of breath, pain in the walls of the chest, and/or abdominal pain.

III. Respirators and Protective Clothing

A. Respirators: You are required to wear a respirator when performing tasks that result in asbestos exposure that exceeds the permissible exposure limit (PEL) of 0.2 f/cc. These conditions can occur while your employer is in the process of installing engineering controls to reduce asbestos exposure, or where engineering controls are not feasible to reduce asbestos exposure. Air-purifying respirators equipped with a high-efficiency particulate air (HEPA) filter can be used where airborne asbestos fiber concentrations do not exceed 2 f/cc; otherwise, air-supplied, positive-pressure, full facepiece respirators must be used. Disposable respirators or dust masks are not permitted to be used for asbestos work. For effective protection, respirators must fit your face and head snugly. Your employer is required to conduct fit tests when you are first assigned a respirator and every 6 months thereafter. Respirators should not be loosened or removed in work situations where their use is required.

B. Protective Clothing: You are required to wear protective clothing in work areas where asbestos fiber concentrations exceed the permissible exposure limit (PEL) of 0.2 f/cc to prevent contamination of the skin. Where protective clothing is required, your employer must provide you with clean garments. Unless you are working on a large asbestos removal or demolition project, your employer must also provide a change room and separate lockers for your street clothes and contaminated work clothes. If you are working on a large asbestos removal or demolition project, and where it is feasible to do so, your employer must provide a clean room, shower, and decontamination room contiguous to the work area. When leaving the work area, you must remove contaminated clothing before proceeding to the shower. If the shower is not adjacent to the work area, you must vacuum your clothing before proceeding to the change room and shower. To prevent inhaling fibers in contaminated change rooms and showers, leave your respirator on until you leave the shower and enter the clean change room.

IV. Disposal Procedures and Cleanup

A. Wastes that are generated by processes where asbestos is present include:

1. Empty asbestos shipping containers.
2. Process wastes such as cuttings, trimmings, or reject material.
3. Housekeeping waste from sweeping or vacuuming.
4. Asbestos fireproofing or insulating material that is removed from buildings.
5. Building products that contain asbestos removed during building renovation or demolition.
6. Contaminated disposable protective clothing.

B. Empty shipping bags can be flattened under exhaust hoods and packed into airtight containers for disposal. Empty shipping drums are difficult to clean and should be sealed.

C. Vacuum bags or disposable paper filters should not be cleaned, but should be sprayed with a fine water mist and placed into a labeled waste container.

D. Process waste and housekeeping waste should be wetted with water or a mixture of water and surfactant prior to packaging in disposable containers.

E. Material containing asbestos that is removed from buildings must be disposed of in leak-tight 6-mil thick plastic bags, plastic-lined cardboard containers, or plastic-lined metal containers. These wastes, which are removed while wet, should be sealed in containers before they dry out to minimize the release of asbestos fibers during handling.

V. Access to Information

A. Each year, your employer is required to inform you of the information contained in this standard and appendices for asbestos. In addition, your employer must instruct you in the proper work practices for handling materials containing asbestos, and the correct use of protective equipment.

B. Your employer is required to determine whether you are being exposed to asbestos. You or your representative has the right to observe employee measurements and to record the results obtained. Your employer is required to inform you of your exposure, and, if you are exposed above the permissible limit, he or she is required to inform you of the actions that are being taken to reduce your exposure to within the permissible limit.

C. Your employer is required to keep records of your exposures and medical examinations. These exposure records must be kept for at least thirty (30) years. Medical records must be kept for the period of your employment plus thirty (30) years.

D. Your employer is required to release your exposure and medical records to your physician or designated representative upon your written request.

APPENDIX H TO § 1910.1001—MEDICAL SURVEILLANCE GUIDELINES FOR ASBESTOS NON-MANDATORY

I. Route of Entry Inhalation, Ingestion

II. Toxicology

Clinical evidence of the adverse effects associated with exposure to asbestos is present in the form of several well-conducted epidemiological studies of occupationally exposed workers, family contacts of workers, and persons living near asbestos mines. These studies have shown a definite association between exposure to asbestos and an increased incidence of lung cancer, pleural and peritoneal mesothelioma, gastrointestinal cancer, and asbestosis. The latter is a disabling fibrotic lung disease that is caused only by exposure to asbestos. Exposure to asbestos has also been associated with an increased incidence of esophageal, kidney, laryngeal, pharyngeal, and buccal cavity cancers. As with other known chronic occupational diseases, disease associated with asbestos generally appears about 20 years following the first occurrence of exposure: There are no known acute effects associated with exposure to asbestos.

Epidemiological studies indicate that the risk of lung cancer among exposed workers who smoke cigarettes is greatly increased over the risk of lung cancer among non-exposed smokers or exposed nonsmokers. These studies suggest that cessation of smoking will reduce the risk of lung cancer for a person exposed to asbestos but will not reduce it to the same level of risk as that existing for an exposed worker who has never smoked.

III. Signs and Symptoms of Exposure-Related Disease

The signs and symptoms of lung cancer or gastrointestinal cancer induced by exposure to asbestos are not unique, except that a chest X-ray of an exposed patient with lung cancer may show pleural plaques, pleural calcification, or pleural fibrosis. Symptoms characteristic of mesothelioma include shortness of breath, pain in the walls of the chest, or abdominal pain. Mesothelioma has a much longer latency period compared with lung cancer (40 years versus 15-20 years), and mesothelioma is therefore more likely to be found among workers who were first exposed to asbestos at an early age. Mesothelioma is always fatal.

Asbestosis is pulmonary fibrosis caused by the accumulation of asbestos fibers in the lungs. Symptoms include shortness of breath, coughing, fatigue, and vague feelings of sickness. When the fibrosis worsens, shortness of breath occurs even at rest. The diagnosis of asbestosis is based on a history of exposure to asbestos, the presence of characteristic radiologic changes, end-inspiratory crackles (rales), and other clinical features of fibrosing lung disease. Pleural plaques and thickening are observed on X-rays taken during the early stages of the disease. Asbestosis is often a progressive disease even in the absence of continued exposure, although this appears to be a highly individualized characteristic. In severe cases, death may be caused by respiratory or cardiac failure.

IV. Surveillance and Preventive Considerations

As noted above, exposure to asbestos has been linked to an increased risk of lung cancer, mesothelioma, gastrointestinal cancer, and asbestosis among occupationally exposed workers. Adequate screening tests to determine an employee's potential for developing serious chronic diseases, such as cancer, from exposure to asbestos do not presently exist. However, some tests, particularly chest X-rays and pulmonary function tests, may indicate that an employee has been overexposed to asbestos increasing his or her risk of developing exposure-related chronic diseases. It is important for the physician to become familiar with the operating conditions in which occupational exposure to asbestos is likely to occur. This is particularly important in evaluating medical and work histories and in conducting physical examinations. When an active employee has been identified as having been overexposed to asbestos, measures taken by the employer to eliminate or mitigate further exposure should also lower the risk of serious long-term consequences.

The employer is required to institute a medical surveillance program for all employees who are or will be exposed to asbestos at or above the action level (0.1 fiber per cubic centimeter of air). All examinations and procedures must be performed by or under the supervision of a licensed physician, at a reasonable time and place, and at no cost to the employee.

Although broad latitude is given to the physician in prescribing specific tests to be included in the medical surveillance program, OSHA requires inclusion of the following elements in the routine examination:

(i) Medical and work histories with special emphasis directed to symptoms of the respiratory system, cardiovascular system, and digestive tract.

(ii) Completion of the respiratory disease questionnaire contained in Appendix D.

(iii) A physical examination including a chest roentgenogram and pulmonary function test that includes measurement of the employee's forced vital capacity (FVC) and forced expiratory volume at one second (FEV_1).

(iv) Any laboratory or other test that the examining physician deems by sound medical practice to be necessary.

The employer is required to make the prescribed tests available at least annually to those employees covered; more often than specified if recommended by the examining physician; and upon termination of employment.

The employer is required to provide the physician with the following information: A copy of this standard and appendices; a description of the mployee's duties as they relate to asbestos exposure; the employee's representative level of exposure to asbestos; a description of any personal protective and respiratory equipment used; and information from previous medical examinations of the affected employee that is not otherwise available to the physician. Making this information available to the physician will aid in the evaluation of the employee's health in relation to assigned duties and fitness to wear personal protective equipment, if required.

The employer is required to obtain a written opinion from the examining physician containing the results of the medical examination; the physician's opinion as to whether the employee has any detected medical conditions that would place the employee at an increased risk of exposure-related disease; any recommended limitations on the employee or on the use of personal protective equipment; and a statement that the employee has been informed by the physician of the results of the medical examination and of any medical conditions related to asbestos exposure that require further explanation or treatment. This written opinion must not reveal specific findings or diagnoses unrelated to exposure to asbestos, and a copy of the opinion must be provided to the affected employee.

APPENDIX I TO § 1910.1001—SMOKING CESSATION PROGRAM INFORMATION FOR ASBESTOS—NON-MANDATORY

The following organizations provide smoking cessation information and program material.

1. The National Cancer Institute operates a toll-free Cancer Information Service (CIS) with trained personnel to help you. Call 1–800–4–CANCER* to reach the CIS office serving your area, or write: Office of Cancer Communications, National Cancer Institute, National Institutes of Health, Building 31, Room 10A24, Bethesda, Maryland 20892.

2. American Cancer Society, 3340 Peachtree Road, NE., Atlanta, Georgia 30062, (404) 320–3333.

The American Cancer Society (ACS) is a voluntary organization composed of 58 divisions and 3,100 local units. Through "The Great American Smokeout" in November, the annual Cancer Crusade in April, and numerous educational materials, ACS helps people learn about the health hazards of smoking and become successful ex-smokers.

3. American Heart Association, 7320 Greenville Avenue, Dallas, Texas 75231, (214) 750–5300.

The American Heart Association (AHA) is a voluntary organization with 130,000 members (physicians, scientists, and laypersons) in 55 state and regional groups. AHA produces a variety of publications and audiovisual materials about the effects of smoking on the heart. AHA also has developed a guidebook for incorporating a weight-control component into smoking cessation programs.

4. American Lung Association, 1740 Broadway, New York, New York 10019, (212) 245–8000.

A voluntary organization of 7,500 members (physicians, nurses, and laypersons), the American Lung Association (ALA) conducts numerous public information programs about the health effect of smoking. ALA has 59 state and 85 local units. The organization actively supports legislation and information campaigns for non-smokers' rights and provides help for smokers who want to quit, for example, through "Freedom From Smoking," a self-help smoking cessation program.

5. Office on Smoking and Health, U.S. Department of Health and, Human Services, 5600 Fishers Lane, Park Building, Room 110, Rockville, Maryland 20857.

The Office on Smoking and Health (OSH) is the Department of Health and Human Services' lead agency in smoking control. OSH has sponsored distribution of publications on smoking-realted topics, such as free flyers on relapse after initial quitting, helping a friend or family member quit smoking, the health hazards of smoking, and the effects of parental smoking on teenagers.

*In Hawaii, on Oahu call 524–1234 (call collect from neighboring islands),

Spanish-speaking staff members are available during daytime hours to callers from the following areas: California, Florida, Georgia, Illinois, New Jersey (area code 210), New York, and Texas. Consult your local telephone directory for listings of local chapters.

(Reporting and recordkeeping requirements in paragraphs (d)(2), (3), (5), and (7), (f)(2) and (3)(i), (j)(5), (l), and (m) as they apply to the excursion limit have been approved by the Office of Management and Budget under control numbers 1218–0133 and 1218–0134. The OMB clearance expires on February 29, 1992.) (Reporting and recordkeeping requirements in paragraph (j)(5)(iv)(C) have received OMB paperwork clearance under OMB clearance number 1218–0133. The OMB clearance expires on April 30, 1993.)

(Approved by the Office of Management and Budget under control number 1218–0133)

[51 FR 22733, June 20, 1986, as amended at 51 FR 37004, Oct. 17, 1986; 52 FR 17754, 17755, May 12, 1987; 53 FR 35625, September 14, 1988; 54 FR 24334, June 7, 1989; 54 FR 29546, July 13, 1989; 54 FR 52027, Dec. 20, 1989, 55 FR 3731, Feb. 5, 1990; 55 FR 34710, Aug. 24, 1990; 57 FR 24330, June 8, 1992]

§ 1910.1002 Coal tar pitch volatiles; interpretation of term.

As used in § 1910.1000 (Table Z-1), coal tar pitch volatiles include the fused polycyclic hydrocarbons which volatilize from the distillation residues of coal, petroleum (excluding asphalt), wood, and other organic matter. Asphalt (CAS 8052–42–4, and CAS 64742–93–4) is not covered under the "coal tar pitch volatiles" standard.

[48 FR 2768, Jan. 21, 1983]

§ 1910.1003 4-Nitrobiphenyl.

(a) Scope and application. (1) This section applies to any area in which 4-Nitrobiphenyl, Chemical Abstracts Service Registry Number 92933 is man-

29 CFR 1910.1030

BLOODBORNE

PATHOGENS

§ 1910.1030 Bloodborne pathogens.

(a) *Scope and Application.* This section applies to all occupational exposure to blood or other potentially infectious materials as defined by paragraph (b) of this section.

(b) *Definitions.* For purposes of this section, the following shall apply:

Assistant Secretary means the Assistant Secretary of Labor for Occupational Safety and Health, or designated representative.

Blood means human blood, human blood components, and products made from human blood.

Bloodborne Pathogens means pathogenic microorganisms that are present in human blood and can cause disease in humans. These pathogens include, but are not limited to, hepatitis B virus (HBV) and human immunodeficiency virus (HIV).

Clinical Laboratory means a workplace where diagnostic or other screening procedures are performed on blood or other potentially infectious materials.

Contaminated means the presence or the reasonably anticipated presence of blood or other potentially infectious materials on an item or surface.

Contaminated Laundry means laundry which has been soiled with blood or other potentially infectious materials or may contain sharps.

Contaminated Sharps means any contaminated object that can penetrate the skin including, but not limited to, needles, scalpels, broken glass, broken capillary tubes, and exposed ends of dental wires.

Decontamination means the use of physical or chemical means to remove, inactivate, or destroy bloodborne pathogens on a surface or item to the point where they are no longer capable of transmitting infectious particles and the surface or item is rendered safe for handling, use, or disposal.

Director means the Director of the National Institute for Occupational Safety and Health, U.S. Department of Health and Human Services, or designated representative.

Engineering Controls means controls (e.g., sharps disposal containers, self-sheathing needles) that isolate or remove the bloodborne pathogens hazard from the workplace.

Exposure Incident means a specific eye, mouth, other mucous membrane, non-intact skin, or parenteral contact with blood or other potentially infectious materials that results from the performance of an employee's duties.

Handwashing Facilities means a facility providing an adequate supply of running potable water, soap and single use towels or hot air drying machines.

Licensed Healthcare Professional is a person whose legally permitted scope of practice allows him or her to independently perform the activities required by paragraph (f) Hepatitis B Vaccination and Post-exposure Evaluation and Follow-up.

HBV means hepatitis B virus.

HIV means human immunodeficiency virus.

Occupational Exposure means reasonably anticipated skin, eye, mucous membrane, or parenteral contact with blood or other potentially infectious materials that may result from the performance of an employee's duties.

Other Potentially Infectious Materials means

(1) The following human body fluids: semen, vaginal secretions, cerebrospinal fluid, synovial fluid, pleural fluid, pericardial fluid, peritoneal fluid, amniotic fluid, saliva in dental procedures, any body fluid that is visibly contaminated with blood, and all body fluids in situations where it is difficult or impossible to differentiate between body fluids;

(2) Any unfixed tissue or organ (other than intact skin) from a human (living or dead); and

(3) HIV-containing cell or tissue cultures, organ cultures, and HIV- or HBV-containing culture medium or other solutions; and blood, organs, or other tissues from experimental animals infected with HIV or HBV.

Parenteral means piercing mucous membranes or the skin barrier through such events as needlesticks, human bites, cuts, and abrasions.

Personal Protective Equipment is specialized clothing or equipment worn by an employee for protection against a hazard. General work clothes (e.g., uniforms, pants, shirts or blouses) not intended to function as protection against a hazard are not considered to be personal protective equipment.

Production Facility means a facility engaged in industrial-scale, large-volume or high concentration production of HIV or HBV.

Regulated Waste means liquid or semi-liquid blood or other potentially infectious materials; contaminated items that would release blood or other potentially infectious materials in a liquid or semi-liquid state if compressed; items that are caked with dried blood or other potentially infectious materials and are capable of releasing these materials during handling; contaminated sharps; and pathological and microbiological wastes containing blood or other potentially infectious materials.

Research Laboratory means a laboratory producing or using research-laboratory-scale amounts of HIV or HBV. Research laboratories may produce high concentrations of HIV or HBV but not in the volume found in production facilities.

Source Individual means any individual, living or dead, whose blood or other potentially infectious materials may be a source of occupational exposure to the employee. Examples include, but are not limited to, hospital and clinic patients; clients in institutions for the developmentally disabled; trauma victims; clients of drug and alcohol treatment facilities; residents of hospices and nursing homes; human remains; and individuals who donate or sell blood or blood components.

Sterilize means the use of a physical or chemical procedure to destroy all microbial life including highly resistant bacterial endospores.

Universal Precautions is an approach to infection control. According to the concept of Universal Precautions, all human blood and certain human body fluids are treated as if known to be infectious for HIV, HBV, and other bloodborne pathogens.

Work Practice Controls means controls that reduce the likelihood of exposure by altering the manner in which a task is performed (e.g., prohibiting recapping of needles by a two-handed technique).

(c) *Exposure control—*(1) *Exposure Control Plan.* (i) Each employer having an employee(s) with occupational exposure as defined by paragraph (b) of this section shall establish a written Exposure Control Plan designed to eliminate or minimize employee exposure.

(ii) The Exposure Control Plan shall contain at least the following elements:

(A) The exposure determination required by paragraph(c)(2),

(B) The schedule and method of implementation for paragraphs (d) Methods of Compliance, (e) HIV and HBV Research Laboratories and Production Facilities, (f) Hepatitis B Vaccination and Post-Exposure Evaluation and Follow-up, (g) Communication of Hazards to Employees, and (h) Recordkeeping, of this standard, and

(C) The procedure for the evaluation of circumstances surrounding exposure

incidents as required by paragraph (f)(3)(i) of this standard.

(iii) Each employer shall ensure that a copy of the Exposure Control Plan is accessible to employees in accordance with 29 CFR 1910.20(e).

(iv) The Exposure Control Plan shall be reviewed and updated at least annually and whenever necessary to reflect new or modified tasks and procedures which affect occupational exposure and to reflect new or revised employee positions with occupational exposure.

(v) The Exposure Control Plan shall be made available to the Assistant Secretary and the Director upon request for examination and copying.

(2) *Exposure determination.* (i) Each employer who has an employee(s) with occupational exposure as defined by paragraph (b) of this section shall prepare an exposure determination. This exposure determination shall contain the following:

(A) A list of all job classifications in which all employees in those job classifications have occupational exposure;

(B) A list of job classifications in which some employees have occupational exposure, and

(C) A list of all tasks and procedures or groups of closely related task and procedures in which occupational exposure occurs and that are performed by employees in job classifications listed in accordance with the provisions of paragraph (c)(2)(i)(B) of this standard.

(ii) This exposure determination shall be made without regard to the use of personal protective equipment.

(d) *Methods of compliance—*(1) *General—*Universal precautions shall be observed to prevent contact with blood or other potentially infectious materials. Under circumstances in which differentiation between body fluid types is difficult or impossible, all body fluids shall be considered potentially infectious materials.

(2) *Engineering and work practice controls.* (i) Engineering and work practice controls shall be used to eliminate or minimize employee exposure. Where occupational exposure remains after institution of these controls, personal protective equipment shall also be used.

(ii) Engineering controls shall be examined and maintained or replaced on a regular schedule to ensure their effectiveness.

(iii) Employers shall provide handwashing facilities which are readily accessible to employees.

(iv) When provision of handwashing facilities is not feasible, the employer shall provide either an appropriate antiseptic hand cleanser in conjunction with clean cloth/paper towels or antiseptic towelettes. When antiseptic hand cleansers or towelettes are used, hands shall be washed with soap and running water as soon as feasible.

(v) Employers shall ensure that employees wash their hands immediately or as soon as feasible after removal of gloves or other personal protective equipment.

(vi) Employers shall ensure that employees wash hands and any other skin with soap and water, or flush mucous membranes with water immediately or as soon as feasible following contact of such body areas with blood or other potentially infectious materials.

(vii) Contaminated needles and other contaminated sharps shall not be bent, recapped, or removed except as noted in paragraphs (d)(2)(vii)(A) and (d)(2)(vii)(B) below. Shearing or breaking of contaminated needles is prohibited.

(A) Contaminated needles and other contaminated sharps shall not be bent, recapped or removed unless the employer can demonstrate that no alternative is feasible or that such action is required by a specific medical or dental procedure.

(B) Such bending, recapping or needle removal must be accomplished through the use of a mechanical device or a one-handed technique.

(viii) Immediately or as soon as possible after use, contaminated reusable sharps shall be placed in appropriate containers until properly reprocessed. These containers shall be:

(A) Puncture resistant;

(B) Labeled or color-coded in accordance with this standard;

(C) Leakproof on the sides and bottom; and

(D) In accordance with the requirements set forth in paragraph (d)(4)(ii)(E) for reusable sharps.

(ix) Eating, drinking, smoking, applying cosmetics or lip balm, and handling contact lenses are prohibited in work areas where there is a reasonable likelihood of occupational exposure.

(x) Food and drink shall not be kept in refrigerators, freezers, shelves, cabinets or on countertops or benchtops where blood or other potentially infectious materials are present.

(xi) All procedures involving blood or other potentially infectious materials shall be performed in such a manner as to minimize splashing, spraying, spattering, and generation of droplets of these substances.

(xii) Mouth pipetting/suctioning of blood or other potentially infectious materials is prohibited.

(xiii) Specimens of blood or other potentially infectious materials shall be placed in a container which prevents leakage during collection, handling, processing, storage, transport, or shipping.

(A) The container for storage, transport, or shipping shall be labeled or color-coded according to paragraph (g)(1)(i) and closed prior to being stored, transported, or shipped. When a facility utilizes Universal Precautions in the handling of all specimens, the labeling/color-coding of specimens is not necessary provided containers are recognizable as containing specimens. This exemption only applies while such specimens/containers remain within the facility. Labeling or color-coding in accordance with paragraph (g)(1)(i) is required when such specimens/containers leave the facility.

(B) If outside contamination of the primary container occurs, the primary container shall be placed within a second container which prevents leakage during handling, processing, storage, transport, or shipping and is labeled or color-coded according to the requirements of this standard.

(C) If the specimen could puncture the primary container, the primary container shall be placed within a secondary container which is puncture-resistant in addition to the above characteristics.

(xiv) Equipment which may become contaminated with blood or other potentially infectious materials shall be examined prior to servicing or shipping and shall be decontaminated as necessary, unless the employer can demonstrate that decontamination of such equipment or portions of such equipment is not feasible.

(A) A readily observable label in accordance with paragraph (g)(1)(i)(H) shall be attached to the equipment stating which portions remain contaminated.

(B) The employer shall ensure that this information is conveyed to all affected employees, the servicing representative, and/or the manufacturer, as appropriate, prior to handling, servicing, or shipping so that appropriate precautions will be taken.

(3) *Personal protective equipment*—(i) Provision. When there is occupational exposure, the employer shall provide, at no cost to the employee, appropriate personal protective equipment such as, but not limited to, gloves, gowns, laboratory coats, face shields or masks and eye protection, and mouthpieces, resuscitation bags, pocket masks, or other ventilation devices. Personal protective equipment will be considered "appropriate" only if it does not permit blood or other potentially infectious materials to pass through to or reach the employee's work clothes, street clothes, undergarments, skin, eyes, mouth, or other mucous membranes under normal conditions of use and for the duration of time which the protective equipment will be used.

(ii) Use. The employer shall ensure that the employee uses appropriate personal protective equipment unless the employer shows that the employee temporarily and briefly declined to use personal protective equipment when, under rare and extraordinary circumstances, it was the employee's professional judgment that in the specific instance its use would have prevented the delivery of health care or public safety services or would have posed an increased hazard to the safety of the worker or co-worker. When the employee makes this judgement, the circumstances shall be investigated and documented in order to determine whether changes can be instituted to prevent such occurences in the future.

(iii) Accessibility. The employer shall ensure that appropriate personal protective equipment in the appropriate sizes is readily accessible at the worksite or is issued to employees.

Hypoallergenic gloves, glove liners, powderless gloves, or other similar alternatives shall be readily accessible to those employees who are allergic to the gloves normally provided.

(iv) Cleaning, Laundering, and Disposal. The employer shall clean, launder, and dispose of personal protective equipment required by paragraphs (d) and (e) of this standard, at no cost to the employee.

(v) Repair and Replacement. The employer shall repair or replace personal protective equipment as needed to maintain its effectiveness, at no cost to the employee.

(vi) If a garment(s) is penetrated by blood or other potentially infectious materials, the garment(s) shall be removed immediately or as soon as feasible.

(vii) All personal protective equipment shall be removed prior to leaving the work area.

(viii) When personal protective equipment is removed it shall be placed in an appropriately designated area or container for storage, washing, decontamination or disposal.

(ix) Gloves. Gloves shall be worn when it can be reasonably anticipated that the employee may have hand contact with blood, other potentially infectious materials, mucous membranes, and non-intact skin; when performing vascular access procedures except as specified in paragraph (d)(3)(ix)(D); and when handling or touching contaminated items or surfaces.

(A) Disposable (single use) gloves such as surgical or examination gloves, shall be replaced as soon as practical when contaminated or as soon as feasible if they are torn, punctured, or when their ability to function as a barrier is compromised.

(B) Disposable (single use) gloves shall not be washed or decontaminated for re-use.

(C) Utility gloves may be decontaminated for re-use if the integrity of the glove is not compromised. However, they must be discarded if they are cracked, peeling, torn, punctured, or exhibit other signs of deterioration or when their ability to function as a barrier is compromised.

(D) If an employer in a volunteer blood donation center judges that routine gloving for all phlebotomies is not necessary then the employer shall:

(1) Periodically reevaluate this policy;

(2) Make gloves available to all employees who wish to use them for phlebotomy;

(3) Not discourage the use of gloves for phlebotomy; and

(4) Require that gloves be used for phlebotomy in the following circumstances:

(i) When the employee has cuts, scratches, or other breaks in his or her skin;

(ii) When the employee judges that hand contamination with blood may occur, for example, when performing phlebotomy on an uncooperative source individual; and

(iii) When the employee is receiving training in phlebotomy.

(x) Masks, Eye Protection, and Face Shields. Masks in combination with eye protection devices, such as goggles or glasses with solid side shields, or chin-length face shields, shall be worn whenever splashes, spray, spatter, or droplets of blood or other potentially infectious materials may be generated and eye, nose, or mouth contamination can be reasonably anticipated.

(xi) Gowns, Aprons, and Other Protective Body Clothing. Appropriate protective clothing such as, but not limited to, gowns, aprons, lab coats, clinic jackets, or similar outer garments shall be worn in occupational exposure situations. The type and characteristics will depend upon the task and degree of exposure anticipated.

(xii) Surgical caps or hoods and/or shoe covers or boots shall be worn in instances when gross contamination can reasonably be anticipated (e.g., autopsies, orthopaedic surgery).

(4) *Housekeeping.* (i) General. Employers shall ensure that the worksite is maintained in a clean and sanitary condition. The employer shall determine and implement an appropriate written schedule for cleaning and method of decontamination based upon the location within the facility, type of surface to be cleaned, type of soil present, and tasks or procedures being performed in the area.

(ii) All equipment and environmental and working surfaces shall be cleaned and decontaminated after contact with blood or other potentially infectious materials.

(A) Contaminated work surfaces shall be decontaminated with an appropriate disinfectant after completion of procedures; immediately or as soon as feasible when surfaces are overtly contaminated or after any spill of blood or other potentially infectious materials; and at the end of the work shift if the surface may have become contaminated since the last cleaning.

(B) Protective coverings, such as plastic wrap, aluminum foil, or imperviously-backed absorbent paper used to cover equipment and environmental surfaces, shall be removed and replaced as soon as feasible when they become overtly contaminated or at the end of the workshift if they may have become contaminated during the shift.

(C) All bins, pails, cans, and similar receptacles intended for reuse which have a reasonable likelihood for becoming contaminated with blood or other potentially infectious materials shall be inspected and decontaminated on a regularly scheduled basis and cleaned and decontaminated immediately or as soon as feasible upon visible contamination.

(D) Broken glassware which may be contaminated shall not be picked up directly with the hands. It shall be cleaned up using mechanical means, such as a brush and dust pan, tongs, or forceps.

(E) Reusable sharps that are contaminated with blood or other potentially infectious materials shall not be stored or processed in a manner that requires employees to reach by hand into the containers where these sharps have been placed.

(iii) Regulated Waste.

(A) Contaminated Sharps Discarding and Containment. (1) Contaminated sharps shall be discarded immediately or as soon as feasible in containers that are:

(i) Closable;

(ii) Puncture resistant;

(iii) Leakproof on sides and bottom; and

(*iv*) Labeled or color-coded in accordance with paragraph (g)(1)(i) of this standard.

(2) During use, containers for contaminated sharps shall be:

(*i*) Easily accessible to personnel and located as close as is feasible to the immediate area where sharps are used or can be reasonably anticipated to be found (e.g., laundries);

(*ii*) Maintained upright throughout use; and

(*iii*) Replaced routinely and not be allowed to overfill.

(3) When moving containers of contaminated sharps from the area of use, the containers shall be:

(*i*) Closed immediately prior to removal or replacement to prevent spillage or protrusion of contents during handling, storage, transport, or shipping;

(*ii*) Placed in a secondary container if leakage is possible. The second container shall be:

(*A*) Closable;

(*B*) Constructed to contain all contents and prevent leakage during handling, storage, transport, or shipping; and

(*C*) Labeled or color-coded according to paragraph (g)(1)(i) of this standard.

(4) Reusable containers shall not be opened, emptied, or cleaned manually or in any other manner which would expose employees to the risk of percutaneous injury.

(B) Other Regulated Waste Containment. (1) Regulated waste shall be placed in containers which are:

(*i*) Closable;

(*ii*) Constructed to contain all contents and prevent leakage of fluids during handling, storage, transport or shipping;

(*iii*) Labeled or color-coded in accordance with paragraph (g)(1)(i) this standard; and

(*iv*) Closed prior to removal to prevent spillage or protrusion of contents during handling, storage, transport, or shipping.

(2) If outside contamination of the regulated waste container occurs, it shall be placed in a second container. The second container shall be:

(*i*) Closable;

(*ii*) Constructed to contain all contents and prevent leakage of fluids dur-

ing handling, storage, transport or shipping;

(*iii*) Labeled or color-coded in accordance with paragraph (g)(1)(i) of this standard; and

(*iv*) Closed prior to removal to prevent spillage or protrusion of contents during handling, storage, transport, or shipping.

(C) Disposal of all regulated waste shall be in accordance with applicable regulations of the United States, States and Territories, and political subdivisions of States and Territories.

(iv) Laundry.

(A) Contaminated laundry shall be handled as little as possible with a minimum of agitation. (1) Contaminated laundry shall be bagged or containerized at the location where it was used and shall not be sorted or rinsed in the location of use.

(2) Contaminated laundry shall be placed and transported in bags or containers labeled or color-coded in accordance with paragraph (g)(1)(i) of this standard. When a facility utilizes Universal Precautions in the handling of all soiled laundry, alternative labeling or color-coding is sufficient if it permits all employees to recognize the containers as requiring compliance with Universal Precautions.

(3) Whenever contaminated laundry is wet and presents a reasonable likelihood of soak-through of or leakage from the bag or container, the laundry shall be placed and transported in bags or containers which prevent soak-through and/or leakage of fluids to the exterior.

(B) The employer shall ensure that employees who have contact with contaminated laundry wear protective gloves and other appropriate personal protective equipment.

(C) When a facility ships contaminated laundry off-site to a second facility which does not utilize Universal Precautions in the handling of all laundry, the facility generating the contaminated laundry must place such laundry in bags or containers which are labeled or color-coded in accordance with paragraph (g)(1)(i).

(e) *HIV and HBV Research Laboratories and Production Facilities.* (1) This paragraph applies to research laboratories and production facilities engaged in the culture, production, concentration, experimentation, and manipulation of HIV and HBV. It does not apply to clinical or diagnostic laboratories engaged solely in the analysis of blood, tissues, or organs. These requirements apply in addition to the other requirements of the standard.

(2) Research laboratories and production facilities shall meet the following criteria:

(i) Standard microbiological practices. All regulated waste shall either be incinerated or decontaminated by a method such as autoclaving known to effectively destroy bloodborne pathogens.

(ii) Special practices.

(A) Laboratory doors shall be kept closed when work involving HIV or HBV is in progress.

(B) Contaminated materials that are to be decontaminated at a site away from the work area shall be placed in a durable, leakproof, labeled or color-coded container that is closed before being removed from the work area.

(C) Access to the work area shall be limited to authorized persons. Written policies and procedures shall be established whereby only persons who have been advised of the potential biohazard, who meet any specific entry requirements, and who comply with all entry and exit procedures shall be allowed to enter the work areas and animal rooms.

(D) When other potentially infectious materials or infected animals are present in the work area or containment module, a hazard warning sign incorporating the universal biohazard symbol shall be posted on all access doors. The hazard warning sign shall comply with paragraph (g)(1)(ii) of this standard.

(E) All activities involving other potentially infectious materials shall be conducted in biological safety cabinets or other physical-containment devices within the containment module. No work with these other potentially infectious materials shall be conducted on the open bench.

(F) Laboratory coats, gowns, smocks, uniforms, or other appropriate protective clothing shall be used in the work area and animal rooms. Protective clothing shall not be worn outside of the work area and shall be decontaminated before being laundered.

(G) Special care shall be taken to avoid skin contact with other potentially infectious materials. Gloves shall be worn when handling infected animals and when making hand contact with other potentially infectious materials is unavoidable.

(H) Before disposal all waste from work areas and from animal rooms shall either be incinerated or decontaminated by a method such as autoclaving known to effectively destroy bloodborne pathogens.

(I) Vacuum lines shall be protected with liquid disinfectant traps and high-efficiency particulate air (HEPA) filters or filters of equivalent or superior efficiency and which are checked routinely and maintained or replaced as necessary.

(J) Hypodermic needles and syringes shall be used only for parenteral injection and aspiration of fluids from laboratory animals and diaphragm bottles. Only needle-locking syringes or disposable syringe-needle units (i.e., the needle is integral to the syringe) shall be used for the injection or aspiration of other potentially infectious materials. Extreme caution shall be used when handling needles and syringes. A needle shall not be bent, sheared, replaced in the sheath or guard, or removed from the syringe following use. The needle and syringe shall be promptly placed in a puncture-resistant container and autoclaved or decontaminated before reuse or disposal.

(K) All spills shall be immediately contained and cleaned up by appropriate professional staff or others properly trained and equipped to work with potentially concentrated infectious materials.

(L) A spill or accident that results in an exposure incident shall be immediately reported to the laboratory director or other responsible person.

(M) A biosafety manual shall be prepared or adopted and periodically reviewed and updated at least annually or more often if necessary. Personnel shall be advised of potential hazards, shall be required to read instructions on practices and procedures, and shall be required to follow them.

(iii) *Containment equipment.* (A) Certified biological safety cabinets (Class I, II, or III) or other appropriate combinations of personal protection or physical containment devices, such as special protective clothing, respirators, centrifuge safety cups, sealed centrifuge rotors, and containment caging for animals, shall be used for all activities with other potentially infectious materials that pose a threat of exposure to droplets, splashes, spills, or aerosols.

(B) Biological safety cabinets shall be certified when installed, whenever they are moved and at least annually.

(3) HIV and HBV research laboratories shall meet the following criteria:

(i) Each laboratory shall contain a facility for hand washing and an eye wash facility which is readily available within the work area.

(ii) An autoclave for decontamination of regulated waste shall be available.

(4) HIV and HBV production facilities shall meet the following criteria:

(i) The work areas shall be separated from areas that are open to unrestricted traffic flow within the building. Passage through two sets of doors shall be the basic requirement for entry into the work area from access corridors or other contiguous areas. Physical separation of the high-containment work area from access corridors or other areas or activities may also be provided by a double-doored clothes-change room (showers may be included), airlock, or other access facility that requires passing through two sets of doors before entering the work area.

(ii) The surfaces of doors, walls, floors and ceilings in the work area shall be water resistant so that they can be easily cleaned. Penetrations in these surfaces shall be sealed or capable of being sealed to facilitate decontamination.

(iii) Each work area shall contain a sink for washing hands and a readily available eye wash facility. The sink shall be foot, elbow, or automatically operated and shall be located near the exit door of the work area.

(iv) Access doors to the work area or containment module shall be self-closing.

(v) An autoclave for decontamination of regulated waste shall be available within or as near as possible to the work area.

(vi) A ducted exhaust-air ventilation system shall be provided. This system shall create directional airflow that draws air into the work area through the entry area. The exhaust air shall not be recirculated to any other area of the building, shall be discharged to the outside, and shall be dispersed away from occupied areas and air intakes. The proper direction of the airflow shall be verified (i.e., into the work area).

(5) *Training Requirements.* Additional training requirements for employees in HIV and HBV research laboratories and HIV and HBV production facilities are specified in paragraph (g)(2)(ix).

(f) *Hepatitis B vaccination and post-exposure evaluation and follow-up—*(1) *General.* (i) The employer shall make available the hepatitis B vaccine and vaccination series to all employees who have occupational exposure, and post-exposure evaluation and follow-up to all employees who have had an exposure incident.

(ii) The employer shall ensure that all medical evaluations and procedures including the hepatitis B vaccine and vaccination series and post-exposure evaluation and follow-up, including prophylaxis, are:

(A) Made available at no cost to the employee;

(B) Made available to the employee at a reasonable time and place;

(C) Performed by or under the supervision of a licensed physician or by or under the supervision of another licensed healthcare professional; and

(D) Provided according to recommendations of the U.S. Public Health Service current at the time these evaluations and procedures take place, except as specified by this paragraph (f).

(iii) The employer shall ensure that all laboratory tests are conducted by an accredited laboratory at no cost to the employee.

(2) *Hepatitis B Vaccination.* (i) Hepatitis B vaccination shall be made available after the employee has received the training required in paragraph (g)(2)(vii)(I) and within 10 working days

of initial assignment to all employees who have occupational exposure unless the employee has previously received the complete hepatitis B vaccination series, antibody testing has revealed that the employee is immune, or the vaccine is contraindicated for medical reasons.

(ii) The employer shall not make participation in a prescreening program a prerequisite for receiving hepatitis B vaccination.

(iii) If the employee initially declines hepatitis B vaccination but at a later date while still covered under the standard decides to accept the vaccination, the employer shall make available hepatitis B vaccination at that time.

(iv) The employer shall assure that employees who decline to accept hepatitis B vaccination offered by the employer sign the statement in appendix A.

(v) If a routine booster dose(s) of hepatitis B vaccine is recommended by the U.S. Public Health Service at a future date, such booster dose(s) shall be made available in accordance with section (f)(1)(ii).

(3) *Post-exposure Evaluation and Follow-up.* Following a report of an exposure incident, the employer shall make immediately available to the exposed employee a confidential medical evaluation and follow-up, including at least the following elements:

(i) Documentation of the route(s) of exposure, and the circumstances under which the exposure incident occurred;

(ii) Identification and documentation of the source individual, unless the employer can establish that identification is infeasible or prohibited by state or local law;

(A) The source individual's blood shall be tested as soon as feasible and after consent is obtained in order to determine HBV and HIV infectivity. If consent is not obtained, the employer shall establish that legally required consent cannot be obtained. When the source individual's consent is not required by law, the source individual's blood, if available, shall be tested and the results documented.

(B) When the source individual is already known to be infected with HBV or HIV, testing for the source individual's known HBV or HIV status need not be repeated.

(C) Results of the source individual's testing shall be made available to the exposed employee, and the employee shall be informed of applicable laws and regulations concerning disclosure of the identity and infectious status of the source individual.

(iii) Collection and testing of blood for HBV and HIV serological status;

(A) The exposed employee's blood shall be collected as soon as feasible and tested after consent is obtained.

(B) If the employee consents to baseline blood collection, but does not give consent at that time for HIV serologic testing, the sample shall be preserved for at least 90 days. If, within 90 days of the exposure incident, the employee elects to have the baseline sample tested, such testing shall be done as soon as feasible.

(iv) Post-exposure prophylaxis, when medically indicated, as recommended by the U.S. Public Health Service;

(v) Counseling; and

(vi) Evaluation of reported illnesses.

(4) *Information Provided to the Healthcare Professional.* (i) The employer shall ensure that the healthcare professional responsible for the employee's Hepatitis B vaccination is provided a copy of this regulation.

(ii) The employer shall ensure that the healthcare professional evaluating an employee after an exposure incident is provided the following information:

(A) A copy of this regulation;

(B) A description of the exposed employee's duties as they relate to the exposure incident;

(C) Documentation of the route(s) of exposure and circumstances under which exposure occurred;

(D) Results of the source individual's blood testing, if available; and

(E) All medical records relevant to the appropriate treatment of the employee including vaccination status which are the employer's responsibility to maintain.

(5) *Healthcare Professional's Written Opinion.* The employer shall obtain and provide the employee with a copy of the evaluating healthcare professional's written opinion within 15 days of the completion of the evaluation.

(i) The healthcare professional's written opinion for Hepatitis B vaccination shall be limited to whether Hepatitis B vaccination is indicated for an employee, and if the employee has received such vaccination.

(ii) The healthcare professional's written opinion for post-exposure evaluation and follow-up shall be limited to the following information:

(A) That the employee has been informed of the results of the evaluation; and

(B) That the employee has been told about any medical conditions resulting from exposure to blood or other potentially infectious materials which require further evaluation or treatment.

(iii) All other findings or diagnoses shall remain confidential and shall not be included in the written report.

(6) *Medical recordkeeping.* Medical records required by this standard shall be maintained in accordance with paragraph (h)(1) of this section.

(g) *Communication of hazards to employees*—(1) *Labels and signs.* (i) Labels. (A) Warning labels shall be affixed to containers of regulated waste, refrigerators and freezers containing blood or other potentially infectious material; and other containers used to store, transport or ship blood or other potentially infectious materials, except as provided in paragraph (g)(1)(i)(E), (F) and (G).

(B) Labels required by this section shall include the following legend:

BIOHAZARD

(C) These labels shall be fluorescent orange or orange-red or predominantly so, with lettering and symbols in a contrasting color.

(D) Labels shall be affixed as close as feasible to the container by string, wire, adhesive, or other method that prevents their loss or unintentional removal.

(E) Red bags or red containers may be substituted for labels.

(F) Containers of blood, blood components, or blood products that are labeled as to their contents and have been released for transfusion or other clinical use are exempted from the labeling requirements of paragraph (g).

(G) Individual containers of blood or other potentially infectious materials that are placed in a labeled container during storage, transport, shipment or disposal are exempted from the labeling requirement.

(H) Labels required for contaminated equipment shall be in accordance with this paragraph and shall also state which portions of the equipment remain contaminated.

(I) Regulated waste that has been decontaminated need not be labeled or color-coded.

(ii) Signs. (A) The employer shall post signs at the entrance to work areas specified in paragraph (e), HIV and HBV Research Laboratory and Production Facilities, which shall bear the following legend:

BIOHAZARD

(Name of the Infectious Agent)
(Special requirements for entering the area)
(Name, telephone number of the laboratory director or other responsible person.)

(B) These signs shall be fluorescent orange-red or predominantly so, with lettering and symbols in a contrasting color.

(2) *Information and Training.* (i) Employers shall ensure that all employees with occupational exposure participate in a training program which must be provided at no cost to the employee and during working hours.

(ii) Training shall be provided as follows:

(A) At the time of initial assignment to tasks where occupational exposure may take place;

(B) Within 90 days after the effective date of the standard; and

(C) At least annually thereafter.

(iii) For employees who have received training on bloodborne pathogens in the year preceding the effective date of the standard, only training with respect to the provisions of the standard which were not included need be provided.

(iv) Annual training for all employees shall be provided within one year of their previous training.

(v) Employers shall provide additional training when changes such as modification of tasks or procedures or institution of new tasks or procedures affect the employee's occupational exposure. The additional training may be limited to addressing the new exposures created.

(vi) Material appropriate in content and vocabulary to educational level, literacy, and language of employees shall be used.

(vii) The training program shall contain at a minimum the following elements:

(A) An accessible copy of the regulatory text of this standard and an explanation of its contents;

(B) A general explanation of the epidemiology and symptoms of bloodborne diseases;

(C) An explanation of the modes of transmission of bloodborne pathogens;

(D) An explanation of the employer's exposure control plan and the means by which the employee can obtain a copy of the written plan;

(E) An explanation of the appropriate methods for recognizing tasks and other activities that may involve exposure to blood and other potentially infectious materials;

(F) An explanation of the use and limitations of methods that will prevent or reduce exposure including appropriate engineering controls, work practices, and personal protective equipment;

(G) Information on the types, proper use, location, removal, handling, decontamination and disposal of personal protective equipment;

(H) An explanation of the basis for selection of personal protective equipment;

(I) Information on the hepatitis B vaccine, including information on its efficacy, safety, method of administration, the benefits of being vaccinated, and that the vaccine and vaccination will be offered free of charge;

(J) Information on the appropriate actions to take and persons to contact in an emergency involving blood or other potentially infectious materials;

(K) An explanation of the procedure to follow if an exposure incident occurs, including the method of reporting the incident and the medical follow-up that will be made available;

(L) Information on the post-exposure evaluation and follow-up that the employer is required to provide for the employee following an exposure incident;

(M) An explanation of the signs and labels and/or color coding required by paragraph (g)(1); and

(N) An opportunity for interactive questions and answers with the person conducting the training session.

(viii) The person conducting the training shall be knowledgeable in the subject matter covered by the elements contained in the training program as it relates to the workplace that the training will address.

(ix) Additional Initial Training for Employees in HIV and HBV Laboratories and Production Facilities. Employees in HIV or HBV research laboratories and HIV or HBV production facilities shall receive the following initial training in addition to the above training requirements.

(A) The employer shall assure that employees demonstrate proficiency in standard microbiological practices and techniques and in the practices and operations specific to the facility before being allowed to work with HIV or HBV.

(B) The employer shall assure that employees have prior experience in the handling of human pathogens or tissue cultures before working with HIV or HBV.

(C) The employer shall provide a training program to employees who have no prior experience in handling human pathogens. Initial work activities shall not include the handling of infectious agents. A progression of work activities shall be assigned as techniques are learned and proficiency is developed. The employer shall assure that employees participate in work activities involving infectious agents only after proficiency has been demonstrated.

(h) *Recordkeeping*—(1) *Medical Records.* (i) The employer shall establish and maintain an accurate record for each employee with occupational exposure, in accordance with 29 CFR 1910.20.

(ii) This record shall include:

(A) The name and social security number of the employee;

(B) A copy of the employee's hepatitis B vaccination status including the dates of all the hepatitis B vaccinations and any medical records relative to the employee's ability to receive vaccination as required by paragraph (f)(2);

(C) A copy of all results of examinations, medical testing, and follow-up procedures as required by paragraph (f)(3);

(D) The employer's copy of the healthcare professional's written opinion as required by paragraph (f)(5); and

(E) A copy of the information provided to the healthcare professional as required by paragraphs (f)(4)(ii)(B)(C) and (D).

(iii) *Confidentiality.* The employer shall ensure that employee medical records required by paragraph (h)(1) are:

(A) Kept confidential; and

(B) Not disclosed or reported without the employee's express written consent to any person within or outside the workplace except as required by this section or as may be required by law.

(iv) The employer shall maintain the records required by paragraph (h) for at least the duration of employment plus 30 years in accordance with 29 CFR 1910.20.

(2) *Training Records.* (i) Training records shall include the following information:

(A) The dates of the training sessions;

(B) The contents or a summary of the training sessions;

(C) The names and qualifications of persons conducting the training; and

(D) The names and job titles of all persons attending the training sessions.

(ii) Training records shall be maintained for 3 years from the date on which the training occurred.

(3) *Availability.* (i) The employer shall ensure that all records required to be maintained by this section shall be made available upon request to the Assistant Secretary and the Director for examination and copying.

(ii) Employee training records required by this paragraph shall be provided upon request for examination and copying to employees, to employee representatives, to the Director, and to the Assistant Secretary.

(iii) Employee medical records required by this paragraph shall be provided upon request for examination and copying to the subject employee, to anyone having written consent of the subject employee, to the Director, and to the Assistant Secretary in accordance with 29 CFR 1910.20.

(4) *Transfer of Records.* (i) The employer shall comply with the requirements involving transfer of records set forth in 29 CFR 1910.20(h).

(ii) If the employer ceases to do business and there is no successor employer to receive and retain the records for the prescribed period, the employer shall notify the Director, at least three months prior to their disposal and transmit them to the Director, if required by the Director to do so, within that three month period.

(i) *Dates*—(1) *Effective Date.* The standard shall become effective on March 6, 1992.

(2) The Exposure Control Plan required by paragraph (c) of this section shall be completed on or before May 5, 1992.

(3) Paragraph (g)(2) Information and Training and (h) Recordkeeping shall take effect on or before June 4, 1992.

(4) Paragraphs (d)(2) Engineering and Work Practice Controls, (d)(3) Personal Protective Equipment, (d)(4) Housekeeping, (e) HIV and HBV Research Laboratories and Production Facilities, (f) Hepatitis B Vaccination and Post-Exposure Evaluation and Follow-

up, and (g) (1) Labels and Signs, shall take effect July 6, 1992.

APPENDIX A TO SECTION 1910.1030—HEPATITIS
B VACCINE DECLINATION (MANDATORY)

I understand that due to my occupational exposure to blood or other potentially infectious materials I may be at risk of acquiring hepatitis B virus (HBV) infection. I have been given the opportunity to be vaccinated with hepatitis B vaccine, at no charge to myself. However, I decline hepatitis B vaccination at this time. I understand that by declining this vaccine, I continue to be at risk of acquiring hepatitis B, a serious disease. If in the future I continue to have occupational exposure to blood or other potentially infectious materials and I want to be vaccinated with hepatitis B vaccine, I can receive the vaccination series at no charge to me.

(Apporved by the Office of Management and Budget under control number 1218–0180)

[56 FR 64175, Dec. 6, 1991, as amended at 57 FR 12717, Apr. 13, 1992; 57 FR 29206, July 1, 1992]

29 CFR 1910.1450

OCCUPATIONAL EXPOSURE TO HAZARDOUS CHEMICALS IN LABORATORIES

§ 1910.1450 Occupational exposure to hazardous chemicals in laboratories.

(a) *Scope and application.* (1) This section shall apply to all employers engaged in the laboratory use of hazardous chemicals as defined below.

(2) Where this section applies, it shall supersede, for laboratories, the requirements of all other OSHA health standards in 29 CFR part 1910, subpart Z, except as follows:

(i) For any OSHA health standard, only the requirement to limit employee exposure to the specific permissible exposure limit shall apply for laboratories, unless that particular standard states otherwise or unless the conditions of paragraph (a)(2)(iii) of this section apply.

(ii) Prohibition of eye and skin contact where specified by any OSHA health standard shall be observed.

(iii) Where the action level (or in the absence of an action level, the permissible exposure limit) is routinely exceeded for an OSHA regulated substance with exposure monitoring and medical surveillance requirements, paragraphs (d) and (g)(1)(ii) of this section shall apply.

(3) This section shall not apply to:

(i) Uses of hazardous chemicals which do not meet the definition of laboratory use, and in such cases, the employer shall comply with the relevant standard in 29 CFR part 1910, subpart Z, even if such use occurs in a laboratory.

(ii) Laboratory uses of hazardous chemicals which provide no potential for employee exposure. Examples of such conditions might include:

(A) Procedures using chemically-impregnated test media such as Dip-and-Read tests where a reagent strip is dipped into the specimen to be tested and the results are interpreted by comparing the color reaction to a color chart supplied by the manufacturer of the test strip; and

(B) Commercially prepared kits such as those used in performing pregnancy tests in which all of the reagents needed to conduct the test are contained in the kit.

(b) *Definitions—*

Action level means a concentration designated in 29 CFR part 1910 for a specific substance, calculated as an eight (8)-hour time-weighted average, which initiates certain required activities such as exposure monitoring and medical surveillance.

Assistant Secretary means the Assistant Secretary of Labor for Occupational Safety and Health, U.S. Department of Labor, or designee.

Carcinogen (see *select carcinogen*).

Chemical Hygiene Officer means an employee who is designated by the employer, and who is qualified by training or experience, to provide technical guidance in the development and implementation of the provisions of the Chemical Hygiene Plan. This definition is not intended to place limitations on the position description or job classification that the designated indvidual shall hold within the employer's organizational structure.

Chemical Hygiene Plan means a written program developed and implemented by the employer which sets forth procedures, equipment, personal protective equipment and work practices that (i) are capable of protecting employees from the health hazards presented by hazardous chemicals used in that particular workplace and (ii) meets the requirements of paragraph (e) of this section.

Combustible liquid means any liquid having a flashpoint at or above 100 °F (37.8 °C), but below 200 °F (93.3 °C), except any mixture having components with flashpoints of 200 °F (93.3 °C), or higher, the total volume of which make up 99 percent or more of the total volume of the mixture.

Compressed gas means:

(i) A gas or mixture of gases having, in a container, an absolute pressure exceeding 40 psi at 70 °F (21.1 °C); or

(ii) A gas or mixture of gases having, in a container, an absolute pressure exceeding 104 psi at 130 °F (54.4 °C) regardless of the pressure at 70 °F (21.1 °C); or

(iii) A liquid having a vapor pressure exceeding 40 psi at 100 °F (37.8 °C) as determined by ASTM D–323–72.

Designated area means an area which may be used for work with "select carcinogens," reproductive toxins or substances which have a high degree of acute toxicity. A designated area may be the entire laboratory, an area of a laboratory or a device such as a laboratory hood.

Emergency means any occurrence such as, but not limited to, equipment failure, rupture of containers or failure of control equipment which results in an uncontrolled release of a hazardous chemical into the workplace.

Employee means an individual employed in a laboratory workplace who may be exposed to hazardous chemicals in the course of his or her assignments.

Explosive means a chemical that causes a sudden, almost instantaneous release of pressure, gas, and heat when subjected to sudden shock, pressure, or high temperature.

Flammable means a chemical that falls into one of the following categories:

(i) *Aerosol, flammable* means an aerosol that, when tested by the method described in 16 CFR 1500.45, yields a flame protection exceeding 18 inches at full valve opening, or a flashback (a flame extending back to the valve) at any degree of valve opening;

(ii) *Gas, flammable* means:

(A) A gas that, at ambient temperature and pressure, forms a flammable mixture with air at a concentration of 13 percent by volume or less; or

(B) A gas that, at ambient temperature and pressure, forms a range of flammable mixtures with air wider than 12 percent by volume, regardless of the lower limit.

(iii) *Liquid, flammable* means any liquid having a flashpoint below 100 °F (37.8 °C), except any mixture having components with flashpoints of 100 °F (37.8 °C) or higher, the total of which make up 99 percent or more of the total volume of the mixture.

(iv) *Solid, flammable* means a solid, other than a blasting agent or explosive as defined in § 1910.109(a), that is liable to cause fire through friction, absorption of moisture, spontaneous chemical change, or retained heat from manufacturing or processing, or which can be ignited readily and when ignited burns so vigorously and persistently as to create a serious hazard. A chemical shall be considered to be a flammable solid if, when tested by the method described in 16 CFR 1500.44, it ignites and burns with a self-sustained flame at a rate greater than one-tenth of an inch per second along its major axis.

Flashpoint means the minimum temperature at which a liquid gives off a vapor in sufficient concentration to ignite when tested as follows:

(i) Tagliabue Closed Tester (See American National Standard Method of Test for Flash Point by Tag Closed Tester, Z11.24–1979 (ASTM D 56–79))-for liquids with a viscosity of less than 45 Saybolt Universal Seconds (SUS) at 100 °F (37.8 °C), that do not contain suspended solids and do not have a tendency to form a surface film under test; or

(ii) Pensky-Martens Closed Tester (see American National Standard Method of Test for Flash Point by Pensky-Martens Closed Tester, Z11.7–1979 (ASTM D 93–79))-for liquids with a viscosity equal to or greater than 45 SUS at 100 °F (37.8 °C), or that contain suspended solids, or that have a tendency to form a surface film under test; or

(iii) Setaflash Closed Tester (see American National Standard Method of Test for Flash Point by Setaflash Closed Tester (ASTM D 3278–78)).

Organic peroxides, which undergo autoaccelerating thermal decomposition, are excluded from any of the flashpoint determination methods specified above.

Hazardous chemical means a chemical for which there is statistically significant evidence based on at least one study conducted in accordance with established scientific principles that acute or chronic health effects may occur in exposed employees. The term *health hazard* includes chemicals which are carcinogens, toxic or highly toxic agents, reproductive toxins, irritants, corrosives, sensitizers, hepatotoxins, nephrotoxins, neurotoxins, agents which act on the hematopoietic systems, and agents which damage the

Occupational Safety and Health Admin., Labor   **§ 1910.1450**

lungs, skin, eyes, or mucous membranes.

Appendices A and B of the Hazard Communication Standard (29 CFR 1910.1200) provide further guidance in defining the scope of health hazards and determining whether or not a chemical is to be considered hazardous for purposes of this standard.

Laboratory means a facility where the "laboratory use of hazardous chemicals" occurs. It is a workplace where relatively small quantities of hazardous chemicals are used on a non-production basis.

Laboratory scale means work with substances in which the containers used for reactions, transfers, and other handling of substances are designed to be easily and safely manipulated by one person. "Laboratory scale" excludes those workplaces whose function is to produce commercial quantities of materials.

Laboratory-type hood means a device located in a laboratory, enclosure on five sides with a moveable sash or fixed partial enclosed on the remaining side; constructed and maintained to draw air from the laboratory and to prevent or minimize the escape of air contaminants into the laboratory; and allows chemical manipulations to be conducted in the enclosure without insertion of any portion of the employee's body other than hands and arms.

Walk-in hoods with adjustable sashes meet the above definition provided that the sashes are adjusted during use so that the airflow and the exhaust of air contaminants are not compromised and employees do not work inside the enclosure during the release of airborne hazardous chemicals.

Laboratory use of hazardous chemicals means handling or use of such chemicals in which all of the following conditions are met:

(i) Chemical manipulations are carried out on a "laboratory scale;"

(ii) Multiple chemical procedures or chemicals are used;

(iii) The procedures involved are not part of a production process, nor in any way simulate a production process; and

(iv) "Protective laboratory practices and equipment" are available and in common use to minimize the potential

for employee exposure to hazardous chemicals.

Medical consultation means a consultation which takes place between an employee and a licensed physician for the purpose of determining what medical examinations or procedures, if any, are appropriate in cases where a significant exposure to a hazardous chemical may have taken place.

Organic peroxide means an organic compound that contains the bivalent $-O-O-$ structure and which may be considered to be a structural derivative of hydrogen peroxide where one or both of the hydrogen atoms has been replaced by an organic radical.

Oxidizer means a chemical other than a blasting agent or explosive as defined in § 1910.109(a), that initiates or promotes combustion in other materials, thereby causing fire either of itself or through the release of oxygen or other gases.

Physical hazard means a chemical for which there is scientifically valid evidence that it is a combustible liquid, a compressed gas, explosive, flammable, an organic peroxide, an oxidizer, pyrophoric, unstable (reactive) or water-reactive.

Protective laboratory practices and equipment means those laboratory procedures, practices and equipment accepted by laboratory health and safety experts as effective, or that the employer can show to be effective, in minimizing the potential for employee exposure to hazardous chemicals.

Reproductive toxins means chemicals which affect the reproductive capabilities including chromosomal damage (mutations) and effects on fetuses (teratogenesis)

Select carcinogen means any substance which meets one of the following criteria:

(i) It is regulated by OSHA as a carcinogen; or

(ii) It is listed under the category, "known to be carcinogens," in the Annual Report on Carcinogens published by the National Toxicology Program (NTP) (latest edition); or

(iii) It is listed under Group 1 ("carcinogenic to humans") by the International Agency for Research on Cancer Monographs (IARC) (latest editions); or

(iv) It is listed in either Group 2A or 2B by IARC or under the category, "reasonably anticipated to be carcinogens" by NTP, and causes statistically significant tumor incidence in experimental animals in accordance with any of the following criteria:

(A) After inhalation exposure of 6–7 hours per day, 5 days per week, for a significant portion of a lifetime to dosages of less than 10 mg/m³;

(B) After repeated skin application of less than 300 (mg/kg of body weight) per week; or

(C) After oral dosages of less than 50 mg/kg of body weight per day.

Unstable (reactive) means a chemical which is the pure state, or as produced or transported, will vigorously polymerize, decompose, condense, or will become self-reactive under conditions of shocks, pressure or temperature.

Water-reactive means a chemical that reacts with water to release a gas that is either flammable or presents a health hazard.

(c) *Permissible exposure limits.* For laboratory uses of OSHA regulated substances, the employer shall assure that laboratory employees' exposures to such substances do not exceed the permissible exposure limits specified in 29 CFR part 1910, subpart Z.

(d) *Employee exposure determination—* (1) *Initial monitoring.* The employer shall measure the employee's exposure to any substance regulated by a standard which requires monitoring if there is reason to believe that exposure levels for that substance routinely exceed the action level (or in the absence of an action level, the PEL).

(2) *Periodic monitoring.* If the initial monitoring prescribed by paragraph (d)(1) of this section discloses employee exposure over the action level (or in the absence of an action level, the PEL), the employer shall immediately comply with the exposure monitoring provisions of the relevant standard.

(3) *Termination of monitoring.* Monitoring may be terminated in accordance with the relevant standard.

(4) *Employee notification of monitoring results.* The employer shall, within 15 working days after the receipt of any monitoring results, notify the employee of these results in writing either individually or by posting results in an appropriate location that is accessible to employees.

(e) *Chemical hygiene plan—General.* (Appendix A of this section is non-mandatory but provides guidance to assist employers in the development of the Chemical Hygiene Plan.)

(1) Where hazardous chemicals as defined by this standard are used in the workplace, the employer shall develop and carry out the provisions of a written Chemical Hygiene Plan which is:

(i) Capable of protecting employees from health hazards associated with hazardous chemicals in that laboratory and

(ii) Capable of keeping exposures below the limits specified in paragraph (c) of this section.

(2) The Chemical Hygiene Plan shall be readily available to employees, employee representatives and, upon request, to the Assistant Secretary.

(3) The Chemical Hygiene Plan shall include each of the following elements and shall indicate specific measures that the employer will take to ensure laboratory employee protection:

(i) Standard operating procedures relevant to safety and health considerations to be followed when laboratory work involves the use of hazardous chemicals;

(ii) Criteria that the employer will use to determine and implement control measures to reduce employee exposure to hazardous chemicals including engineering controls, the use of personal protective equipment and hygiene practices; particular attention shall be given to the selection of control measures for chemicals that are known to be extremely hazardous;

(iii) A requirement that fume hoods and other protective equipment are functioning properly and specific measures that shall be taken to ensure proper and adequate performance of such equipment;

(iv) Provisions for employee information and training as prescribed in paragraph (f) of this section;

(v) The circumstances under which a particular laboratory operation, procedure or activity shall require prior approval from the employer or the employer's designee before implementation;

(vi) Provisions for medical consultation and medical examinations in accordance with paragraph (g) of this section;

(vii) Designation of personnel responsible for implementation of the Chemical Hygiene Plan including the assignment of a Chemical Hygiene Officer and, if appropriate, establishment of a Chemical Hygiene Committee; and

(viii) Provisions for additional employee protection for work with particularly hazardous substances. These include "select carcinogens," reproductive toxins and substances which have a high degree of acute toxicity. Specific consideration shall be given to the following provisions which shall be included where appropriate:

(A) Establishment of a designated area;

(B) Use of containment devices such as fume hoods or glove boxes;

(C) Procedures for safe removal of contaminated waste; and

(D) Decontamination procedures.

(4) The employer shall review and evaluate the effectiveness of the Chemical Hygiene Plan at least annually and update it as necessary.

(f) *Employee information and training.* (1) The employer shall provide employees with information and training to ensure that they are apprised of the hazards of chemicals present in their work area.

(2) Such information shall be provided at the time of an employee's initial assignment to a work area where hazardous chemicals are present and prior to assignments involving new exposure situations. The frequency of refresher information and training shall be determined by the employer.

(3) *Information.* Employees shall be informed of:

(i) The contents of this standard and its appendices which shall be made available to employees;

(ii) The location and availability of the employer's Chemical Hygiene Plan;

(iii) The permissible exposure limits for OSHA regulated substances or recommended exposure limits for other hazardous chemicals where there is no applicable OSHA standard;

(iv) Signs and symptoms associated with exposures to hazardous chemicals used in the laboratory; and

(v) The location and availability of known reference material on the hazards, safe handling, storage and disposal of hazardous chemicals found in the laboratory including, but not limited to, Material Safety Data Sheets received from the chemical supplier.

(4) *Training.* (i) Employee training shall include:

(A) Methods and observations that may be used to detect the presence or release of a hazardous chemical (such as monitoring conducted by the employer, continuous monitoring devices, visual appearance or odor of hazardous chemicals when being released, etc.);

(B) The physical and health hazards of chemicals in the work area; and

(C) The measures employees can take to protect themselves from these hazards, including specific procedures the employer has implemented to protect employees from exposure to hazardous chemicals, such as appropriate work practices, emergency procedures, and personal protective equipment to be used.

(ii) The employee shall be trained on the applicable details of the employer's written Chemical Hygiene Plan.

(g) *Medical consultation and medical examinations.* (1) The employer shall provide all employees who work with hazardous chemicals an opportunity to receive medical attention, including any follow-up examinations which the examining physician determines to be necessary, under the following circumstances:

(i) Whenever an employee develops signs or symptoms associated with a hazardous chemical to which the employee may have been exposed in the laboratory, the employee shall be provided an opportunity to receive an appropriate medical examination.

(ii) Where exposure monitoring reveals an exposure level routinely above the action level (or in the absence of an action level, the PEL) for an OSHA regulated substance for which there are exposure monitoring and medical surveillance requirements, medical surveillance shall be established for the affected employee as prescribed by the particular standard.

(iii) Whenever an event takes place in the work area such as a spill, leak, explosion or other occurrence resulting in the likelihood of a hazardous exposure, the affected employee shall be provided an opportunity for a medical consultation. Such consultation shall be for the purpose of determining the need for a medical examination.

(2) All medical examinations and consultations shall be performed by or under the direct supervision of a licensed physician and shall be provided without cost to the employee, without loss of pay and at a reasonable time and place.

(3) *Information provided to the physician.* The employer shall provide the following information to the physician:

(i) The identity of the hazardous chemical(s) to which the employee may have been exposed;

(ii) A description of the conditions under which the exposure occurred including quantitative exposure data, if available; and

(iii) A description of the signs and symptoms of exposure that the employee is experiencing, if any.

(4) *Physician's written opinion.* (i) For examination or consultation required under this standard, the employer shall obtain a written opinion from the examining physician which shall include the following:

(A) Any recommendation for further medical follow-up;

(B) The results of the medical examination and any associated tests,

(C) Any medical condition which may be revealed in the course of the examination which may place the employee at increased risk as a result of exposure to a hazardous chemical found in the workplace; and

(D) A statement that the employee has been informed by the physician of the results of the consultation or medical examination and any medical condition that may require further examination or treatment.

(ii) The written opinion shall not reveal specific findings of diagnoses unrelated to occupational exposure.

(h) *Hazard identification.* (1) With respect to labels and material safety data sheets:

(i) Employers shall ensure that labels on incoming containers of hazardous chemicals are not removed or defaced.

(ii) Employers shall maintain any material safety data sheets that are received with incoming shipments of hazardous chemicals, and ensure that they are readily accessible to laboratory employees.

(2) The following provisions shall apply to chemical substances developed in the laboratory:

(i) If the composition of the chemical substance which is produced exclusively for the laboratory's use is known, the employer shall determine if it is a hazardous chemical as defined in paragraph (b) of this section. If the chemical is determined to be hazardous, the employer shall provide appropriate training as required under paragraph (f) of this section.

(ii) If the chemical produced is a by-product whose composition is not known, the employer shall assume that the substance is hazardous and shall implement paragraph (e) of this section.

(iii) If the chemical substance is produced for another user outside of the laboratory, the employer shall comply with the Hazard Communication Standard (29 CFR 1910.1200) including the requirements for preparation of material safety data sheets and labeling.

(i) *Use of respirators.* Where the use of respirators is necessary to maintain exposure below permissible exposure limits, the employer shall provide, at no cost to the employee, the proper respiratory equipment. Respirators shall be selected and used in accordance with the requirements of 29 CFR 1910.134.

(j) *Recordkeeping.* (1) The employer shall establish and maintain for each employee an accurate record of any measurements taken to monitor employee exposures and any medical consultation and examinations including tests or written opinions required by this standard.

(2) The employer shall assure that such records are kept, transferred, and made available in accordance with 29 CFR 1910.20.

(k) *Dates*—(1) *Effective date.* This section shall become effective May 1, 1990.

(2) *Start-up dates.* (i) Employers shall have developed and implemented a written Chemical Hygiene Plan no later than January 31, 1991.

(ii) Paragraph (a)(2) of this section shall not take effect until the employer has developed and implemented a written Chemical Hygiene Plan.

(1) *Appendices.* The information contained in the appendices is not intended, by itself, to create any additional obligations not otherwise imposed or to detract from any existing obligation.

[55 FR 3327, Jan. 31, 1990, 55 FR 7967, Mar. 6, 1990, 55 FR 12111, Mar. 30, 1990]

APPENDIX A TO §1910.1450—NATIONAL RESEARCH COUNCIL RECOMMENDATIONS CONCERNING CHEMICAL HYGIENE IN LABORATORIES (NON-MANDATORY)

TABLE OF CONTENTS

Foreword

Foreword

As guidance for each employer's development of an appropriate laboratory Chemical Hygiene Plan, the following non-mandatory recommendations are provided. They were extracted from "Prudent Practices for Handling Hazardous Chemicals in Laboratories" (referred to below as "Prudent Practices"), which was published in 1981 by the National Research Council and is available from the National Academy Press, 2101 Constitution Ave., NW., Washington DC 20418.

"Prudent Practices" is cited because of its wide distribution and acceptance and because of its preparation by members of the laboratory community through the sponsorship of the National Research Council. However, none of the recommendations given here will modify any requirements of the laboratory standard. This Appendix merely presents pertinent recommendations from "Prudent Practices", organized into a form convenient for quick reference during operation of a laboratory facility and during development and application of a Chemical Hygiene Plan. Users of this appendix should consult "Prudent Practices" for a more extended presentation and justification for each recommendation.

"Prudent Practices" deals with both safety and chemical hazards while the laboratory standard is concerned primarily with chemical hazards. Therefore, only those recommendations directed primarily toward control of toxic exposures are cited in this appendix, with the term "chemical hygiene" being substituted for the word "safety". However, since conditions producing or threatening physical injury often pose toxic risks as well, page references concerning major categories of safety hazards in the laboratory are given in section F.

The recommendations from "Prudent Practices" have been paraphrased, combined, or otherwise reorganized, and headings have been added. However, their sense has not been changed.

§ 1910.1450, App. A

Corresponding Sections of the Standard and this Appendix

The following table is given for the convenience of those who are developing a Chemical Hygiene Plan which will satisfy the requirements of paragraph (e) of the standard. It indicates those sections of this appendix which are most pertinent to each of the sections of paragraph (e) and related paragraphs.

Paragraph and topic in laboratory standard	Relevant appendix section
(e)(3)(i) Standard operating procedures for handling toxic chemicals.	C, D, E
(e)(3)(ii) Criteria to be used for implementation of measures to reduce exposures.	D
(e)(3)(iii) Fume hood performance	C4b
(e)(3)(iv) Employee information and training (including emergency procedures).	D10, D9
(e)(3)(v) Requirements for prior approval of laboratory activities.	E2b, E4b
(e)(3)(vi) Medical consultation and medical examinations.	D5, E4f
(e)(3)(vii) Chemical hygiene responsibilities ...	B
(e)(3)(viii) Special precautions for work with particularly hazardous substances.	E2, E3, E4

In this appendix, those recommendations directed primarily at administrators and supervisors are given in sections A–D. Those recommendations of primary concern to employees who are actually handling laboratory chemicals are given in section E. (Reference to page numbers in "Prudent Practices" are given in parentheses.)

A. General Principles for Work with Laboratory Chemicals

In addition to the more detailed recommendations listed below in sections B–E, "Prudent Practices" expresses certain general principles, including the following:

1. *It is prudent to minimize all chemical exposures.* Because few laboratory chemicals are without hazards, general precautions for handling all laboratory chemicals should be adopted, rather than specific guidelines for particular chemicals (2, 10). Skin contact with chemicals should be avoided as a cardinal rule (198).

2. *Avoid underestimation of risk.* Even for substances of no known significant hazard, exposure should be minimized; for work with substances which present special hazards, special precautions should be taken (10, 37, 38). One should assume that any mixture will be more toxic than its most toxic component (30, 103) and that all substances of unknown toxicity are toxic (3, 34).

3. *Provide adequate ventilation.* The best way to prevent exposure to airborne substances is to prevent their escape into the working atmosphere by use of hoods and other ventilation devices (32, 198).

4. *Institute a chemical hygiene program.* A mandatory chemical hygiene program designed to minimize exposures is needed; it should be a regular, continuing effort, not merely a standby or short-term activity (6, 11). Its recommendations should be followed in academic teaching laboratories as well as by full-time laboratory workers (13).

5. *Observe the PELs, TLVs.* The Permissible Exposure Limits of OSHA and the Threshold Limit Values of the American Conference of Governmental Industrial Hygienists should not be exceeded (13).

B. Chemical Hygiene Responsibilities

Responsibility for chemical hygiene rests at all levels (6, 11, 21) including the:

1. *Chief executive officer,* who has ultimate responsibility for chemical hygiene within the institution and must, with other administrators, provide continuing support for institutional chemical hygiene (7, 11).

2. *Supervisor of the department or other administrative unit,* who is responsible for chemical hygiene in that unit (7).

3. *Chemical hygiene officer(s),* whose appointment is essential (7) and who must:

(a) Work with administrators and other employees to develop and implement appropriate chemical hygiene policies and practices (7);

(b) Monitor procurement, use, and disposal of chemicals used in the lab (8);

(c) See that appropriate audits are maintained (8);

(d) Help project directors develop precautions and adequate facilities (10);

(e) Know the current legal requirements concerning regulated substances (50); and

(f) Seek ways to improve the chemical hygiene program (8, 11).

4. *Laboratory supervisor,* who has overall responsibility for chemical hygiene in the laboratory (21) including responsibility to:

(a) Ensure that workers know and follow the chemical hygiene rules, that protective equipment is available and in working order, and that appropriate training has been provided (21, 22);

(b) Provide regular, formal chemical hygiene and housekeeping inspections including routine inspections of emergency equipment (21, 171);

(c) Know the current legal requirements concerning regulated substances (50, 231);

(d) Determine the required levels of protective apparel and equipment (156, 160, 162); and

(e) Ensure that facilities and training for use of any material being ordered are adequate (215).

5. *Project director or director of other specific operation,* who has primary responsibility for chemical hygiene procedures for that operation (7).

6. *Laboratory worker,* who is responsible for:

(a) Planning and conducting each operation in accordance with the institutional chemical hygiene procedures (7, 21, 22, 230); and

(b) Developing good personal chemical hygiene habits (22).

C. The Laboratory Facility

1. *Design.* The laboratory facility should have:

(a) An appropriate general ventilation system (see C4 below) with air intakes and exhausts located so as to avoid intake of contaminated air (194);

(b) Adequate, well-ventilated stockrooms/storerooms (218, 219);

(c) Laboratory hoods and sinks (12, 162);

(d) Other safety equipment including eyewash fountains and drench showers (162, 169); and

(e) Arrangements for waste disposal (12, 240).

2. *Maintenance.* Chemical-hygiene-related equipment (hoods, incinerator, etc.) should undergo continuing appraisal and be modified if inadequate (11, 12).

3. *Usage.* The work conducted (10) and its scale (12) must be appropriate to the physical facilities available and, especially, to the quality of ventilation (13).

4. *Ventilation—*(a) *General laboratory ventilation.* This system should: Provide a source of air for breathing and for input to local ventilation devices (199); it should not be relied on for protection from toxic substances released into the laboratory (198); ensure that laboratory air is continually replaced, preventing increase of air concentrations of toxic substances during the working day (194); direct air flow into the laboratory from non-laboratory areas and out to the exterior of the building (194).

(b) *Hoods.* A laboratory hood with 2.5 linear feet of hood space per person should be provided for every 2 workers if they spend most of their time working with chemicals (199); each hood should have a continuous monitoring device to allow convenient confirmation of adequate hood performance before use (200, 209). If this is not possible, work with substances of unknown toxicity should be avoided (13) or other types of local ventilation devices should be provided (199). See pp. 201–206 for a discussion of hood design, construction, and evaluation.

(c) *Other local ventilation devices.* Ventilated storage cabinets, canopy hoods, snorkels, etc. should be provided as needed (199). Each canopy hood and snorkel should have a separate exhaust duct (207).

(d) *Special ventilation areas.* Exhaust air from glove boxes and isolation rooms should be passed through scrubbers or other treatment before release into the regular exhaust system (208). Cold rooms and warm rooms should have provisions for rapid escape and for escape in the event of electrical failure (209).

(e) *Modifications.* Any alteration of the ventilation system should be made only if thorough testing indicates that worker protection from airborne toxic substances will continue to be adequate (12, 193, 204).

(f) *Performance.* Rate: 4–12 room air changes/hour is normally adequate general ventilation if local exhaust systems such as hoods are used as the primary method of control (194).

(g) *Quality.* General air flow should not be turbulent and should be relatively uniform throughout the laboratory, with no high velocity or static areas (194, 195); airflow into and within the hood should not be excessively turbulent (200); hood face velocity should be adequate (typically 60–100 lfm) (200, 204).

(h) *Evaluation.* Quality and quantity of ventilation should be evaluated on installation (202), regularly monitored (at least every 3 months) (6, 12, 14, 195), and reevaluated whenever a change in local ventilation devices is made (12, 195, 207). See pp. 195–198 for methods of evaluation and for calculation of estimated airborne contaminant concentrations.

D. Components of the Chemical Hygiene Plan

1. Basic Rules and Procedures (Recommendations for these are given in section E, below)

2. Chemical Procurement, Distribution, and Storage

(a) *Procurement.* Before a substance is received, information on proper handling, storage, and disposal should be known to those who will be involved (215, 216). No container should be accepted without an adequate identifying label (216). Preferably, all substances should be received in a central location (216).

(b) *Stockrooms/storerooms.* Toxic substances should be segregated in a well-identified area with local exhaust ventilation (221). Chemicals which are highly toxic (227) or other chemicals whose containers have been opened should be in unbreakable secondary containers (219). Stored chemicals should be examined periodically (at least annually) for replacement, deterioration, and container integrity (218–19).

Stockrooms/storerooms should not be used as preparation or repackaging areas, should be open during normal working hours, and should be controlled by one person (219).

(c) *Distribution.* When chemicals are hand carried, the container should be placed in an outside container or bucket. Freight-only elevators should be used if possible (223).

(d) *Laboratory storage.* Amounts permitted should be as small as practical. Storage on bench tops and in hoods is inadvisable. Exposure to heat or direct sunlight should be avoided. Periodic inventories should be conducted, with unneeded items being discarded or returned to the storeroom/stockroom (225–6, 229).

3. Environmental Monitoring

Regular instrumental monitoring of airborne concentrations is not usually justified or practical in laboratories but may be appropriate when testing or redesigning hoods or other ventilation devices (12) or when a highly toxic substance is stored or used regularly (e.g., 3 times/week) (13).

4. Housekeeping, Maintenance, and Inspections

(a) Cleaning. Floors should be cleaned regularly (24).

(b) Inspections. Formal housekeeping and chemical hygiene inspections should be held at least quarterly (6, 21) for units which have frequent pesonnel changes and semiannually for others; informal inspections should be continual (21).

(c) *Maintenance.* Eye wash fountains should be inspected at intervals of not less than 3 months (6). Respirators for routine use should be inspected periodically by the laboratory supervisor (169). Safety showers should be tested routinely (169). Other safety equipment should be inspected regularly. (e.g., every 3–6 months) (6, 24, 171). Procedures to prevent restarting of out of service equipment should be established (25).

(d) *Passageways.* Stairways and hallways should not be used as storage areas (24). Access to exits, emergency equipment, and utility controls should never be blocked (24).

5. Medical Program

(a) *Compliance with regulations.* Regular medical surveillance should be established to the extent required by regulations (12).

(b) *Routine surveillance.* Anyone whose work involves regular and frequent handling of toxicologically significant quantities of a chemical should consult a qualified physician to determine on an individual basis whether a regular schedule of medical surveillance is desirable (11, 50).

(c) *First aid.* Personnel trained in first aid should be available during working hours and an emergency room with medical personnel should be nearby (173). See pp. 176–178 for description of some emergency first aid procedures.

6. Protective Apparel and Equipment

These should include for each laboratory:
(a) Protective apparel compatible with the required degree of protection for substances being handled (158–161);
(b) An easily accessible drench-type safety shower (162, 169);
(c) An eyewash fountain (162);
(d) A fire extinguisher (162–164);

(e) Respiratory protection (164–9), fire alarm and telephone for emergency use (162) should be available nearby; and
(f) Other items designated by the laboratory supervisor (156, 160).

7. Records

(a) Accident records should be written and retained (174).
(b) Chemical Hygiene Plan records should document that the facilities and precautions were compatible with current knowledge and regulations (7).
(c) Inventory and usage records for high-risk substances should be kept as specified in sections E3e below
(d) Medical records should be retained by the institution in accordance with the requirements of state and federal regulations (12).

8. Signs and Labels

Prominent signs and labels of the following types should be posted:
(a) Emergency telephone numbers of emergency personnel/facilities, supervisors, and laboratory workers (28);
(b) Identity labels, showing contents of containers (including waste receptacles) and associated hazards (27, 48);
(c) Location signs for safety showers, eyewash stations, other safety and first aid equipment, exits (27) and areas where food and beverage consumption and storage are permitted (24); and
(d) Warnings at areas or equipment where special or unusual hazards exist (27).

9. Spills and Accidents

(a) A written emergency plan should be established and communicated to all personnel; it should include procedures for ventilation failure (200), evacuation, medical care, reporting, and drills (172).
(b) There should be an alarm system to alert people in all parts of the facility including isolation areas such as cold rooms (172).
(c) A spill control policy should be developed and should include consideration of prevention, containment, cleanup, and reporting (175).
(d) All accidents or near accidents should be carefully analyzed with the results distributed to all who might benefit (8, 28).

10. Information and Training Program

(a) Aim: To assure that all individuals at risk are adequately informed about the work in the laboratory, its risks, and what to do if an accident occurs (5, 15).
(b) Emergency and Personal Protection Training: Every laboratory worker should know the location and proper use of available protective apparel and equipment (154, 169).

Some of the full-time personnel of the laboratory should be trained in the proper use of emergency equipment and procedures (6).

Such training as well as first aid instruction should be available to (154) and encouraged for (176) everyone who might need it.

(c) Receiving and stockroom/storeroom personnel should know about hazards, handling equipment, protective apparel, and relevant regulations (217).

(d) Frequency of Training: The training and education program should be a regular, continuing activity—not simply an annual presentation (15).

(e) Literature/Consultation: Literature and consulting advice concerning chemical hygiene should be readily available to laboratory personnel, who should be encouraged to use these information resources (14).

11. *Waste Disposal Program.*

(a) Aim: To assure that minimal harm to people, other organisms, and the environment will result from the disposal of waste laboratory chemicals (5).

(b) Content (14, 232, 233, 240): The waste disposal program should specify how waste is to be collected, segregated, stored, and transported and include consideration of what materials can be incinerated. Transport from the institution must be in accordance with DOT regulations (244).

(c) Discarding Chemical Stocks: Unlabeled containers of chemicals and solutions should undergo prompt disposal; if partially used, they should not be opened (24, 27).

Before a worker's employment in the laboratory ends, chemicals for which that person was responsible should be discarded or returned to storage (226).

(d) Frequency of Disposal: Waste should be removed from laboratories to a central waste storage area at least once per week and from the central waste storage area at regular intervals (14).

(e) Method of Disposal: Incineration in an environmentally acceptable manner is the most practical disposal method for combustible laboratory waste (14, 238, 241).

Indiscriminate disposal by pouring waste chemicals down the drain (14, 231, 242) or adding them to mixed refuse for landfill burial is unacceptable (14).

Hoods should not be used as a means of disposal for volatile chemicals (40, 200).

Disposal by recycling (233, 243) or chemical decontamination (40, 230) should be used when possible.

E. *Basic Rules and Procedures for Working with Chemicals*

The Chemical Hygiene Plan should require that laboratory workers know and follow its rules and procedures. In addition to the procedures of the sub programs mentioned

above, these should include the rules listed below.

1. General Rules

The following should be used for essentially all laboratory work with chemicals:

(a) *Accidents and spills*—Eye Contact: Promptly flush eyes with water for a prolonged period (15 minutes) and seek medical attention (33, 172).

Ingestion: Encourage the victim to drink large amounts of water (178).

Skin Contact: Promptly flush the affected area with water (33, 172, 178) and remove any contaminated clothing (172, 178). If symptoms persist after washing, seek medical attention (33).

Clean-up. Promptly clean up spills, using appropriate protective apparel and equipment and proper disposal (24 33). See pp. 233–237 for specific clean-up recommendations.

(b) *Avoidance of "routine" exposure:* Develop and encourage safe habits (23); avoid unnecessary exposure to chemicals by any route (23);

Do not smell or taste chemicals (32). Vent apparatus which may discharge toxic chemicals (vacuum pumps, distillation columns, etc.) into local exhaust devices (199).

Inspect gloves (157) and test glove boxes (208) before use.

Do not allow release of toxic substances in cold rooms and warm rooms, since these have contained recirculated atmospheres (209).

(c) *Choice of chemicals:* Use only those chemicals for which the quality of the available ventilation system is appropriate (13).

(d) *Eating, smoking, etc.:* Avoid eating, drinking, smoking, gum chewing, or application of cosmetics in areas where laboratory chemicals are present (22, 24, 32, 40); wash hands before conducting these activities (23, 24).

Avoid storage, handling or consumption of food or beverages in storage areas, refrigerators, glassware or utensils which are also used for laboratory operations (23, 24, 226).

(e) *Equipment and glassware:* Handle and store laboratory glassware with care to avoid damage; do not use damaged glassware (25). Use extra care with Dewar flasks and other evacuated glass apparatus; shield or wrap them to contain chemicals and fragments should implosion occur (25). Use equipment only for its designed purpose (23, 26).

(f) *Exiting:* Wash areas of exposed skin well before leaving the laboratory (23).

(g) *Horseplay:* Avoid practical jokes or other behavior which might confuse, startle or distract another worker (23).

(h) *Mouth suction:* Do not use mouth suction for pipeting or starting a siphon (23, 32).

(i) *Personal apparel:* Confine long hair and loose clothing (23, 158). Wear shoes at all times in the laboratory but do not wear sandals, perforated shoes, or sneakers (158).

(j) *Personal housekeeping:* Keep the work area clean and uncluttered, with chemicals and equipment being properly labeled and stored; clean up the work area on completion of an operation or at the end of each day (24).

(k) *Personal protection:* Assure that appropriate eye protection (154–156) is worn by all persons, including visitors, where chemicals are stored or handled (22, 23, 33, 154).

Wear appropriate gloves when the potential for contact with toxic materials exists (157); inspect the gloves before each use, wash them before removal, and replace them periodically (157). (A table of resistance to chemicals of common glove materials is given on p. 159).

Use appropriate (164–168) respiratory equipment when air contaminant concentrations are not sufficiently restricted by engineering controls (164–5), inspecting the respirator before use (169).

Use any other protective and emergency apparel and equipment as appropriate (22, 157–162).

Avoid use of contact lenses in the laboratory unless necessary; if they are used, inform supervisor so special precautions can be taken (155).

Remove laboratory coats immediately on significant contamination (161).

(l) *Planning:* Seek information and advice about hazards (7), plan appropriate protective procedures, and plan positioning of equipment before beginning any new operation (22, 23).

(m) *Unattended operations:* Leave lights on, place an appropriate sign on the door, and provide for containment of toxic substances in the event of failure of a utility service (such as cooling water) to an unattended operation (27, 128).

(n) *Use of hood:* Use the hood for operations which might result in release of toxic chemical vapors or dust (198–9).

As a rule of thumb, use a hood or other local ventilation device when working with any appreciably volatile substance with a TLV of less than 50 ppm (13).

Confirm adequate hood performance before use; keep hood closed at all times except when adjustments within the hood are being made (200); keep materials stored in hoods to a minimum and do not allow them to block vents or air flow (200).

Leave the hood "on" when it is not in active use if toxic substances are stored in it or if it is uncertain whether adequate general laboratory ventilation will be maintained when it is "off" (200).

(o) *Vigilance:* Be alert to unsafe conditions and see that they are corrected when detected (22).

(p) *Waste disposal:* Assure that the plan for each laboratory operation includes plans and training for waste disposal (230).

Deposit chemical waste in appropriately labeled receptacles and follow all other waste disposal procedures of the Chemical Hygiene Plan (22, 24).

Do not discharge to the sewer concentrated acids or bases (231); highly toxic, malodorous, or lachrymatory substances (231); or any substances which might interfere with the biological activity of waste water treatment plants, create fire or explosion hazards, cause structural damage or obstruct flow (242).

(q) *Working alone:* Avoid working alone in a building; do not work alone in a laboratory if the procedures being conducted are hazardous (28).

2. Working with Allergens and Embryotoxins

(a) *Allergens* (examples: diazomethane, isocyanates, bichromates): Wear suitable gloves to prevent hand contact with allergens or substances of unknown allergenic activity (35).

(b) *Embryotoxins* (34–5) (examples: organomercurials, lead compounds, formamide): If you are a woman of childbearing age, handle these substances only in a hood whose satisfactory performance has been confirmed, using appropriate protective apparel (especially gloves) to prevent skin contact.

Review each use of these materials with the research supervisor and review continuing uses annually or whenever a procedural change is made.

Store these substances, properly labeled, in an adequately ventilated area in an unbreakable secondary container.

Notify supervisors of all incidents of exposure or spills; consult a qualified physician when appropriate.

3. Work with Chemicals of Moderate Chronic or High Acute Toxicity

EXAMPLES: diisopropylflurophosphate (41), hydrofluoric acid (43), hydrogen cyanide (45).

Supplemental rules to be followed in addition to those mentioned above (Procedure B of "Prudent Practices", pp. 39–41):

(a) *Aim:* To minimize exposure to these toxic substances by any route using all reasonable precautions (39).

(b) *Applicability:* These precautions are appropriate for substances with moderate chronic or high acute toxicity used in significant quantities (39).

(c) *Location:* Use and store these substances only in areas of restricted access with special warning signs (40, 229).

Always use a hood (previously evaluated to confirm adequate performance with a face velocity of at least 60 linear feet per minute) (40) or other containment device for procedures which may result in the generation of aerosols or vapors containing the substance

(39); trap released vapors to prevent their discharge with the hood exhaust (40).

(d) *Personal protection:* Always avoid skin contact by use of gloves and long sleeves (and other protective apparel as appropriate) (39). Always wash hands and arms immediately after working with these materials (40).

(e) *Records:* Maintain records of the amounts of these materials on hand, amounts used, and the names of the workers involved (40, 229).

(f) *Prevention of spills and accidents:* Be prepared for accidents and spills (41).

Assure that at least 2 people are present at all times if a compound in use is highly toxic or of unknown toxicity (39).

Store breakable containers of these substances in chemically resistant trays; also work and mount apparatus above such trays or cover work and storage surfaces with removable, absorbent, plastic backed paper (40).

If a major spill occurs outside the hood, evacuate the area; assure that cleanup personnel wear suitable protective apparel and equipment (41).

(g) *Waste:* Thoroughly decontaminate or incinerate contaminated clothing or shoes (41). If possible, chemically decontaminate by chemical conversion (40).

Store contaminated waste in closed, suitably labeled, impervious containers (for liquids, in glass or plastic bottles half-filled with vermiculite) (40).

4. Work with Chemicals of High Chronic Toxicity

(Examples: dimethylmercury and nickel carbonyl (48), benzo-a-pyrene (51), N-nitrosodiethylamine (54), other human carcinogens or substances with high carcinogenic potency in animals (38).)

Further supplemental rules to be followed, in addition to all these mentioned above, for work with substances of known high chronic toxicity (in quantities above a few milligrams to a few grams, depending on the substance) (47). (Procedure A of "Prudent Practices" pp. 47–50).

(a) *Access:* Conduct all transfers and work with these substances in a "controlled area": a restricted access hood, glove box, or portion of a lab, designated for use of highly toxic substances, for which all people with access are aware of the substances being used and necessary precautions (48).

(b) *Approvals:* Prepare a plan for use and disposal of these materials and obtain the approval of the laboratory supervisor (48).

(c) *Non-contamination/Decontamination:* Protect vacuum pumps against contamination by scrubbers or HEPA filters and vent them into the hood (49). Decontaminate vacuum pumps or other contaminated equipment, including glassware, in the hood before removing them from the controlled area (49, 50).

Decontaminate the controlled area before normal work is resumed there (50).

(d) *Exiting:* On leaving a controlled area, remove any protective apparel (placing it in an appropriate, labeled container) and thoroughly wash hands, forearms, face, and neck (49).

(e) *Housekeeping:* Use a wet mop or a vacuum cleaner equipped with a HEPA filter instead of dry sweeping if the toxic substance was a dry powder (50).

(f) *Medical surveillance:* If using toxicologically significant quantities of such a substance on a regular basis (*e.g.*, 3 times per week), consult a qualified physician concerning desirability of regular medical surveillance (50).

(g) *Records:* Keep accurate records of the amounts of these substances stored (229) and used, the dates of use, and names of users (48).

(h) *Signs and labels:* Assure that the controlled area is conspicuously marked with warning and restricted access signs (49) and that all containers of these substances are appropriately labeled with identity and warning labels (48).

(i) *Spills:* Assure that contingency plans, equipment, and materials to minimize exposures of people and property in case of accident are available (233–4).

(j) *Storage:* Store containers of these chemicals only in a ventilated, limited access (48, 227, 229) area in appropriately labeled, unbreakable, chemically resistant, secondary containers (48, 229).

(k) *Glove boxes:* For a negative pressure glove box, ventilation rate must be at least 2 volume changes/hour and pressure at least 0.5 inches of water (48). For a positive pressure glove box, thoroughly check for leaks before each use (49). In either case, trap the exit gases or filter them through a HEPA filter and then release them into the hood (49).

(l) *Waste:* Use chemical decontamination whenever possible; ensure that containers of contaminated waste (including washings from contaminated flasks) are transferred from the controlled area in a secondary container under the supervision of authorized personnel (49, 50, 233).

5. Animal Work with Chemicals of High Chronic Toxicity

(a) *Access:* For large scale studies, special facilities with restricted access are preferable (56).

(b) *Administration of the toxic substance:* When possible, administer the substance by injection or gavage instead of in the diet. If administration is in the diet, use a caging system under negative pressure or under laminar air flow directed toward HEPA filters (56).

(c) *Aerosol suppression:* Devise procedures which minimize formation and dispersal of contaminated aerosols, including those from food, urine, and feces (e.g., use HEPA filtered vacuum equipment for cleaning, moisten contaminated bedding before removal from the cage, mix diets in closed containers in a hood) (55, 56).

(d) *Personal protection:* When working in the animal room, wear plastic or rubber gloves, fully buttoned laboratory coat or jumpsuit and, if needed because of incomplete suppression of aerosols, other apparel and equipment (shoe and head coverings, respirator) (56).

(e) *Waste disposal:* Dispose of contaminated animal tissues and excreta by incineration if the available incinerator can convert the contaminant to non-toxic products (238); otherwise, package the waste appropriately for burial in an EPA-approved site (239).

F. Safety Recommendations

The above recommendations from "Prudent Practices" do not include those which are directed primarily toward prevention of physical injury rather than toxic exposure. However, failure of precautions against injury will often have the secondary effect of causing toxic exposures. Therefore, we list below page references for recommendations concerning some of the major categories of safety hazards which also have implications for chemical hygiene:

1. Corrosive agents: (35 6)
2. Electrically powered laboratory apparatus: (179–92)
3. Fires, explosions: (26, 57–74, 162–4, 174–5, 219–20, 226–7)
4. Low temperature procedures: (26, 88)
5. Pressurized and vacuum operations (including use of compressed gas cylinders): (27, 75 101)

G. Material Safety Data Sheets

Material safety data sheets are presented in "Prudent Practices" for the chemicals listed below. (Asterisks denote that comprehensive material safety data sheets are provided).

*Acetyl peroxide (105)
*Acrolein (106)
*Acrylonilrile (107)
Ammonia (anhydrous) (91)
*Aniline (109)
*Benzene (110)
*Benzo[a]pyrene (112)
*Bis(chloromethyl) ether (113)
Boron trichloride (91)
Boron trifluoride (92)
Bromine (114)
*Tert-butyl hydroperoxide (148)
*Carbon disulfide (116)
Carbon monoxide (92)
*Carbon tetrachloride (118)
*Chlorine (119)
Chlorine trifluoride (94)
*Chloroform (121)
Chloromethane (93)

*Diethyl ether (122)
Diisopropyl fluorophosphate (41)
*Dimethylformamide (123)
*Dimethyl sulfate (125)
*Dioxane (126)
*Ethylene dibromide (128)
*Fluorine (95)
*Formaldehyde (130)
*Hydrazine and salts (132)
Hydrofluoric acid (43)
Hydrogen bromide (98)
Hydrogen chloride (98)
*Hydrogen cyanide (133)
*Hydrogen sulfide (135)
Mercury and compounds (52)
*Methanol (137)
*Morpholine (138)
*Nickel carbonyl (99)
*Nitrobenzene (139)
Nitrogen dioxide (100)
N-nitrosodiethylamine (54)
*Peracetic acid (141)
*Phenol (142)
*Phosgene (143)
*Pyridine (144)
*Sodium azide (145)
*Sodium cyanide (147)
Sulfur dioxide (101)
*Trichloroethylene (149)
*Vinyl chloride (150)

APPENDIX B TO § 1910 1450—REFERENCES (NON-MANDATORY)

The following references are provided to assist the employer in the development of a Chemical Hygiene Plan. The materials listed below are offered as non-mandatory guidance. References listed here do not imply specific endorsement of a book, opinion, technique, policy or a specific solution for a safety or health problem. Other references not listed here may better meet the needs of a specific laboratory. (a) Materials for the development of the Chemical Hygiene Plan:

1. American Chemical Society, Safety in Academic Chemistry Laboratories, 4th edition, 1985.
2. Fawcett, H.H. and W. S. Wood, Safety and Accident Prevention in Chemical Operations, 2nd edition, Wiley-Interscience, New York, 1982.
3. Flury, Patricia A., Environmental Health and Safety in the Hospital Laboratory, Charles C. Thomas Publisher, Springfield IL, 1978.
4. Green, Michael E. and Turk, Amos, Safety in Working with Chemicals, Macmillan Publishing Co., NY, 1978.
5. Kaufman, James A., Laboratory Safety Guidelines, Dow Chemical Co., Box 1713, Midland, MI 48640, 1977.
6. National Institutes of Health, NIH Guidelines for the Laboratory use of Chemical Carcinogens, NIH Pub. No. 81-2385, GPO, Washington, DC 20402, 1981.
7. National Research Council, Prudent Practices for Disposal of Chemicals from

Laboratories, National Academy Press, Washington, DC, 1983.

8. National Research Council, Prudent Practices for Handling Hazardous Chemicals in Laboratories, National Academy Press, Washington, DC, 1981.

9. Renfrew, Malcolm, Ed., Safety in the Chemical Laboratory, Vol. IV, *J. Chem. Ed.*, American Chemical Society, Easlon, PA, 1981.

10. Steere, Norman V., Ed., Safety in the Chemical Laboratory, *J. Chem. Ed.* American Chemical Society, Easlon, PA, 18042, Vol. I, 1967, Vol. II, 1971, Vol. III 1974.

11. Steere, Norman V., Handbook of Laboratory Safety, the Chemical Rubber Company Cleveland, OH, 1971.

12. Young, Jay A., Ed., Improving Safety in the Chemical Laboratory, John Wiley & Sons, Inc. New York, 1987.

(b) Hazardous Substances Information:

1. American Conference of Governmental Industrial Hygienists, Threshold Limit Values for Chemical Substances and Physical Agents in the Workroom Environment with Intended Changes, 6500 Glenway Avenue, Bldg. D–7 Cincinnati, OH 45211–4438 (latest edition).

2. Annual Report on Carcinogens, National Toxicology Program U.S. Department of Health and Human Services, Public Health Service, U.S. Government Printing Office, Washington, DC, (latest edition).

3. Best Company, Best Safety Directory, Vols. I and II, Oldwick, N.J., 1981.

4. Bretherick, L., Handbook of Reactive Chemical Hazards, 2nd edition, Butterworths, London, 1979.

5. Bretherick, L., Hazards in the Chemical Laboratory, 3rd edition, Royal Society of Chemistry, London, 1986.

6. Code of Federal Regulations, 29 CFR part 1910 subpart Z. U.S. Govt. Printing Office, Washington, DC 20402 (latest edition).

7. IARC Monographs on the Evaluation of the Carcinogenic Risk of Chemicals to Man, World Health Organization Publications Center, 49 Sheridan Avenue, Albany, New York 12210 (latest editions).

8. NIOSH/OSHA Pocket Guide to Chemical Hazards. NIOSH Pub. No. 85–114, U.S. Government Printing Office, Washington, DC, 1985 (or latest edition).

9. Occupational Health Guidelines, NIOSH/OSHA NIOSH Pub. No. 81–123 U.S. Government Printing Office, Washington, DC, 1981.

10. Patty, F.A., Industrial Hygiene and Toxicology, John Wiley & Sons, Inc., New York, NY (Five Volumes).

11. Registry of Toxic Effects of Chemical Substances, U.S. Department of Health and Human Services, Public Health Service, Centers for Disease Control, National Institute for Occupational Safety and Health, Revised Annually, for sale from Superintendent of Documents U.S. Govt. Printing Office, Washington, DC 20402.

12. The Merck Index: An Encyclopedia of Chemicals and Drugs. Merck and Company Inc. Rahway, N.J., 1976 (or latest edition).

13. Sax, N.I. Dangerous Properties of Industrial Materials, 5th edition, Van Nostrand Reinhold, NY., 1979.

14. Sittig, Marshall, Handbook of Toxic and Hazardous Chemicals, Noyes Publications, Park Ridge, NJ, 1981.

(c) Information on Ventilation:

1. American Conference of Governmental Industrial Hygienists Industrial Ventilation (latest edition), 6500 Glenway Avenue, Bldg. D–7, Cincinnati, Ohio 45211–4438.

2. American National Standards Institute, Inc. American National Standards Fundamentals Governing the Design and Operation of Local Exhaust Systems ANSI Z 9.2–1979 American National Standards Institute, N.Y. 1979.

3. Imad, A.P. and Watson, C.L. Ventilation Index: An Easy Way to Decide about Hazardous Liquids, Professional Safety pp 15–18, April 1980.

4. National Fire Protection Association, Fire Protection for Laboratories Using Chemicals NFPA–45, 1982.

Safety Standard for Laboratories in Health Related Institutions, NFPA, 56c, 1980.

Fire Protection Guide on Hazardous Materials, 7th edition, 1978.

National Fire Protection Association, Batterymarch Park, Quincy, MA 02269.

5. Scientific Apparatus Makers Association (SAMA), Standard for Laboratory Fume Hoods, SAMA LF7–1980, 1101 16th Street, NW., Washington, DC 20036.

(d) Information on Availability of Referenced Material:

1. American National Standards Institute (ANSI), 1430 Broadway, New York, NY 10018.

2. American Society for Testing and Materials (ASTM), 1916 Race Street, Philadelphia, PA 19103.

(Approved by the Office of Management and Budget under control number 1218–0131)

[55 FR 3327, Jan. 31, 1990; 55 FR 7967, Mar. 6, 1990; 57 FR 29204, July 1, 1992]

Appendix 5A

WORKPLACE INJURY & ILLNESS PREVENTION SAMPLE PROGRAMS

Workplace Injury & Illness Prevention Sample Programs

with sample record forms

CAL OSHA — STATE OF CALIFORNIA — DEPARTMENT OF INDUSTRIAL RELATIONS

CS-1A revised January 1993   Cal/OSHA Consultation Service
State of California—Department of Industrial Relations—Division of Occupational Safety & Health

Cal/OSHA Consultation Service Offices

Headquarters
455 Golden Gate Avenue, Room 5246
San Francisco, CA 94102

Fresno
1901 North Gateway Blvd, Suite 102
Fresno, CA 93727
Telephone (209) 454-1295

Sacramento
2424 Arden Way, Suite 410
Sacramento, CA 95825
Telephone (916) 263-2855

San Diego
7827 Convoy Court, Suite 406
San Diego, CA 92111
Telephone (619) 279-3771

San Mateo
3 Waters Park Drive, Suite 230
San Mateo, CA 94403
Telephone (415) 573-3862

Santa Fe Springs
10350 Heritage Park Drive, Suite 201
Santa Fe Springs, CA 90670
Telephone (310) 944-9366

This publication (CS-1A) can be ordered from:

Department of Industrial Relations
Cal/OSHA Publications
Post Office Box 420603
San Francisco, CA 94142-0603

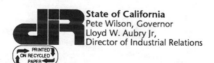

State of California
Pete Wilson, Governor
Lloyd W. Aubry Jr,
Director of Industrial Relations

PRINTED
ON RECYCLED
PAPER

Table of Contents

1

About These Sample Programs

California Senate Bill 198 of 1989 requires every employer in the state, regardless of size or industry, to implement an Injury and Illness Prevention Program (IIPP). It must be a written plan that describes the procedures to be put into practice.

These sample programs—the first for employers whose operations are not complex, and the second for employers who require a more complex IIPP—can be used as a guide for employers to follow in developing their own specific program. The samples were assembled from a variety of plans reviewed by Cal/OSHA Consultation Service staff.

All the required elements of Title 8 (T8) Section 3203 of the *California Code of Regulations* (CCR) are addressed in both samples.

Since each sample was written for a broad spectrum of employers, it may not match your facility exactly. However, it does provide the essential framework needed to customize an Injury and Illness Prevention Program.

The format is not rigid—what is essential is that you have all the required elements in your individual program. You need to develop and carry out specific procedures to transform the sample program into an IIPP that is effective in your workplace.

We have included a sampling of forms that you are welcome to use or revise according to your own needs.

The scope of this program is limited to satisfying the employer's requirement for an IIPP. T8 CCR contains a multitude of other safety and health standards that employers need to learn about and comply with.

Also, employers who have collective bargaining relationships should note that they may have an obligation to bargain over portions of an IIPP.

If you desire further assistance, please contact one of the Cal/OSHA Consultation offices listed on the inside front cover.

2

Sample Injury & Illness Prevention Program for Less Complex Operations

Policy

_____
(Company name)

will institute and administer a comprehensive and continuous occupational Injury and Illness Prevention Program (IIPP) for all employees. The health and safety of the individual employee, whether in the field, factory or office, takes precedence over all other concerns. Management's goal is to prevent accidents, to reduce personal injury and occupational illness, and to comply with all safety and health standards.

Responsibility

The program administrator, _____
(Name)
_____, has the authority and is responsible for overall management and administration of the Injury and Illness Prevention Program. All supervisors are responsible for carrying out the IIPP in their work areas. A copy of the IIPP shall be available from each supervisor, who can answer employee questions about the program.

Employee Compliance

Employees who follow safe and healthful work practices will have this fact recognized and documented on their performance reviews.

Employees who are unaware of correct safety and health procedures will be trained or retrained (see *Training* section).

Willful violations of safe work practices (see *Safety & Health Compliance Process*) may result in disciplinary action in accordance with company policies.

Communication

Matters concerning occupational safety and health will be communicated to employees by means of written documentation, staff meetings, formal and informal training and posting.

Exception: Employers with fewer than 10 employees shall be permitted to communicate to and instruct employees orally in general safe work practices, with specific instructions regarding hazards unique to the employees' job assignments.

Communication from employees to supervisors and/or safety representatives about unsafe or unhealthy conditions is encouraged and may be verbal or written, as the employee chooses. The employee may use the *Report of Safety Hazard* form and remain anonymous.

No employee shall be retaliated against for reporting hazards or potential hazards, or for making suggestions related to safety.

The results of the investigation of any employee safety suggestion or report of hazard will be distributed to all employees affected by the hazard, or posted on appropriate bulletin boards.

Inspections

Each supervisor and/or safety representative will conduct inspections/investigations to identify unsafe work conditions and practices:

1. _____
(Frequency)
in all work areas.

2. Whenever new substances, processes, procedures or equipment introduced into the workplace present a new occupational safety and health hazard.

3. Whenever the supervisor/safety representative is made aware of a new or previously unrecognized hazard.

The *Hazard Checklist* or *Hazard Assessment Form* will be used to document these inspections/investigations.

3

Injury/Illness Investigation

Occupational injuries and illness will be investigated in accordance with established procedures and documented, as described in *Basic Rules for Accident Investigation*.

Correction of Unsafe or Unhealthful Conditions

Whenever an unsafe or unhealthful condition, practice or procedure is observed, discovered or reported, the program administrator or designee will take appropriate corrective measures in a timely manner based upon the severity of the hazard. Employees will be informed of the hazard, and interim protective measures taken until the hazard is corrected.

Employees may not enter an imminent hazard area without appropriate protective equipment, training, and prior specific approval given by the program administrator or designee.

Training

The program administrator or designee shall assure that supervisors receive training on recognizing the safety and health hazards to which employees under their immediate direction and control may be exposed.

Supervisors are responsible for seeing that those under their direction receive training on general workplace safety, and specific instructions regarding hazards unique to any job assignment.

This training is provided:

1. To all employees and those given new job assignments for which training was not previously received—the *Employee Safety Checklist* should be used to document this training.

2. Whenever new substances, processes, procedures or equipment introduced to the workplace present a new hazard.

3. Whenever the employer is made aware of a new or previously unrecognized hazard.

When supervisors are unable to provide the required training themselves, they should request that the training be given by others through notifying the program administrator or designee. The *Request for Training* form should be used.

(A list of specific requirements for employee instruction or training contained in Title 8 of the *California Code of Regulations* is given at the end of this guide.)

Recordkeeping

The program administrator or designee shall keep records of inspections, including the name of the person(s) conducting the inspection, the unsafe conditions and work practices identified, and action taken to correct these identified unsafe conditions and work practices. The records shall be maintained for three (3) years.

Exception: Employers with fewer than 10 employees may elect to maintain the inspection records only until the hazard is corrected.

The program administrator or designee shall also keep documentation of safety and health training attended by each employee, including employee name or other identifier, training dates, type(s) of training, and training providers. This documentation shall be maintained for three (3) years.

Exception: Employers with fewer than 10 employees can substantially comply with the documentation provision by maintaining a log of the instructions given the employee regarding hazards unique to the employee's job assignment when first hired or assigned new duties.

(The *Training* section contains a variety of sample forms for documentation of training/communication.)

4

Sample Injury & Illness Prevention Program for More Complex Operations

Policy

_____
(Company name)

believes that everyone benefits from a safe and healthful work environment. We are committed to maintaining an injury-free and illness-free workplace, and to complying with applicable laws and regulations governing workplace safety.

To achieve this goal the Company has adopted an Injury and Illness Prevention Program (IIPP). This program is everyone's responsibility as we work together to identify and eliminate conditions and practices that reduce the benefits of a safe and healthful work environment.

Responsibility

All employees are expected to work conscientiously to implement and maintain the IIPP program. _____ (Name) the program administrator, has the authority and responsibility for implementing the provisions of this program. Any questions regarding the program should be directed to the program administrator.

Senior Management

Senior management must set policy and provide leadership by participation, example, and a demonstrated interest in the program.

Responsibilities include:
* developing policy
* allocating adequate resources
* ensuring responsibility
* reviewing and evaluating results.

IIPP Program Administrator

The program administrator is responsible for ensuring that all provisions of the IIPP are implemented.

Responsibilities include:
* advising senior management on safety and health policy issues
* maintaining current information on local, state and federal safety and health regulations
* acting as liaison with government agencies
* planning, organizing and coordinating safety training
* preparing and distributing company policies and procedures on workplace safety and health issues
* developing a code of safe practices and inspection guidelines
* arranging safety and health inspections and followup to ensure that necessary corrective action is completed
* making sure that an adequate supply of personal protective equipment is available
* establishing accident report and investigation procedures, and maintaining injury and illness records (OSHA log 200)
* reviewing injury and illness trends
* establishing a system for maintaining records of inspection, hazard abatement, and training.

Supervisors

Supervisors are responsible for ensuring that employees know and abide by the Company policy and procedures on safety. They are expected to do everything within their control to assure a safe workplace in their area.

Responsibilities include:
* keeping abreast of safety and health regulations affecting operations they supervise
* ensuring that each subordinate is able to and understands how to complete each assigned task safely
* conducting on-the-job safety training of those they supervise

5

• advising the program administrator of training needs of subordinates
• making sure equipment and machines are in safe operating condition
• ascertaining that subordinates follow safe work practices and health regulations
• ensuring that employees under their direction wear required protective equipment
• correcting unsafe and unhealthful conditions within their power
• investigating accidents to discover cause(s) and identifying corrective action to prevent future occurrences
• conducting periodic inspections of their work areas according to the appropriate inspection checklist(s).

Compliance

Management is responsible for ensuring that Company safety and health policies and procedures are clearly communicated and understood by all employees. Managers and supervisors are expected to enforce the rules fairly and uniformly.

All employees are responsible for using safe work practices, for following all directives, policies and procedures, and for assisting in maintaining a safe work environment.

As part of an employee's regular performance review, the employee will be evaluated on his/her compliance with safe work practices.

Employees who make a significant contribution to the maintenance of a safe workplace, as determined by the program administrator, will receive written acknowledgment that is maintained in the employee's personnel file.

Employees who are unaware of correct safety and health procedures will be trained or retrained (see *Training* section).

Employees who deliberately fail to follow safe work practices and/or procedures, or who violate the Company's safety rules or directives, will be subject to disciplinary action, up to and including termination (see *Safety & Health Compliance Process*).

Communication

The Company recognizes that open, two-way communication between management and staff on health and safety issues is essential to an injury-free, productive workplace. The following system of communication is designed to facilitate a continuous flow of safety and health information between management and staff in a form that is readily understandable.

1. The new-employee orientation will include review of the Company's IIPP and a discussion of policy and procedures that the employee is expected to follow (see *Employee Communication & Compliance* section).

2. The Company will schedule a time at general employee meetings when safety is freely and openly discussed by all present. Such meetings will be regularly scheduled and announced to all employees, so that maximum participation can occur.

3. From time to time, the Company will post and/or distribute written safety notifications. Employees should check Company bulletin boards regularly for such posting(s).

Safety-related memos and documents are to be read promptly. Questions about the meaning or implementation of this information should be directed to the supervisor.

4. Other methods of communicating pertinent health and safety information include electronic mail or a safety committee.

5. All employees are encouraged to inform their supervisor, the program administrator or designee of any matter which they perceive to be a workplace hazard and/or a potential workplace hazard. Employees are also encouraged to make safety suggestions and safety training suggestions.

If an employee so wishes, he/she may make such notification anonymously by depositing it in the program administrator's mailbox. A *Report of Safety Hazard* form may be used by the employee.

6. *No employee shall be retaliated against for reporting hazards or potential hazards, or for making suggestions related to safety.*

6

7. All suggestions will be reviewed by the program administrator or designee, who will initiate an investigation of each report of a hazard, potential hazard or safety suggestion in accordance with Company procedures for hazard control.

8. Any directives issued as a result of the investigation shall be distributed to all employees affected by the hazard, or shall be posted on appropriate bulletin boards.

Workplace Hazard Evaluation and Abatement

Hazard control is the heart of an effective IIPP program. The Company's hazard control procedure is: identify hazards that exist or develop in the workplace, describe how to correct those hazards, and initiate steps to prevent their recurrence.

Assessment of Hazards

Inspection of the workplace is our primary tool used to identify unsafe conditions and practices. While we encourage all employees to continuously identify and correct hazards and poor safety practices, certain situations require formal evaluation and documentation.

Along with each inspection/investigation, the program administrator or designee shall evaluate the severity of the hazard identified, and if it can not be abated immediately, suggest priority for corrective action. The *Hazard Checklist* or *Hazard Assessment Form* is to be used to document inspections/investigations.

The program administrator or designee will conduct an inspection or investigation whenever any of the following occur:

1. Routinely in each work area, ————
————————— the time and frequency of
(daily, monthly, weekly)
inspection will be set by the program administrator or designee according to the type of work being performed in each worksite.

Prior to the periodic inspection, the inspector should review workplace injury reports and inspection reports which have been filed since the last investigation or inspection.

The *Hazard Checklist* for the appropriate work area is to be used by the inspector(s).

2. The introduction of new substances, processes, procedures or equipment present a new safety/health hazard.

Each supervisor is responsible for promptly reporting to the program administrator or designee whenever a new substance (such as a chemical or solvent), new work procedure or technique, and/or new equipment is introduced which may pose a safety risk. A *Report of Safety Hazard* form shall be used by the supervisor.

Each supervisor's report should include an evaluation of the potential hazard(s), training and/or other steps to be taken to provide abatement solutions for any potential hazard(s).

Based upon the information, the program administrator or designee will conduct an inspection and issue any directive that may be necessary.

3. The program administrator becomes aware of a new or previously unrecognized hazard, either independently or by receipt of information from an employee, including receipt of a *Report of Safety Hazard* form.

4. An occupational injury, occupational illness, or near-miss accident occurs (see *Accident Investigation* section).

5. From time to time, the program administrator or designee may conduct unannounced inspections.

All investigations and findings shall be fully documented on the *Hazard Assessment Form* and filed as directed in *Recordkeeping*.

Abatement of Hazards

It is the Company's intention to eliminate all hazards and unsafe work practices immediately. Some corrective actions require more time. Priority will be given to severe and imminent hazards.

7

The *Hazard Checklist / Hazard Assessment* forms completed during the inspection/investigation will be used by the program administrator or designee to describe measures taken to abate the hazard or correct the unsafe work practice. Actions to be taken may include, but are not limited to:

- fixing or replacing defective equipment
- implementing safer procedures
- installing guards, modifying equipment
- employee training
- posting warning notices.

All such actions taken and the dates they are completed shall be documented on the appropriate forms.

When corrective action involves multiple steps or cannot be completed promptly, an action plan needs to be developed. The *Hazard Abatement Record* is to be used for this purpose and filed as directed in *Recordkeeping*.

While corrective action is in progress, necessary precautions are to be taken to protect or remove employees from exposure to the hazard.

Employees shall not enter an imminent hazard area without prior specific approval of the program administrator or designee. Employees expected to correct the imminent hazard shall be properly trained and provided with necessary safeguards.

Accident Investigation

The purpose of an accident investigation is to find the cause of an accident and prevent further occurrences—not to assign blame.

A thorough and properly completed accident investigation is necessary to obtain facts. The investigation should focus on causes and hazards. Analysis of what happened and why it happened is aimed at determining how it can be prevented in the future.

Injury and Illness

The occurrence of an occupational injury and/or illness precipitates a document called *Employer's Report of Injury*. This report is completed by the injured employee's supervi-

sor, and a copy of the report is to be sent to the program administrator or designee within 24 hours of the occurrence. Upon receipt, the program administrator:

1. Reports fatalities and serious injuries or illness *immediately* by phone or FAX to the nearest office of the Division of Occupational Safety and Health (CCR Title 8, Section 342).

2. Investigates the incident by visiting the site and interviewing the victim and witnesses.

Accidents

The majority of accidents do not cause injury or illness, yet result in property damage and/or lost time. Such mishaps usually indicate an unsafe act, faulty procedure or hidden hazard. Investigations of these occurrences are conducted at the discretion of the supervisor, program administrator or designee.

All investigation facts, findings and recommendations shall be fully documented on the *Accident / Exposure Investigation Report* form. This report is filed in accordance with the instructions in *Recordkeeping*.

Training

Training is essential to maximizing the skills and knowledge of employees. It is the key to productivity.

The Company has a duty to include safety as an integral part of employee training. Employees need to work safely as well as productively and efficiently. The supervisor is the essential link in ensuring the proper outcome.

Supervisors must know how to perform a designated job, and be aware of safety and health hazards facing employees under their immediate supervision. Supervisors are responsible for ensuring that they themselves and those under their direction receive training on general workplace safety, as well as on safety and health issues specific to each job.

With this in mind, training will be conducted with the following considerations:

Supervisors

The program administrator or designee will consult with department administrators or supervisors to determine training topics and needs of supervisors—these include human relations, trainer skills, production/ process skills, and familiarization with hazards and risks faced by employees.

Supervisors who recognize their own need for training are encouraged to submit a direct request for training in any area in which they feel deficient.

Employees

Supervisors are expected to assess training needs of all employees under their direction. They are to train those they supervise in general workplace safety and give them specific instructions regarding hazards unique to any job assignment, to the extent that such information was not already covered in other trainings (see *Employee Safety Checklist*).

The Company recognizes that continuing safety and health training is needed for:

1. Employees given a job assignment for which they have not previously received training. If the position is supervisory, such training shall include familiarization with hazards and risks faced by the employees under the supervisor's direction.

2. Whenever new substances, processes, procedures or equipment pose a new hazard.

3. Whenever the supervisor, program administrator or designee becomes aware of a previously unrecognized hazard.

4. All employees in periodic refresher safety training involving general workplace safety, job-specific hazards, and/or hazardous materials as applicable.

All training shall be documented on one of the training record forms and filed as directed in *Recordkeeping*. (A list of specific requirements for employee instruction or training contained in Title 8 of the *California Code of Regulations* is given at the end of this guide.)

Recordkeeping

No operation can be successful without recordkeeping that enables the Company to learn from past experience and make corrections for future operations. In addition, the IIPP regulation requires records to be kept of the steps taken to establish and maintain the Company's Injury and Illness Prevention Program.

Injury and Illness Prevention Program Records

Each supervisor will maintain an updated copy of the Company's IIPP. The program administrator will retain the following records on file for at least three (3) years:

• master copy of IIPP, changes/updates
• documents verifying that the Company has maintained ongoing two-way communication with employees, such as —
    –memos, letters to employees on safety and health issues
    –new employee safety orientation session acknowledgment form
    –employee suggestions and Company response
• all records of inspections/investigations—including date, name of person who performed the inspection/investigation, unsafe conditions and work practices identified, corrective action taken and date of correction—forms covered in this category include:
    –*Report of Safety Hazard*
    –*Hazard Checklist*
    –*Hazard Assessment Form*
    –*Hazard Abatement Record*
    –*Accident / Exposure Investigation Report*
• records of safety and health training received by employees—containing the employee's name, training date, type of training and identification of trainer—examples are:
    –*Employee Safety Meeting Attendance*
    –*Employee Safety Checklist*
    –*Employee Safety Training Verification*

Employee Communication & Compliance

Sample :

Safety & Health Compliance Process

Disciplinary measures are progressive and involve four steps:

1. Should a safety and health violation be noted, the supervisor is to informally discuss the behavior with the employee—stating the potential dangerous result and outlining the correct procedure—then to retrain the employee to ensure understanding.

2. A second violation should generate either a formal verbal warning or a written warning to the employee, depending on the severity of the violation.

3. A third infraction results in a formal written warning or employee suspension.

4. A fourth violation may lead to employee termination.

These suggested disciplinary measures should be reviewed in the context of any collective bargaining agreement which may exist.

Sample :

Acknowledgment of Receipt & Review of Code of Safe Practices

TO ALL EMPLOYEES:

Attached is a copy of the code of safe practices. These guidelines are provided for your safety.

It is the responsibility of

_____
(Name)
to provide and review this code with each employee.

It is the employee's responsibility to read and comply with this code.

The attached copy of the code of safe practices is for you to keep.

Please sign and date below and return *only* this page to:

_____
(Name)

I have read and understand the code of safe practices.

Date _____

Signed _____
(Employee)

10

Employee Communication & Compliance

Construction Safety Orders
Code of Safe Practices

This is a suggested format, general in nature, intended as a basis for preparing a code of safe practices that is tailored to fit the contractor's operations.

General

1. All persons shall follow these safe practices rules, render every possible aid to safe operations, and report all unsafe conditions or practices to the foreman or superintendent.

2. Foremen shall insist on employees observing and obeying every applicable Company, state or federal regulation and order necessary to the safe conduct of the work, and take action as necessary to obtain compliance.

3. All employees shall be given frequent accident prevention instruction. Instruction shall be given at least every 10 working days.

4. Anyone known to be under the influence of drugs or intoxicating substances, which impair the employee's ability to safely perform assigned duties, shall not be allowed on the job while in that condition.

5. Horseplay, scuffling, or other acts that tend to adversely influence the safety or well-being of the employees shall be prohibited.

6. Work shall be well planned and supervised to prevent injuries in materials handling and working together with equipment.

7. No employees shall knowingly be permitted or required to work while their ability or alertness is so impaired by fatigue, illness, or other causes that they might unnecessarily expose themselves or others to injury.

8. Employees shall not enter manholes, underground vaults, chambers, tanks, silos, or other similar places receiving little ventilation, unless these places are determined safe to enter.

9. Employees shall be instructed to ensure that all guards and other protective devices are in the proper places and adjusted, and shall report deficiencies promptly to the foreman or superintendent.

10. Crowding or pushing when boarding or leaving any vehicle or other conveyance shall be prohibited.

11. Workers shall not handle or tamper with any electrical equipment, machinery, or air or water lines in a manner not within the scope of their duties, unless they receive instructions from their foreman.

12. All injuries shall be reported promptly to the foreman or superintendent so arrangements can be made for medical or first aid treatment.

13. When lifting heavy objects, the large muscles of the leg instead of the smaller muscles of the back shall be used.

14. Inappropriate footwear or shoes with thin or badly worn soles must not be worn.

15. Materials, tools, or other objects shall not be thrown from buildings or structures until proper precautions are taken to protect others from the falling objects.

16. Employees shall cleanse themselves thoroughly after handling hazardous substances, and follow special instructions from authorized sources.

17. Hod carriers should avoid using extension ladders when carrying loads. Though such ladders may provide adequate strength, the

11

rung position and rope arrangement make climbing difficult and hazardous for this trade.

18. Work shall be arranged so that employees are able to face a ladder and use both hands while climbing.

19. Gasoline shall not be used for cleaning purposes.

20. No burning, welding, or other source of ignition shall be applied to any enclosed tank or vessel, even if there are some openings, until it has first been determined that no possibility of explosion exists, and authority for the work is obtained from the foreman or superintendent.

21. Any damage to scaffolds, falsework, or other supporting structures shall be immediately reported to the foreman and repaired before use.

Use of Tools & Equipment

22. All tools and equipment shall be maintained in good condition.

23. Damaged tools or equipment shall be removed from service and tagged "DEFECTIVE."

24. Pipe or Stillson wrenches shall not be used as a substitute for other wrenches.

25. Only appropriate tools shall be used for a specific job.

26. Wrenches shall not be altered by the addition of handle-extensions or "cheaters."

27. Files shall be equipped with handles and not used to punch or pry.

28. Screwdrivers shall not be used as chisels.

29. Wheelbarrows shall not be pushed with handles in an upright position.

30. Portable electric tools shall not be lifted or lowered by means of the power cord. Ropes shall be used.

31. Electric cords shall not be exposed to damage by vehicles.

32. In locations where using a portable power tool is difficult, the tool shall be supported by means of a rope or similar support of adequate strength.

Machinery & Vehicles

33. Only authorized persons shall operate machinery or equipment.

34. Loose or frayed clothing, long hair, dangling ties, or finger rings shall not be worn around moving machinery or other places where they may become entangled.

35. Machinery shall not be serviced, repaired or adjusted while in operation, nor shall oiling of moving parts be attempted, except on equipment designed or fitted with safeguards to protect the person performing the work.

36. Where appropriate, lock-out procedures shall be used.

37. Employees shall not work under vehicles supported by jacks or chain hoists without protective blocking to prevent injury if jacks or hoists should fail.

38. Air hoses shall not be disconnected at compressors until the hose line has been bled.

39. All excavations shall be visually inspected before backfilling to ensure that it is safe to backfill.

40. Excavating equipment shall not be operated near tops of cuts, banks, or cliffs if employees are working below.

41. Tractors, bulldozers, scrapers and carry-alls shall not operate where there is a possibility of overturning in dangerous areas like edges of deep fills, cut banks and steep slopes.

42. When loading where there is a probability of dangerous slides or movement of material, the wheels or treads of loading equipment, other than that riding on rails, should be turned in the direction which will facilitate escape in case of danger, except in a situation where this position of the wheels or treads would cause a greater operational hazard.

12

Employee Communication & Compliance

General Industry Safety Orders
Code of Safe Practices

This is a suggested format, general in nature, intended as a basis for preparing a code of safe practices that is tailored to fit the employer's operations.

It is our policy that everything possible will be done to protect employees, customers and visitors from accidents. Safety is a cooperative undertaking that requires participation by every employee. Failure by any employee to comply with safety rules will be grounds for corrective discipline. Supervisors shall insist that employees observe all applicable Company, state and federal safety rules and practices, and take action as necessary to obtain compliance.

To carry out this policy:

1. Employees shall report all unsafe conditions and equipment to the supervisor or safety coordinator.

2. Employees shall report immediately all accidents, injuries and illnesses to the supervisor or safety coordinator.

3. Anyone known to be under the influence of intoxicating liquor or drugs shall not be allowed on the job while in that condition.

4. Horseplay, scuffling, or other acts that tend to adversely influence the safety or well-being of the employees are prohibited.

5. Means of egress shall be kept unblocked, well lighted and unlocked during work hours.

6. In the event of fire, sound the alarm and evacuate.

7. Upon hearing a fire alarm, stop work and proceed to the nearest clear exit. Gather at the designated location.

8. Only workers trained for it may attempt to respond to a fire or other emergency.

9. Exit doors must comply with fire safety regulations during business hours.

10. Keep stairways clear of items that can be tripped over. All areas under stairways that are egress routes should not be used to store combustibles.

11. Materials and equipment will not be stored against doors or exits, fire ladders or fire extinguisher stations.

12. Aisles must be kept clear at all times.

13. Work areas should be maintained in a neat, orderly manner. Throw trash and refuse into proper waste containers.

14. All spills shall be wiped up promptly.

15. Always use the correct lifting technique. Never attempt to lift or push an object that is too heavy. Contact the supervisor when help is needed to move a heavy object.

16. Never stack material precariously on top of lockers, file cabinets or other high places.

17. When carrying objects, use caution in watching for and avoiding obstructions or loose material.

18. Do not stack material in an unstable manner.

19. Report exposed wiring and cords that are frayed or have deteriorated insulation, so that they can be repaired promptly.

13

20. Never use a metal ladder where it could come in contact with energized parts of equipment, fixtures or circuit conductors.

21. Maintain sufficient access and working space around all electrical equipment for ready and safe operations and maintenance.

22. Do not use any portable electrical equipment or tools that are not grounded or double insulated.

23. Plug all electrical equipment into appropriate wall receptacles, or into an extension of only one cord of similar size and capacity. Three-pronged plugs should be used to ensure continuity of ground.

24. All cords running into walk areas must be taped down or inserted through rubber protectors to prevent tripping hazards.

25. Inspect motorized vehicles and other mechanized equipment daily or prior to use.

26. Shut off engine, set brakes and block wheels prior to loading or unloading vehicles.

27. Inspect pallets and their loads for integrity and stability before loading or moving.

28. Do not store compressed gas cylinders in areas that are exposed to heat sources, electric arcs or high temperature lines.

29. Do not use compressed air for cleaning off clothing unless pressure is less than 10 psi.

30. Identify contents of pipelines prior to initiating any work that affects the integrity of the pipe.

31. Wear hearing protection in all areas identified as having high noise exposure.

32. Goggles or face shields must be worn when grinding.

33. Do not use any faulty or worn hand tools.

34. Guard floor openings by a cover, guardrail, or equivalent.

35. Do not enter into a confined space unless tests for toxic substances, explosive concentrations, and oxygen deficiency have been taken.

36. Always keep flammable or toxic chemicals in closed containers when not in use.

37. Do not eat in areas where hazardous chemicals are present.

38. Be aware of potential hazards involving various chemicals stored or used in the workplace.

39. Cleaning supplies should be stored away from edible items on kitchen shelves.

40. Store cleaning solvents and flammable liquids in appropriate containers.

41. Keep solutions that may be poisonous or are not intended for consumption in well labeled containers.

42. When working with a VDT, have all furniture adjusted, positioned and arranged to minimize strain on all parts of the body.

43. Never leave lower desk or cabinet drawers open, a tripping hazard. Use care when opening and closing drawers to avoid pinching fingers.

44. Do not open more than one upper drawer at a time, particularly the top two drawers on tall file cabinets.

45. Keep individual heaters at work areas clear of combustible materials such as drapes or waste from wastebaskets. Use newer heaters that are equipped with tip-over switches.

46. Keep appliances such as coffeepots or microwave ovens in working order and inspect them for signs of wear, heat or frayed cords.

47. Fans used in work areas should be guarded, and guards must not allow fingers to be inserted through the mesh. Newer fans are equipped with proper guards.

14

Employee Communication & Compliance

General Office Code of Safe Practices

This is a suggested format, general in nature, intended as a basis for preparing a code of safe practices that is tailored to fit the employer's operations.

It is our policy that everything possible will be done to protect employees, customers and visitors from accidents. Safety is a cooperative undertaking that requires participation by every employee. Failure by any employee to comply with safety rules will be grounds for corrective discipline. Supervisors shall insist that employees observe all applicable Company, state and federal safety rules and practices, and take action as necessary to obtain compliance.

To carry out this policy:

1. Employees shall report all unsafe conditions and equipment to the supervisor or safety coordinator.

2. Employees shall report immediately all accidents, injuries and illnesses to the supervisor or safety coordinator.

3. Means of egress shall be kept unblocked, well lighted and unlocked during work hours.

4. In the event of fire, sound the alarm and evacuate.

5. Upon hearing a fire alarm, stop work and proceed to the nearest clear exit. Gather at the designated location.

6. Only workers trained for it may attempt to respond to a fire or other emergency.

7. Exit doors must comply with fire safety regulations during business hours.

8. Keep stairways clear of items that can be tripped over. All areas under stairways that are egress routes should not be used to store combustibles.

9. Do not store materials and equipment against doors or exits, fire ladders or fire extinguisher stations.

10. Keep aisles clear at all times.

11. Maintain work areas in a neat, orderly manner. Throw trash and refuse into proper waste containers.

12. Wipe up all spills promptly.

13. Store files and supplies in a manner that prevents damage to supplies or injury to personnel when they are moved. Store heaviest items closest to the floor and lightweight items above.

14. All cords running into walk areas must be taped down or inserted through rubber protectors to prevent tripping hazards.

15. Never stack material precariously on top of lockers, file cabinets or other high places.

16. Never leave lower desk or cabinet drawers open, a tripping hazard. Use care when opening and closing drawers to avoid pinching fingers.

17. Do not open more than one upper drawer at a time, particularly the top two drawers on tall file cabinets.

18. Always use the correct lifting technique. Never attempt to lift or push an object that is too heavy. Contact the supervisor when help is needed to move a heavy object.

19. When carrying objects, use caution in watching for and avoiding obstructions or loose material.

20. Plug all electrical equipment into appropriate wall receptacles, or into an extension of only one cord of similar size and capacity. Three-pronged plugs should be used to ensure continuity of ground.

21. Keep individual heaters at work areas clear of combustible materials such as drapes or waste from wastebaskets. Use newer heaters that are equipped with tip-over switches.

22. Keep appliances such as coffeepots or microwave ovens in working order and inspect them for signs of wear, heat or frayed cords.

23. Fans used in work areas should be guarded, and guards must not allow fingers to be inserted through the mesh. Newer fans are equipped with proper guards.

24. Use equipment such as scissors or staplers for their intended purposes only, and do not misuse them as hammers, pry bars, screwdrivers. Misuse can cause damage to the equipment and possible injury to the user.

25. Store cleaning supplies away from edible items on kitchen shelves.

26. Store cleaning solvents and flammable liquids in appropriate containers.

27. Keep solutions that may be poisonous or are not intended for consumption in well labeled containers.

15

Employee Communication & Compliance

Report of Safety Hazard	Year		Number
Name (optional)	**Date**	**Supervisor's Name**	

Describe Substance, Equipment, Process, Practice or Workplace Condition	Health and/or Safety Hazard	Suggestions for Minimizing or Abating Hazard — or for Training	Action

Make additional copies of this form as needed.

16

Hazard Evaluation & Abatement

Hazard Checklist	Company/Entity Name & Location
Inspected by **Date**	

Rating evaluations: S=Satisfactory   U=Unsatisfactory   NA=Not applicable
If Unsatisfactory, prioritize by severity:
U1=Immediate   U2=Within 48 hours   U3=Within 2 weeks   U4=Abatement plan needed

Checklist Item	S	U	NA	Corrective Action Taken & Date
Employer Posting				
Is the Cal/OSHA poster "Safety and Health Protection on the Job" displayed in a prominent location where all employees are likely to see it?				
Are emergency telephone numbers posted where they can be easily found in case of emergency?				
Where employees may be exposed to any toxic substances or harmful physical agents, has appropriate information on employee access to medical and exposure records and Material Safety Data Sheets been posted or otherwise made easily available?				
Are signs posted where appropriate to inform of building exits, room capacities, floor loading, and exposure to x-ray, microwave, or other harmful radiation or substances?				
Are other California posters properly displayed—				
▪Industrial Welfare Commission orders regulating wages, hours, and working conditions?				
▪Discrimination in employment prohibited by law?				
▪Notice to employees of unemployment and disability insurance?				
▪Payday notice?				
Emergency Action Plan				
Are alarm systems properly maintained and tested regularly?				
Is the emergency action plan reviewed and revised periodically?				
Do employees know their responsibilities—				
▪For reporting emergencies?				
▪During an emergency?				
▪For conducting rescue and medical duties?				

Make additional copies of this form as needed.

17

Hazard Evaluation & Abatement

Hazard Checklist

Company/Entity Name & Location	
Inspected by	**Date**

Rating evaluations: S=Satisfactory   U=Unsatisfactory   NA=Not applicable
If Unsatisfactory, prioritize by severity:
U1=Immediate   U2=Within 48 hours   U3=Within 2 weeks   U4=Abatement plan needed

Checklist Item	S	U	NA	Corrective Action Taken & Date
Fire Protection Do you have a fire prevention plan?				
Does your plan describe the type of fire protection equipment and/or system?				
Have you established practices and procedures to control potential fire hazards and ignition sources?				
Is your local fire department well acquainted with your facilities, location and specific hazards?				
If you have a fire alarm system, is it certified as required?				
If you have a fire alarm system, is it tested at least annually?				
Are fire doors and shutters in good operating condition?				
Are automatic sprinkler system water control valves, air and water pressures checked weekly/periodically as required?				
Is maintenance of automatic sprinkler systems assigned to responsible persons, or to a sprinkler contractor?				

Make additional copies of this form as needed.

18

Hazard Evaluation & Abatement

# Hazard Checklist	Company/Entity Name & Location
Inspected by **Date**	

Rating evaluations: S=Satisfactory   U=Unsatisfactory   NA=Not applicable
If Unsatisfactory, prioritize by severity:
U1=Immediate   U2=Within 48 hours   U3=Within 2 weeks   U4=Abatement plan needed

Checklist Item	S	U	NA	Corrective Action Taken & Date
Exiting or Egress				
Are all exits marked with an exit sign and illuminated by a reliable light source?				
Are the directions to exits, when not immediately apparent, marked with visible signs?				
Are doors, passageways or stairways, which are neither exits nor access to exits, and which could be mistaken for exits, appropriately marked "NOT AN EXIT", "TO BASEMENT", "STOREROOM", or in such a way that they will not be mistaken for exits?				
Are all exits kept free of obstructions?				
Are there sufficient exits to permit prompt escape in case of emergency?				
Are special precautions taken to protect employees during construction and repair operations?				
Where exiting will be through frameless glass doors or glass exit doors, are the doors of fully tempered glass and do they meet the safety requirements for human impact?				

Make additional copies of this form as needed.

19

Hazard Evaluation & Abatement

Hazard Checklist

Inspected by	Date

Company/Entity Name & Location

Rating evaluations:　　S=Satisfactory　　　U=Unsatisfactory　　　NA=Not applicable
If Unsatisfactory, prioritize by severity:
U1=Immediate　U2=Within 48 hours　U3=Within 2 weeks　U4=Abatement plan needed

Checklist Item	S	U	NA	Corrective Action Taken & Date
General Work Environment Are all worksites clean and orderly?				
Are work surfaces kept dry, or appropriate means taken to assure the surfaces are slip-resistant?				
Are all spilled materials or liquids cleaned up immediately?				
Are the minimum number of toilets and washing facilities provided?				
Are all toilets and washing facilities clean and sanitary?				
Are all work areas adequately illuminated?				
Walkways Are aisles and passageways kept clear?				
Are aisles and walkways marked as appropriate?				
Are wet surfaces covered with non-slip materials?				
Are holes in the floor, sidewalk or other walking surface repaired properly, covered or otherwise made safe?				

Make additional copies of this form as needed.

20

Hazard Evaluation & Abatement

Hazard Checklist

Company/Entity Name & Location

Inspected by	Date

Rating evaluations: S=Satisfactory U=Unsatisfactory NA=Not applicable
If Unsatisfactory, prioritize by severity:
U1=Immediate U2=Within 48 hours U3=Within 2 weeks U4=Abatement plan needed

Checklist Item	S	U	NA	Corrective Action Taken & Date
Medical Services & First Aid If medical and first aid facilities are not in proximity of your workplace, is at least one employee on each shift currently qualified to render first aid?				
Are medical personnel readily available for advice and consultation on matters of employee health?				
Are emergency phone numbers posted?				
Are first aid kits easily accessible to each work area, with necessary supplies available, periodically inspected and replenished as needed?				
Have first aid kit supplies been approved by a physician, indicating they are adequate for a particular area or operation?				
Miscellaneous (Note to Employer/Inspector: Please add applicable questions below.)				

Make additional copies of this form as needed.

21

Hazard Evaluation & Abatement

Sample :

Hazard Assessment Form
Investigation/Inspection & Abatement Record

Date of Investigation/Inspection

Reason for Inspection:

☐ New Equipment/Substance
Explain:

_____

☐ New Process
Explain:

_____

☐ New or Revised Procedure
Explain:

Name of Person(s) Conducting Investigation:

Name of Person(s) Consulted:

Description of Investigation: (attach additional sheets as necessary)

Findings—Including Identification of Hazard & Severity: (attach additional sheets as necessary)

Steps Taken to Abate Hazard & Date of These Steps: (attach additional sheets as necessary)

22

Hazard Evaluation & Abatement

Sample :

Hazard Abatement Record

Safety/Health items identified during ———(Date)——— inspection/investigation will be submitted to
————(Name)———————— for review, and an action plan will be developed to resolve each
specific safety/health item (such as hazards, needed policies) by a fixed completion date, and by those
assigned responsibility This form will be used to document identified problems, steps to be taken,
and completion deadline.

Overall Action Plan

Major action steps to be taken:	Priority assign each step a number	Projected Completion Date	Date Completed
1.			
2.			
3.			
4.			
5.			

23

Accident Investigation

Basic Rules for Accident Investigation

Every employer shall report *immediately*— within 24 hours—by telephone or telegraph to the nearest district office of the California Division of Occupational Safety and Health— any serious injury or illness or death of an employee, occuring in a place of employment or in connection with any employment (see CCR Title 8, Section 342).

● The purpose of an investigation is to find the cause of an accident and prevent further occurrences, *not* to fix blame. An unbiased approach is necessary for obtaining objective findings.

● Visit the accident scene as soon as possible while the facts are fresh, and before witnesses forget important details.

● If possible, interview the injured worker at the scene of the accident and "walk" him or her through a mock re-enactment.

● All interviews should be conducted as privately as possible. Interview witnesses one at a time. Talk with everyone who has knowledge of the accident, even if they did not actually witness it.

● Consider taking signed statements in cases where facts are unclear or there is an element of controversy.

● Document details graphically. Use sketches, diagrams and photos as needed, and take measurements when appropriate.

● Focus on causes and hazards. Develop an analysis of what happened, how it happened and how it could have been prevented. Determine what caused the accident itself, not just the injury.

● Every investigation should include an action plan. How will you prevent such accidents in the future?

● If a third party or defective product contributed to the accident, save any evidence. It could be critical to the recovery of claims costs.

24

Accident Investigation

Accident/Exposure Investigation Report

Company	**Date**

Investigation Team

Employee's Name & ID

Sex   Age   Job Description

Department & Location

Accident Date & Time

Date & Time Accident Reported to Supervisor

Nature of Incident

Nature of Injury

Referred to Medical Facility/Doctor	**Yes**	**No**

Employee Returned to Work	**Yes**	**Date/Time**	**No**

Injured Employee Interview/Statement—Attached

Witnesses

Witnesses Interviews/Statements—Attached

Photographs of Site—Attached

Diagrams of Site—Attached

Equipment Records—Attached—Reviewed	**Yes**	**No**

Accident/Exposure Incident Description

_____

_____

_____

_____

_____

_____

_____

_____

_____

_____

Make additional copies of this form as needed. (form provided courtesy of Safety Publications of California © 1990)

25

Accident Investigation

Accident/Exposure Investigation Report

Accident Description

_____

_____

Date & Time　　　　　　　　　**Location**

_____

Employees Involved

_____

Preventive Action Recommendations

_____

_____

_____

_____

_____

_____

Corrective Actions Completed	Manager Responsible	Date Completed

—Employee Lost Time—Temporary Help—Cleanup—Repair—Discussion—

Accident Cost Analysis	Investigation	Compliance	Total Cost
Medical			
Production Loss			

Report Prepared By　　　　　　　　**Date Completed**

Safety Committee Review　　　Yes　　　**No**

Corrective Action　　　　　　　　**Date Started**

Safety Communication Notice Prepared　　　**Date**

Safety Director Signature

Make additional copies of this form as needed. (form provided courtesy of Safety Publications of California © 1990)

26

Accident Investigation

Accident/Exposure Investigation Report

Accident Description

Date & Time   **Location**

Employees Involved

Employee Interview/Statement—Injured Employee—Witness

Employee Name

Interviewed By

Accident Diagram/Photographs

Make additional copies of this form as needed. (form provided courtesy of Safety Publications of California © 1990)

27

Training

Sample :

Employee Safety Checklist

This report is to be completed by the supervisor and new or reassigned employee within_____ days after employment or reassignment and filed with ⎯⎯⎯⎯⎯⎯⎯⎯⎯⎯⎯ .

                (Name)

Employee Name

⎯⎯⎯⎯⎯⎯⎯⎯⎯⎯⎯⎯⎯⎯⎯⎯⎯⎯⎯⎯⎯⎯⎯
(print   First   Middle   Last Name)

Date Employed   Date Checklist
or Reassigned   Completed

Department Assigned

Type of Work

Outline employee's past work experience

Ask employee: Do you have any physical conditions or handicaps which might limit your ability to perform this job? If so, what reasonable accommodation can be made by us?

Did employee have a pre-placement physical? Yes ____ No ____
If yes, any work restrictions indicated?

The supervisor and new employee are to review the following safety concerns, check and discuss those which apply:

☐ Applicable Company, state and federal safety policies and programs

☐ Applicable Company, state and federal safety rules, general and specific to job assignment

☐ Company safety rule enforcement procedures

☐ Company policy on medical treatment for work-related injuries

☐ Use of tools and equipment

☐ Proper guarding of equipment

☐ Proper work shoes and other personal protective equipment, as needed

☐ Handling of product

☐ Use of specific lifting equipment, such as hoists, hand truck

☐ How, when and where to report injuries

☐ Importance of housekeeping

☐ Special hazards of job

☐ When and where to report unsafe conditions

☐ Emergency procedures

☐ Employee responsibility for the prevention of accidents

☐ Training on any toxic material which employee might be exposed to

☐ Fire safety

☐ Safe operation of vehicle(s)

☐ Employee is to receive special additional instruction and guidance

☐ Supervisor will adequately and frequently review performance of new employee: superior behavior will be rewarded, substandard behavior will be corrected

☐ Probationary period

☐ Supervisor will formally review employee's performance on (mark calendar)

☐ Employee agrees to fully cooperate with the safety efforts of the employer, follow all safety rules and use good judgment concerning safe work behavior

⎯⎯⎯⎯⎯⎯⎯⎯⎯⎯⎯   ⎯⎯⎯⎯⎯⎯⎯⎯⎯⎯⎯
Supervisor   Employee
signature   signature

28

Training

Sample :

Request for Training

Employees must be given safety training on the performance of their duties.

Name _____

Department _____

The employee has been given the safety indoctrination, advised of Company safety rules, and needs additional training indicated below:

Training Topic	Must be Trained by Date	Date Training Completed	Initials Trainer	Employee

Sample :

Employee Safety Meeting Attendance

Date & Time _____

Conducted By _____
(Name & title)

Subject Discussed _____

Signatures of Employees

_____	_____	_____
_____	_____	_____
_____	_____	_____
_____	_____	_____
_____	_____	_____

Approved By _____ Date_____
(Manager)

Make meetings brief, 15 to 20 minutes. Cover only one specific subject. Use an object to focus the attention of the employees. Involve them in the talk.

29

Training

Employee Safety Training Verification

Company

Employee's Name & ID

Hire Date   **Job Description**

Training Program	Date Completed	Instructor	Comments

Make additional copies of this form as needed. (form provided courtesy of Safety Publications of California © 1990)

30

Training Requirements in
California Code of Regulations Title 8, January 1993

Specific requirements for employee instruction or training are contained in Title 8, Division 1, Chapter 4 of the *California Code of Regulations*, and are listed sequentially here by their subject titles.

CCR T8 Construction Safety Orders

1509 (a) & (e) Injury and Illness Prevention Program

1510 (a) & (c) Safety Instructions for Employees

1512 (b),(d) & (j) Emergency Medical Service

1529 (o)(1)(A) Asbestos

1531 (c) Respiratory Protective Equipment

1532 Confined Space (see CCR T8, 5157 General Industry Safety Orders)

1637 (k)(1) Scaffold Erection and Dismantling

1662 (a) Boatswains Chairs

1585 (a)(1) Powder Actuated Tools, Operator and Instructor

1585 (b)(1) Qualifications

1599 (f) Vehicle Traffic Control, Flaggers, Barricades and Warning Signs

1740 (k)(l) Use of Fuel Gas (Liquid Propane)

1801 (a) Ionizing Radiation, High Voltage Electrical Safety Orders

2940 Work Procedures (Inspection of Safety Devices)

CCR T8 General Industry Safety Orders

3203 (a)(1) Injury and Illness Prevention Program

3220 (g) Emergency Action Plan

3221 (d) Fire Prevention Plan

3282 (f) Window Cleaning Operations

3286 (f)(2) Boatswains Chairs

3314 (a) Cleaning, Repairing, Servicing and Adjusting Prime Movers, Machinery and Equipment

3326 (c) Servicing Single, Split and Multi-piece Rims or Wheels

3333 (d) Blue Stop Signs (Railcars)

3400 (b) Medical Service and First Aid

3411 (c) Private Fire Brigades

3421 (c), (f) & (j) Tree-work Maintenance and Removal

3439 (b) Agricultural Operations, First Aid

3441 (a) Operation of Agricultural Equipment, Operating Instructions Marine Terminal Operations

3463 (b)(5)(A) Respiratory Protective Equipment (reference to 5144)

3464 (a)(1) Accident Prevention and First Aid

3472 (b)(1) Qualifications of Machinery Operation

3638 (d) Elevating Work Platform

3648 (l)(7) Aerial Devices (Towering)

3657 (h) Elevating Employees with Lift Trucks

3664 (a)(1) Operating Rules (Industrial Trucks)

4203 (b) Power Press Operation

4243 (a)(6) Forging Machinery and Equipment

4355 (a)(2) Operating Rules for Compaction Equipment

4402 Pulp and Paper Mills

4445 (3) Hand-fed Engraving Press

4494 (a) Operating Rules, Laundry and Dry Cleaning

4799 (a) Training of Operators, Gas Systems and for Welding and Cutting

4848 (a)(21) Fire Prevention and Suppression Procedure

5006 (a) Crane, Hoists, Derrick Operators Qualifications

5099 (a) Control of Noise Exposure

5144 (c) Respiratory Protective Equipment

5154 (j)(1) Open Surface Tank Operations

5157 (b) Confined Spaces

5166 (a) Cleaning, Repairing or Altering Containers

5185 (a) Changing and Charging Storage Batteries

5189 (g) Process Safety Management of Acutely Hazardous Materials

5190 (i) Cotton Dust

5191 (f) Occupational Exposure to Hazardous Chemicals in Laboratories

5192 (e) & (l)(3)(D) Hazardous Waste Operations and Emergency Response— Uncontrolled Waste Site Operations

31

5192 (p)(2), (p)(7) & (p)(8)(C) Hazardous Waste
Operations and Emergency Response—
RCRA Operations

5192 (q)(6) Hazardous Waste Operations and
Emergency Response—Emergency
Response Operations

5193 (c)(5) & (g)(2) Bloodborne Pathogens

5194 (b)(1) Hazard Communication, Employee
Information and Training

5208 (o)(1) Asbestos

5208.1 (n)(1)(B) Non Asbestiform Minerals

5209 (e)(5) Carcinogens

5210 (j) Vinyl Chloride

5211 (t)(1) Coke Oven Emissions

5212 (r)(1) 1, 2 Dibromo–3 Chloropropane
(DBCP)

5213 (o)(1) Acrylonitrile (AN)

5214 (m)(1) Inorganic Arsenic

5215 (j)(1) 4, 4'–Methylenebis
(2-Chloroaniline), MBOCA

5216 (l)(1) Lead

5217 (n) Formaldehyde

5218 (j)(3) Benzene

5219 (j) Ethylene Dibromide

5220 (i)(1) Ethylene Oxide (EtO)

5221 (c) Fumigation: General

5229 Protection (Labels)

5239 Handle or Transport Explosives

5322 Manufacture of Explosives and
Fireworks

5571 (g) Service Stations (Portable Fire
Extinguishers)

6052 (d)(1) Diving Operations (Dive Team
Training)

Fire Protection

6151 (g)(1) Portable Fire Extinguishers

6165 (f)(2)(F) Standpipe and Hose Systems

6175 (a)(10) Fixed Extinguishers Systems

Logging and Sawmills

6251 (d) First Aid Training

Petroleum Safety Orders: Drilling and Production

6507 (A) Safety Training and Instruction

Petroleum Safety Orders: Refining, Transportation, Handling

6760 (A) Safety Training and Instruction

Mine Safety Orders and Instruction

6963 Safety Training and Instruction

6967 Certification of Safety Representative at
Underground Mines

6968 (a), (b) & (c) First Aid Training

7074 (d) Emergency Plan (Underground)

7083 (c) Mine Rescue Stations

7085 (a) Mine Rescue Training and
Procedure

7150 (d) Qualified Hoistmen (Persons)

7201 Explosives

Ship Building, Ship Repairing and Ship Breaking Safety Orders

8355 (b) Hazardous Work

8397.1(b) Radioactive Material

Tunnel Safety Orders

8407 Safety Instructions for New
Employees

8421 (a) First Aid Training

8430 (a) Rescue Apparatus (Trained
Rescue Crew)

8455 (a) Mechanical Tunneling Methods and
Equipment

8499 (b) Hoisting Engineers

8506 Explosives

Tunnel Safety Orders Appendix B—Labor Code Excerpts Part 9 Tunnel and Mine Safety

7952 Trained DOSH Safety Engineers

7958 Trained Rescue Crews

7990 Explosives Blasters Licensed

7999 Gas Testers and Safety Representatives

Telecommunication Orders

8603 Training

Elevator Safety Orders

3003 (c) Certified Elevator Inspectors

Aerial Passenger Tramway Safety Orders

3157.1(c)(2) Operator Experience and Training

93 83776

29 CFR 1926.21
SAFETY TRAINING
AND EDUCATION

§ 1926.21 **Safety training and education.**

(a) *General requirements.* The Secretary shall, pursuant to section 107(f) of the Act, establish and supervise programs for the education and training of employers and employees in the recognition, avoidance and prevention of unsafe conditions in employments covered by the act.

(b) *Employer responsibility.* (1) The employer should avail himself of the safety and health training programs the Secretary provides.

(2) The employer shall instruct each employee in the recognition and avoidance of unsafe conditions and the regulations applicable to his work environment to control or eliminate any hazards or other exposure to illness or injury.

(3) Employees required to handle or use poisons, caustics, and other harmful substances shall be instructed regarding the safe handling and use, and be made aware of the potential hazards, personal hygiene, and personal protective measures required.

(4) In job site areas where harmful plants or animals are present, employees who may be exposed shall be instructed regarding the potential hazards, and how to avoid injury, and the first aid procedures to be used in the event of injury.

(5) Employees required to handle or use flammable liquids, gases, or toxic materials shall be instructed in the safe handling and use of these materials and made aware of the specific requirements contained in subparts D, F, and other applicable subparts of this part.

(6)(i) All employees required to enter into confined or enclosed spaces shall be instructed as to the nature of the hazards involved, the necessary precautions to be taken, and in the use of protective and emergency equipment required. The employer shall comply with any specific regulations that apply to work in dangerous or potentially dangerous areas.

(ii) For purposes of paragraph (b)(6)(i) of this section, "confined or enclosed space" means any space having a limited means of egress, which is subject to the accumulation of toxic or flammable contaminants or has an oxygen deficient atmosphere. Confined or enclosed spaces include, but are not limited to, storage tanks, process vessels, bins, boilers, ventilation or exhaust ducts, sewers, underground utility vaults, tunnels, pipelines, and open top spaces more than 4 feet in depth such as pits, tubs, vaults, and vessels.

29 CFR 1910.120

HAZARDOUS WASTE OPERATIONS AND EMERGENCY RESPONSE

§ 1910.120 Hazardous waste operations and emergency response.

(a) *Scope, application, and definitions—* (1) *Scope.* This section covers the following operations, unless the employer can demonstrate that the operation does not involve employee exposure or the reasonable possibility for employee exposure to safety or health hazards:

(i) Clean-up operations required by a governmental body, whether Federal, state, local or other involving hazardous substances that are conducted at ,uncontrolled hazardous waste sites (including, but not limited to, the EPA's National Priority Site List (NPL), state priority site lists, sites recommended for the EPA NPL, and initial investigations of government identified sites which are conducted before the presence or absence of hazardous substances has been ascertained);

(ii) Corrective actions involving clean-up operations at sites covered by the Resource Conservation and Recovery Act of 1976 (RCRA) as amended (42 U.S.C. 6901 *et seq.*);

(iii) Voluntary clean-up operations at sites recognized by Federal, state, local or other governmental bodies as uncontrolled hazardous waste sites;

(iv) Operations involving hazardous wastes that are conducted at treatment, storage, and disposal (TSD) facilities regulated by 40 CFR parts 264 and 265 pursuant to RCRA; or by agencies under agreement with U.S.E.P.A. to implement RCRA regulations; and

(v) Emergency response operations for releases of, or substantial threats of releases of, hazardous substances without regard to the location of the hazard.

(2) *Application.* (i) All requirements of part 1910 and part 1926 of title 29 of the Code of Federal Regulations apply pursuant to their terms to hazardous waste and emergency response operations whether covered by this section or not. If there is a conflict or overlap, the provision more protective of em-

ployee safety and health shall apply without regard to 29 CFR 1910.5(c)(1).

(ii) Hazardous substance clean-up operations within the scope of paragraphs (a)(1)(i) through (a)(1)(iii) of this section must comply with all paragraphs of this section except paragraphs (p) and (q).

(iii) Operations within the scope of paragraph (a)(1)(iv) of this section must comply only with the requirements of paragraph (p) of this section.

Notes and Exceptions: (A) All provisions of paragraph (p) of this section cover any treatment, storage or disposal (TSD) operation regulated by 40 CFR parts 264 and 265 or by state law authorized under RCRA, and required to have a permit or interim status from EPA pursuant to 40 CFR 270.1 or from a state agency pursuant to RCRA.

(B) Employers who are not required to have a permit or interim status because they are conditionally exempt small quantity generators under 40 CFR 261.5 or are generators who qualify under 40 CFR 262.34 for exemptions from regulation under 40 CFR parts 264, 265 and 270 ("excepted employers") are not covered by paragraphs (p)(1) through (p)(7) of this section. Excepted employers who are required by the EPA or state agency to have their employees engage in emergency response or who direct their employees to engage in emergency response are covered by paragraph (p)(8) of this section, and cannot be exempted by (p)(8)(i) of this section. Excepted employers who are not required to have employees engage in emergency response, who direct their employees to evacuate in the case of such emergencies and who meet the requirements of paragraph (p)(8)(i) of this section are exempt from the balance of paragraph (p)(8) of this section.

(C) If an area is used primarily for treatment, storage or disposal, any emergency response operations in that area shall comply with paragraph (p)(8) of this section. In other areas not used primarily for treatment, storage, or disposal, any emergency response operations shall comply with paragraph (q) of this section. Compliance with the requirements of paragraph (q) of this section shall be deemed to be in compliance with the requirements of paragraph (p)(8) of this section.

(iv) Emergency response operations for releases of, or substantial threats of releases of, hazardous substances which are not covered by paragraphs (a)(1)(i) through (a)(1)(iv) of this section must only comply with the requirements of paragraph (q) of this section.

(3) *Definitions*—"*Buddy system* means a system of organizing employees into work groups in such a manner that each employee of the work group is designated to be observed by at least one other employee in the work group. The purpose of the buddy system is to provide rapid assistance to employees in the event of an emergency.

Clean-up operation means an operation where hazardous substances are removed, contained, incinerated, neutralized, stabilized, cleared-up, or in any other manner processed or handled with the ultimate goal of making the site safer for people or the environment.

Decontamination means the removal of hazardous substances from employees and their equipment to the extent necessary to preclude the occurrence of foreseeable adverse health affects.

Emergency response orresponding to *emergencies* means a response effort by employees from outside the immediate release area or by other designated responders (i.e., mutual-aid groups, local fire departments, etc.) to an occurrence which results, or is likely to result, in an uncontrolled release of a hazardous substance. Responses to incidental releases of hazardous substances where the substance can be absorbed, neutralized, or otherwise controlled at the time of release by employees in the immediate release area, or by maintenance personnel are not considered to be emergency responses within the scope of this standard. Responses to releases of hazardous substances where there is no potential safety or health hazard (i.e., fire, explosion, or chemical exposure) are not considered to be emergency responses.

Facility means (A) any building, structure, installation, equipment, pipe or pipeline (including any pipe into a sewer or publicly owned treatment works), well, pit, pond, lagoon, impoundment, ditch, storage container, motor vehicle, rolling stock, or aircraft, or (B) any site or area where a hazardous substance has been deposited, stored, disposed of, or placed, or otherwise come to be located; but does not include any consumer product in consumer use or any water-borne vessel.

Hazardous materials response (HAZMAT) team means an organized group of employees, designated by the employer, who are expected to perform work to handle and control actual or potential leaks or spills of hazardous substances requiring possible close approach to the substance. The team members perform responses to releases or potential releases of hazardous substances for the purpose of control or stabilization of the incident. A HAZMAT team is not a fire brigade nor is a typical fire brigade a HAZMAT team. A HAZMAT team, however, may be a separate component of a fire brigade or fire department.

Hazardous substance means any substance designated or listed under paragraphs (A) through (D) of this definition, exposure to which results or may result in adverse affects on the health or safety of employees:

(A) Any substance defined under section 101(14) of CERCLA;

(B) Any biological agent and other disease-causing agent which after release into the environment and upon exposure, ingestion, inhalation, or assimilation into any person, either directly from the environment or indirectly by ingestion through food chains, will or may reasonably be anticipated to cause death, disease, behavioral abnormalities, cancer, genetic mutation, physiological malfunctions (including malfunctions in reproduction) or physical deformations in such persons or their offspring;

(C) Any substance listed by the U.S. Department of Transportation as hazardous materials under 49 CFR 172.101 and appendices; and

(D) Hazardous waste as herein defined.

Hazardous waste means—

(A) A waste or combination of wastes as defined in 40 CFR 261.3, or

(B) Those substances defined as hazardous wastes in 49 CFR 171.8.

Hazardous waste operation means any operation conducted within the scope of this standard.

Hazardous waste site or *Site* means any facility or location within the scope of this standard at which hazardous waste operations take place.

Health hazard means a chemical, mixture of chemicals or a pathogen for which there is statistically significant evidence based on at least one study conducted in accordance with estab-

lished scientific principles that acute or chronic health effects may occur in exposed employees. The term "health hazard" includes chemicals which are carcinogens, toxic or highly toxic agents, reproductive toxins, irritants, corrosives, sensitizers, heptaotoxins, nephrotoxins, neurotoxins, agents which act on the hematopoietic system, and agents which damage the lungs, skin, eyes, or mucous membranes. It also includes stress due to temperature extremes. Further definition of the terms used above can be found in appendix A to 29 CFR 1910.1200.

IDLH or *Immediately dangerous to life or health* means an atmospheric concentration of any toxic, corrosive or asphyxiant substance that poses an immediate threat to life or would cause irreversible or delayed adverse health effects or would interfere with an individual's ability to escape from a dangerous atmosphere.

Oxygen deficiency means that concentration of oxygen by volume below which atmosphere supplying respiratory protection must be provided. It exists in atmospheres where the percentage of oxygen by volume is less than 19.5 percent oxygen.

Permissible exposure limit means the exposure, inhalation or dermal permissible exposure limit specified in 29 CFR part 1910 subparts G and Z.

Published exposure level means the exposure limits published in "NIOSH Recommendations for Occupational Health Standards" dated 1986 incorporated by reference, or if none is specified, the exposure limits published in the standards specified by the American Conference of Governmental Industrial Hygienists in their publication "Threshold Limit Values and Biological Exposure Indices for 1987–88" dated 1987 incorporated by reference.

Post emergency response means that portion of an emergency response performed after the immediate threat of a release has been stabilized or eliminated and clean-up of the site has begun. If post emergency response is performed by an employer's own employees who were part of the initial emergency response, it is considered to be part of the initial response and not post emergency response. However, if a group of an employer's own employees, separate from the group providing initial response, performs the clean-up operation, then the separate group of employees would be considered to be performing post-emergency response and subject to paragraph (q)(11) of this section.

Qualified person means a person with specific training, knowledge and experience in the area for which the person has the responsibility and the authority to control.

Site safety and health supervisor (or official) means the individual located on a hazardous waste site who is responsible to the employer and has the authority and knowledge necessary to implement the site safety and health plan and verify compliance with applicable safety and health requirements.

Small quantity generator means a generator of hazardous wastes who in any calendar month generates no more than 1,000 kilograms (2,205 pounds) of hazardous waste in that month.

Uncontrolled hazardous waste site, means an area identified as an uncontrolled hazardous waste site by a governmental body, whether Federal, state, local or other where an accumulation of hazardous substances creates a threat to the health and safety of individuals or the environment or both. Some sites are found on public lands such as those created by former municipal, county or state landfills where illegal or poorly managed waste disposal has taken place. Other sites are found on private property, often belonging to generators or former generators of hazardous substance wastes. Examples of such sites include, but are not limited to, surface impoundments, landfills, dumps, and tank or drum farms. Normal operations at TSD sites are not covered by this definition.

(b) *Safety and health program.*

NOTE TO (b): Safety and health programs developed and implemented to meet other Federal, state, or local regulations are considered acceptable in meeting this requirement if they cover or are modified to cover the topics required in this paragraph. An additional or separate safety and health program is not required by this paragraph.

(1) *General.* (i) Employers shall develop and implement a written safety and health program for their employees involved in hazardous waste operations. The program shall be designed to identify, evaluate, and control safety and health hazards, and provide for emergency response for hazardous waste operations.

(ii) The written safety and health program shall incorporate the following:

(A) An organizational structure;

(B) A comprehensive workplan;

(C) A site-specific safety and health plan which need not repeat the employer's standard operating procedures required in paragraph (b)(1)(ii)(F) of this section;

(D) The safety and health training program;

(E) The medical surveillance program;

(F) The employer's standard operating procedures for safety and health; and

(G) Any necessary interface between general program and site specific activities.

(iii) *Site excavation.* Site excavations created during initial site preparation or during hazardous waste operations shall be shored or sloped as appropriate to prevent accidental collapse in accordance with subpart P of 29 CFR part 1926.

(iv) *Contractors and sub-contractors.* An employer who retains contractor or sub-contractor services for work in hazardous waste operations shall inform those contractors, sub-contractors, or their representatives of the site emergency response procedures and any potential fire, explosion, health, safety or other hazards of the hazardous waste operation that have been identified by the employer, including those identified in the employer's information program.

(v) *Program availability.* The written safety and health program shall be made available to any contractor or subcontractor or their representative who will be involved with the hazardous waste operation; to employees; to employee designated representatives; to OSHA personnel, and to personnel of other Federal, state, or local agencies with regulatory authority over the site.

(2) *Organizational structure part of the site program*—(i) The organizational structure part of the program shall es-

tablish the specific chain of command and specify the overall responsibilities of supervisors and employees. It shall include, at a minimum, the following elements:

(A) A general supervisor who has the responsibility and authority to direct all hazardous waste operations.

(B) A site safety and health supervisor who has the responsibility and authority to develop and implement the site safety and health plan and verify compliance.

(C) All other personnel needed for hazardous waste site operations and emergency response and their general functions and responsibilities.

(D) The lines of authority, responsibility, and communication.

(ii) The organizational structure shall be reviewed and updated as necessary to reflect the current status of waste site operations.

(3) *Comprehensive workplan part of the site program.* The comprehensive workplan part of the program shall address the tasks and objectives of the site operations and the logistics and resources required to reach those tasks and objectives.

(i) The comprehensive workplan shall address anticipated clean-up activities as well as normal operating procedures which need not repeat the employer's procedures available elsewhere.

(ii) The comprehensive workplan shall define work tasks and objectives and identify the methods for accomplishing those tasks and objectives.

(iii) The comprehensive workplan shall establish personnel requirements for implementing the plan.

(iv) The comprehensive workplan shall provide for the implementation of the training required in paragraph (e) of this section.

(v) The comprehensive workplan shall provide for the implementation of the required informational programs required in paragraph (i) of this section.

(vi) The comprehensive workplan shall provide for the implementation of the medical surveillance program described in paragraph (f) of this section.

(4) *Site-specific safety and health plan part of the program*—(i) *General.* The site safety and health plan, which must be kept on site, shall address the safety and health hazards of each phase of site operation and include the requirements and procedures for employee protection.

(ii) *Elements.* The site safety and health plan, as a minimum, shall address the following:

(A) A safety and health risk or hazard analysis for each site task and operation found in the workplan.

(B) Employee training assignments to assure compliance with paragraph (e) of this section.

(C) Personal protective equipment to be used by employees for each of the site tasks and operations being conducted as required by the personal protective equipment program in paragraph (g)(5) of this section.

(D) Medical surveillance requirements in accordance with the program in paragraph (f) of this section.

(E) Frequency and types of air monitoring, personnel monitoring, and environmental sampling techniques and instrumentation to be used, including methods of maintenance and calibration of monitoring and sampling equipment to be used.

(F) Site control measures in accordance with the site control program required in paragraph (d) of this section.

(G) Decontamination procedures in accordance with paragraph (k) of this section.

(H) An emergency response plan meeting the requirements of paragraph (l) of this section for safe and effective responses to emergencies, including the necessary PPE and other equipment.

(I) Confined space entry procedures.

(J) A spill containment program meeting the requirements of paragraph (j) of this section.

(iii) *Pre-entry briefing.* The site specific safety and health plan shall provide for pre-entry briefings to be held prior to initiating any site activity, and at such other times as necessary to ensure that employees are apprised of the site safety and health plan and that this plan is being followed. The information and data obtained from site characterization and analysis work required in paragraph (c) of this section shall be used to prepare and update the site safety and health plan.

(iv) *Effectiveness of site safety and health plan.* Inspections shall be conducted by the site safety and health supervisor or, in the absence of that individual, another individual who is knowledgeable in occupational safety and health, acting on behalf of the employer as necessary to determine the effectiveness of the site safety and health plan. Any deficiencies in the effectiveness of the site safety and health plan shall be corrected by the employer.

(c) *Site characterization and analysis—* (1) *General.* Hazardous waste sites shall be evaluated in accordance with this paragraph to identify specific site hazards and to determine the appropriate safety and health control procedures needed to protect employees from the identified hazards.

(2) *Preliminary evaluation.* A preliminary evaluation of a site's characteristics shall be performed prior to site entry by a qualified person in order to aid in the selection of appropriate employee protection methods prior to site entry. Immediately after initial site entry, a more detailed evaluation of the site's specific characteristics shall be performed by a qualified person in order to further identify existing site hazards and to further aid in the selection of the appropriate engineering controls and personal protective equipment for the tasks to be performed.

(3) *Hazard identification.* All suspected conditions that may pose inhalation or skin absorption hazards that are immediately dangerous to life or health (IDLH), or other conditions that may cause death or serious harm, shall be identified during the preliminary survey and evaluated during the detailed survey. Examples of such hazards include, but are not limited to, confined space entry, potentially explosive or flammable situations, visible vapor clouds, or areas where biological indicators such as dead animals or vegetation are located.

(4) *Required information.* The following information to the extent available shall be obtained by the employer prior to allowing employees to enter a site:

(i) Location and approximate size of the site.

(ii) Description of the response activity and/or the job task to be performed.

(iii) Duration of the planned employee activity.

(iv) Site topography and accessibility by air and roads.

(v) Safety and health hazards expected at the site.

(vi) Pathways for hazardous substance dispersion.

(vii) Present status and capabilities of emergency response teams that would provide assistance to hazardous waste clean-up site employees at the time of an emergency.

(viii) Hazardous substances and health hazards involved or expected at the site, and their chemical and physical properties.

(5) *Personal protective equipment.* Personal protective equipment (PPE) shall be provided and used during initial site entry in accordance with the following requirements:

(i) Based upon the results of the preliminary site evaluation, an ensemble of PPE shall be selected and used during initial site entry which will provide protection to a level of exposure below permissible exposure limits and published exposure levels for known or suspected hazardous substances and health hazards, and which will provide protection against other known and suspected hazards identified during the preliminary site evaluation. If there is no permissible exposure limit or published exposure level, the employer may use other published studies and information as a guide to appropriate personal protective equipment.

(ii) If positive-pressure self-contained breathing apparatus is not used as part of the entry ensemble, and if respiratory protection is warranted by the potential hazards identified during the preliminary site evaluation, an escape self-contained breathing apparatus of at least five minute's duration shall be carried by employees during initial site entry.

(iii) If the preliminary site evaluation does not produce sufficient information to identify the hazards or suspected hazards of the site, an ensemble providing protection equivalent to Level B PPE shall be provided as minimum protection, and direct reading instruments shall be used as appropriate for identifying IDLH conditions. (See appendix B for a description of Level B hazards and the recommendations for Level B protective equipment.)

(iv) Once the hazards of the site have been identified, the appropriate PPE shall be selected and used in accordance with paragraph (g) of this section.

(6) *Monitoring.* The following monitoring shall be conducted during initial site entry when the site evaluation produces information that shows the potential for ionizing radiation or IDLH conditions, or when the site information is not sufficient reasonably to eliminate these possible conditions:

(i) Monitoring with direct reading instruments for hazardous levels of ionizing radiation.

(ii) Monitoring the air with appropriate direct reading test equipment (i.e., combustible gas meters, detector tubes) for IDLH and other conditions that may cause death or serious harm (combustible or explosive atmospheres, oxygen deficiency, toxic substances).

(iii) Visually observing for signs of actual or potential IDLH or other dangerous conditions.

(iv) An ongoing air monitoring program in accordance with paragraph (h) of this section shall be implemented after site characterization has determined the site is safe for the start-up of operations.

(7) *Risk identification.* Once the presence and concentrations of specific hazardous substances and health hazards have been established, the risks associated with these substances shall be identified. Employees who will be working on the site shall be informed of any risks that have been identified. In situations covered by the Hazard Communication Standard, 29 CFR 1910.1200, training required by that standard need not be duplicated.

NOTE TO (c)(7).—Risks to consider include, but are not limited to:

(a) Exposures exceeding the permissible exposure limits and published exposure levels.

(b) IDLH concentrations.

(c) Potential skin absorption and irritation sources.

(d) Potential eye irritation sources.

(e) Explosion sensitivity and flammability ranges.

(f) Oxygen deficiency.

(8) *Employee notification.* Any information concerning the chemical, physical, and toxicologic properties of each substance known or expected to be present on site that is available to the employer and relevant to the duties an employee is expected to perform shall be made available to the affected employees prior to the commencement of their work activities. The employer may utilize information developed for the hazard communication standard for this purpose.

(d) *Site control*—(1) *General.* Appropriate site control procedures shall be implemented to control employee exposure to hazardous substances before clean-up work begins.

(2) *Site control program.* A site control program for protecting employees which is part of the employer's site safety and health program required in paragraph (b) of this section shall be developed during the planning stages of a hazardous waste clean-up operation and modified as necessary as new information becomes available.

(3) *Elements of the site control program.* The site control program shall, as a minimum, include: A site map; site work zones; the use of a "buddy system"; site communications including alerting means for emergencies; the standard operating procedures or safe work practices; and, identification of the nearest medical assistance. Where these requirements are covered elsewhere they need not be repeated.

(e) *Training*—(1) *General.* (i) All employees working on site (such as but not limited to equipment operators, general laborers and others) exposed to hazardous substances, health hazards, or safety hazards and their supervisors and management responsible for the site shall receive training meeting the requirements of this paragraph before they are permitted to engage in hazardous waste operations that could expose them to hazardous substances, safety, or health hazards, and they shall receive review training as specified in this paragraph.

(ii) Employees shall not be permitted to participate in or supervise field activities until they have been trained to a level required by their job function and responsibility.

(2) *Elements to be covered.* The training shall thoroughly cover the following:

(i) Names of personnel and alternates responsible for site safety and health;

(ii) Safety, health and other hazards present on the site;

(iii) Use of personal protective equipment;

(iv) Work practices by which the employee can minimize risks from hazards;

(v) Safe use of engineering controls and equipment on the site;

(vi) Medical surveillance requirements, including recognition of symptoms and signs which might indicate overexposure to hazards; and

(vii) The contents of paragraphs (G) through (J) of the site safety and health plan set forth in paragraph (b)(4)(ii) of this section.

(3) *Initial training.* (i) General site workers (such as equipment operators, general laborers and supervisory personnel) engaged in hazardous substance removal or other activities which expose or potentially expose workers to hazardous substances and health hazards shall receive a minimum of 40 hours of instruction off the site, and a minimum of three days actual field experience under the direct supervision of a trained, experienced supervisor.

(ii) Workers on site only occasionally for a specific limited task (such as, but not limited to, ground water monitoring, land surveying, or geo-physical surveying) and who are unlikely to be exposed over permissible exposure limits and published exposure limits shall receive a minimum of 24 hours of instruction off the site, and the minimum of one day actual field experience under the direct supervision of a trained, experienced supervisor.

(iii) Workers regularly on site who work in areas which have been monitored and fully characterized indicating that exposures are under permissible exposure limits and published exposure limits where respirators are not necessary, and the characterization indicates that there are no health hazards or the possibility of an emergency developing, shall receive a minimum of 24 hours of instruction off the site and the minimum of one day actual field experience under the direct supervision of a trained, experienced supervisor.

(iv) Workers with 24 hours of training who are covered by paragraphs (e)(3)(ii) and (e)(3)(iii) of this section, and who become general site workers or who are

required to wear respirators, shall have the additional 16 hours and two days of training necessary to total the training specified in paragraph (e)(3)(i).

(4) *Management and supervisor training.* On-site management and supervisors directly responsible for, or who supervise employees engaged in, hazardous waste operations shall receive 40 hours initial training, and three days of supervised field experience (the training may be reduced to 24 hours and one day if the only area of their responsibility is employees covered by paragraphs (e)(3)(ii) and (e)(3)(iii)) and at least eight additional hours of specialized training at the time of job assignment on such topics as, but not limited to, the employer's safety and health program and the associated employee training program, personal protective equipment program, spill containment program, and health hazard monitoring procedure and techniques.

(5) *Qualifications for trainers.* Trainers shall be qualified to instruct employees about the subject matter that is being presented in training. Such trainers shall have satisfactorily completed a training program for teaching the subjects they are expected to teach, or they shall have the academic credentials and instructional experience necessary for teaching the subjects. Instructors shall demonstrate competent instructional skills and knowledge of the applicable subject matter.

(6) *Training certification.* Employees and supervisors that have received and successfully completed the training and field experience specified in paragraphs (e)(1) through (e)(4) of this section shall be certified by their instructor or the head instructor and trained supervisor as having successfully completed the necessary training. A written certificate shall be given to each person so certified. Any person who has not been so certified or who does not meet the requirements of paragraph (e)(9) of this section shall be prohibited from engaging in hazardous waste operations.

(7) *Emergency response.* Employees who are engaged in responding to hazardous emergency situations at hazardous waste clean-up sites that may expose them to hazardous substances

shall be trained in how to respond to such expected emergencies.

(8) *Refresher training.* Employees specified in paragraph (e)(1) of this section, and managers and supervisors specified in paragraph (e)(4) of this section, shall receive eight hours of refresher training annually on the items specified in paragraph (e)(2) and/or (e)(4) of this section, any critique of incidents that have occurred in the past year that can serve as training examples of related work, and other relevant topics.

(9) *Equivalent training.* Employers who can show by documentation or certification that an employee's work experience and/or training has resulted in training equivalent to that training required in paragraphs (e)(1) through (e)(4) of this section shall not be required to provide the initial training requirements of those paragraphs to such employees and shall provide a copy of the certification or documentation to the employee upon request. However, certified employees or employees with equivalent training new to a site shall receive appropriate, site specific training before site entry and have appropriate supervised field experience at the new site. Equivalent training includes any academic training or the training that existing employees might have already received from actual hazardous waste site work experience.

(f) *Medical surveillance*—(1) *General.* Employers engaged in operations specified in paragraphs (a)(1)(i) through (a)(1)(iv) of this section and not covered by (a)(2)(iii) exceptions and employers of employees specified in paragraph (q)(9) shall institute a medical surveillance program in accordance with this paragraph.

(2) *Employees covered.* The medical surveillance program shall be instituted by the employer for the following employees:

(i) All employees who are or may be exposed to hazardous substances or health hazards at or above the permissible exposure limits or, if there is no permissible exposure limit, above the published exposure levels for these substances, without regard to the use of respirators, for 30 days or more a year;

(ii) All employees who wear a respirator for 30 days or more a year or as required by § 1910.134;

(iii) All employees who are injured, become ill or develop signs or symptoms due to possible overexposure involving hazardous substances or health hazards from an emergency response or hazardous waste operation; and

(iv) Members of HAZMAT teams.

(3) *Frequency of medical examinations and consultations.* Medical examinations and consultations shall be made available by the employer to each employee covered under paragraph (f)(2) of this section on the following schedules:

(i) For employees covered under paragraphs (f)(2)(i), (f)(2)(ii), and (f)(2)(iv):

(A) Prior to assignment;

(B) At least once every twelve months for each employee covered unless the attending physician believes a longer interval (not greater than biennially) is appropriate;

(C) At termination of employment or reassignment to an area where the employee would not be covered if the employee has not had an examination within the last six months;

(D) As soon as possible upon notification by an employee that the employee has developed signs or symptoms indicating possible overexposure to hazardous substances or health hazards, or that the employee has been injured or exposed above the permissible exposure limits or published exposure levels in an emergency situation;

(E) At more frequent times, if the examining physician determines that an increased frequency of examination is medically necessary.

(ii) For employees covered under paragraph (f)(2)(iii) and for all employees including those of employers covered by paragraph (a)(1)(v) who may have been injured, received a health impairment, developed signs or symptoms which may have resulted from exposure to hazardous substances resulting from an emergency incident, or exposed during an emergency incident to hazardous substances at concentrations above the permissible exposure limits or the published exposure levels without the necessary personal protective equipment being used:

(A) As soon as possible following the emergency incident or development of signs or symptoms;

(B) At additional times, if the examining physician determines that follow-up examinations or consultations are medically necessary.

(4) *Content of medical examinations and consultations.* (i) Medical examinations required by paragraph (f)(3) of this section shall include a medical and work history (or updated history if one is in the employee's file) with special emphasis on symptoms related to the handling of hazardous substances and health hazards, and to fitness for duty including the ability to wear any required PPE under conditions (i.e., temperature extremes) that may be expected at the work site.

(ii) The content of medical examinations or consultations made available to employees pursuant to paragraph (f) shall be determined by the attending physician. The guidelines in the *Occupational Safety and Health Guidance Manual for Hazardous Waste Site Activities* (See appendix D, Reference #10) should be consulted.

(5) *Examination by a physician and costs.* All medical examinations and procedures shall be performed by or under the supervision of a licensed physician, preferably one knowledgeable in occupational medicine, and shall be provided without cost to the employee, without loss of pay, and at a reasonable time and place.

(6) *Information provided to the physician.* The employer shall provide one copy of this standard and its appendices to the attending physician, and in addition the following for each employee:

(i) A description of the employee's duties as they relate to the employee's exposures.

(ii) The employee's exposure levels or anticipated exposure levels.

(iii) A description of any personal protective equipment used or to be used.

(iv) Information from previous medical examinations of the employee which is not readily available to the examining physician.

(v) Information required by §1910.134.

(7) *Physician's written opinion.* (i) The employer shall obtain and furnish the employee with a copy of a written opinion from the attending physician containing the following:

(A) The physician's opinion as to whether the employee has any detected medical conditions which would place the employee at increased risk of material impairment of the employee's health from work in hazardous waste operations or emergency response, or from respirator use.

(B) The physician's recommended limitations upon the employee's assigned work.

(C) The results of the medical examination and tests if requested by the employee.

(D) A statement that the employee has been informed by the physician of the results of the medical examination and any medical conditions which require further examination or treatment.

(ii) The written opinion obtained by the employer shall not reveal specific findings or diagnoses unrelated to occupational exposures.

(8) *Recordkeeping.* (i) An accurate record of the medical surveillance required by paragraph (f) of this section shall be retained. This record shall be retained for the period specified and meet the criteria of 29 CFR 1910.20.

(ii) The record required in paragraph (f)(8)(i) of this section shall include at least the following information:

(A) The name and social security number of the employee;

(B) Physician's written opinions, recommended limitations, and results of examinations and tests;

(C) Any employee medical complaints related to exposure to hazardous substances;

(D) A copy of the information provided to the examining physician by the employer, with the exception of the standard and its appendices.

(g) *Engineering controls, work practices, and personal protective equipment for employee protection.* Engineering controls, work practices, personal protective equipment, or a combination of these shall be implemented in accordance with this paragraph to protect employees from exposure to hazardous substances and safety and health hazards.

(1) *Engineering controls, work practices and PPE for substances regulated in subparts G and Z.* (i) Engineering controls and work practices shall be instituted to reduce and maintain employee exposure to or below the permissible exposure limits for substances regulated by 29 CFR part 1910, to the extent required by subpart Z, except to the extent that such controls and practices are not feasible.

NOTE TO (g)(1)(i): Engineering controls which may be feasible include the use of pressurized cabs or control booths on equipment, and/or the use of remotely operated material handling equipment. Work practices which may be feasible are removing all non-essential employees from potential exposure during opening of drums, wetting down dusty operations and locating employees upwind of possible hazards.

(ii) Whenever engineering controls and work practices are not feasible or not required, any reasonable combination of engineering controls, work practices and PPE shall be used to reduce and maintain employee exposures to or below the permissible exposure limits or dose limits for substances regulated by 29 CFR part 1910, subpart Z.

(iii) The employer shall not implement a schedule of employee rotation as a means of compliance with permissible exposure limits or dose limits except when there is no other feasible way of complying with the airborne or dermal dose limits for ionizing radiation.

(iv) The provisions of 29 CFR, subpart G, shall be followed.

(2) *Engineering controls, work practices, and PPE for substances not regulated in subparts G and Z.* An appropriate combination of engineering controls, work practices and personal protective equipment shall be used to reduce and maintain employee exposure to or below published exposure levels for hazardous substances and health hazards not regulated by 29 CFR part 1910, subparts G and Z. The employer may use the published literature and MSDS as a guide in making the employer's determination as to what level of protection the employer believes is appropriate for hazardous substances and health hazards for which there is no permissible exposure limit or published exposure limit.

(3) *Personal protective equipment selection.* (i) Personal protective equipment (PPE) shall be selected and used which will protect employees from the hazards and potential hazards they are likely to encounter as identified during the site characterization and analysis.

(ii) Personal protective equipment selection shall be based on an evaluation of the performance characteristics of the PPE relative to the requirements and limitations of the site, the task-specific conditions and duration, and the hazards and potential hazards identified at the site.

(iii) Positive pressure self-contained breathing apparatus, or positive pressure air-line respirators equipped with an escape air supply, shall be used when chemical exposure levels present will create a substantial possibility of immediate death, immediate serious illness or injury, or impair the ability to escape.

(iv) Totally-encapsulating chemical protective suits (protection equivalent to Level A protection as recommended in appendix B) shall be used in conditions where skin absorption of a hazardous substance may result in a substantial possibility of immediate death, immediate serious illness or injury, or impair the ability to escape.

(v) The level of protection provided by PPE selection shall be increased when additional information on site conditions indicates that increased protection is necessary to reduce employee exposures below permissible exposure limits and published exposure levels for hazardous substances and health hazards. (See appendix B for guidance on selecting PPE ensembles.)

NOTE TO (g)(3): The level of employee protection provided may be decreased when additional information or site conditions show that decreased protection will not result in hazardous exposures to employees.

(vi) Personal protective equipment shall be selected and used to meet the requirements of 29 CFR part 1910, subpart I, and additional requirements specified in this section.

(4) *Totally-encapsulating chemical protective suits.* (i) Totally-encapsulating suits shall protect employees from the particular hazards which are identified

during site characterization and analysis.

(ii) Totally-encapsulating suits shall be capable of maintaining positive air pressure. (See appendix A for a test method which may be used to evaluate this requirement.)

(iii) Totally-encapsulating suits shall be capable of preventing inward test gas leakage of more than 0.5 percent. (See appendix A for a test method which may be used to evaluate this requirement.)

(5) *Personal protective equipment (PPE) program.* A written personal protective equipment program, which is part of the employer's safety and health program required in paragraph (b) of this section or required in paragraph (p)(1) of this section and which is also a part of the site-specific safety and health plan shall be established. The PPE program shall address the elements listed below. When elements, such as donning and doffing procedures, are provided by the manufacturer of a piece of equipment and are attached to the plan, they need not be rewritten into the plan as long as they adequately address the procedure or element.

(i) PPE selection based upon site hazards,

(ii) PPE use and limitations of the equipment,

(iii) Work mission duration,

(iv) PPE maintenance and storage,

(v) PPE decontamination and disposal,

(vi) PPE training and proper fitting,

(vii) PPE donning and doffing procedures,

(viii) PPE inspection procedures prior to, during, and after use,

(ix) Evaluation of the effectiveness of the PPE program, and

(x) Limitations during temperature extremes, heat stress, and other appropriate medical considerations.

(h) *Monitoring*—(1) *General.* (i) Monitoring shall be performed in accordance with this paragraph where there may be a question of employee exposure to hazardous concentrations of hazardous substances in order to assure proper selection of engineering controls, work practices and personal protective equipment so that employees are not exposed to levels which exceed permissible exposure limits, or published exposure levels if there are no permissible exposure limits, for hazardous substances.

(ii) Air monitoring shall be used to identify and quantify airborne levels of hazardous substances and safety and health hazards in order to determine the appropriate level of employee protection needed on site.

(2) *Initial entry.* Upon initial entry, representative air monitoring shall be conducted to identify any IDLH condition, exposure over permissible exposure limits or published exposure levels, exposure over a radioactive material's dose limits or other dangerous condition such as the presence of flammable atmospheres or oxygen-deficient environments.

(3) *Periodic monitoring.* Periodic monitoring shall be conducted when the possibility of an IDLH condition or flammable atmosphere has developed or when there is indication that exposures may have risen over permissible exposure limits or published exposure levels since prior monitoring. Situations where it shall be considered whether the possibility that exposures have risen are as follows:

(i) When work begins on a different portion of the site.

(ii) When contaminants other than those previously identified are being handled.

(iii) When a different type of operation is initiated (e.g., drum opening as opposed to exploratory well drilling).

(iv) When employees are handling leaking drums or containers or working in areas with obvious liquid contamination (e.g., a spill or lagoon).

(4) *Monitoring of high-risk employees.* After the actual clean-up phase of any hazardous waste operation commences; for example, when soil, surface water or containers are moved or disturbed; the employer shall monitor those employees likely to have the highest exposures to hazardous substances and health hazards likely to be present above permissible exposure limits or published exposure levels by using personal sampling frequently enough to characterize employee exposures. If the employees likely to have the highest exposure are over permissible exposure limits or published exposure limits, then monitoring shall continue to de-

termine all employees likely to be above those limits. The employer may utilize a representative sampling approach by documenting that the employees and chemicals chosen for monitoring are based on the criteria stated above.

NOTE TO (h): It is not required to monitor employees engaged in site characterization operations covered by paragraph (c) of this section.

(i) *Informational programs.* Employers shall develop and implement a program, which is part of the employer's safety and health program required in paragraph (b) of this section, to inform employees, contractors, and subcontractors (or their representative) actually engaged in hazardous waste operations of the nature, level and degree of exposure likely as a result of participation in such hazardous waste operations. Employees, contractors and subcontractors working outside of the operations part of a site are not covered by this standard.

(j) *Handling drums and containers*—(1) *General.* (i) Hazardous substances and contaminated soils, liquids, and other residues shall be handled, transported, labeled, and disposed of in accordance with this paragraph.

(ii) Drums and containers used during the clean-up shall meet the appropriate DOT, OSHA, and EPA regulations for the wastes that they contain.

(iii) When practical, drums and containers shall be inspected and their integrity shall be assured prior to being moved. Drums or containers that cannot be inspected before being moved because of storage conditions (i.e., buried beneath the earth, stacked behind other drums, stacked several tiers high in a pile, etc.) shall be moved to an accessible location and inspected prior to further handling.

(iv) Unlabelled drums and containers shall be considered to contain hazardous substances and handled accordingly until the contents are positively identified and labeled.

(v) Site operations shall be organized to minimize the amount of drum or container movement.

(vi) Prior to movement of drums or containers, all employees exposed to the transfer operation shall be warned of the potential hazards associated with the contents of the drums or containers.

(vii) U.S. Department of Transportation specified salvage drums or containers and suitable quantities of proper absorbent shall be kept available and used in areas where spills, leaks, or ruptures may occur.

(viii) Where major spills may occur, a spill containment program, which is part of the employer's safety and health program required in paragraph (b) of this section, shall be implemented to contain and isolate the entire volume of the hazardous substance being transferred.

(ix) Drums and containers that cannot be moved without rupture, leakage, or spillage shall be emptied into a sound container using a device classified for the material being transferred.

(x) A ground-penetrating system or other type of detection system or device shall be used to estimate the location and depth of buried drums or containers.

(xi) Soil or covering material shall be removed with caution to prevent drum or container rupture.

(xii) Fire extinguishing equipment meeting the requirements of 29 CFR part 1910, subpart L, shall be on hand and ready for use to control incipient fires.

(2) *Opening drums and containers.* The following procedures shall be followed in areas where drums or containers are being opened:

(i) Where an airline respirator system is used, connections to the source of air supply shall be protected from contamination and the entire system shall be protected from physical damage.

(ii) Employees not actually involved in opening drums or containers shall be kept a safe distance from the drums or containers being opened.

(iii) If employees must work near or adjacent to drums or containers being opened, a suitable shield that does not interfere with the work operation shall be placed between the employee and the drums or containers being opened to protect the employee in case of accidental explosion.

(iv) Controls for drum or container opening equipment, monitoring equipment, and fire suppression equipment shall be located behind the explosion-resistant barrier.

(v) When there is a reasonable possibility of flammable atmospheres being present, material handling equipment and hand tools shall be of the type to prevent sources of ignition.

(vi) Drums and containers shall be opened in such a manner that excess interior pressure will be safely relieved. If pressure can not be relieved from a remote location, appropriate shielding shall be placed between the employee and the drums or containers to reduce the risk of employee injury.

(vii) Employees shall not stand upon or work from drums or containers.

(3) *Material handling equipment.* Material handling equipment used to transfer drums and containers shall be selected, positioned and operated to minimize sources of ignition related to the equipment from igniting vapors released from ruptured drums or containers.

(4) *Radioactive wastes.* Drums and containers containing radioactive wastes shall not be handled until such time as their hazard to employees is properly assessed.

(5) *Shock sensitive wastes.* As a minimum, the following special precautions shall be taken when drums and containers containing or suspected of containing shock-sensitive wastes are handled:

(i) All non-essential employees shall be evacuated from the area of transfer.

(ii) Material handling equipment shall be provided with explosive containment devices or protective shields to protect equipment operators from exploding containers.

(iii) An employee alarm system capable of being perceived above surrounding light and noise conditions shall be used to signal the commencement and completion of explosive waste handling activities.

(iv) Continuous communications (i.e., portable radios, hand signals, telephones, as appropriate) shall be maintained between the employee-in-charge of the immediate handling area and both the site safety and health supervisor and the command post until such time as the handling operation is completed. Communication equipment or methods that could cause shock sensitive materials to explode shall not be used.

(v) Drums and containers under pressure, as evidenced by bulging or swelling, shall not be moved until such time as the cause for excess pressure is determined and appropriate containment procedures have been implemented to protect employees from explosive relief of the drum.

(vi) Drums and containers containing packaged laboratory wastes shall be considered to contain shock-sensitive or explosive materials until they have been characterized.

CAUTION: Shipping of shock sensitive wastes may be prohibited under U.S. Department of Transportation regulations. Employers and their shippers should refer to 49 CFR 173.21 and 173.50.

(6) *Laboratory waste packs.* In addition to the requirements of paragraph (j)(5) of this section, the following precautions shall be taken, as a minimum, in handling laboratory waste packs (lab packs):

(i) Lab packs shall be opened only when necessary and then only by an individual knowledgeable in the inspection, classification, and segregation of the containers within the pack according to the hazards of the wastes.

(ii) If crystalline material is noted on any container, the contents shall be handled as a shock-sensitive waste until the contents are identified.

(7) *Sampling of drum and container contents.* Sampling of containers and drums shall be done in accordance with a sampling procedure which is part of the site safety and health plan developed for and available to employees and others at the specific worksite.

(8) *Shipping and transport.* (i) Drums and containers shall be identified and classified prior to packaging for shipment.

(ii) Drum or container staging areas shall be kept to the minimum number necessary to identify and classify materials safely and prepare them for transport.

(iii) Staging areas shall be provided with adequate access and egress routes.

(iv) Bulking of hazardous wastes shall be permitted only after a thorough characterization of the materials has been completed.

(9) *Tank and vault procedures.* (i) Tanks and vaults containing hazardous substances shall be handled in a manner similar to that for drums and containers, taking into consideration the size of the tank or vault.

(ii) Appropriate tank or vault entry procedures as described in the employer's safety and health plan shall be followed whenever employees must enter a tank or vault.

(k) *Decontamination*—(1) *General.* Procedures for all phases of decontamination shall be developed and implemented in accordance with this paragraph.

(2) *Decontamination procedures.* (i) A decontamination procedure shall be developed, communicated to employees and implemented before any employees or equipment may enter areas on site where potential for exposure to hazardous substances exists.

(ii) Standard operating procedures shall be developed to minimize employee contact with hazardous substances or with equipment that has contacted hazardous substances.

(iii) All employees leaving a contaminated area shall be appropriately decontaminated; all contaminated clothing and equipment leaving a contaminated area shall be appropriately disposed of or decontaminated.

(iv) Decontamination procedures shall be monitored by the site safety and health supervisor to determine their effectiveness. When such procedures are found to be ineffective, appropriate steps shall be taken to correct any deficiencies.

(3) *Location.* Decontamination shall be performed in geographical areas that will minimize the exposure of uncontaminated employees or equipment to contaminated employees or equipment.

(4) *Equipment and solvents.* All equipment and solvents used for decontamination shall be decontaminated or disposed of properly.

(5) *Personal protective clothing and equipment.* (i) Protective clothing and equipment shall be decontaminated, cleaned, laundered, maintained or replaced as needed to maintain their effectiveness.

(ii) Employees whose non-impermeable clothing becomes wetted with hazardous substances shall immediately remove that clothing and proceed to shower. The clothing shall be disposed of or decontaminated before it is removed from the work zone.

(6) *Unauthorized employees.* Unauthorized employees shall not remove protective clothing or equipment from change rooms.

(7) *Commercial laundries or cleaning establishments.* Commercial laundries or cleaning establishments that decontaminate protective clothing or equipment shall be informed of the potentially harmful effects of exposures to hazardous substances.

(8) *Showers and change rooms.* Where the decontamination procedure indicates a need for regular showers and change rooms outside of a contaminated area, they shall be provided and meet the requirements of 29 CFR 1910.141. If temperature conditions prevent the effective use of water, then other effective means for cleansing shall be provided and used.

(l) *Emergency response by employees at uncontrolled hazardous waste sites*—(1) *Emergency response plan.* (i) An emergency response plan shall be developed and implemented by all employers within the scope of paragraphs (a)(1)(i)–(ii) of this section to handle anticipated emergencies prior to the commencement of hazardous waste operations. The plan shall be in writing and available for inspection and copying by employees, their representatives, OSHA personnel and other governmental agencies with relevant responsibilities.

(ii) Employers who will evacuate their employees from the danger area when an emergency occurs, and who do not permit any of their employees to assist in handling the emergency, are exempt from the requirements of this paragraph if they provide an emergency action plan complying with § 1910.38(a) of this part.

(2) *Elements of an emergency response plan.* The employer shall develop an emergency response plan for emergencies which shall address, as a minimum, the following:

(i) Pre-emergency planning.

(ii) Personnel roles, lines of authority, and communication.

(iii) Emergency recognition and prevention.

(iv) Safe distances and places of refuge.

(v) Site security and control.

(vi) Evacuation routes and procedures.

(vii) Decontamination procedures which are not covered by the site safety and health plan.

(viii) Emergency medical treatment and first aid.

(ix) Emergency alerting and response procedures.

(x) Critique of response and follow-up.

(xi) PPE and emergency equipment.

(3) *Procedures for handling emergency incidents.* (i) In addition to the elements for the emergency response plan required in paragraph (1)(2) of this section, the following elements shall be included for emergency response plans:

(A) Site topography, layout, and prevailing weather conditions.

(B) Procedures for reporting incidents to local, state, and federal governmental agencies.

(ii) The emergency response plan shall be a separate section of the Site Safety and Health Plan.

(iii) The emergency response plan shall be compatible and integrated with the disaster, fire and/or emergency response plans of local, state, and federal agencies.

(iv) The emergency response plan shall be rehearsed regularly as part of the overall training program for site operations.

(v) The site emergency response plan shall be reviewed periodically and, as necessary, be amended to keep it current with new or changing site conditions or information.

(vi) An employee alarm system shall be installed in accordance with 29 CFR 1910.165 to notify employees of an emergency situation; to stop work activities if necessary; to lower background noise in order to speed communication; and to begin emergency procedures.

(vii) Based upon the information available at time of the emergency, the employer shall evaluate the incident and the site response capabilities and proceed with the appropriate steps to implement the site emergency response plan.

(m) *Illumination.* Areas accessible to employees shall be lighted to not less than the minimum illumination intensities listed in the following Table H–120.1 while any work is in progress:

TABLE H–120.1—MINIMUM ILLUMINATION INTENSITIES IN FOOT-CANDLES

Foot-candles	Area or operations
5	General site areas.
3	Excavation and waste areas, accessways, active storage areas, loading platforms, refueling, and field maintenance areas.
5	Indoors: Warehouses, corridors, hallways, and exitways.
5	Tunnels, shafts, and general underground work areas. (Exception: Minimum of 10 foot-candles is required at tunnel and shaft heading during drilling mucking, and scaling. Mine Safety and Health Administration approved cap lights shall be acceptable for use in the tunnel heading.)
10	General shops (e.g., mechanical and electrical equipment rooms, active storerooms, barracks or living quarters, locker or dressing rooms, dining areas, and indoor toilets and workrooms.)
30	First aid stations, infirmaries, and offices.

(n) *Sanitation at temporary workplaces*—(1) *Potable water.* (i) An adequate supply of potable water shall be provided on the site.

(ii) Portable containers used to dispense drinking water shall be capable of being tightly closed, and equipped with a tap. Water shall not be dipped from containers.

(iii) Any container used to distribute drinking water shall be clearly marked as to the nature of its contents and not used for any other purpose.

(iv) Where single service cups (to be used but once) are supplied, both a sanitary container for the unused cups and a receptacle for disposing of the used cups shall be provided.

(2) *Nonpotable water.* (i) Outlets for nonpotable water, such as water for firefighting purposes, shall be identified to indicate clearly that the water is unsafe and is not to be used for drinking, washing, or cooking purposes.

(ii) There shall be no cross-connection, open or potential, between a system furnishing potable water and a system furnishing nonpotable water.

(3) *Toilet facilities.* (i) Toilets shall be provided for employees according to the following Table H–120.2.

TABLE H–120.2—TOILET FACILITIES

Number of employees	Minimum number of facilities
20 or fewer	One.
More than 20, fewer than 200	One toilet seat and one urinal per 40 employees.
More than 200	One toilet seat and one urinal per 50 employees.

(ii) Under temporary field conditions, provisions shall be made to assure that at least one toilet facility is available.

(iii) Hazardous waste sites not provided with a sanitary sewer shall be provided with the following toilet facilities unless prohibited by local codes:

(A) Chemical toilets;

(B) Recirculating toilets;

(C) Combustion toilets; or

(D) Flush toilets.

(iv) The requirements of this paragraph for sanitation facilities shall not apply to mobile crews having transportation readily available to nearby toilet facilities.

(v) Doors entering toilet facilities shall be provided with entrance locks controlled from inside the facility.

(4) *Food handling.* All food service facilities and operations for employees shall meet the applicable laws, ordinances, and regulations of the jurisdictions in which they are located.

(5) *Temporary sleeping quarters.* When temporary sleeping quarters are provided, they shall be heated, ventilated, and lighted.

(6) *Washing facilities.* The employer shall provide adequate washing facilities for employees engaged in operations where hazardous substances may be harmful to employees. Such facilities shall be in near proximity to the worksite; in areas where exposures are below permissible exposure limits and published exposure levels and which are under the controls of the employer; and shall be so equipped as to enable employees to remove hazardous substances from themselves.

(7) *Showers and change rooms.* When hazardous waste clean-up or removal operations commence on a site and the duration of the work will require six months or greater time to complete, the employer shall provide showers and change rooms for all employees exposed to hazardous substances and health hazards involved in hazardous waste clean-up or removal operations.

(i) Showers shall be provided and shall meet the requirements of 29 CFR 1910.141(d)(3).

(ii) Change rooms shall be provided and shall meet the requirements of 29 CFR 1910.141(e). Change rooms shall consist of two separate change areas separated by the shower area required in paragraph (n)(7)(i) of this section. One change area, with an exit leading off the worksite, shall provide employees with a clean area where they can remove, store, and put on street clothing. The second area, with an exit to the worksite, shall provide employees with an area where they can put on, remove and store work clothing and personal protective equipment.

(iii) Showers and change rooms shall be located in areas where exposures are below the permissible exposure limits and published exposure levels. If this cannot be accomplished, then a ventilation system shall be provided that will supply air that is below the permissible exposure limits and published exposure levels.

(iv) Employers shall assure that employees shower at the end of their work shift and when leaving the hazardous waste site.

(o) *New technology programs.* (1) The employer shall develop and implement procedures for the introduction of effective new technologies and equipment developed for the improved protection of employees working with hazardous waste clean-up operations, and the same shall be implemented as part of the site safety and health program to assure that employee protection is being maintained.

(2) New technologies, equipment or control measures available to the industry, such as the use of foams, absorbents, adsorbents, neutralizers, or other means to suppress the level of air contaminates while excavating the site or for spill control, shall be evaluated by employers or their representatives. Such an evaluation shall be done to determine the effectiveness of the new methods, materials, or equipment before implementing their use on a large scale for enhancing employee protection. Information and data from manufacturers or suppliers may be used as

part of the employer's evaluation effort. Such evaluations shall be made available to OSHA upon request.

(p) *Certain Operations Conducted Under the Resource Conservation and Recovery Act of 1976 (RCRA).* Employers conducting operations at treatment, storage and disposal (TSD) facilities specified in paragraph (a)(1)(iv) of this section shall provide and implement the programs specified in this paragraph. See the "Notes and Exceptions" to paragraph (a)(2)(iii) of this section for employers not covered.)".

(1) *Safety and health program.* The employer shall develop and implement a written safety and health program for employees involved in hazardous waste operations that shall be available for inspection by employees, their representatives and OSHA personnel. The program shall be designed to identify, evaluate and control safety and health hazards in their facilities for the purpose of employee protection, to provide for emergency response meeting the requirements of paragraph (p)(8) of this section and to address as appropriate site analysis, engineering controls, maximum exposure limits, hazardous waste handling procedures and uses of new technologies.

(2) *Hazard communication program.* The employer shall implement a hazard communication program meeting the requirements of 29 CFR 1910.1200 as part of the employer's safety and program.

NOTE TO 1910.120—The exemption for hazardous waste provided in § 1910.1200 is applicable to this section.

(3) *Medical surveillance program.* The employer shall develop and implement a medical surveillance program meeting the requirements of paragraph (f) of this section.

(4) *Decontamination program.* The employer shall develop and implement a decontamination procedure meeting the requirements of paragraph (k) of this section.

(5) *New technology program.* The employer shall develop and implement procedures meeting the requirements of paragraph (o) of this section for introducing new and innovative equipment into the workplace.

(6) *Material handling program.* Where employees will be handling drums or

containers, the employer shall develop and implement procedures meeting the requirements of paragraphs (j)(1) (ii) through (viii) and (xi) of this section, as well as (j)(3) and (j)(8) of this section prior to starting such work.

(7) *Training program*—(i) *New employees.* The employer shall develop and implement a training program, which is part of the employer's safety and health program, for employees exposed to health hazards or hazardous substances at TSD operations to enable the employees to perform their assigned duties and functions in a safe and healthful manner so as not to endanger themselves or other employees. The initial training shall be for 24 hours and refresher training shall be for eight hours annually. Employees who have received the initial training required by this paragraph shall be given a written certificate attesting that they have successfully completed the necessary training.

(ii) *Current employees.* Employers who can show by an employee's previous work experience and/or training that the employee has had training equivalent to the initial training required by this paragraph, shall be considered as meeting the initial training requirements of this paragraph as to that employee. Equivalent training includes the training that existing employees might have already received from actual site work experience. Current employees shall receive eight hours of refresher training annually.

(iii) *Trainers.* Trainers who teach initial training shall have satisfactorily completed a training course for teaching the subjects they are expected to teach or they shall have the academic credentials and instruction experience necessary to demonstrate a good command of the subject matter of the courses and competent instructional skills.

(8) *Emergency response program*—(i) *Emergency response plan.* An emergency response plan shall be developed and implemented by all employers. Such plans need not duplicate any of the subjects fully addressed in the employer's contingency planning required by permits, such as those issued by the U.S. Environmental Protection Agency, provided that the contingency plan

is made part of the emergency response plan. The emergency response plan shall be a written portion of the employers safety and health program required in paragraph (p)(1) of this section. Employers who will evacuate their employees from the worksite location when an emergency occurs and who do not permit any of their employees to assist in handling the emergency are exempt from the requirements of paragraph (p)(8) if they provide an emergency action plan complying with § 1910.38(a) of this part.

(ii) *Elements of an emergency response plan.* The employer shall develop an emergency response plan for emergencies which shall address, as a minimum, the following areas to the extent that they are not addressed in any specific program required in this paragraph:

(A) Pre-emergency planning and coordination with outside parties.

(B) Personnel roles, lines of authority, and communication.

(C) Emergency recognition and prevention.

(D) Safe distances and places of refuge.

(E) Site security and control.

(F) Evacuation routes and procedures.

(G) Decontamination procedures.

(H) Emergency medical treatment and first aid.

(I) Emergency alerting and response procedures.

(J) Critique of response and follow-up.

(K) PPE and emergency equipment.

(iii) *Training.* (A) Training for emergency response employees shall be completed before they are called upon to perform in real emergencies. Such training shall include the elements of the emergency response plan, standard operating procedures the employer has established for the job, the personal protective equipment to be worn and procedures for handling emergency incidents.

Exception #1: An employer need not train all employees to the degree specified if the employer divides the work force in a manner such that a sufficient number of employees who have responsibility to control emergencies have the training specified, and all other employees, who may first respond to an emergency incident, have sufficient awareness training to recognize that an emergency response situation exists and that they are instructed in that case to summon the fully trained employees and not attempt control activities for which they are not trained.

Exception #2: An employer need not train all employees to the degree specified if arrangements have been made in advance for an outside fully-trained emergency response team to respond in a reasonable period and all employees, who may come to the incident first, have sufficient awareness training to recognize that an emergency response situation exists and they have been instructed to call the designated outside fully-trained emergency response team for assistance.

(B) Employee members of TSD facility emergency response organizations shall be trained to a level of competence in the recognition of health and safety hazards to protect themselves and other employees. This would include training in the methods used to minimize the risk from safety and health hazards; in the safe use of control equipment; in the selection and use of appropriate personal protective equipment; in the safe operating procedures to be used at the incident scene; in the techniques of coordination with other employees to minimize risks; in the appropriate response to over exposure from health hazards or injury to themselves and other employees; and in the recognition of subsequent symptoms which may result from over exposures.

(C) The employer shall certify that each covered employee has attended and successfully completed the training required in paragraph (p)(8)(iii) of this section, or shall certify the employee's competency at least yearly. The method used to demonstrate competency for certification of training shall be recorded and maintained by the employer.

(iv) *Procedures for handling emergency incidents.* (A) In addition to the elements for the emergency response plan required in paragraph (p)(8)(ii) of this section, the following elements shall be included for emergency response plans to the extent that they do not repeat any information already contained in the emergency response plan:

(1) Site topography, layout, and prevailing weather conditions.

(2) Procedures for reporting incidents to local, state, and federal governmental agencies.

(B) The emergency response plan shall be compatible and integrated with the disaster, fire and/or emergency response plans of local, state, and federal agencies.

(C) The emergency response plan shall be rehearsed regularly as part of the overall training program for site operations.

(D) The site emergency response plan shall be reviewed periodically and, as necessary, be amended to keep it current with new or changing site conditions or information.

(E) An employee alarm system shall be installed in accordance with 29 CFR 1910.165 to notify employees of an emergency situation; to stop work activities if necessary; to lower background noise in order to speed communication; and to begin emergency procedures.

(F) Based upon the information available at time of the emergency, the employer shall evaluate the incident and the site response capabilities and proceed with the appropriate steps to implement the site emergency response plan.

(q) *Emergency response to hazardous substance releases.* This paragraph covers employers whose employees are engaged in emergency response no matter where it occurs except that it does not cover employees engaged in operations specified in paragraphs (a)(1)(i) through (a)(1)(iv) of this section. Those emergency response organizations who have developed and implemented programs equivalent to this paragraph for handling releases of hazardous substances pursuant to section 303 of the Superfund Amendments and Reauthorization Act of 1986 (Emergency Planning and Community Right-to-Know Act of 1986, 42 U.S.C. 11003) shall be deemed to have met the requirements of this paragraph.

(1) *Emergency response plan.* An emergency response plan shall be developed and implemented to handle anticipated emergencies prior to the commencement of emergency response operations. The plan shall be in writing and available for inspection and copying by employees, their representatives and OSHA personnel. Employers who will evacuate their employees from the danger area when an emergency occurs, and who do not permit any of their employees to assist in handling the emergency, are exempt from the requirements of this paragraph if they provide an emergency action plan in accordance with § 1910.38(a) of this part.

(2) *Elements of an emergency response plan.* The employer shall develop an emergency response plan for emergencies which shall address, as a minimum, the following to the extent that they are not addressed elsewhere:

(i) Pre-emergency planning and coordination with outside parties.

(ii) Personnel roles, lines of authority, training, and communication.

(iii) Emergency recognition and prevention.

(iv) Safe distances and places of refuge.

(v) Site security and control.

(vi) Evacuation routes and procedures.

(vii) Decontamination.

(viii) Emergency medical treatment and first aid.

(ix) Emergency alerting and response procedures.

(x) Critique of response and follow-up.

(xi) PPE and emergency equipment.

(xii) Emergency response organizations may use the local emergency response plan or the state emergency response plan or both, as part of their emergency response plan to avoid duplication. Those items of the emergency response plan that are being properly addressed by the SARA Title III plans may be substituted into their emergency plan or otherwise kept together for the employer and employee's use.

(3) *Procedures for handling emergency response.* (i) The senior emergency response official responding to an emergency shall become the individual in charge of a site-specific Incident Command System (ICS). All emergency responders and their communications shall be coordinated and controlled through the individual in charge of the ICS assisted by the senior official present for each employer.

NOTE TO (q)(3)(i).—The "senior official" at an emergency response is the most senior official on the site who has the responsibility for controlling the operations at the site. Initially it is the senior officer on the first-due piece of responding emergency apparatus to arrive on the incident scene. As more senior officers arrive (i.e., battalion chief, fire chief, state law enforcement official, site coordinator, etc.) the position is passed up the line of authority which has been previously established.

(ii) The individual in charge of the ICS shall identify, to the extent possible, all hazardous substances or conditions present and shall address as appropriate site analysis, use of engineering controls, maximum exposure limits, hazardous substance handling procedures, and use of any new technologies.

(iii) Based on the hazardous substances and/or conditions present, the individual in charge of the ICS shall implement appropriate emergency operations, and assure that the personal protective equipment worn is appropriate for the hazards to be encountered. However, personal protective equipment shall meet, at a minimum, the criteria contained in 29 CFR 1910.156(e) when worn while performing fire fighting operations beyond the incipient stage for any incident.

(iv) Employees engaged in emergency response and exposed to hazardous substances presenting an inhalation hazard or potential inhalation hazard shall wear positive pressure self-contained breathing apparatus while engaged in emergency response, until such time that the individual in charge of the ICS determines through the use of air monitoring that a decreased level of respiratory protection will not result in hazardous exposures to employees.

(v) The individual in charge of the ICS shall limit the number of emergency response personnel at the emergency site, in those areas of potential or actual exposure to incident or site hazards, to those who are actively performing emergency operations. However, operations in hazardous areas shall be performed using the buddy system in groups of two or more.

(vi) Back-up personnel shall stand by with equipment ready to provide assistance or rescue. Advance first aid support personnel, as a minimum, shall also stand by with medical equipment and transportation capability.

(vii) The individual in charge of the ICS shall designate a safety official, who is knowledgable in the operations being implemented at the emergency response site, with specific responsibility to identify and evaluate hazards and to provide direction with respect to the safety of operations for the emergency at hand.

(viii) When activities are judged by the safety official to be an IDLH condition and/or to involve an imminent danger condition, the safety official shall have the authority to alter, suspend, or terminate those activities. The safety official shall immediately inform the individual in charge of the ICS of any actions needed to be taken to correct these hazards at the emergency scene.

(ix) After emergency operations have terminated, the individual in charge of the ICS shall implement appropriate decontamination procedures.

(x) When deemed necessary for meeting the tasks at hand, approved self-contained compressed air breathing apparatus may be used with approved cylinders from other approved self-contained compressed air breathing apparatus provided that such cylinders are of the same capacity and pressure rating. All compressed air cylinders used with self-contained breathing apparatus shall meet U.S. Department of Transportation and National Institute for Occupational Safety and Health criteria.

(4) *Skilled support personnel.* Personnel, not necessarily an employer's own employees, who are skilled in the operation of certain equipment, such as mechanized earth moving or digging equipment or crane and hoisting equipment, and who are needed temporarily to perform immediate emergency support work that cannot reasonably be performed in a timely fashion by an employer's own employees, and who will be or may be exposed to the hazards at an emergency response scene, are not required to meet the training required in this paragraph for the employer's regular employees. However, these personnel shall be given an initial briefing at the site prior to their participation in any emergency response. The initial briefing shall include instruction in the wearing of ap-

propriate personal protective equipment, what chemical hazards are involved, and what duties are to be performed. All other appropriate safety and health precautions provided to the employer's own employees shall be used to assure the safety and health of these personnel.

(5) *Specialist employees.* Employees who, in the course of their regular job duties, work with and are trained in the hazards of specific hazardous substances, and who will be called upon to provide technical advice or assistance at a hazardous substance release incident to the individual in charge, shall receive training or demonstrate competency in the area of their specialization annually.

(6) *Training.* Training shall be based on the duties and function to be performed by each responder of an emergency response organization. The skill and knowledge levels required for all new responders, those hired after the effective date of this standard, shall be conveyed to them through training before they are permitted to take part in actual emergency operations on an incident. Employees who participate, or are expected to participate, in emergency response, shall be given training in accordance with the following paragraphs:

(i) *First responder awareness level.* First responders at the awareness level are individuals who are likely to witness or discover a hazardous substance release and who have been trained to initiate an emergency response sequence by notifying the proper authorities of the release. They would take no further action beyond notifying the authorities of the release. First responders at the awareness level shall have sufficient training or have had sufficient experience to objectively demonstrate competency in the following areas:

(A) An understanding of what hazardous substances are, and the risks associated with them in an incident.

(B) An understanding of the potential outcomes associated with an emergency created when hazardous substances are present.

(C) The ability to recognize the presence of hazardous substances in an emergency.

(D) The ability to identify the hazardous substances, if possible.

(E) An understanding of the role of the first responder awareness individual in the employer's emergency response plan including site security and control and the U.S. Department of Transportation's Emergency Response Guidebook.

(F) The ability to realize the need for additional resources, and to make appropriate notifications to the communication center.

(ii) *First responder operations level.* First responders at the operations level are individuals who respond to releases or potential releases of hazardous substances as part of the initial response to the site for the purpose of protecting nearby persons, property, or the environment from the effects of the release. They are trained to respond in a defensive fashion without actually trying to stop the release. Their function is to contain the release from a safe distance, keep it from spreading, and prevent exposures. First responders at the operational level shall have received at least eight hours of training or have had sufficient experience to objectively demonstrate competency in the following areas in addition to those listed for the awareness level and the employer shall so certify:

(A) Knowledge of the basic hazard and risk assessment techniques.

(B) Know how to select and use proper personal protective equipment provided to the first responder operational level.

(C) An understanding of basic hazardous materials terms.

(D) Know how to perform basic control, containment and/or confinement operations within the capabilities of the resources and personal protective equipment available with their unit.

(E) Know how to implement basic decontamination procedures.

(F) An understanding of the relevant standard operating procedures and termination procedures.

(iii) *Hazardous materials technician.* Hazardous materials technicians are individuals who respond to releases or potential releases for the purpose of stopping the release. They assume a more aggressive role than a first responder at the operations level in that they will approach the point of release in order to plug, patch or otherwise stop the release of a hazardous substance. Hazardous materials technicians shall have received at least 24 hours of training equal to the first responder operations level and in addition have competency in the following areas and the employer shall so certify:

(A) Know how to implement the employer's emergency response plan.

(B) Know the classification, identification and verification of known and unknown materials by using field survey instruments and equipment.

(C) Be able to function within an assigned role in the Incident Command System.

(D) Know how to select and use proper specialized chemical personal protective equipment provided to the hazardous materials technician.

(E) Understand hazard and risk assessment techniques.

(F) Be able to perform advance control, containment, and/or confinement operations within the capabilities of the resources and personal protective equipment available with the unit.

(G) Understand and implement decontamination procedures.

(H) Understand termination procedures.

(I) Understand basic chemical and toxicological terminology and behavior.

(iv) *Hazardous materials specialist.* Hazardous materials specialists are individuals who respond with and provide support to hazardous materials technicians. Their duties parallel those of the hazardous materials technician, however, those duties require a more directed or specific knowledge of the various substances they may be called upon to contain. The hazardous materials specialist would also act as the site liaison with Federal, state, local and other government authorities in regards to site activities. Hazardous materials specialists shall have received at least 24 hours of training equal to the technician level and in addition have competency in the following areas and the employer shall so certify:

(A) Know how to implement the local emergency response plan.

(B) Understand classification, identification and verification of known and unknown materials by using advanced survey instruments and equipment.

(C) Know of the state emergency response plan.

(D) Be able to select and use proper specialized chemical personal protective equipment provided to the hazardous materials specialist.

(E) Understand in-depth hazard and risk techniques.

(F) Be able to perform specialized control, containment, and/or confinement operations within the capabilities of the resources and personal protective equipment available.

(G) Be able to determine and implement decontamination procedures.

(H) Have the ability to develop a site safety and control plan.

(I) Understand chemical, radiological and toxicological terminology and behavior.

(v) *On scene incident commander.* Incident commanders, who will assume control of the incident scene beyond the first responder awareness level, shall receive at least 24 hours of training equal to the first responder operations level and in addition have competency in the following areas and the employer shall so certify:

(A) Know and be able to implement the employer's incident command system.

(B) Know how to implement the employer's emergency response plan.

(C) Know and understand the hazards and risks associated with employees working in chemical protective clothing.

(D) Know how to implement the local emergency response plan.

(E) Know of the state emergency response plan and of the Federal Regional Response Team.

(F) Know and understand the importance of decontamination procedures.

(7) *Trainers.* Trainers who teach any of the above training subjects shall have satisfactorily completed a training course for teaching the subjects they are expected to teach, such as the courses offered by the U.S. National Fire Academy, or they shall have the training and/or academic credentials and instructional experience necessary to demonstrate competent instruc-

tional skills and a good command of the subject matter of the courses they are to teach.

(8) *Refresher training.* (i) Those employees who are trained in accordance with paragraph (q)(6) of this section shall receive annual refresher training of sufficient content and duration to maintain their competencies, or shall demonstrate competency in those areas at least yearly.

(ii) A statement shall be made of the training or competency, and if a statement of competency is made, the employer shall keep a record of the methodology used to demonstrate competency.

(9) *Medical surveillance and consultation.* (i) Members of an organized and designated HAZMAT team and hazardous materials specialists shall receive a baseline physical examination and be provided with medical surveillance as required in paragraph (f) of this section.

(ii) Any emergency response employees who exhibits signs or symptoms which may have resulted from exposure to hazardous substances during the course of an emergency incident, either immediately or subsequently, shall be provided with medical consultation as required in paragraph (f)(3)(ii) of this section.

(10) *Chemical protective clothing.* Chemical protective clothing and equipment to be used by organized and designated HAZMAT team members, or to be used by hazardous materials specialists, shall meet the requirements of paragraphs (g) (3) through (5) of this section.

(11) *Post-emergency response operations.* Upon completion of the emergency response, if it is determined that it is necessary to remove hazardous substances, health hazards, and materials contaminated with them (such as contaminated soil or other elements of the natural environment) from the site of the incident, the employer conducting the clean-up shall comply with one of the following:

(i) Meet all of the requirements of paragraphs (b) through (o) of this section; or

(ii) Where the clean-up is done on plant property using plant or workplace employees, such employees shall have completed the training requirements of the following: 29 CFR 1910.38(a); 1910.134; 1910.1200, and other appropriate safety and health training made necessary by the tasks that they are expected to be performed such as personal protective equipment and decontamination procedures. All equipment to be used in the performance of the clean-up work shall be in serviceable condition and shall have been inspected prior to use.

APPENDICES TO § 1910.120—HAZARDOUS WASTE OPERATIONS AND EMERGENCY RESPONSE

NOTE: The following appendices serve as non-mandatory guidelines to assist employees and employers in complying with the appropriate requirements of this section. However paragraph 1910.120(g) makes mandatory in certain circumstances the use of Level A and Level B PPE protection.

APPENDIX A TO § 1910.120—PERSONAL PROTECTIVE EQUIPMENT TEST METHODS

This appendix sets forth the non-mandatory examples of tests which may be used to evaluate compliance with § 1910.120 (g)(4) (ii) and (iii). Other tests and other challenge agents may be used to evaluate compliance.

A. Totally-encapsulating chemical protective suit pressure test

1.0—Scope
1.1 This practice measures the ability of a gas tight totally-encapsulating chemical protective suit material, seams, and closures to maintain a fixed positive pressure. The results of this practice allow the gas tight integrity of a totally-encapsulating chemical protective suit to be evaluated.
1.2 Resistance of the suit materials to permeation, penetration, and degradation by specific hazardous substances is not determined by this test method.
2.0—Definition of terms
2.1 *Totally-encapsulated chemical protective suit (TECP suit)* means a full body garment which is constructed of protective clothing materials; covers the wearer's torso, head, arms, legs and respirator; may cover the wearer's hands and feet with tightly attached gloves and boots; completely encloses the wearer and respirator by itself or in combination with the wearer's gloves and boots.
2.2 *Protective clothing material* means any material or combination of materials used in an item of clothing for the purpose of isolating parts of the body from direct contact with a potentially hazardous liquid or gaseous chemicals.
2.3 *Gas tight* means, for the purpose of this test method, the limited flow of a gas under pressure from the inside of a TECP suit to

atmosphere at a prescribed pressure and time interval.

3.0—Summary of test method

3.1 The TECP suit is visually inspected and modified for the test. The test apparatus is attached to the suit to permit inflation to the pre-test suit expansion pressure for removal of suit wrinkles and creases. The pressure is lowered to the test pressure and monitored for three minutes. If the pressure drop is excessive, the TECP suit fails the test and is removed from service. The test is repeated after leak location and repair.

4.0—Required Supplies

4.1 Source of compressed air.

4.2 Test apparatus for suit testing, including a pressure measurement device with a sensitivity of at least ¼ inch water gauge.

4.3 Vent valve closure plugs or sealing tape.

4.4 Soapy water solution and soft brush.

4.5 Stop watch or appropriate timing device.

5.0—Safety Precautions

5.1 Care shall be taken to provide the correct pressure safety devices required for the source of compressed air used.

6.0—Test Procedure

6.1 Prior to each test, the tester shall perform a visual inspection of the suit. Check the suit for seam integrity by visually examining the seams and gently pulling on the seams. Ensure that all air supply lines, fittings, visor, zippers, and valves are secure and show no signs of deterioration.

6.1.1 Seal off the vent valves along with any other normal inlet or exhaust points (such as umbilical air line fittings or face piece opening) with tape or other appropriate means (caps, plugs, fixture etc.) Care should be exercised in the sealing process not to damage any of the suit components.

6.1.2 Close all closure assemblies.

6.1.3 Prepare the suit for inflation by providing an improvised connection point on the suit for connecting an airline. Attach the pressure test apparatus to the suit to permit suit inflation from a compressed air source equipped with a pressure indicating regulator. The leak tightness of the pressure test apparatus should be tested before and after each test by closing off the end of the tubing attached to the suit and assuring a pressure of three inches water gauge for three minutes can be maintained. If a component is removed for the test, that component shall be replaced and a second test conducted with another component removed to permit a complete test of the ensemble.

6.1.4 The pre-test expansion pressure (A) and the suit test pressure (B) shall be supplied by the suit manufacturer, but in no case shall they be less than: (A)=three inches water gauge; and (B)=two inches water gauge. The ending suit pressure (C) shall be no less than 80 percent of the test pressure

(B); i.e., the pressure drop shall not exceed 20 percent of the test pressure (B).

6.1.5 Inflate the suit until the pressure inside is equal to pressure (A), the pre-test expansion suit pressure. Allow at least one minute to fill out the wrinkles in the suit. Release sufficient air to reduce the suit pressure to pressure (B), the suit test pressure. Begin timing. At the end of three minutes, record the suit pressure as pressure (C), the ending suit pressure. The difference between the suit test pressure and the ending suit test pressure (B–C) shall be defined as the suit pressure drop.

6.1.6 If the suit pressure drop is more than 20 percent of the suit test pressure (B) during the three-minute test period, the suit fails the test and shall be removed from service.

7.0—Retest Procedure

7.1 If the suit fails the test check for leaks by inflating the suit to pressure (A) and brushing or wiping the entire suit (including seams, closures, lens gaskets, glove-to-sleeve joints, etc.) with a mild soap and water solution. Observe the suit for the formation of soap bubbles, which is an indication of a leak. Repair all identified leaks.

7.2 Retest the TECP suit as outlined in Test procedure 6.0.

8.0—Report

8.1 Each TECP suit tested by this practice shall have the following information recorded:

8.1.1 Unique identification number, identifying brand name, date of purchase, material of construction, and unique fit features, e.g., special breathing apparatus.

8.1.2 The actual values for test pressures (A), (B), and (C) shall be recorded along with the specific observation times. If the ending pressure (C) is less than 80 percent of the test pressure (B), the suit shall be identified as failing the test. When possible, the specific leak location shall be identified in the test records. Retest pressure data shall be recorded as an additional test.

8.1.3 The source of the test apparatus used shall be identified and the sensitivity of the pressure gauge shall be recorded.

8.1.4 Records shall be kept for each pressure test even if repairs are being made at the test location.

CAUTION

Visually inspect all parts of the suit to be sure they are positioned correctly and secured tightly before putting the suit back into service. Special care should be taken to examine each exhaust valve to make sure it is not blocked.

Care should also be exercised to assure that the inside and outside of the suit is completely dry before it is put into storage.

B. Totally-encapsulating chemical protective suit qualitative leak test

1.0—Scope

1.1 This practice semi-qualitatively tests gas tight totally-encapsulating chemical protective suit integrity by detecting inward leakage of ammonia vapor. Since no modifications are made to the suit to carry out this test, the results from this practice provide a realistic test for the integrity of the entire suit.

1.2 Resistance of the suit materials to permeation, penetration, and degradation is not determined by this test method. ASTM test methods are available to test suit materials for these characteristics and the tests are usually conducted by the manufacturers of the suits.

2.0—Definition of terms

2.1 *Totally-encapsulated chemical protective suit (TECP suit)* means a full body garment which is constructed of protective clothing materials; covers the wearer's torso, head, arms, legs and respirator; may cover the wearer's hands and feet with tightly attached gloves and boots; completely encloses the wearer and respirator by itself or in combination with the wearer's gloves, and boots.

2.2 *Protective clothing material* means any material or combination of materials used in an item of clothing for the purpose of isolating parts of the body from direct contact with a potentially hazardous liquid or gaseous chemicals.

2.3 *Gas tight* means, for the purpose of this test method, the limited flow of a gas under pressure from the inside of a TECP suit to atmosphere at a prescribed pressure and time interval.

2.4 *Intrusion Coefficient* means a number expressing the level of protection provided by a gas tight totally-encapsulating chemical protective suit. The intrusion coefficient is calculated by dividing the test room challenge agent concentration by the concentration of challenge agent found inside the suit. The accuracy of the intrusion coefficient is dependent on the challenge agent monitoring methods. The larger the intrusion coefficient the greater the protection provided by the TECP suit.

3.0—Summary of recommended practice

3.1 The volume of concentrated aqueous ammonia solution (ammonia hydroxide NH_4OH) required to generate the test atmosphere is determined using the directions outlined in 6.1. The suit is donned by a person wearing the appropriate respiratory equipment (either a positive pressure self-contained breathing apparatus or a positive pressure supplied air respirator) and worn inside the enclosed test room. The concentrated aqueous ammonia solution is taken by the suited individual into the test room and poured into an open plastic pan. A two-minute evaporation period is observed

before the test room concentration is measured, using a high range ammonia length of stain detector tube. When the ammonia vapor reaches a concentration of between 1000 and 1200 ppm, the suited individual starts a standardized exercise protocol to stress and flex the suit. After this protocol is completed, the test room concentration is measured again. The suited individual exits the test room and his stand-by person measures the ammonia concentration inside the suit using a low range ammonia length of stain detector tube or other more sensitive ammonia detector. A stand-by person is required to observe the test individual during the test procedure; aid the person in donning and doffing the TECP suit; and monitor the suit interior. The intrusion coefficient of the suit can be calculated by dividing the average test area concentration by the interior suit concentration. A colorimetric ammonia indicator strip of bromophenol blue or equivalent is placed on the inside of the suit face piece lens so that the suited individual is able to detect a color change and know if the suit has a significant leak. If a color change is observed the individual shall leave the test room immediately.

4.0—Required supplies

4.1 A supply of concentrated aqueous ammonium hydroxide (58% by weight).

4.2 A supply of bromophenol/blue indicating paper or equivalent, sensitive to 5–10 ppm ammonia or greater over a two-minute period of exposure. [pH 3.0 (yellow) to pH 4.6 (blue)]

4.3 A supply of high range (0.5–10 volume percent) and low range (5–700 ppm) detector tubes for ammonia and the corresponding sampling pump. More sensitive ammonia detectors can be substituted for the low range detector tubes to improve the sensitivity of this practice.

4.4 A shallow plastic pan (PVC) at least 12˝:14˝:1˝ and a half pint plastic container (PVC) with tightly closing lid.

4.5 A graduated cylinder or other volumetric measuring device of at least 50 milliliters in volume with an accuracy of at least ± 1 milliliters.

5.0—Safety precautions

5.1 Concentrated aqueous ammonium hydroxide, NH_4OH, is a corrosive volatile liquid requiring eye, skin, and respiratory protection. The person conducting the test shall review the MSDS for aqueous ammonia.

5.2 Since the established permissible exposure limit for ammonia is 35 ppm as a 15 minute STEL, only persons wearing a positive pressure self-contained breathing apparatus or a positive pressure supplied air respirator shall be in the chamber. Normally only the person wearing the totally-encapsulating suit will be inside the chamber. A stand-by person shall have a positive pressure self-contained breathing apparatus, or a positive pressure supplied air respirator available to enter the test area should the suited individual need assistance.

5.3 A method to monitor the suited individual must be used during this test. Visual contact is the simplest but other methods using communication devices are acceptable.

5.4 The test room shall be large enough to allow the exercise protocol to be carried out and then to be ventilated to allow for easy exhaust of the ammonia test atmosphere after the test(s) are completed.

5.5 Individuals shall be medically screened for the use of respiratory protection and checked for allergies to ammonia before participating in this test procedure.

6.0—Test procedure

6.1.1 Measure the test area to the nearest foot and calculate its volume in cubic feet. Multiply the test area volume by 0.2 milliliters of concentrated aqueous ammonia solution per cubic foot of test area volume to determine the approximate volume of concentrated aqueous ammonia required to generate 1000 ppm in the test area.

6.1.2 Measure this volume from the supply of concentrated aqueous ammonia and place it into a closed plastic container.

6.1.3 Place the container, several high range ammonia detector tubes, and the pump in the clean test pan and locate it near the test area entry door so that the suited individual has easy access to these supplies.

6.2.1 In a non-contaminated atmosphere, open a pre-sealed ammonia indicator strip and fasten one end of the strip to the inside of the suit face shield lens where it can be seen by the wearer. Moisten the indicator strip with distilled water. Care shall be taken not to contaminate the detector part of the indicator paper by touching it. A small piece of masking tape or equivalent should be used to attach the indicator strip to the interior of the suit face shield.

6.2.2 If problems are encountered with this method of attachment, the indicator strip can be attached to the outside of the respirator face piece lens being used during the test.

6.3 Don the respiratory protective device normally used with the suit, and then don the TECP suit to be tested. Check to be sure all openings which are intended to be sealed (zippers, gloves, etc.) are completely sealed. DO NOT, however, plug off any venting valves.

6.4 Step into the enclosed test room such as a closet, bathroom, or test booth, equipped with an exhaust fan. No air should be exhausted from the chamber during the test because this will dilute the ammonia challenge concentrations.

6.5 Open the container with the pre-measured volume of concentrated aqueous ammonia within the enclosed test room, and pour the liquid into the empty plastic test pan.

Wait two minutes to allow for adequate volatilization of the concentrated aqueous ammonia. A small mixing fan can be used near the evaporation pan to increase the evaporation rate of the ammonia solution.

6.6 After two minutes a determination of the ammonia concentration within the chamber should be made using the high range colorimetric detector tube. A concentration of 1000 ppm ammonia or greater shall be generated before the exercises are started.

6.7. To test the integrity of the suit the following four minute exercise protocol should be followed:

6.7.1 Raising the arms above the head with at least 15 raising motions completed in one minute.

6.7.2 Walking in place for one minute with at least 15 raising motions of each leg in a one-minute period.

6.7.3 Touching the toes with a least 10 complete motions of the arms from above the head to touching of the toes in a one-minute period.

6.7.4 Knee bends with at least 10 complete standing and squatting motions in a one-minute period.

6.8 If at any time during the test the colorimetric indicating paper should change colors, the test should be stopped and section 6.10 and 6.12 initiated (See ¶4.2).

6.9 After completion of the test exercise the test area concentration should be measured again using the high range colorimetric detector tube.

6.10 Exit the test area.

6.11 The opening created by the suit zipper or other appropriate suit penetration should be used to determine the ammonia concentration in the suit with the low range length of stain detector tube or other ammonia monitor. The internal TECP suit air should be sampled far enough from the enclosed test area to prevent a false ammonia reading.

6.12 After completion of the measurement of the suit interior ammonia concentration the test is concluded and the suit is doffed and the respirator removed.

6.13 The ventilating fan for the test room should be turned on and allowed to run for enough time to remove the ammonia gas. The fan shall be vented to the outside of the building.

6.14 Any detectable ammonia in the suit interior (five ppm ammonia (NH_3) or more for the length of stain detector tube) indicates that the suit has failed the test. When other ammonia detectors are used a lower level of detection is possible, and it should be specified as the pass/fail criteria.

6.15 By following this test method, an intrusion coefficient of approximately 200 or more can be measured with the suit in a completely operational condition. If the intrusion coefficient is 200 or more, then the suit is suitable for emergency response and field use.

7.0—Retest procedures

7.1 If the suit fails this test, check for leaks by following the pressure test in test A above.

7.2 Retest the TECP suit as outlined in the test procedure 6.0.

8.0—Report

8.1 Each gas tight totally-encapsulating chemical protective suit tested by this practice shall have the following information recorded.

8.1.1 Unique identification number, identifying brand name, date of purchase, material of construction, and unique suit features; e.g., special breathing apparatus.

8.1.2 General description of test room used for test.

8.1.3 Brand name and purchase date of ammonia detector strips and color change data.

8.1.4 Brand name, sampling range, and expiration date of the length of stain ammonia detector tubes. The brand name and model of the sampling pump should also be recorded. If another type of ammonia detector is used, it should be identified along with its minimum detection limit for ammonia.

8.1.5 Actual test results shall list the two test area concentrations, their average, the interior suit concentration, and the calculated intrusion coefficient. Retest data shall be recorded as an additional test.

8.2 The evaluation of the data shall be specified as "suit passed" or "suit failed," and the date of the test. Any detectable ammonia (five ppm or greater for the length of stain detector tube) in the suit interior indicates the suit has failed this test. When other ammonia detectors are used, a lower level of detection is possible and it should be specified as the pass fail criteria.

CAUTION

Visually inspect all parts of the suit to be sure they are positioned correctly and secured tightly before putting the suit back into service. Special care should be taken to examine each exhaust valve to make sure it is not blocked.

Care should also be exercised to assure that the inside and outside of the suit is completely dry before it is put into storage.

APPENDIX B TO § 1910.120—GENERAL DESCRIPTION AND DISCUSSION OF THE LEVELS OF PROTECTION AND PROTECTIVE GEAR

This appendix sets forth information about personal protective equipment (PPE) protection levels which may be used to assist employers in complying with the PPE requirements of this section.

As required by the standard, PPE must be selected which will protect employees from the specific hazards which they are likely to encounter during their work on-site.

Selection of the appropriate PPE is a complex process which should take into consideration a variety of factors. Key factors involved in this process are identification of the hazards, or suspected hazards; their routes of potential hazard to employees (inhalation, skin absorption, ingestion, and eye or skin contact); and the performance of the PPE *materials* (and seams) in providing a barrier to these hazards. The amount of protection provided by PPE is material-hazard specific. That is, protective equipment materials will protect well against some hazardous substances and poorly, or not at all, against others. In many instances, protective equipment materials cannot be found which will provide continuous protection from the particular hazardous substance. In these cases the breakthrough time of the protective material should exceed the work durations.

Other factors in this selection process to be considered are matching the PPE to the employee's work requirements and task-specific conditions. The durability of PPE materials, such as tear strength and seam strength, should be considered in relation to the employee's tasks. The effects of PPE in relation to heat stress and task duration are a factor in selecting and using PPE. In some cases layers of PPE may be necessary to provide sufficient protection, or to protect expensive PPE inner garments, suits or equipment.

The more that is known about the hazards at the site, the easier the job of PPE selection becomes. As more information about the hazards and conditions at the site becomes available, the site supervisor can make decisions to up-grade or down-grade the level of PPE protection to match the tasks at hand.

The following are guidelines which an employer can use to begin the selection of the appropriate PPE. As noted above, the site information may suggest the use of combinations of PPE selected from the different protection levels (i.e., A, B, C, or D) as being more suitable to the hazards of the work. It should be cautioned that the listing below does not fully address the performance of the specific PPE material in relation to the specific hazards at the job site, and that PPE selection, evaluation and re-selection is an ongoing process until sufficient information about the hazards and PPE performance is obtained.

Part A. Personal protective equipment is divided into four categories based on the degree of protection afforded. (See Part B of this appendix for further explanation of Levels A, B, C, and D hazards.)

I. *Level A*—To be selected when the greatest level of skin, respiratory, and eye protection is required.

The following constitute Level A equipment; it may be used as appropriate;

1. Positive pressure, full face-piece self-contained breathing apparatus (SCBA), or positive pressure supplied air respirator with escape SCBA, approved by the National Institute for Occupational Safety and Health (NIOSH).

2. Totally-encapsulating chemical-protective suit.

3. Coveralls.[1]

4. Long underwear.[1]

5. Gloves, outer, chemical-resistant.

6. Gloves, inner, chemical-resistant.

7. Boots, chemical-resistant, steel toe and shank.

8. Hard hat (under suit).[1]

9. Disposable protective suit, gloves and boots (depending on suit construction, may be worn over totally-encapsulating suit).

II. *Level B*—The highest level of respiratory protection is necessary but a lesser level of skin protection is needed.

The following constitute Level B equipment; it may be used as appropriate.

1. Positive pressure, full-facepiece self-contained breathing apparatus (SCBA), or positive pressure supplied air respirator with escape SCBA (NIOSH approved).

2. Hooded chemical-resistant clothing (overalls and long-sleeved jacket; coveralls; one or two-piece chemical-splash suit; disposable chemical-resistant overalls).

3. Coveralls.[1]

4. Gloves, outer, chemical-resistant.

5. Gloves, inner, chemical-resistant.

6. Boots, outer, chemical-resistant steel toe and shank.

7. Boot-covers, outer, chemical-resistant (disposable).[1]

8. Hard hat.[1]

9. [Reserved]

10. Face shield.[1]

III. *Level C*—The concentration(s) and type(s) of airborne substance(s) is known and the criteria for using air purifying respirators are met.

The following constitute Level C equipment; it may be used as appropriate.

1. Full-face or half-mask, air purifying respirators (NIOSH approved).

2. Hooded chemical-resistant clothing (overalls; two-piece chemical-splash suit; disposable chemical-resistant overalls).

3. Coveralls.[1]

4. Gloves, outer, chemical-resistant.

5. Gloves, inner, chemical-resistant.

6. Boots (outer), chemical-resistant steel toe and shank.[1]

7. Boot-covers, outer, chemical-resistant (disposable)[1].

---

[1] Optional, as applicable.

8. Hard hat.[1]

9. Escape mask.[1]

10. Face shield.[1]

IV. *Level D*—A work uniform affording minimal protection, used for nuisance contamination only.

The following constitute Level D equipment; it may be used as appropriate:

1. Coveralls.

2. Gloves.[1]

3. Boots/shoes, chemical-resistant steel toe and shank.

4. Boots, outer, chemical-resistant (disposable).[1]

5. Safety glasses or chemical splash goggles*.

6. Hard hat.[1]

7. Escape mask.[1]

8. Face shield.[1]

Part B. The types of hazards for which levels A, B, C, and D protection are appropriate are described below:

I. *Level A*—Level A protection should be used when:

1. The hazardous substance has been identified and requires the highest level of protection for skin, eyes, and the respiratory system based on either the measured (or potential for) high concentration of atmospheric vapors, gases, or particulates; or the site operations and work functions involve a high potential for splash, immersion, or exposure to unexpected vapors, gases, or particulates of materials that are harmful to skin or capable of being absorbed through the skin;

2. Substances with a high degree of hazard to the skin are known or suspected to be present, and skin contact is possible; or

3. Operations are being conducted in confined, poorly ventilated areas, and the absence of conditions requiring Level A have not yet been determined.

II. *Level B*—Level B protection should be used when:

1. The type and atmospheric concentration of substances have been identified and require a high level of respiratory protection, but less skin protection;

2. The atmosphere contains less than 19.5 percent oxygen; or

3. The presence of incompletely identified vapors or gases is indicated by a direct-reading organic vapor detection instrument, but vapors and gases are not suspected of containing high levels of chemicals harmful to skin or capable of being absorbed through the skin.

NOTE: This involves atmospheres with IDLH concentrations of specific substances that present severe inhalation hazards and that do not represent a severe skin hazard; or that do not meet the criteria for use of air-purifying respirators.

III. *Level C*—Level C protection should be used when:

1. The atmospheric contaminants, liquid splashes, or other direct contact will not adversely affect or be absorbed through any exposed skin;

2. The types of air contaminants have been identified, concentrations measured, and an air-purifying respirator is available that can remove the contaminants; and

3. All criteria for the use of air-purifying respirators are met.

IV. *Level D*—Level D protection should be used when:

1. The atmosphere contains no known hazard; and

2. Work functions preclude splashes, immersion, or the potential for unexpected inhalation of or contact with hazardous levels of any chemicals.

NOTE: As stated before, combinations of personal protective equipment other than those described for Levels A, B, C, and D protection may be more appropriate and may be used to provide the proper level of protection.

As an aid in selecting suitable chemical protective clothing, it should be noted that the National Fire Protection Association is developing standards on chemical protective clothing. These standards are currently undergoing public review prior to adoption, including:

NFPA 1991—Standard on Vapor-Protective Suits for Hazardous Chemical Emergencies (EPA Level A Protective Clothing)

NFPA 1992—Standard on Liquid Splash-Protective Suits for Hazardous Chemical Emergencies (EPA Level B Protective Clothing)

NFPA 1993—Standard on Liquid Splash-Protective Suits for Non-emergency, Nonflammable Hazardous Chemical Situations (EPA Level B Protective Clothing)

These standards would apply documentation and performance requirements to the manufacture of chemical protective suits. Chemical protective suits meeting these requirements would be labelled as compliant with the appropriate standard. When these standards are adopted by the National Fire Protection Association, it is recommended that chemical protective suits which meet these standards be used.

APPENDIX C TO § 1910.120—COMPLIANCE GUIDELINES

1. *Occupational Safety and Health Program.* Each hazardous waste site clean-up effort will require an occupational safety and health program headed by the site coordinator or the employer's representative. The purpose of the program will be the protection of employees at the site and will be an extension of the employer's overall safety and health program. The program will need to be developed before work begins on the site and implemented as work proceeds as stated in paragraph (b). The program is to facilitate coordination and communication of safety and health issues among personnel responsible for the various activities which will take place at the site. It will provide the overall means for planning and implementing the needed safety and health training and job orientation of employees who will be working at the site. The program will provide the means for identifying and controlling worksite hazards and the means for monitoring program effectiveness. The program will need to cover the responsibilities and authority of the site coordinator or the employer's manager on the site for the safety and health of employees at the site, and the relationships with contractors or support services as to what each employer's safety and health responsibilities are for their employees on the site. Each contractor on the site needs to have its own safety and health program so structured that it will smoothly interface with the program of the site coordinator or principal contractor.

Also those employers involved with treating, storing or disposal of hazardous waste as covered in paragraph (p) must have implemented a safety and health program for their employees. This program is to include the hazard communication program required in paragraph (p)(1) and the training required in paragraphs (p)(7) and (p)(8) as parts of the employers comprehensive overall safety and health program. This program is to be in writing.

Each site or workplace safety and health program will need to include the following: (1) Policy statements of the line of authority and accountability for implementing the program, the objectives of the program and the role of the site safety and health supervisor or manager and staff; (2) means or methods for the development of procedures for identifying and controlling workplace hazards at the site; (3) means or methods for the development and communication to employees of the various plans, work rules, standard operating procedures and practices that pertain to individual employees and supervisors; (4) means for the training of supervisors and employees to develop the needed skills and knowledge to perform their work in a safe and healthful manner; (5) means to anticipate and prepare for emergency situations; and (6) means for obtaining information feedback to aid in evaluating the program and for improving the effectiveness of the program. The management and employees should be trying continually to improve the effectiveness of the program thereby enhancing the protection being afforded those working on the site.

Accidents on the site or workplace should be investigated to provide information on how such occurrences can be avoided in the future. When injuries or illnesses occur on the site or workplace, they will need to be investigated to determine what needs to be done to prevent this incident from occurring again. Such information will need to be used as feedback on the effectiveness of the program and the information turned into positive steps to prevent any reoccurrence. Receipt of employee suggestions or complaints relating to safety and health issues involved with site or workplace activities is also a feedback mechanism that can be used effectively to improve the program and may serve in part as an evaluative tool(s).

For the development and implementation of the program to be the most effective, professional safety and health personnel should be used. Certified Safety Professionals, Board Certified Industrial Hygienists or Registered Professional Safety Engineers are good examples of professional stature for safety and health managers who will administer the employer's program.

2. *Training.* The training programs for employees subject to the requirements of paragraph (e) of this standard should address: the safety and health hazards employees should expect to find on hazardous waste clean-up sites; what control measures or techniques are effective for those hazards; what monitoring procedures are effective in characterizing exposure levels; what makes an effective employer's safety and health program; what a site safety and health plan should include; hands on training with personal protective equipment and clothing they may be expected to use; the contents of the OSHA standard relevant to the employee's duties and function; and, employee's responsibilities under OSHA and other regulations. Supervisors will need training in their responsibilities under the safety and health program and its subject areas such as the spill containment program, the personal protective equipment program, the medical surveillance program, the emergency response plan and other areas.

The training programs for employees subject to the requirements of paragraph (p) of this standard should address: the employers safety and health program elements impacting employees; the hazard communication program; the medical surveillance program; the hazards and the controls for such hazards that employees need to know for their job duties and functions. All require annual refresher training.

The training programs for employees covered by the requirements of paragraph (q) of this standard should address those competencies required for the various levels of response such as: the hazards associated with hazardous substances; hazard identification and awareness; notification of appropriate persons; the need for and use of personal protective equipment including respirators; the decontamination procedures to be used; preplanning activities for hazardous sub-

stance incidents including the emergency reponse plan; company standard operating procedures for hazardous substance emergency responses; the use of the incident command system and other subjects. Hands-on training should be stressed whenever possible. Critiques done after an incident which include an evaluation of what worked and what did not and how could the incident be better handled the next time may be counted as training time.

For hazardous materials specialists (usually members of hazardous materials teams), the training should address the care, use and/or testing of chemical protective clothing including totally encapsulating suits, the medical surveillance program, the standard operating procedures for the hazardous materials team including the use of plugging and patching equipment and other subject areas.

Officers and leaders who may be expected to be in charge at an incident should be fully knowledgeable of their company's incident command system. They should know where and how to obtain additional assistance and be familiar with the local district's emergency response plan and the state emergency response plan.

Specialist employees such as technical experts, medical experts or environmental experts that work with hazardous materials in their regular jobs, who may be sent to the incident scene by the shipper, manufacturer or governmental agency to advise and assist the person in charge of the incident should have training on an annual basis. Their training should include the care and use of personal protective equipment including respirators; knowledge of the incident command system and how they are to relate to it; and those areas needed to keep them current in their respective field as it relates to safety and health involving specific hazardous substances.

Those skilled support personnel, such as employees who work for public works departments or equipment operators who operate bulldozers, sand trucks, backhoes, etc., who may be called to the incident scene to provide emergency support assistance, should have at least a safety and health briefing before entering the area of potential or actual exposure. These skilled support personnel, who have not been a part of the emergency response plan and do not meet the training requirements, should be made aware of the hazards they face and should be provided all necessary protective clothing and equipment required for their tasks.

There are two National Fire Protection Association standards, NFPA 472—"Standard for Professional Competence of Responders to Hazardous Material Incidents" and NFPA 471—"Recommended Practice for Responding to Hazardous Material Incidents", which are excellent resource documents to aid fire departments and other emergency response organizations in developing their training program materials. NFPA 472 provides guidance on the skills and knowledge needed for first responder awareness level, first responder operations level, hazmat technicians, and hazmat specialist. It also offers guidance for the officer corp who will be in charge of hazardous substance incidents.

3. *Decontamination.* Decontamination procedures should be tailored to the specific hazards of the site, and may vary in complexity and number of steps, depending on the level of hazard and the employee's exposure to the hazard. Decontamination procedures and PPE decontamination methods will vary depending upon the specific substance, since one procedure or method may not work for all substances. Evaluation of decontamination methods and procedures should be performed, as necessary, to assure that employees are not exposed to hazards by re-using PPE. References in appendix D may be used for guidance in establishing an effective decontamination program. In addition, the U.S. Coast Guard's Manual, "Policy Guidance for Response to Hazardous Chemical Releases," U.S. Department of Transportation, Washington, DC (COMDTINST M16465.30) is a good reference for establishing an effective decontamination program.

4. *Emergency response plans.* States, along with designated districts within the states, will be developing or have developed local emergency response plans. These state and district plans should be utilized in the emergency response plans called for in the standard. Each employer should assure that its emergency response plan is compatible with the local plan. The major reference being used to aid in developing the state and local district plans is the *Hazardous Materials Emergency Planning Guide*, NRT-1. The current Emergency Response Guidebook from the U.S. Department of Transportation, CMA's CHEMTREC and the Fire Service Emergency Management Handbook may also be used as resources.

Employers involved with treatment, storage, and disposal facilities for hazardous waste, which have the required contingency plan called for by their permit, would not need to duplicate the same planning elements. Those items of the emergency response plan that are properly addressed in the contingency plan may be substituted into the emergency response plan required in 1910.120 or otherwise kept together for employer and employee use.

5. *Personal protective equipment programs.* The purpose of personal protective clothing and equipment (PPE) is to shield or isolate individuals from the chemical, physical, and biologic hazards that may be encountered at a hazardous substance site.

As discussed in appendix B, no single combination of protective equipment and clothing is capable of protecting against all haz-

ards. Thus PPE should be used in conjunction with other protective methods and its effectiveness evaluated periodically.

The use of PPE can itself create significant worker hazards, such as heat stress, physical and psychological stress, and impaired vision, mobility, and communication. For any given situation, equipment and clothing should be selected that provide an adequate level of protection. However, over-protection, as well as under-protection, can be hazardous and should be avoided where possible.

Two basic objectives of any PPE program should be to protect the wearer from safety and health hazards, and to prevent injury to the wearer from incorrect use and/or malfunction of the PPE. To accomplish these goals, a comprehensive PPE program should include hazard identification, medical monitoring, environmental surveillance, selection, use, maintenance, and decontamination of PPE and its associated training.

The written PPE program should include policy statements, procedures, and guidelines. Copies should be made available to all employees, and a reference copy should be made available at the worksite. Technical data on equipment, maintenance manuals, relevant regulations, and other essential information should also be collected and maintained.

6. *Incident command system (ICS).* Paragraph 1910.120(q)(3)(ii) requires the implementation of an ICS. The ICS is an organized approach to effectively control and *manage* operations at an emergency incident. The individual in charge of the ICS is the senior official responding to the incident. The ICS is not much different than the "command post" approach used for many years by the fire service. During large complex fires involving several companies and many pieces of apparatus, a command post would be established. This enabled *one* individual to be in charge of managing the incident, rather than having several officers from different companies making separate, and sometimes conflicting, decisions. The individual in charge of the command post would delegate responsibility for performing various tasks to subordinate officers. Additionally, all communications were routed through the command post to reduce the number of radio transmissions and eliminate confusion. However, strategy, tactics, and all decisions were made by one individual.

The ICS is a very similar system, except it is implemented for emergency response to all incidents, both large and small, that involve hazardous substances.

For a small incident, the individual in charge of the ICS may perform many tasks of the ICS. There may not be any, or little, delegation of tasks to subordinates. For example, in response to a small incident, the individual in charge of the ICS, in addition to normal command activities, may become

407

the safety officer and may designate only one employee (with proper equipment) as a back-up to provide assistance if needed. OSHA does recommend, however, that at least two employees be designated as back-up personnel since the assistance needed may include rescue.

To illustrate the operation of the ICS, the following scenario might develop during a small incident, such as an overturned tank truck with a small leak of flammable liquid.

The first responding senior officer would implement and take command of the ICS. That person would size-up the incident and determine if additional personnel and apparatus were necessary; would determine what actions to take to control the leak; and, determine the proper level of personal protective equipment. If additional assistance is not needed, the individual in charge of the ICS would implement actions to stop and control the leak using the fewest number of personnel that can effectively accomplish the tasks. The individual in charge of the ICS then would designate himself as the safety officer and two other employees as a back-up in case rescue may become necessary. In this scenario, decontamination procedures would not be necessary.

A large complex incident may require many employees and difficult, time-consuming efforts to control. In these situations, the individual in charge of the ICS will want to delegate different tasks to subordinates in order to maintain a span of control that will keep the number of subordinates, that are reporting, to a manageable level.

Delegation of task at large incidents may be by location, where the incident scene is divided into sectors, and subordinate officers coordinate activities within the sector that they have been assigned.

Delegation of tasks can also be by function. Some of the functions that the individual in charge of the ICS may want to delegate at a large incident are: medical services; evacuation; water supply; resources (equipment, apparatus); media relations; safety; and, site control (integrate activities with police for crowd and traffic control). Also for a large incident, the individual in charge of the ICS will designate several employees as back-up personnel; and a number of safety officers to monitor conditions and recommend safety precautions.

Therefore, no matter what size or complexity an incident may be, by implementing an ICS there will be one individual in charge who makes the decisions and gives directions; and, all actions, and communications are coordinated through one central point of command. Such a system should reduce confusion, improve safety, organize and coordinate actions, and should facilitate effective management of the incident.

7. *Site Safety and Control Plans.* The safety and security of response personnel and others in the area of an emergeny response incident site should be of primary concern to the incident commander. The use of a site safety and control plan could greatly assist those in charge of assuring the safety and health of employees on the site.

A comprehensive site safety and control plan should include the following: summary analysis of hazards on the site and a risk analysis of those hazards; site map or sketch; site work zones (clean zone, transition or decontamination zone, work or hot zone); use of the buddy system; site communications; command post or command center; standard operating procedures and safe work practices; medical assistance and triage area; hazard monitoring plan (air contaminate monitoring, etc.); decontamination procedures and area; and other relevant areas. This plan should be a part of the employer's emergency response plan or an extension of it to the specific site.

8. *Medical surveillance programs.* Workers handling hazardous substances may be exposed to toxic chemicals, safety hazards, biologic hazards, and radiation. Therefore, a medical surveillance program is essential to assess and monitor workers' health and fitness for employment in hazardous waste operations and during the course of work; to provide emergency and other treatment as needed; and to keep accurate records for future reference.

The *Occupational Safety and Health Guidance Manual for Hazardous Waste Site Activities* developed by the National Institute for Occupational Safety and Health (NIOSH), the Occupational Safety and Health Administration (OSHA), the U.S. Coast Guard (USCG), and the Environmental Protection Agency (EPA); October 1985 provides an excellent example of the types of medical testing that should be done as part of a medical surveillance program.

9. *New Technology and Spill Containment Programs.* Where hazardous substances may be released by spilling from a container that will expose employees to the hazards of the materials, the employer will need to implement a program to contain and control the spilled material. Diking and ditching, as well as use of absorbents like diatomaceous earth, are traditional techniques which have proven to be effective over the years. However, in recent years new products have come into the marketplace, the use of which complement and increase the effectiveness of these traditional methods. These new products also provide emergency responders and others with additional tools or agents to use to reduce the hazards of spilled materials.

These agents can be rapidly applied over a large area and can be uniformly applied or otherwise can be used to build a small dam, thus improving the workers' ability to control spilled material. These application techniques enhance the intimate contact between the agent and the spilled material allowing for the quickest effect by the agent or quickest control of the spilled material. Agents are available to solidify liquid spilled materials, to suppress vapor generation from spilled materials, and to do both. Some special agents, which when applied as recommended by the manufacturer, will react in a controlled manner with the spilled material to neutralize acids or caustics, or greatly reduce the level of hazard of the spilled material.

There are several modern methods and devices for use by emergency response personnel or others involved with spill control efforts to safely apply spill control agents to control spilled material hazards. These include portable pressurized applicators similar to hand-held portable fire extinguishing devices, and nozzle and hose systems similar to portable fire fighting foam systems which allow the operator to apply the agent without having to come into contact with the spilled material. The operator is able to apply the agent to the spilled material from a remote position.

The solidification of liquids provides for rapid containment and isolation of hazardous substance spills. By directing the agent at run-off points or at the edges of the spill, the reactant solid will automatically create a barrier to slow or stop the spread of the material. Clean-up of hazardous substances is greatly improved when solidifying agents, acid or caustic neutralizers, or activated carbon adsorbents are used. Properly applied, these agents can totally solidify liquid hazardous substances or neutralize or absorb them, which results in materials which are less hazardous and easier to handle, transport, and dispose of. The concept of spill treatment, to create less hazardous substances, will improve the safety and level of protection of employees working at spill clean-up operations or emergency response operations to spills of hazardous substances.

The use of vapor suppression agents for volatile hazardous substances, such as flammable liquids and those substances which present an inhalation hazard, is important for protecting workers. The rapid and uniform distribution of the agent over the surface of the spilled material can provide quick vapor knockdown. There are temporary and long-term foam-type agents which are effective on vapors and dusts, and activated carbon adsorption agents which are effective for vapor control and soaking-up of the liquid. The proper use of hose lines or hand-held portable pressurized applicators provides good mobility and permits the worker to deliver the agent from a safe distance without having to step into the untreated spilled material. Some of these systems can be recharged in the field to provide coverage of larger spill areas than the design limits of a single charged applicator unit. Some of the more effective agents can solidify the liquid flammable hazardous substances and at the same time elevate the flashpoint above 140 °F so the resulting substance may be handled as a nonhazardous waste material if it meets the U.S. Environmental Protection Agency's 40 CFR part 261 requirements (See particularly § 261.21).

All workers performing hazardous substance spill control work are expected to wear the proper protective clothing and equipment for the materials present and to follow the employer's established standard operating procedures for spill control. All involved workers need to be trained in the established operating procedures; in the use and care of spill control equipment; and in the associated hazards and control of such hazards of spill containment work.

These new tools and agents are the things that employers will want to evaluate as part of their new technology program. The treatment of spills of hazardous substances or wastes at an emergency incident as part of the immediate spill containment and control efforts is sometimes acceptable to EPA and a permit exception is described in 40 CFR 264.1(g)(8) and 265.1(c)(11).

APPENDIX D TO § 1910.120—REFERENCES. The following references may be consulted for further information on the subject of this standard:

1. OSHA Instruction DFO CPL 2.70—January 29, 1986, *Special Emphasis Program: Hazardous Waste Sites.*

2. OSHA Instruction DFO CPL 2–2.37A—January 29, 1986, *Technical Assistance and Guidelines for Superfund and Other Hazardous Waste Site Activities.*

3. OSHA Instruction DTS CPL 2.74—January 29, 1986, *Hazardous Waste Activity Form, OSHA 175.*

4. *Hazardous Waste Inspections Reference Manual,* U.S. Department of Labor, Occupational Safety and Health Administration, 1986.

5. Memorandum of Understanding Among the National Institute for Occupational Safety and Health, the Occupational Safety and Health Administration, the United States Coast Guard, and the United States Environmental Protection Agency, *Guidance for Worker Protection During Hazardous Waste Site Investigations and Clean-up and Hazardous Substance Emergencies.* December 18, 1980.

6. *National Priorities List,* 1st Edition, October 1984; U.S. Environmental Protection Agency, Revised periodically.

7. *The Decontamination of Response Personnel,* Field Standard Operating Procedures (F.S.O.P.) 7; U.S. Environmental Protection Agency, Office of Emergency and Remedial Response, Hazardous Response Support Division, December 1984.

8. *Preparation of a Site Safety Plan*, Field Standard Operating Procedures (F.S.O.P.) 9; U.S. Environmental Protection Agency, Office of Emergency and Remedial Response, Hazardous Response Support Division, April 1985.

9. *Standard Operating Safety Guidelines;* U.S. Environmental Protection Agency, Office of Emergency and Remedial Response, Hazardous Response Support Division, Environmental Response Team; November 1984.

10. *Occupational Safety and Health Guidance Manual for Hazardous Waste Site Activities*, National Institute for Occupational Safety and Health (NIOSH), Occupational Safety and Health Administration (OSHA), U.S. Coast Guard (USCG), and Environmental Protection Agency (EPA); October 1985.

11. *Protecting Health and Safety at Hazardous Waste Sites: An Overview*, U.S. Environmental Protection Agency, EPA/625/9-85/006; September 1985.

12. *Hazardous Waste Sites and Hazardous Substance Emergencies*, NIOSH Worker Bulletin, U.S. Department of Health and Human Services, Public Health Service, Centers for Disease Control, National Institute for Occupational Safety and Health; December 1982.

13. *Personal Protective Equipment for Hazardous Materials Incidents: A Selection Guide;* U.S. Department of Health and Human Services, Public Health Service, Centers for Disease Control, National Institute for Occupational Safety and Health; October 1984.

14. *Fire Service Emergency Management Handbook*, International Association of Fire Chiefs Foundation, 101 East Holly Avenue, Unit 10B, Sterling, VA 22170, January 1985.

15. *Emergency Response Guidebook*, U.S Department of Transportation, Washington, DC, 1987.

16. *Report to the Congress on Hazardous Materials Training, Planning and Preparedness*, Federal Emergency Management Agency, Washington, DC, July 1986.

17. *Workbook for Fire Command*, Alan V. Brunacini and J. David Beageron, National Fire Protection Association, Batterymarch Park, Quincy, MA 02269, 1985.

18. *Fire Command*, Alan V. Brunacini, National Fire Protection Association, Batterymarch Park,, Quincy, MA 02269, 1985.

19. *Incident Command System*, Fire Protection Publications, Oklahoma State University, Stillwater, OK 74078, 1983.

20. *Site Emergency Response Planning*, Chemical Manufacturers Association, Washington, DC 20037, 1986.

21. *Hazardous Materials Emergency Planning Guide*, NRT-1, Environmental Protection Agency, Washington, DC, March 1987.

22. *Community Teamwork: Working Together to Promote Hazardous Materials Transportation Safety*. U.S. Department of Transportation, Washington, DC, May 1983.

23. *Disaster Planning Guide for Business and Industry*, Federal Emergency Management Agency, Publication No. FEMA 141, August 1987.

(The Office of Management and Budget has approved the information collection requirements in this section under control number 1218-0139)

[54 FR 9317, Mar. 6, 1989, as amended at 55 FR 14073, Apr. 13, 1990; 56 FR 15832, Apr. 18, 1991]

EXAMPLE: COMPANY INSPECTION PROCEDURE

OSHA INSPECTION
POLICIES AND PROCEDURES OF

_____

POLICY

It is the policy of _____ to permit inspections by representatives of the Occupational Safety and Health Agency (OSHA). Such inspections shall be accomplished in accordance with the following procedures.

PROCEDURES

1. Upon arrival at any company workplace, the OSHA inspector shall be directed to report to [location of first contact with the designated company representative], the "key person."

Optional: All company managers should be immediately informed of the presence of the OSHA inspector.

2. The inspector is to wait for the company's key person.

3. If the key person will not be available within a reasonable period of time (for example, 30 to 60 minutes) the inspector is to be informed of that fact. The inspector should be told that the company does *not* require an inspection warrant, but that policy requires the presence of the company representative during the inspection and that the inspection may *not* proceed without this individual. It should be politely suggested that the inspection take place on another day.

Optional: If a back-up or substitute key person has been appointed and is available, that individual would assume responsibility for the inspection.

4. Before the commencement of the opening conference, if the inspector is unknown to the key person, the key person is to review the identification documents of the inspector and verify the inspector's identity with an appropriate OSHA official.

5. If the key person is available, it is likely that the inspector will immediately commence an opening conference.

6. During the opening conference, attempt to determine the reason for the inspection.

If the key person does learn of the basis for the inspection, try and limit the scope of the inspection to the subject matter which is the basis for the inspection. That is, if the inspector wants to inspect a given machine, try to limit the inspection to that machine.

Remember: An OSHA inspector does have the right to conduct an inspection of the entire company workplace.

7. During or upon completion of the opening conference, the inspector should seek consent to begin the investigation. If the company has a policy to deny the inspection without an inspection warrant, the inspector should be informed of the policy at this point in time, if not already so informed. If the company policy is to permit the inspection without an inspection warrant, the inspection will then commence.

8. The key person should accompany the inspector *throughout* the inspection.

The only exception to this requirement is when the inspector desires to talk to company employees in private. Employees are entitled to privacy when being questioned by the inspector. This right of privacy is for the protection of *the employees*. If the employees have no objection to the presence of the key person during such an interview, they have effectively waived their right to confidentiality, and the key person does have a right to be present. It may be that the employee would feel more comfortable if the key person is present during any such interview.

If the OSHA inspector objects, however, to the presence of the key person at any employee interviews, even though acceptable to the employee(s), allow the interview to proceed in private. You may always talk with the employees after the inspector has left the workplace.

9. It is not advisable to include other company representatives during any stage of the inspection procedure; rather, limit the management team to the key person;

10. Throughout the inspection, the key person should be courteous to the inspector and respond to questions *if* authorized by the company to do so. It may be that the key person will be considered to "speak for management." If so, his/her statements could be considered to be "authorized admissions" by the employer and, therefore, admissible in evidence in a later judicial proceeding.

If the key person has not been expressly authorized by the company to speak "for the company," the inspector should be informed of that fact.

11. Under no circumstances is the key person, or any other employee of the company, to guess or speculate when responding to questions of an inspector. If an answer if to be given, the key person or any employee should answer *only* what he/she *knows* to be the facts. If the key person or employee has no knowledge regarding the question, that should be the response.

12. Detailed explanations are not encouraged as they may tend to confuse or unduly prolong the scope of the investigation. Answer the question and only the question, and then only with known facts. **Do not volunteer information.**

13. The company representative should never admit or concede the existence of an unsafe condition. If corrective measures are taken during an inspection, the key person should either make no statement regarding the abatement action or should state that the corrective measures are to be taken *only* as a result of the inspector's demands.

14. **Never admit a violation.**

15. If the company has commenced its own investigation of an accident regarding a given operation or procedure but has not completed that investigation at the time of the OSHA inspection, answers to any questions regarding the accident, operation, or procedure should be deferred pending the completion of the company investigation.

16. An inspector is allowed to take samples, photographs and/or videotapes (except of trade secrets) during the inspection. If the inspector does perform one of these actions, the company should also consider taking such actions. See paragraph 22 below for instructions regarding the samples, photographs, etc.

17. If, during the inspection or any time thereafter, the inspector asks for copies of written documents or materials, consider *the source* of the document or material.

If the company prepared the document in question, for example, an OSHA Log (200), the inspector should be provided with a copy as soon as reasonably possible.

Remember: Some regulations require *immediate accessibility* to various written documents; for example, a copy of the company's written hazard communication program.

If the company did *not* prepare the document (for example, manufacturer's specifications of a piece of equipment) copies of the document may need to be made available, but only when accompanied by disclaimer language. (See: Attachment 1.)

If a copy of a document from a source other than your company is turned over to the inspector without disclaiming its reliability, it may subsequently be concluded that the company believed in and, therefore, adopted all of the representations included in the document.

18. The key person should keep a record of the scope of the inspection, including the identities of employees to whom the inspector spoke, items of apparent interest to the inspector (for example, a specific machine or machine operation), comments made by the inspector, and individual observations of the key person. See paragraph 22 below for instructions regarding these notes, records, etc.

19. If, at any time during the inspection, it is decided by the key person or other designated company representative that the inspection should be terminated, inform the inspector of the fact, and the inspector will immediately stop the inspection and depart the scene. Realize that such an action may force the inspector to obtain an inspection warrant.

20. Upon completion of the inspection, the inspector should hold a closing conference. If there is some question whether such a conference is to take place, the key person should request the scheduling of a closing conference. It is advisable that more than one company representative attend the closing conference to ensure that the company understands the statements of the inspector.

21. During the closing conference, the inspector should be asked if any citations are to be issued as a result of the inspection. If citations are to be issued, determine what safety orders were allegedly violated. Also attempt to determine the classification of any citations which may be forthcoming as a result of the inspection; for example, "serious," etc. The closing conference is not the time not the place to argue with the inspector. Make no concessions nor admissions during the closing conference. **Never admit a violation.**

22. Upon completion of the inspection and closing conference, the key person should prepare a report of the inspection incorporating any records, notes, samples, photographs, etc., made or taken during the inspection. This report is to be made at the request of the company's attorney and must be labeled or designated as having been so prepared. The report should be forwarded to the attorney. Copies of this report are *not* to be circulated.

[Company name]

Date: _____   by _____
                              Name:

ATTACHMENT 1

[Company] makes no representations regarding the truth or accuracy of the contents of the attached document(s). [Company] makes no representations that it or any authorized representative has knowledge of the contents of the attached document(s), that it or any authorized representative of [Company] admits to, acknowledges or adopts the contents of, or any representations contained in said document(s).

By providing a copy, or access to a review, of the attached document(s), [Company] does not and has not authorized any employee to make a statement for [Company] concerning the subject matter of the document(s) or material(s) in question.

INDEX